SELECTED CAVES

BRITAIN

"TO

SELECTED CAVES
OF
BRITAIN AND IRELAND

Compiled by
Des Marshall F.R.G.S. and Donald Rust

Photographs by
Paul Deakin F.R.P.S. and Tony Baker

CORDEE – LEICESTER

Front cover photo: Abseiling through Top Sink, Lancaster/Easgill System
Rear cover photo: The Streamway Ogof Ffynnon Ddu
Frontispiece: Streamway Ogof Ffynnon Ddu 1. Photo: Tony Baker

ISBN 1 87189043 8

British Library Cataloguing in Publication Data
A catalogue record for this book is available from the British Library

All trade enquiries to:
Cordee, 3a De Montfort Street, Leicester LE1 7HD

This book is available from all specialist equipment shops and major booksellers.
It can, along with all the maps mentioned in the text, be obtained direct from the
publishers. Please write for a copy of our comprehensive stocklist of outdoor
recreation and travel books and maps.

CORDEE
3a De Montfort Street, Leicester LE1 7HD

CONTENTS

MAPS

The compilers

Des Marshall first went underground in 1962. He has caved all over Europe, America, Papua New Guinea and Indonesia including some caving in the Himalayas and East Africa. As a freelance instructor for many years operating all over the British Isles, he organises and runs specialist caving holidays along with climbing and trekking trips to East Africa, Himalayas and Europe. He is a Fellow of the Royal Geographical Society and a CIC holder, registered as an assessor for the N.C.A. Local Cave Leader Scheme. Des is also a Director of an Outdoor Pursuits Centre in the Swansea Valley.

Donald Rust started caving in 1974 and has explored caves throughout the British Isles and Europe. He has caved in Iran, Poland, Greece, Ecuador, Columbia and USA. He was a member of the Polish Team that were first to descend the Gouffre Jean Bernard from the highest entrance to the bottom in 1980. As a cave diver he has explored many of the caves in his home patch of South Wales where he now runs an Outdoor Pursuits Centre in the Swansea Valley.

Disclaimer

Caving/potholing is a potentially dangerous sport. It is essential that anyone descending the caves/pots described herein be fully conversant with the techniques involved in order that a descent and ascent is accomplished safely. The descriptions in this guidebook attempt to provide an informative, accurate and safe means of descending and ascending these.

The inclusion of a cave or pothole does not imply that it will remain in the same condition as described. Conditions underground can change very rapidly, rock deteriorates, bolt threads become unusable, water courses change, hangers and any in-situ gear wears. All cavers and potholers must rely on their own ability and judgement to gauge the appropriate use of any fixed gear including old rope and slings 'tat' left by previous parties. DO NOT be tempted to use 'tat', take and use your own and remove after trip.

All Eco hangers should be checked before use. A physical check should be a twisting motion of the anchor using the fingers, while observing any movement. Slight flexing or rotational movement (+/−1mm) of the anchor may be noticed, this is acceptable. The following points should be checked before using or loading the anchors:

Groves or abrasive areas within the inside of the outer curvature of the anchor. E.g. the inside contact area of the anchor.

Excessive rotation of the resin within the drilled hole.

Rotation of the anchor within the resin.

Fracturing of the rock within 20cm of the anchor placement.

Egress of the anchor from the resin or the resin from the drilled hole.

Should any of these defects be noticed, please telephone N.C.A. representatives on 01695 728673 or 01270 768522 9am-9pm. All suspected defective anchors are checked within 5 days of being reported. The following information is required when reporting suspected defective anchors:

Name of cave.

Route on which defective anchor is.

Traverse or pitch number/name.

Anchor number, counting from the start of that group of anchors.

Neither the Editors nor the various authors of this guidebook accept any liability whatsoever for any injury caused to cavers/potholers, third parties or damage to property arising from the use of it. Whilst the content of the guidebook is believed to be accurate, no responsibility is accepted for any error, omission or misstatement. Users must rely on their own judgement and are recommended to insure against injury to person and property as well as third party risks.

Most caves/potholes in this guidebook are on private property and permission must be sought from the landowner before descending. The inclusion of a cave or pothole in this guidebook does not mean any member of the public has a right of descent or access to caves or potholes.

Acknowledgements

Without the efforts and support of many people – especially the section writers – this guide would not exist. We would like to thank these people, along with all the others who helped in offering advice, criticism, as well as writing the odd description or two and companions on many a trip, sometimes in adverse weather. In particular: Tim Allen, Lee Cartledge, C.N.C.C. technical Group, Adam Collinge, Peter Francis, Stuart Halford, Bill Hogarth, Tony Jarratt, Greg Jones, Liam Kealy, Andrew Kirk, Dave Lacey, Richard Mercer, Paul Monico, Michelle Nickerson, Dave Nixon, Tony Oldham, Neil Pacey, Rachel Robins, Richard Rushton, Alan Steele, John Stevens and Andy Walsh. Especial thanks to Paul Deakin and Tony Baker for supplying some of their fine photographs.

Preface

Most cavers do not want to know where every hollow in the ground is even though there is a requirement for every one to be documented as a potential cave site. On talking to various people it became apparent that there was a need to provide a 'selective' cave guide to Britain and Ireland.

Caving for most is fun, done for the enjoyment of being underground, as well as the sporting aspect. Many cavers only need the information required to do the best trip down a cave or trips within a system. Only the dedicated digger or explorer will require the whereabouts of every hollow with a view to finding a 'new' system.

We have not included mines although an odd, very short mined passage is described if it leads to natural passages e.g. Maskhill Mine, which is then described through to the East Canal in Giants Hole. The book is essentially a guide to the best of the wild caves.

INTRODUCTION

The purpose of this guide is to inform the sport caver of the wealth of really good trips to be had in Britain and Ireland. Only the main caving areas are included Assynt in Scotland (together with a description of the major Isle of Skye cave); Yorkshire; Derbyshire; North Wales; South Wales; Mendip and Devon on mainland Britain; Fermanagh and County Clare in Ireland. Other areas of limestone exist, notably along the South Coast of England and Counties Cork, Sligo, Cavan, Kerry and Tipperary in Ireland. Although the definitive guides describe every hollow in the ground or give references to them, this guide is for cavers who want information about the classic trip(s) down each cave or system described. Side passages are not described apart from being mentioned in the text.

Access agreements to caves in each particular area will be dealt with before the different cave description. It is of paramount importance that everyone adheres to the access agreements of all the caves described and indeed to any other cave.

Most of the old descriptions describe ladder as the means of descending caves. This somewhat arcane means of descent has been superseded by SRT. As such all the descriptions are new and brought into the 20th Century by using SRT as the usual method of descending vertical pitches. Some caves, however, will still be descended using ladder as the preferred method of descent. (It seems somewhat pedantic to describe SRT for the '20' in Swildons for example as it does to describe 'Dihedral' Route in Gaping Gill for ladder!). SRT has enabled many cavers to operate outside of club activities. It is not uncommon for parties of two or three to descend even the deepest caves in Yorkshire for instance. Solo caving is also possible down deep holes using SRT. Obviously the people involved are experienced and leave messages where they have gone!

Although ladders do occasionally have their use, modern caving techniques are safer, quicker and much less energetic than lugging huge piles of electron ladders and ropes to the depths. Cavers stay drier because ropes are positioned way out of the water instead of nonsensically down waterfalls – which was supposed to be character building! As such there were many accidents caused by 'macho' cavers climbing ladders without safety checks.

Although the most popular trips will have obvious fixed bolts or spits (bolt sleeves) to screw your hangers into, just like a dot to dot exercise, the less popular ones will tax the ingenuity of any rope technician and great care must be taken to ensure rub free rigging.

Surveys have not been included as they serve, mostly, to confuse with their small scale and lack of definitive information. However, a reference, where known, will be given whether a survey has been made at the end of each cave description. These are often obtainable from caving equipment suppliers. Unfortunately some of them may be out of print or become so within the lifespan of this guide. Even then it will still be feasible to obtain photocopies of surveys from club libraries or, if a member of the B.C.R.A., their library in Matlock.

The caves described are our own or the section writers selection and although regarded as, perhaps, the best trips they may not fall in to your idea as the best. There is something for everyone in the guide and we, as well as the various other authors hope you have as much fun as they have over the years.

It would be appreciated that any comments regarding the cave selection or their descriptions be sent to us at the address below in order for us to rectify any

Des Marshall and Donald Rust, happy to have the guide finished.
Photo: Nona Nash

omission(s) in future editions. C/O Cordee, 3a De Montfort Street, Leicester LE1 7HD.

A CAVING CODE

Before venturing underground always tell a responsible person where you are going – to what cave and which trip you are doing. For example, it is no use telling someone that you are going to Easegill as there are many miles of passages, not to mention the numerous entrances. Be precise, state which entrance and which trip. Also let that person know what time you expect to be out and how long to allow before calling out the rescue team.

Remember the country code and practise it; especially, close all gates, DO NOT climb over walls and fences look for a stile or gate and PLEASE TAKE ALL YOUR LITTER HOME. Please keep to designated access paths.

Ensure that all your equipment is sound and that your party is properly equipped with each person having the right clothing, helmet, lighting (carbide is not allowed in some caves) and, if doing a vertical pot, a full SRT kit. On a long trip ensure that you will have enough light and food.

Some of the caves described have fixed aids in-situ, e.g. the ladder at Maypole Inlet in Ogof Ffynnon Ddu and the ladder on Comic Act Cascade in Giant's Hole. Whereas the ladder at Maypole Inlet is maintained by the South Wales Caving Club, the ladder on Comic Act Cascade is not maintained at all. The need for each party to check in-situ equipment is paramount. Do not assume that because a rope is in place that it is safe. Care must be exercised at all times with fixed aids.

Treat caves with great care. Too much damage has already been done in this very fragile environment. Remember, TAKE NOTHING BUT PICTURES AND LEAVE NOTHING BUT FOOTPRINTS. If using carbide lighting please bring your spent carbide out with you and DO NOT deposit it for all to see on a mud bank in the cave.

If you want to start caving get in touch with a club or read the caving press for the various courses being run throughout the year by Nationally Qualified Instructors.

CONSERVATION

Caves are very fragile, it is easy to damage formations inside. What may have taken thousands of years to form is easily ruined by a careless or thoughtless act spoiling that area for those coming behind. When in delicate areas it is of paramount importance that great care is taken. Mud formations may just seem exactly that, but are an important cave phenomenon and need protection from careless feet. Do not let anyone break off formations or take fallen ones out of a cave. Leave cave pearls for others to see.

Conservation Code

Clumsiness can wreck cave formations.

Observe taped routes – they are there to safeguard the cave.

Never leave litter spent carbide in a cave – pollution kills cave life.

Set others a good example when caving – persuade them to follow it.

Enlist the help of experts to record anything new you may find.

Responsible leaders will avoid taking novices where they may accidentally cause damage.

Vandalism means damage to stals, mud floors, gour pools, etc., help prevent it.

Alert your regional Caving Council to developments which may possibly damage or destroy caves.

Take care not to disturb cave life, especially bats, or remains which may be of archaeological or historical interest.

Initiate measures to help look after caves, collect litter, clean off graffiti, etc.

Offer your support to others who initiate conservation measures.

Natural caves are part of our natural heritage – help protect them.

BATS

There are 15 different types in Britain which hibernate in a few of the caves described. Whilst not often on the main routes it is a criminal act to disturb them and punishable by a hefty fine.

Conservation Code
Do not handle bats.
Do not photograph roosting bats.
Do not warm up hibernating bats.
Do not shine bright lights on bats.
Do not use carbide lamps in bat roosts.
Do not smoke or make excessive noise.
Do not take large parties into bat roosts in winter.
Do seek advice before blasting or digging.

CAVE RESCUE CALL OUT PROCEDURE

Dial 999 and ask for the Police. Then ask for Cave Rescue. You will be asked for the following information: name of caller, position and number of telephone, name of cave and it's grid reference (if known), nature of accident with fullest possible details including position of victim(s) in cave, number of people injured, number and ability of other members of the party remaining in the cave. Any other information which you think is useful e.g. name(s) of victim(s) can also be given. STAY at the telephone until a Cave Rescue Controller contacts you.

Using the guide

LOCATION

Each cave is provided with a 6 figure map reference and the relevant map which the reference refers to. An area map at the beginning of each section will help in determining the relative position of each cave. The altitude is also given which further helps in identifying the correct location.

MAPS

We have used the O.S. Outdoor Leisure Series (yellow covers) 1:25,000 wherever possible. This is because there is greater detail with the hole often being named on the map. Where this has not been possible we have used the O.S. Landranger (pink covers) series 1:50,000. The map number has also been given along with the map title for both series.

ACCESS

Access procedures and approach routes are the most up to date available. As time goes by this information is liable to change as ownership and usage alters. Be polite if approached by a farmer or landowner. Many access problems are those of attitude. The caving press, however, publishes any changes to access arrangements. There are some caves that need to be booked weeks in advance which has to be done through a club. Pirating is to be frowned on as this spoils other legitimate parties fun and causes a lot of ill feeling, as well as jeopardising access agreements.

GRADING

Grading is and can only be a guide. It gives a notional idea as to the length and seriousness of a cave together with stamina required to get to the end – and back out – for the average caver.

Grade 1 Easy cave: no pitches or difficulties.
Grade 2 Moderate caves and small pitches.
Grade 3 Caves and potholes without any particularly hazardous, difficult or strenuous sections.
Grade 4 Caves and potholes which present some hazard, difficulty or large underground pitch.
Grade 5 Caves and potholes which include very strenuous sections or large and wet underground pitches.

SUMPS

There are no descriptions for sump diving. However, some trips do have short dives (or long ducks) e.g. Sump 1 in Swildon's as part of the trip. It is very important that any attempt at these sumps be accompanied by a person who knows the sump and is an experienced diver especially if it is your first one!

FLOODING

Any stream cave or pothole can flood. Some quicker than others and some very unpredictably. Many caves which appear dry can also flood. Warnings given before each cave description are for guidance only and cannot cover every circumstance. No warning does not mean no hazard. Many caves are now more flood prone due to 'gripping', that is drainage ditches being dug into open holes in the ground which may or may not be a cave entrance. These ditches certainly alter the hydrology of caves. The safest maxim is – 'If in doubt, stay out!'

OTHER HAZARDS

Safety is of paramount importance to any party underground. Minimise objective dangers such as stonefall at head of pitches. Ensure that NOBODY climbs ladders without a lifeline. Know how to help a tired caver on a ladder especially if a foot has gone through a rung. Knowledge of fixing a ladder that can be released under load will be very useful, particularly if taking novices, as well as knowledge and ability to use a hauling system.

There are many other potential hazards awaiting the unwary in any cave or pothole, whatever the grade. Make sure that you know the way or have someone in your party that does. Many trips are complicated defying adequate descriptions and as such there is no substitute for an experienced leader.

WEATHER

Weather has a most important effect on cave exploration. Having disregard for forecasts can land you in dead trouble! Flooding directly or indirectly is the single most important factor in caving accidents. It can turn a routine trip into a desperate struggle for survival. The climate of most of the caving areas in this guide is wet because they are in mountainous regions where rain tends to fall far more frequently. It is therefore of great importance that every caver is aware of the current weather trends BEFORE going into a cave.

Recorded weather forecasts, updated every twelve hours can be obtained by ringing the following numbers:

Scotland – 0891 500 425
Yorkshire – 0891 500 417
Derbyshire – 0891 500 412
North Wales – 0891 500 415
South Wales – 0891 500 409
Mendip – 0891 500 405
Devon – 0891 500 404
Fermanagh – 0891 500 427

These calls cost 36p per minute cheap rate, 48p per minute at all other times (Sept 1996).

Information above supplied by Telephone Information Services plc., 24 West Smithfield, London EC1A 9OL, Tel: 0171 975 9000.

Clare – (00 353) 155 012 3850
Irish Special Forecast Services – (00 353) 1 842 4655

FIXED AIDS

The mention of any fixed aids in a cave or pothole is NO guarantee that they are still in place or even safe to use. Some have been in place many years so please check fixed tackle carefully and don't go blithely on.

SINGLE ROPE TECHNIQUES

This is the means by which modern cavers descend vertical caves. The caves in this guide are described using SRT with a few exceptions for a small number of short isolated pitches. Early SRT descents followed the 'traditional' ladder and lifeline routes! However, modern ideals and concepts have done away with this nonsense and now follow 'dry' ways down wet shafts. The gear list for each cave states the amount of rope needed for each pitch and will inevitably include rope for a traverse to avoid the water. The number of hangers to be used is given as a general guide to get you down the hole and back out again. You may find there are other sleeves that can be utilised for your style of rigging, so it is politic to take a few more hangers to account for this. With SRT it is most important that ropes are placed to avoid rub points. It goes without saying that everyone in the team is FULLY conversant with all the techniques involved and that you know how to rescue an unfortunate person stuck on a rope. If in doubt about any of your techniques then a couple of hours in a tree, gym or even at a climbing wall venue to brush up on something you are not sure about will pay dividends underground.

Many 8mm anchors are now untrustworthy, so when rigging be aware of the consequences of a failure. These 8mm anchors are gradually being replaced with stainless steel glue in bolts (ECO hangers), needing only a krab.

It is an easy matter to slide down a rope as very little energy is required. Bear in mind the return journey because it is always more energetic on the way out.

ORIENTATION

Directions given in the descriptions, 'up', 'down', 'right' and 'left' refer to the route as seen in the direction of travel in to a cave or pothole.

ABBREVIATIONS USED IN THE GUIDE

A.C.G.	Axbridge Caving Group
ATLAS	Association of Thrupe Lane Advanced Speleologists
B.C.C.	Burnley Caving Club
B.C.R.A.	British Cave Research Association
B.E.C.	Bristol Exploration Club
B.I.C.C.	Bentham and Ingleton Caving Club
B.N.S.S.S.	British Nylon Spinners Speleological Society
B.S.A.	British Speleological Association
B.U.S.S.	Birmingham University Speleological Society
C.C.C.	Charterhouse Caving Committee
C.C.P.C.	Crewe Caving and Potholing Club
C.D.G.	Cave Diving Group
C.N.C.C.	Council of Northern Caving Clubs
C.P.C.	Craven Potholing Club
C.P.G.	Cave Projects Group
C.S.S.	Chelsea Speleological Society
C.C.C.	Cerberus Caving Club
C.U.C.C.	Cambridge University Caving Club
D.C.A.	Derbyshire Caving Association
D.C.C.	Derbyshire Caving Club
D.H.S.S.	Dent House Speleological Society
D.S.S.	Devon Speleological Society
D.U.G.	Disley Underground Group
E.P.C.	Eldon Pothole Club
E.P.C.	Earby Pothole Club
E.S.C.C.	East Somerset Caving Club
G.C.	Gritstone Club
G.O.C.A.F.	Grwp Ogofeidd Craig-a-Ffynnon
G.S.G.	Grampian Speleological Group
G.S.S.	Glasgow Speleological Society
G.S.S.	Gloucester Speleological Society
H.C.C.	Hereford Caving Club
H.W.C.P.C.	Happy Wanderers Caving and Potholing Club
I.C.D.G.	Independent Cave Diving Group
I.C.R.O.	Irish Cave Rescue Orgnisation

K.C.C.	Kendal Caving Club
L.U.C.C.	London University Caving Club
L.U.S.S.	Lancaster University Speleological Society
M.C.G.	Mendip Caving Group
M.N.R.C.	Mendip Nature Research Committee
M.S.G.	Moldywarps Speleological Group
M.U.S.S.	Manchester University Speleological Society
N.C.A.	National Caving Association
N.C.C.	Northern Caving Club
N.C.F.C.	Northen Cavern and Fell Club
N.H.A.S.A.	North Hill Association for Speleological Advancement
N.P.C.	Northern Pennine Club
N.R.C.G.	North Ribblesdale Caving Group
N.S.G.	Northern Speleological Group
N.W.C.C.	North Wales Caving Club
N.W.P.C.	North-west Pothole Club
O.C.C.	Orpheus Caving Club
P.C.C.	Preston Caving Club
P.C.G.	Plymouth Caving Group
P.P.S.G.	Preston Polytechnic Speleological Group
R.F.D.C.C.	Royal Forest of Dean Caving Club
R.R.C.P.C.	Red Rose Caving and Potholing Club
R.S.C.	Rock Steady Crew
S.M.C.C.	Shepton Mallet Caving Club
S.S.S.I.	Special Site of Scientific Interest
S.U.I.	Speleological Union of Ireland
S.U.M.C.C.	Sheffield University Mountaineering and Caving Club
S.U.S.S.	Sheffield University Speleological Society
S.V.C.C.	Severn Valley Caving Group
S.W.C.C.	South Wales Caving Club
S.W.E.T.C.C.	South West Essex Technical Caving Club
T.S.G.	Technical Speleological Group
T.V.C.G.	Teifi Valley Caving Group
U.B.S.S.	University of Bristol Speleological Society
U.L.S.A.	University of Leeds Speleological Association
W.C.C.	Wessex Caving Club
W.N.H.A.S.	Wells Natural History & Archaeological Society
W.R.P.C.	White Rose Pothole Club
Y.R.C.	Yorkshire Ramblers Club
Y.S.A.	Yorkshire Speleological Assocition
Y.S.S.	Yorkshire Subterannean Society
Y.U.R.T.	Yorkshire Underground Research Team

SCOTLAND
by Alan Jeffreys

Alan Jeffreys, B.E.M. began caving in the late 1950's, inspired by the achievements of Norbert Casteret (and Rupert Bear!). He has caved all over the British Isles and contributed to new explorations in Somerset, Yorkshire and County Clare. With his main interest being channelled into the development of Speleology in Scotland, he founded the Grampian Speleological Group in 1961 and in 1996 established the Scottish Cave Rescue Organisation. He writes extensively on caving and has produced several monographs on the subject and is currently the regional correspondent for Descent Magazine. He has a significant number of Scottish discoveries to his credit.

PRINCIPAL CAVING AREAS IN SCOTLAND

INTRODUCTION

Despite its rich highland landscape, Scotland does not possess extensive caving areas, although large exposures of limestone are known.

The principle caving districts are situated in:

1. N.W.Sutherland. Cambrian limestones outcrop at Durness on the extreme north coast, and again in Assynt Parish, 50 miles further south.

2. Kishorn. The same Cambrian exposures feature at Kishorn, where a few small caves have been recorded.

3. Applecross. Jurassic limestone houses at least one significant system.

4. Skye. Cambrian limestones near Broadford, and some Jurassic outcrops, are penetrated by a prolific number of stream caves.

5. Appin, Argyll. Large areas of metamorphosed limestones have been found to be cavernous. Many sporting systems have been explored here in the last two decades.

6. Schiehallion, Perthshire. Slim exposures of metamorphosed limestones at the base of the mountain possess small, awkward caves in three main groups.

Many other limestone caves have been discovered away from these main areas, and their number increases year by year. They are all recorded by the Grampian Speleological Group, which is the Scottish caving club most active north of the border. The Group also maintain a field base in Sutherland.

USEFUL ADDRESSES

Tourist Information Office,
Meall House,
Portree,
Isle of Skye
Tel 01478 612137

Tourist Information Office,
West Shore Street,
Ullapool,
Ross-shire
Tel 01854 612135

Contact address for the G.S.G.
8 Scone Gardens,
Edinburgh EH8 7DQ

ACCOMMODATION

The G.S.G. maintain a field hut at Knockan hamlet and another at Elphin. Keys from
P. Dowswell,
58 Victoria Road,
Kirkcaldy,
Fife

Assynt, N.W. Sutherland

Assynt Parish contains Scotland's finest and longest limestone caves. Cambrian outcrops are most well developed at Traligill, above the hamlet of Inchnadamph in the Allt nan Uamh Valley some three kilometres further south and in a basin behind the village of Elphin, on the Ullapool road. Thrust faults and glaciation have modified or dominated cave development, particularly in Traligill, where wide sloping streamways are common. Recent explorations have revealed caverns much older than previously suspected and the possibility of large, integrated systems is now much more likely.

ALLT NAN UAMH VALLEY, ASSYNT, SUTHERLAND

UAMH AN CLAONAITE (Cave of the Sloping Rock)   Grade 3

**Grid Ref: NC 270165   O.S. Landranger Series No 15 – Loch Assynt,
1:50,000.   Altitude: 343m   Length: 1,800m   Depth: 58m**

First explored by K.C.C. in 1967. Extended, S.W.C.C. in 1978 and thereafter by
G.S.G. 1979 – 83.

Permission: Check with keeper in Stroncrubie Cottage during the deer stalking
season.

WARNING: Most of the system lies beyond a sump bypass which will become
treacherous in high water and may sump. CARE: The entrance passes through a
boulder choke of dubious stability.

Claonaite is THE Scottish river cave, providing an excellent trip in a varied and
challenging environment.

The entrance lies under a small cliff at the head of a dry watercourse leading off
southwards from the head of Allt nan Uamh Valley, and thence by a 3m thrutch

through boulders to a spacious streamway (upstream impassable). A 5m waterfall may be free-climbed but drier route is a roof level traverse to the right descending by ledges to the main cavern. At the far end the roof dips to a deep pool where an abrupt left hand corner offers an aqueous eyehole to a bouldery continuation and easy going to Sump 1 (30m, not free diveable).

The bypass is a low angled crawl to the left of the sump pool. In dry weather a crawl straight forward leads to roomier going but the normal route is a partial duck under a rock arch on the right a metre in. Beyond, boulder floored passages lead back to the main stream at the Sump 1 exit. On the opposite side an obvious route leads into The Igloo and Levitation Sump Series.

Follow the main stream in a comfortable low tunnel to a 2m fall into Bottomless Pillar Pool, best passed by a careful traverse on the left (footholds below water level) to a junction with Capital Series on the right and twin waterfalls taking the river sharp left. At the foot a wide ponded area ends where the cave turns right to exploit the vertical junction between two limestones (Cavity Wall Passage) which culminates after 60m in two remarkable 'Watershoots' (care needed in high water) connected by a deep pool. At the foot of the second Watershoot the river enters Sump 2 but an obvious climb on the right gains a dry cavern strewn with breakdown, which can be crossed to a short rock tunnel and a boulder pile which gradually descends about 15m to Sump 3 (23m), the end of the cave for non-divers. The cave continues to Sump 6, the present terminus, in mainly cramped passages.

At the top of the final boulder pile, a cairn marks the junction with Mud Passage, an upward crawl ending in The East Bloc, a series of old dry, phreatic caverns. At the far end a complex choke may be passed to enter Infinite Improbability Inlet, a narrow, entertaining passage currently blocked by a huge mud choke after 100m. Survey ref: Uamh An Claonaite, G.S.G.

ALLT NAN UAMH STREAM CAVE (Burn of the Caves)   Grade 2/4

Grid Ref: NC 274171   O.S. Landranger Series No 15 – Loch Assynt, 1:50,000.   Altitude: 320m   Length: 1,500m   Vertical range: 40m

Permission: The cave lies on Nature Conservancy Reserve, and a check should be made with the keeper at Stroncrubie Cottage during the deer stalking season.

Located parallel to a streambed only active in flood, ANUS Cave was opened by S.U.M.C.C. in 1948, after chiselling away obstructions. A major extension was achieved from the upstream sump by S.W.C.C. in 1976 and other discoveries have been made by G.S.G. in the years since then.

Follow the Allt nan Uamh Valley to its head, and take the left hand fork. The entrance will be found at the foot of a small cliff on the left bank, just after the point where a high level footpath is interrupted by a scree slope.

A cemented boulder dam marks the entrance which consists of a body length thrutch down a rock tube into a spacious, flat floored cavern. Easy walking to Piccadilly Junction and a choice of routes.

Straight on a mud slope leads up into the impressive Oxford Street and Breakdown Chamber and at the far end a small left hand tunnel develops into Parallel Crawl, a sporting trip which brings the visitor back to the vicinity of Piccadilly, forming an entertaining round trip.

Below the floor of the junction runs the active stream series becoming seriously tight at the furthest upstream point. Downstream it enters the First Stream Chamber and sumps.

From Piccadilly, a short traverse around the left wall above First Stream Chamber opens into a large passage which extends for 25m to Drip Chamber and a choice of ways on which lead either to The Pit (where the main water emerges from a sump) or in a downstream direction to Second Stream Chamber, easily recognisable from the impressive syphon used to maintain access to the Static Sump Series beyond, where some unpleasant crawls end in disgusting aqua-mud filled bifurcations.

Beyond the 85m sump in The Pit lies a considerable extension which almost certainly will possess a surface entrance in the near future.

Survey ref: Allt nan Uamh Stream Cave, G.S.G.

CNOC NAN UAMH SYSTEM (Hill of the Caves)   Grade 2/3

Grid Ref: NC 276206   O.S. Landranger Series No 15 – Loch Assynt, 1:50,000.   Altitude: 221m   Length: 1,400m   Vertical range: 83m

First published exploration by Y.R.C. in 1935. Cave fully explored by S.U.M.C.C. in 1947-50 and extended in 1975 by U.B.S.S.

WARNING: In flood the Waterslide becomes extremely dangerous.

Permission: The cave is on a footpath within a Nature Conservancy Reserve.

TRALIGILL VALLEY, SUTHERLAND

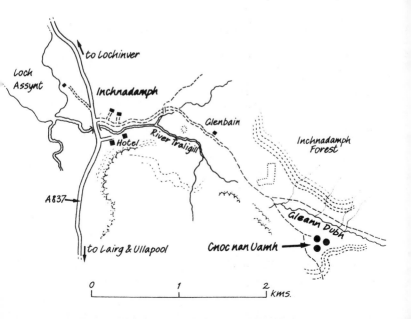

Courtesy demands a check with the keeper at Inchnadamph during the deer stalking season.

"Cnockers" is a deservedly popular tourist trip and consequently has suffered the usual stalactite depravation, but still offers good, undemanding sport. It lies beside a well worn footpath at the head of Traligill Valley, on the western slope of Cnoc nan Uamh.

The three entrances lie in close proximity. The Waterslide, a remarkable thrust fault feature open at the top; Uamh and Uisge, a 20m open shaft a few metres uphill and Uamh an Tartair, an open rock shelter further round the corner of the hill. Access is thus gained to the central section of the cave, and explorations are feasible up and downstream.

From Uamh an Tartair a low crawl from daylight enters a large cavern, First Stream Chamber, with a substantial river flowing from left to right. By crossing straight over, several small exits will be found in the opposite wall which lead to a complicated multi-level phreatic area complete with decorated caverns and waterlogged lower levels. All routes to the right eventually peter out and a choice of routes to the left lead back to the river culminating upstream in a 2m spouting waterfall climb.

Above, a spacious passage formed through piles of large breakdown leads into Landslide Chamber, the largest cavern in Assynt, where much of the floor is comprised of a deep lake. High above, at the summit of a steep gravel slope, are entrances to the Rabbit Warren and Inner Circuit, a collection of greasy crawls and squeezes.

Beyond Landslide Chamber, obvious exits at floor level coalesce into a fine rectangular passage extending for 30m to a long, steepening mud slope and the unpleasant Static Sump (45m). This has been passed into the upstream continuation of the river via several long dives.

Back at First Stream Chamber, by following water downstream, an exhilarating traverse of a narrow streamway with copious amounts of deep water eventually opens into Uamh an Uisge and the Waterslide.

Formed by the Traligill Thrust Plane, this is a spectacular 30 degree decent down a very wide cavern filled with the roar of predominantly white water. At the foot, some 100 metres below, a short lateral passage ends at the main downstream sump. In wet conditions, the lower reaches of the Waterslide will be sumped.

Survey ref: Cnoc nan Uamh System, Obtainable from Mendip Cave Survey Scheme.

Skye

The Cambrian limestone outcrop on Skye lies south of the A831 and immediately east of Loch Slapin. Due to an upthrust gabbro plug in the centre, run off occurs all round the limestone hillsides giving rise to dozens of excellent, if short, caving trips. Of the longer systems, High Pasture Cave and Valley Head Cave are perhaps the best.

UAMH CINN GHLINN (Valley Head Cave)   Grade 4

Grid Ref: NG 601182   O.S. Landranger Series No 32 – South Skye and Arisaig, 1:50,000.   Altitude: 156m   Length: 376m   Depth: 23m

Moldywarps Speleo Group opened up the system in two separate sections between 1971 and 1973. In 1972, U.C.L.S.S. penetrated the upstream sink and

ALLT NAN LEAC VALLEY, SKYE

this was extended by M.S.G. the following year. The first, connecting through trip was achieved by the same club in 1975.

WARNING: The lower reaches of this cave are waterlogged, and sump easily. Not to be attempted as a through trip in wet weather.

The system really consists of two caves, Cinn Ghlinn (the lower half) and Uamh Ceann Mullach a'Chlinn (Upper Valley Head Cave) embracing the top sink and subsequent extension. The top entrance lies some metres north of a grassy climb out of the head of the Allt nan Leac valley which commences at the shore of Loch Slapin.

It is possible to enter the cave at its sink point, but a tight duck there is most unpleasant whilst 20m downstream an excavated 4m drop through earth and gravel is the most popular way in.

A narrow but easy fissure extends for 21m through very decorative rock to a sudden diminution at the first duck – a 10m wallow through a small triangular tunnel – and easier crawling to the start of some stimulating cascades. The Spiral Staircase, enhanced by red garnet coloration, terminates in a small chamber. An aven on the left here almost certainly leads to a choked entrance.

Crawling forward in the stream, a series of small cascades create an invigorating descent to a narrow fissure in unstable rock which after some 10m develops into a bedding crawl floored by a jagged chert-ridden surface. The low section ends with a 3m climb into Campanile Chamber, the biggest void in the cave. Huge blocks of breakdown obscure the way on but a choice of tightish exits reunite in the lower section of the system, whose deeply waterlogged passages should be followed with care to a duck and further low airspace crawls – The Anabaptist Series. A small chamber with a large block in the floor marks the free diveable sump (minimal airspace in dry weather), 1m long, into a ponded chamber of Uamh Cinn Ghlinn. Wet crawls of more comfortable dimensions end at Chantry Chamber, a boulder-floored cavern with blind high level exits. The main route is a low wet crawl for 24m leading to the Lower Entrance at a boulder fall.

Survey ref: Uamh Cinn Ghlinn, M.S.G.

Appin Area, Western Argyll

Caves here are formed in metamorphosed Ballachulish limestones, and are located in distinct pockets at Glen Duror, Glen Stockdale and Glen Creran. Dense afforestation has rendered the northern reaches of Glen Stockdale extremely difficult to traverse, and some caves may be almost impossible to locate.

Uamh nan Claig-ionn however, is easily approached. Cars should be parked at the head of a forestry track where a gate closes the way into Glen Stockdale. Walk up the track round a sharp left and then right hand turn. Leave the track at the next left turn and cross to the hillside straight ahead. The cave lies just inside the plantation tree line where a small burn runs down into the limestone.

UAMH NAN CLAIG-IONN (Cave of the Skulls)   Grade 3

Grid Ref: NM 982513   O.S. Landranger Series No 49 – Oban and East Mull, 1:50,000.   Altitude: 215m   Length: 160m   Depth: 48m

First explored by G.S.G. in 1977, and explored to the sump. Extensions beyond sump 1 made in 1977-78, also by G.S.G.

Argyll specialises in decorative cave entrances and Claig-ionn is no exception, consisting of a pretty 4m waterfall flanked by ferns which discharges a small stream into an open rift, accessed by a greasy sloping ledge at the south end.

A narrow, triangular passage slopes gradually out of daylight, degrading over a distance of 10m into a low crawl where it turns through a sharp 'S' bend before developing into comfortable hands and knees going for 6m. The end coincides with a drop down and directly under the way in. An awkward tube ends abruptly at a 5m pitch, free climbable with care by those with long legs. (In wet weather the whole shaft is filled with cold, stinging spray). Below, an easy 2m climb leads into Nutwood High Street, a lofty stream passage running N-S.

Upstream, the going quickly closes in to a low triangular crawl for 100m to a usually silted up exit into Uamh Mnathan an Duror, the main sink.

Downstream at the point of entry, Nutwood High Street develops into a handsome rift passage in shiny black rock and suddenly opens out half way down a 25m shaft. Water crashes down a vertical 13m pitch topped by enormous sloping boulders which provide ample belay points. A rock pinnacle to the right gives a free SRT hang.

Below, a flat circular chamber leads to a tall sinuous fissure, practically choked at one point by poised flakes – the House of Cards. Just beyond, the floor peters out along a diminishing ledge and the way on is over a rock lip on the left, a 4m wet pitch into a stormy basin (Dealer's Drop).

The cave has now developed into a high rift which ultimately bells out to form the final chamber. Some 2m traversing forward from Dealer's Drop leads to a ledge

Glenstockdale – Appin Argyll

where it is possible to straddle the final drop, Chest Pot, whose upper section is tight and awkward.

A sandy floored chamber 15m long ends at a blank wall, but the river flows away under the left hand side and a flat out 3m wet crawl – which may silt up – can be passed into easier going. Hands and knees progress along a distorted little passage ends with a sharp right turn into Sump 1. This is usually short, but is not recommended as a free dive, due to obstructions in the roof.

Tackle:

	Rope length required	Bolts	Remarks
Pitch 1	15m	3	Slings.
Pitch 2		1	8m ladder recommended, belay to bolt in floor, 15m safety line.
Pitch 3	12m		Rope or ladder belayed to rawlbolt in left wall above pitch.

Survey ref: Uamh nan Claig-ionn, G.S.G.

Applecross, Ross-Shire

Applecross is one of the remoter villages in western Scotland. It has a small exposure of Jurassic limestone and very few cave features. However, there is one system worth visiting. Potential exists for extensions here and elsewhere in the district.

UAMH AN BREAGAIRE (Cave of the Liar)   Grade 3/4

Grid Ref: NG 717438   O.S. Landranger Series No 24 – Raasay, Applecross and Loch Torridon, 1:50,000.   Altitude: 122m   Length: 517m Depth: 43m

The cave appears to have first been entered by staff at the nearby West Highland School of Adventure in 1974. The lower entrance was added by the G.S.G. in 1975.

Permission: Best to enquire in the village, but it is possible to visit the cave by leaving the A896 from above the hillside and traversing down the Allt na Breagaire.

From the seaside hamlet of Milton follow the Allt na Breagaire upstream to a limestone gill. The entrances will be found on the left bank where the gill describes a 'Z' bend.

Two entrances are presently open – the upper main entrance being a small 3m vertical drop into a cramped streamway. The subsidiary, Lower entrance lies some 20m further downstream at a small, insignificant cliff opening in the bank. Both entrance routes run straight into the hillside on parallel courses and may from time to time be blocked by flood waters in the ravine.

Climbing down the main entrance (beware of loose rock) a 5m crawl leads forward into easier going and walking passage for 20m to a junction where the stream is captured by a low, cobblestone tunnel to the right. The obvious, larger route is a spacious crawl for 22m to a sharp left turn and a wider section of crawl ending in a boulder strewn chamber with several oxbows leading off. Above the rubble at the left wall a joint controlled fissure develops into an uncomfortable crawl, Jawbone Passage, which gains in size before reaching daylight at the Lower Entrance after 60m.

APPLECROSS, ROSS-SHIRE

From the chamber, a triangular thrutch opposite the point of entry leads to a series of breakdown dominated passages with abrupt right angled corners and a tight squeeze before the natural line of the cave is regained. Some further crawling opens into Breakdown (alternatively Balcony) Chamber where straw formations affected by rock movement can be seen. Passing the formations with care, particularly the gour pools in the flat out crawl which follows, access is gained to walking height passage ending at a sharp left turn into Flowstone Pot. This 10m shaft is entirely filled by excellent formations and should not be descended as there is no way out at the bottom.

A 'T' junction on the right some metres before Flowstone Pot leads to a small widening with an athletic squirm through an eyehole into a larger chamber. The exit is a horizontal slot, extremely tight, which continues as hands and knees crawl for some 20m over breakdown, ending at Straw Chamber, a spectacular hall liberally decorated with long straw stalactites. Rubble on the floor descends steeply to a

miserable sandy crawl which pinches in after 30m. Several blind inlets occur in the lower reaches of the chamber.
Survey ref: Uamh an Breagaire, M.S.G.

Bibliography

Jeffreys, A.L. (1984) Scotland Underground. Out of print.
Jeffreys, A.L. (1977) Uamh nan Claig-ionn. G.S.G. Bulletin, 2nd Series Vol 2 No 1.
Lawson, T. et al (1988) Caves of Assynt. G.S.G. Occ. Publ. No 6.
Mehew, R.D. (1977) Uamh an Breagaire. G.S.G. Bulletin, 2nd Series Vol 1 No 5.
Ryder, P. (1982) Expedition to Skye and Applecross. G.S.G. Bulletin, 2nd Series Vol 3 No 5
Ryder, P.F.R. (1976) New Explorations. M.S.G. Journal 8.
Young, I. (1978) Appin Cave Guide. G.S.G. Special Publication No 1.

YORKSHIRE
by Des Marshall and Nigel Robertson

Nigel Robertson started caving in 1977 with both Aberdeen and Manchester Universities followed by a year working for Whernside Manor. Whilst living in Scotland for 10 years he was an active member of the Grampian Speleological Group. For the last 5 years he has lived in the Yorkshire Dales working at Inglesport and becoming the Equipment Officer of the C.R.O.

INTRODUCTION

The premier region for potholing in Britain, Yorkshire possess the longest system in Britain – the Easegill system – and the deepest underground pitch (other than mine shafts) – Vulcan – in Nick Pot.

There are over 1,000 square mile of mountains and spectacular wild moorlands overlaying the limestone in the region with each area having it's own style of caving. For instance the caves around Ingleborough, Penyghent, Kingsdale and Leck Fell are in general vertical before developing horizontally whilst further east in the other caving areas the caves are mainly horizontal in nature having shorter pitches if any at all. It is this diversity that makes Yorkshire such a fine area. Many of the pots and caves carry large streams which add interest and excitement.

The region is easily accessible by road and travel between each caving area is fairly straightforward. The main centre in the west and, perhaps, the focal point of the region, is Ingleton easily reached from the M6 – junction 34 – along the A683 and A687.

The region has been split into separate area sections for ease of reference and are: Alum Pot; Kingsdale; Easegill; Leck Fell and Marble Steps; Fountains Fell, Penyghent and Birkwith; Great Whernside, Wharfedale, Langstrothdale, Lower Littondale, Darnbrook and Penyghent Gill and finally Nidderdale and Dentdale.

Caving started here in the mists of time with one of the first recorded explorations being of Gaping Gill Main Shaft by J. Birkwith, who reached the ledge named after him, some 60m down, in the 1840's. Since then exploration of the caves gathered momentum with the golden age being the latter end of the 1800's to 1920 when all the major vertical pots were discovered and partially, if not fully, explored. The history of Yorkshire caving is tinged with many epics and sagas of exploration, especially as equipment in those far off days was, to say the least, rudimentary. Clothing was bulky and soaked up water, hemp ropes and ladders having wooden rungs did not make for lightweight caving as equipment was generally hung down the direct line of any waterfall. A far cry from today's lightweight, warm clothing and state of the art SRT equipment with modern technology enabling bolting to be done to avoid water on vertical pitches. What was once a weekend trip to rig and de-rig, a pot can now be done in a matter of hours.

Accommodation abounds in Yorkshire, from the many B and B's to bunkhouse style in the caving club huts and private enterprise.

ACCESS AGREEMENTS

As access agreements frequently change it is advisable to check on the current status with the C.N.C.C. Access and Conservation Officer enclosing an S.A.E.

EASEGILL

Midweek access can be arranged through T. Bowring.
For weekend access apply to Pete Muckalt.
Access to Easegill caves is via Hellot Scales Barn and NOT over the moor.
Destination board at Bull Pot Farm (the R.R.C.P.C. hut) must be filled in. Permission now needs to be obtained for Aygill Caverns.

LECK FELL

Only two permits per day plus one in Pippikin.
Written application to C.N.C.C. 1 month in advance.
Right to withdraw permits for shooting.
Routes to caves must be strictly adhered to.
Permits to be shown at Bank House Farm.
NO potholing between 1st April and 30th June.

PENYGHENT AND FOUNTAINS FELL

Written application to C.N.C.C. 1 month in advance.
Only 1 club per pothole to be permited on any day.
Right to withdraw permits for shooting days in August / September / October.
For caves in the Penyghent area (west of Stainforth – Halton Gill road) please call on the gamekeeper, Mr G. Perfect at Brackenbottom in Horton-in-Ribblesdale.
For Fountains Fell the farmer renews the situation annually.
Please submit requests by the end of January of the year in question.

BIRKS FELL CAVE

The agreed access is through Birks Fell Cave entrance ONLY unless written consent is obtained from the agents and tenant of Redmire Farm. The agents are Messrs Dacre Son & Hartley.
No cars to be taken to Redmire Farm. Please park in Buckden car park.
Access is only granted to C.N.C.C. member clubs, one per day.
NO access between 1st November and 15th April the following year.
When going to the cave please call at Redmire Farm as well as on return.
The tenant may deny access on any day giving reasonable notice.
The owner retains the right to terminate the agreement at any time by giving written notice.

CLOSED SEASONS

LECK FELL	1st April–30th June.
PIPPIKIN / NIPPIKIN / ETC	April, May and June.
BIRKS FELL	1st November–15th April the following year.
ALLOTMENT, All Pots	31st March–1st October.
FOUNTAINS FELL	1st November–2nd week end in May.

Access to Langcliffe Pot and Mossdale Caverns

Due to poor relations with the owners of the land around Langcliffe and Mossdale they have not been described in this guide. If the situation improves they will be included in a future edition.
If any cave requires permission to enter then it is imperative that this permission is sought before entering.

For further information please see the Handbook of the C.N.C.C. 1993 and subsequent updates.

USEFUL ADDRESSES

For access to C.N.C.C. controlled caves your club meets secretary will organise trips by writing to the relevant meets/access secretary

Mr P Parker
C.N.C.C. Access and Conservation Officer
11 Mansion Gardens
Crossgates
Leeds LS15 8EY

P. Muckalt
Casterton Fell (Easegill)
Meet Secretary
96 Low Lane
Torrisholme
Morecambe LA4 6PP
Send s.a.e.

T. Bowering
Hawkshead Farm
Halton Park
Lancaster
LA2 6PD
Tel 01524 811361
Send s.a.e.

For Aygill Caverns write to:
The Estate Office
Cowan Bridge
Via Carnforth
Lancs LA6 2HS
Send s.a.e.

Mr L. Sykes
C.N.C.C. Secretary
49 Manfield
Ashurst, Skelmersdale WN8 6SU
Send s.a.e.

For access to caves on the Allotment, Gaping Gill and Newby Moss apply to:
Dr. J. A. Farrer
Ingleborough Estate Office
Clapham
Via Lancaster
Send s.a.e.
Tel 01524 251302. Office open between 8.30 a.m. and 1 p.m. weekdays only.

Access to Hagg Gill Pot and all other caves on Raisgill land, call at Raisgill Farm or write to:
Mr Charnley
Raisgill Farm
Hubberholme
Buckden
Skipton BD23 5JQ
Send s.a.e.

ACCOMMODATION

Bull Pot Farm (R.R.C.P.C. Hut)
Ron Bliss
9 Summerersgill Road
Lancaster LA1 2RT

Lowstern Cottage (Y.R.C. Hut)
Ken Aldred
5 Tribune Drive
Houghton
Carlisle CA3 0LE

Greenclose (N.P.C. Hut)
Ring Patrick O'Connel on 01792 822014 early evening OR Andy Goddard 01978 812100 during the day.

Station Inn, Ribblehead. 01524 241274

The Old School, Chapel le Dale.
Contact:
Mr & Mrs Wild
0152 4242327

Dalebridge Centre (also lamp hire)
Jon Beavan
Dalebridge Centre
Austwick
Near Settle
LA2 8AZ
0152 42 51021

TOURIST INFORMATION OFFICES

Dales Countryside Museum
Station Yard
Hawes
North Yorkshire DL8 3NT
Tel 01969 667450

Penyghent Cafe
Horton in Ribblesdale
Settle
North Yorkshire BD24 0HE
Tel 01729 860333

Community Centre Car Park
Ingleton
North Yorkshire LA6 3HJ
Tel 015242 41049

Town Hall
Cheapside
Settle
North Yorkshire BD24 9EJ
Tel 01729 825192

GEAR HIRE

Ingleport
11 The Square
Ingleton
Via Carnforth LA6 3EB
Tel 015242 41146

Bernies
4 Main Street
Ingleton
Via Carnforth LA6 3EB
Tel 015242 41802

Cave & Crag
Market Place
Settle
North Yorks BD24 9ED
Tel 01729 823877

Over & Under
Middle Lane
Kettlewell
Skipton
North Yorks BD23 5QX
Tel 01756 760871 Shop Hours
Out of hours 01535 691587

CAFES

Ingleton:
  Inglesport
  Bernies
  Fountain Cafe

PUBS

New Inn, Clapham
Marton Arms, Thornton in Lonsdale, nr Ingleton

Looking up to daylight from the bottom of Alum Pot. Photo: Paul Deakin

A fine array of stalactites in the far reaches of White Scar Cave.
Photo: Paul Deakin

Ingleborough – Alum Pot Area

ALUM POT   Grade 3

Grid Ref: SD 775756   O.S. Outdoor Leisure Series No 2, Yorkshire Dales – Western Area, 1:25,000.   Altitude: 347m   Length: 522m   Depth: 104m

In 1870 Boyd Dawkins and friends made the first direct descent! Extensions made in 1978 and 1990 by the C.D.G.

Please call at Selside Farm for permission. A small access fee is payable.

Park cars to the side of the rough track, tidily so that the farmer has access. Where the track bends left at 90 degrees, a stile, with a gate on the left, is climbed over. Follow a track to the clump of trees surrounding this classic and dramatic hole. There is, unfortunately, not a lot of cave at the bottom, but what there is is quite impressive.

North-west side

This is THE way in! Go over stile at NW corner of enclosure and belay rope to large tree. Drop down to ledge and rebelay. A further dirty descent for another 7m reaches an exposed and rather impressive rebelay point. A magnificent drop of 60m reaches the ledge close to the head of the final pitch. The lower 20m of the shaft can be unpleasantly wet where it descends a mossy section, so a deviation can be arranged at –38m from a thread by swinging across towards the bridge to avoid the wetness. This then drops down onto some boulders close to the last pitch. Down the 11m last pitch to enter darkness. On the left a dry oxbow avoids a cascade and enters the draughty final chamber with the water from Diccan entering on the right. The sump is only a few metres further.

Tackle:

	Rope length required	Bolts	Remarks
North-west side:			
Main pitch	80m	4	Eco hangers, belay rope to trees at surface. Deviation at –38m.
Final pitch	20m	2	Eco hangers, belay rope to boulder 3m from pitch head.

Survey ref: The Caves of the Alum Pot area published by U.L.S.A.

DICCAN POT   Grade 4

Grid Ref: SD 775757   O.S. Outdoor Leisure Series No 2, Yorkshire Dales – Western Area, 1:25,000.   Altitude: 352m   Length: 91m   Depth: 108m

First explored by the Y.R.C. in 1923 with the first complete descent being made in 1932 by the G.C.

Please call Selside Farm for permission. A small access fee is payable.

WARNING: Diccan takes a large stream which responds very quickly to heavy rainfall. It is also a very draughty cave.

A fine sporting, vertical cave.

Approaching as for Alum Pot, Diccan is situated 91m NNW in the first (lower of two) enclosures. The entrance is low, wide and takes the stream. This soon enlarges and reaches a pool, (passage on right links into Lower Long Churn beyond Double Shuffle and Plank pools). Stooping passage continues to a deeper pool and the head of the first pitch. A thread before the pitch on the left gives access to the pitch head where the water spills over the lip and splashes onto a small ledge 5m down. A guide line is in place to keep dry (if you clip a cow's tail to it) on the first part of the pitch and lands in an alcove 5m down. Here a rebelay allows the bottom of the shaft to be reached via a deviation, at a large flat ledge, which is a cold, draughty and wet place, with the second pitch following immediately. A large thread to the right where the shaft is undercut provides a good belay.

The ensuing boulder rift leads to two short drops, best treated as a pitch, the third. Traversing out at a higher level drops close to the head of the spectacular fourth pitch. Traverse across the shaft as far as possible. Descend 10m and pendulum to reach the far side of the shaft and rebelay. Two more rebelays 5 metres apart and a deviation lands on a ledge where a rebelay for the final 8m of the shaft is found.

Tackle:

	Rope length required	Bolts	Remarks
Pitch 1 and 2	60m	5	Thread at head of pitch. Flake for deviation at –14m. Thread at head of pitch 2.
Pitch 3	30m	7	Deviations at –8m and –13m.
Pitch 4	60m	12	Deviation at –23m.

Survey ref: The Caves of the Alum Pot area published by U.L.S.A.

LOWER LONG CHURN   Grade 3

Grid Ref: SD 773757   O.S. Outdoor Leisure Series No 2, Yorkshire Dales – Western Area, 1:25,000.   Altitude: 351m   Length: 366m   Depth: 107m

The first complete descent was, remarkably, accomplished by J Birkbeck and party in 1848!

Please call Selside Farm for permission. A small access fee is payable.

Approaching as for Alum Pot, the Churns are situated some 200m NW in a fenced enclosure. (Do not confuse this one with the lower enclosure, which is Diccan Pot). There are two entrances, the left hand one, with a hawthorn at the top, being Upper Long Churn and the right hand larger one Lower Long Churn. Water emerges from Wilson's Cave and flows into the depression.

A fine though heavily used cave. Follow the bouldery floor to the stream passage, waterfall to the right and follow water downstream to next patch of daylight, seen on the left. Leave the stream to enter obvious large passage. (Stream continues to Diccan Pot). Passage continues past Cross Passage on the right coming from Upper Long Churn. Two amusing pools are crossed in quick succession. Usually, novices get wet here!

The first pool is called Double Shuffle and the second, Plank. Passage on left links into entrance passage of Diccan. Soon after, the passage cuts down in a rift and a climb down reaches the famous Cheese Press. Fatties keep out! This obstacle is avoided on the right by an awkward 3m climb down to enter a large chamber. This point can be reached by going above the Cheese Press, thus avoiding the climb down, to an easy climb down and short stooping passage leading into the large chamber.

Dollytubs pitch is a few metres further on and daylight can be seen glistening on the walls. Although slightly longer than the nearer hang, the 17m pitch is best rigged as far without as possible beyond some boulders, as it is drier. A small flake ledge half way down is traversed out to another hang to land in a large boulder strewn passage which quickly emerges into daylight. A superb view of Alum Pot shaft.

Most novice trips end at this point. From here a wandering route descends to the bottom of the shaft. Initially over boulders on the left to reach the Greasy Slab, a pitch of 10m. A ledge to the right is traversed (care – rope advisable) to The Bridge which spans the shaft obliquely and at a steep angle. Although an easy climb it is better regarded as a pitch. This lands on the ledge at the junction with the South East route down Alum Pot.

Continue as for this route in pitches of 27m (belay to Eco hangers on side of bridge facing Dollytubs and a deviation at –5m) and 11m. Into the dark and follow the stream to a dry oxbow on the left, which avoids a cascade, into a deep pool. A rather noisy chamber, with large waterfall (last pitch of Diccan), is entered with the sump a short distance away.

Tackle:

	Rope length required	Eco hangers	Remarks
Dollytubs	35m	4	1 thread.
Greasy Slab	20m	3	
Traverse & Bridge	35m	6	
Pitch beneath bridge	45m	4	Deviation at −5m.
Final Pitch	20m	2	Belay rope to boulder 3m from pitch head.

Survey ref: The Caves of the Alum Pot area published by U.L.S.A.

UPPER LONG CHURN   Grade 2

Grid Ref: SD 773757 entrance, SD 772755 exit   O.S. Outdoor Leisure Series No 2, Yorkshire Dales – Western Area, 1:25,000.   Altitude: 351m Length: 762m   Depth: +18m

Please call at Selside Farm for permission – lower entrance (small access fee payable) and Gillgarth Farm – if entering via top entrance or exploring Borrins Moor Cave.

Approach as for Lower Long Churn.

Go along stooping passage to a junction with the stream. Downstream leads into Lower Long Churn. Walk upstream (the first passage on the left follows a low damp crawl to Lower Long Churn) following the fine flat roofed passage to Dr. Bannister's Handbasin, where a 5m chute of water descends into a pool. An awkward climb, for the short legged, leads to daylight after a few feet. Care with slippery rock at the exit. There is an Eco hanger 4m back from the chute for a handline, recommended for novices. Return the same way for double the fun, or back over the clints to the NE to cross the wall via a stile to the start. However, Borrins Moor Cave is only a 60m walk away upstream. This makes a good extension, starting off with a wide, wet canal which soon leads into some large drier passages interspersed with lower sections.

Tackle:
Dr. Banister's Handbasin: 10m rope as handline or safety line for novices.
Survey ref: The Caves of the Alum Pot area published by U.L.S.A.

WASHFOLD POT   Grade 5

Grid Ref: SD 774765   O.S. Outdoor Leisure Series No 2, Yorkshire Dales – Western Area, 1:25,000.   Altitude: 366m   Length: 312m   Depth: 112m

First explored in 1933 by the G.C. with the N.C.F.C. completing explorations in 1934.

A C.N.C.C. permit is required for this cave.

One of the less frequently visited deep pots of the Ingleborough area, Washfold is dominated by a fine 40m shaft and displays more than its fair share of relatively unspoilt formations. It is definitely not a trip for novices or the unfit. Despite a perfect hang, the big pitch becomes impassable in flood, sections of the canyon above and stream crawls below, flood to the roof. The big pitch itself is perhaps the most straightforward part of the descent, other sections frequently being awkward and strenuous, succumbing only to a persistent approach.

East of a stream sink and mined stone enclosure, the 'washfold', is a further fenced area containing entrances. The most easterly is a 6m climb into a narrow downstream canyon. This is followed awkwardly for 50m to a short climb up calcite covered walls and a low, well decorated bedding plane.

Moving leftwards through the bedding, a descending calcite climb lands in a chamber. Just across this chamber the stream flows along a narrow rift to the head of the big pitch. Although it is possible to follow the rift at stream level it is better to traverse in the ceiling. Yet more awkward progress allows this section to be passed a traverse (bolt) and 8mm spits (bolt sleeves) to be reached. Neatly rigged via a 'Y' hang with a deviation a few metres down on the opposite wall, the rope lands on a damp and draughty ledge 40m below.

Easy going for a few metres follows the stream into a short crawl after which the passage enlarges once again. Soon, the stream drops away and a traverse over angular chockstones is made to a steep down climb using a calcite covered flake on the right wall of the passage. More streamway is now followed until the water cuts downwards again and it is necessary to traverse at a higher level.

Shortly, a bay on the left, containing numerous calcite straws, is passed. Traversing at the same level passes a second similar bay. Here the way on continues as a series of steep climbs down over further chockstones. The final climb is best protected by a rope belayed directly to a massive fin of rock in the centre of the passage. Following the streamway leads to the final three pitches. Of these, the first two total 9m while the final pitch is 8m. The final pitch lands next to a sump pool which becomes undivable at a depth of 2.5m.

Tackle:

	Rope length required	Bolts	Remarks
Entrance climb			10m handline.
Big Pitch	50m	3	Deviation on far wall –6m.
Chockstone climbs			35m handline.
Pitches 2, 3 &			
Last Pitch	35m	6	

Survey ref: Washfold Pot & Cave, C.P.C. Journal Vol. 4 (5) 1971

The Allotment

JUNIPER GULF   Grade 4

Grid Ref: SD 765733   O.S. Outdoor Leisure Series No 2, Yorkshire Dales – Western Area, 1:25,000.   Altitude: 418m   Length: 244m   Depth: 128m

The entrance rift was descended in 1905 by the Y.R.C. but the major explorations were accomplished by the G.C. in 1924.

Permission is required from the Ingleborough Estate Office, Clapham.

The best approach to the Allotment is from Crummack Farm, grid ref. SD 772714. Turn left off the A65, one mile SW of Clapham, to Austwick. Go through the village heading towards Helwith Bridge. At the far end of the village turn left up Townhead Lane. Initially tarmaced, it turns into an un-metalled track. Park carefully, as the lane is in constant use, 300m before the first gate where a track goes off to

The Allotment

Nick Pot

Juniper Gulf

Long Kin East Cave

Long Kin East Pot

Rift Pot

gate

Crummack

to Austwick

0   500 m

the right. Go through the gate and walk towards Crummack Farm.

A waymarked path goes on through another gate. NW up a shallow valley following a well marked track trending right to emerge onto a large flat area – The Allotment. A cairn marks the point where a track comes across from the left and off to the right. Cross this track to follow another track to a further junction where a small path is followed up to a gate (yellow Bucket on gate post). Over the wall, Juniper Gulf is 300m to the right where the stream sinks.

A magnificent cave. One of the best trips in Yorkshire.

The traditional way into the cave is alongside the waterfall at the end of the classic rift entrance. However, in wet weather the way on can become impassable, especially so down the small cascades. A better way is to descend the surface rift at the opposite (nearer) end of the rift from where it is possible to avoid the small cascades and traverse in the roof to a point where it is possible to rig a 7m pitch to the stream.

The second pitch is reached by a traverse above the narrow trench across an awkward widening to a 14m pitch at the far end of the traverse. The stream cuts down but the way on is to follow the rift traversing at roof level on ledges. At one point these fade out and the Bad Step ensues. This needs to be roped and requires care, especially when wet.

The third pitch is soon reached and is marked by a prominent spike at head level. Narrow at the start the shaft opens out into a classic bell shape to land on large ledges at the bottom. It is possible, if conditions warrant, to traverse a little further and descend an alternative dry pitch.

The final pitch is reached by traversing the large ledges to a scramble up a pile of boulders and a drop down to a large ledge overlooking the impressive final pitch, the descent of which is down the far wall. This is reached by an exposed traverse to the right (facing out) to a drop down a short sloping section to a nose of rock, the belay for the free hang down the airy, beautifully fluted rock to land on a spray lashed platform. A handline descent of 4m regains the stream which is followed to the sump.

Tackle:

	Rope length required	Eco hangers	Remarks
Entrance pitch	45m	10	Avoids cascades.
(Traditional first pitch by waterfall uses 25m rope and 3 bolts).			
Pitch 2	45m	8	2 Threads along traverse.
Bad Step and			
Traverse	30m	7	Fasten rope to spike at head of pitch 3.
Pitch 3	35m	2	Spike at head of pitch.
Pitch 4	90m	12	From bottom of Pitch 3 use roped traverse to enter chamber above big pitch. Fasten rope to thread at bottom of shaft for handline.

Survey ref: Juniper Gulf, U.L.S.A.

LONG KIN EAST POT   Grade 4

**Grid Ref: SD 761729   O.S. Outdoor Leisure Series No 2, Yorkshire Dales
– Western Area, 1:25,000.   Altitude: 408m   Length: 317m   Depth: 113m**

Explored to a junction with Rift Pot in 1906 by the Y.S.A. The main pitch was descended by the G.C. in 1925.

WARNING: The stream rises very quickly during rainfall with the main pitch quickly becoming impassable. The grade assumes dry conditions on the main pitch.

Permission required from the Ingleborough Estate Office, Clapham.

Approach as for Juniper Gulf to the gate post with yellow bucket. Over the gate and walk straight ahead passing to the right of a small grassy knoll (vague path) before heading off to the left to reach a small area of pavement. Long Kin East is a 3m climb down entrance on the knoll side of the pavement.

A fine pot with a superb final shaft. 3m climb down to boulders. Hole between boulders and drop into streamway. Easy walking in canyon passage to head of first cascade quickly followed by second. From bottom of second cascade Waterfall pitch soon follows before reaching head of Final pitch.

Traverse RH wall to drop over edge to small ledge. A further 5m drop reaches large boulder ledge. On LH side traverse out to bolt and descend 5m to 'Y' hang. A marvellous 62m free drop can be made in dry conditions, or via 2 re-belays, one at –26m close to the ledge gained by penduling to the right and another at –48m by an overhang. Gain this by swinging right into a side rift to avoid the water, to the bottom of Rift Pot. An excellent exchange trip can be made between Long Kin East and Rift Pot.

Tackle:

	Rope length required	Bolts	Remarks
Cascades	22m	5	Eco hangers.
Waterfall pitch	13m	4	Eco hangers.
Main Pitch	70m	14	9 Eco hangers + 5 bolts and krabs.

N.B. This cave is in the process of being Eco bolted (November '96).
Survey ref: Long Kin East – Rift Pot system, U.L.S.A.

NICK POT   Grade 4/5

**Grid Ref: SD 770737   O.S. Outdoor Leisure Series No 2, Yorkshire Dales
– Western Area, 1:25,000.   Altitude: 399m   Length: 305m   Depth: 113m**

The crawl at the bottom of the Main Entrance pitch was reached in 1906 by the Y.R.C. with a full descent being made by the N.C.F.C. in 1935. Extensions were made by the W.R.P.C. in 1967 and by U.L.S.A. during 1972–3.

Permission required from the Ingleborough Estate Office, Clapham.

WARNING: The cave responds quickly to rainfall.

A fine Pot with an awe striking big pitch being part of the largest underground pitch in Britain – Vulcan.

Although possible to approach as for the other caves on the Allotment, from Crummackdale, it is better to approach from Horton-in-Ribblesdale by following the track from the station that leads up Ingleborough. Four kilometres up this track and 200m before a fingerpost the cave is found to the right beyond a small stream and wall in a rocky depression. The eastern hole in this depression is the loose and not recommended Hangman's Hole.

Nick Pot itself has several entrances: Main Entrance is nearest Hangman's, the scaffold shoring marks the Direct, whilst 50m away to the west is Thornber's. This is a narrow slot having an even narrower slot on the immediate left. Dawson's Entrance is found 50m away to the west-south-west.

Thornber's Entrance

A short sideways crawl enlarges slightly just before the head of the first pitch where a traverse enables a 'Y' hang to be awkwardly rigged for the descent of the 24m pitch. From the floor of the shaft go under a low bedding or take the slot to the left. Both quickly lead to where the stream is channelled into a trench.

After a short distance the stream plunges down the big pitch. Shortly before this a shale bed is found on the left where by climbing up above the stream a flake can be used to start a long, roped traverse – Traverse in the Gods. After a slippery climb up (care needed on return) a flat out crawl in this narrow bed reaches a short downward sloping gangway to gain a niche. A small passage enters this niche forming a short gully.

From the niche a 'Y' hang is rigged for the first part of the big pitch. Swing over the lip and descend 4m to a 'Y' hang rebelay. A tremendous 43m freehanging descent is then made to the top of the aptly named and remarkable Trouser Flake. DO NOT go behind the flake because the stream is met part way down, making the final 20m very wet, not to mention a lot of rope rub! Instead, a 'Y' hang rebelay is found to the left in smooth rock which permits a further 26m descent down the outside of the flake to the stony floor of the shaft. A short, low and miserable passage slopes down to the sump.

Vulcan Pitch

From just inside Dawson's Entrance a small side crawl leads via several squeezes to a short 5m pitch which enters a chamber. From this chamber the head of the pitch starts from a 'Y' hang as a squeeze down followed by a rebelay just beneath. A further 'Y' hang at -20m allows a freehanging 78m descent to the floor of the shaft.

Tackle:

	Rope length required	Bolts	Remarks
Thornber's:			
Pitch 1	35m	4	Traverse to pitch head.
Traverse in the God's	28m	8	Use flake at start and finish of traverse.
Big pitch	84m	6	Rebelay –4m.
			Rebelay –43m.
Vulcan:			
Pitch 1	5m ladder		1.5m Thread on left at head of pitch.
Vulcan pitch	125m	5	Rebelay –3m.
			Rebelay –20m.

Survey ref: Nick Pot, Hangman's Hole and Sulber Pot, U.L.S.A.

RIFT POT Grade 4

**Grid Ref: SD 761729   O.S. Outdoor Leisure Series No 2, Yorkshire Dales
– Western Area, 1:25,000.   Altitude: 407m   Length: 937m   Depth: 111m**

Exploration by the Y.R.C. in 1904 with extensions by U.L.S.A. in 1968 and the C.D.G. in 1987.

Permission is required from the Ingleborough Estate Office, Clapham.

WARNING: There are many loose boulders which occasionally move, BEWARE.

Approach as for Juniper Gulf to the gate post with the yellow bucket. Over the gate go straight ahead passing to the right of a small grassy knoll before heading off to the left and a small area of pavement. Rift Pot is a long gash in the moor some 250m to the WNW from the pavement.

Carefully descend into the rift down the often muddy slope. Two fixed hangers are used for reaching a very wide 'Y' hang, 2 more fixed hangers, for descent of first part of shaft to further two fixed hangers in a rift allowing free hanging descent to enter long rift chamber. Going up the boulder slope reaches the head of the second pitch.

Descend to the sloping floor and go under a large perched boulder to the top of an enormous jammed boulder. This is descended via a rebelay on the smooth face to enter a large boulder floored chamber.

At the far side of the chamber a hole is descended down to yet another large boulder ledge. A further drop onto more boulders and on to the head of the last pitch at a boulder perched on a ledge. This is descended in three stages to reach the bottom of the fine shaft with water entering from Long Kin East. This can be a very cold and draughty place.

The end of the cave is down the obvious passage following the water via some muddy passage and some nasty ducks. This part is not often bothered with!

Tackle:

	Rope length required	Bolts	Remarks
Pitch 1	55m	6	Hangers in situ.
Pitches 2,3 and 4	60m	9	Thread by the hole at far end of the large boulder floored chamber.
Last Pitch	70m	5	Large rawlbolt in place above boulder on the ledge. Rebelays at –2m, –6m and –20m.

Survey ref: Long Kin East Pot, Rift Pot and Jockey Hole, U.L.S.A. & C.D.G. and Y.S.S.

Gaping Gill Area

BAR POT Grade 3

**Grid Ref: SD 752723   O.S. Outdoor Leisure Series No 2, Yorkshire Dales
– Western Area, 1:25,000.   Altitude: 395m
Length: 274m to SE Passage   Depth: 104m to SE Passage**

Explored in 1949 by the B.S.A. and extended by them in 1959.

Permission is required from Ingleborough Estate Office, Clapham.

Parking in the car park at Clapham follow the route to Gaping Gill via the

Gaping Gill Area

Grange Rigg Pot

Gaping Gill

Christmas Pot

Stream Passage Pot

Disappointment Pot

Wade's Entrance

Hurnel Moss Pot

Bar Pot

Trow Gill

Ingleborough Cave

Clapdale →

Clapham Beck

0   500 m

Ingleborough Trail. A small charge is payable for this scenic walk that passes by
Ingleborough Cave and through the impressive Trow Gill to emerge on the moor.
Twin stiles enable the wall to be crossed to where the cave is situated a few metres
beyond in a large depression on the left.

The most popular and the only all weather way into Gaping Gill. Entrance is a
small hole at the base of the far wall. A slither down a small tube reaches the first
18m pitch which is constricted at the top. At the bottom the way on is down a hole
at the bottom of the chamber onto a slab. This has been the demise of many a
budding caver, so it is advisable to extend the entrance rope, from a belay above
the hole, down this slab. A scree slope spirals down to boulders trending right to a
large boulder filled chamber and the head of the fine second, 35m, pitch. The best
hang is found by taking to the right wall where a traverse out reaches a 'Y' hang
that drops clear to the floor of the shaft.

From the foot of the shaft go left, when facing the wall looking up the pitch. Soon
the scramble down to SE Pot is reached. Great care is needed here as a slip, if un-
roped, will be fatal because the black hole on the left at the bottom of this slippery
climb is 40m down to a sump! Fixing a traverse line will be much safer and does
not take long to install.

From the broad ledge on the right at the bottom of the scramble down, a tunnel
leads off right. This decreases to a flat out crawl over cobbles after a few metres to
reach SE Passage. Follow the draught to the left along a frustratingly sized
passage. A mixture of stooping and crawling (more like a drunken stagger)
eventually reaches a 'T' junction. (Straight on here reaches Sand Caverns and
Stalagmite Chamber. Continuing along a gallery and after passing the top of Mud
Pot, Stream Chamber is reached. By following the water upstream the foot of the
final pitch of Stream Passage Pot is reached).

By turning right at the 'T' junction an easier passage leads to another junction.
Straight on is Pool Chamber but to the right a low arch – The Portcullis – is passed
to a bend in the passage with a junction. Right is Booth-Parsons Crawl. Bearing
left, following the draught, quickly emerges into the stupendous Main Chamber of
Gaping Gill. A magnificent sight. To the right on the floor of the chamber is a way up
boulders to enter Old East Passage and on to Mud Hall.

Tackle:

	Rope length required	Bolts	Remarks
Pitch 1	30m	7	
Pitch 2	55m	7	Fasten rope to boulder at start of traverse out.
Traverse rope	25m	3	

Survey ref: Gaping Gill System including Ingleborough Cave, B.P.C., B.S.A.,
C.P.C., H.W.C.P.C., K.C.C., L.U.S.S., N.R.C.G., U.L.S.A., Y.R.C.
Bar Pot and Flood Entrance Pot, including Wade's Entrance and OBJ Hole, L.U.S.S.

CAR POT Grade 4

**Grid Ref: SD 755725   O.S. Outdoor Leisure Series No 2, Yorkshire Dales
– Western Area, 1:25,000.   Altitude: 396m   Length: 800m   Depth: 104m**

First descended by the Y.R.C. in 1909 but the main exploration was carried out by
the C.P.C. in 1948. The cave was extended in 1948 by the C.P.C. and N.P.C.

Permission required from the Ingleborough Estate Office, Clapham.

WARNING: Baptistry Crawl is liable to become impassable in wet conditions.

Car Pot is the original classic tight Yorkshire pothole. The infamous Baptistry crawl protects its fine formations.

Park in Clapham and follow either the Nature Trail beside Clapham Beck or the lane to the left of the Nature Trail to arrive at Ingleborough Cave. Continue into Trow Gill and to the stiles over to Bar Pot. Do not cross the stiles but continue for 400m to the corner of the field. Car Pot is about 150m SE in a large open pothole, recognisable by a tree and a rock bridge.

Climb down boulders leads to top of first pitch (15m). Chamber below is choked so squeeze down to Baptistry Pitch (9m) which is best tackled on a ladder. Thread belay and bolt on right for lifeline. A letterbox leads to the 10m long Baptistry Crawl with the narrowest section 3m in. Tackle is best pulled through on a rope.

At the other side is a small chamber with the awkward take-off for the third and fourth pitches (30m). Land on a ledge after 10m and traverse over trench to final 20m to floor. Short passage leads to the final pitch (40m) with rebelays on the ledges at 15m and 20m down.

Downstream from foot of pitch is North Craven Passage. The large tunnel continues past the sump doorway to a boulder pile. A climb up boulders leads past a low bedding where there is a visual connection with Brothers Junction in Gaping Gill. Ahead are magnificent formations and the passage continues up a mud slope to a crawl and a mud choke.

Tackle:

	Rope length required	Bolts	Remarks
Pitch 1	20m	2	
Baptistry Pitch			8m ladder, 1.5m belay 15m lifeline
Pitches 3 & 4	40m	6	
Last pitch	45m	4	

Survey ref: Gaping Gill System including Ingleborough Cave, B.P.C., B.S.A., C.P.C., H.W.C.P.C., K.C.C., L.U.S.S., N.R.C.G., U.L.S.A., Y.R.C.

DISAPPOINTMENT POT   Grade 4

Grid Ref: SD 750726   O.S. Outdoor Leisure Series No 2, Yorkshire Dales – Western Area, 1:25,000.   Altitude: 405m   Length: 500m to Hensler's Master Cave.   Depth: 110m to Hensler's Master Cave.

The infamous duck was reached in 1912 by the Y.R.C. with Hensler's Master Cave being reached by the B.S.A. in 1944.

Permission required from the Ingleborough Estate Office, Clapham.

WARNING: The duck, which often wants clearing of stones, and the bedding plane both sump in wet conditions.

Approach as for Bar Pot and the other caves associated with the Gaping Gill system. As the path swings round to the right beyond Wade's Entrance a large, deep shakehole on the left is passed before reaching Gaping Gill. This is Disappointment Pot.

At the bottom of the shakehole climb down onto a boulder slope. Descend this (handline useful) to a stream canyon. Continue along this until it becomes flat out and the duck is reached. The low arch of the Portcullis makes this very wet! Beyond, the passage starts to enlarge as it reaches the first and second pitches. Traverse out to get a hang and rig both together.

A steady passage follows for a while to the third pitch which, like all the others, is rigged by firstly traversing out. Continue onwards to the fourth and final pitches which are split by a slope. The final pitch lands on a boulder slope which is followed down into Hensler's Master Cave. This becomes an impressive stream cavern until the way on spilts. The stream flows down to a sump whilst the dry passage continues to an iron ladder which is the way on to Far Country. Just beyond the ladder is another sump.

Tackle:

	Rope length required	Bolts	Remarks
Entrance			15m handline
Pitch 1	25m	5	
Pitch 2	20m	4	
Pitch 3	20m	5	
Pitch 4	20m	5	
Last Pitch	30m	5	

Survey ref: Gaping Gill System including Ingleborough Cave, B.P.C., B.S.A., C.P.C., H.W.C.P.C., K.C.C., L.U.S.S., N.R.C.G., U.L.S.A., Y.R.C.

FLOOD ENTRANCE POT by WADE'S ENTRANCE   Grade 3

Grid Ref: SD 751724   O.S. Outdoor Leisure Series No 2, Yorkshire Dales – Western Area, 1:25,000.   Altitude: 398m   Length: 258m to SE Passage   Depth: 110m to SE Passage

Wade's is the easier of the two entrances that are Flood Entrance. The proper Flood Entrance is tight to start with, then opens out and ends up at the bottom of the first pitch of Wade's.

Flood Entrance was explored in 1909 and was the first alternative way in to the Gaping Gill system. The sump at the bottom of SE Pot was dived in 1978 by the C.D.G.

Permission is required from the Ingleborough Estate Office, Clapham.

Approach as for Bar Pot but continue along the path for a further 80m to a small dripping shakehole on the right. This is Flood Entrance. A further 30m reaches an even less significant shakehole that is Wade's.

Scramble down the small entrance passage to a cramped position overlooking the pitch. Starting off tight, a ledge and rebelay are found 6m down. Continue to the bottom, landing in a tall but not very wide rift. Upstream leads to Flood Entrance. Downstream, in a small passage, a couple of awkward bends are negotiated to a fine joint controlled passage which is followed as a hands and knees crawl to a pronounced zig-zag. After this the going becomes easier to a chamber with a way out to the right.

A trench in the floor cuts down to the short second, 4m, pitch. This can be free climbed but it is better roped. The pitch lands in a pool from which a bedding plane crawl quickly reaches the third, 12m, pitch. The landing is in a fine joint passage that continues to a cascade. Again this is free climbable but a handline makes things a lot easier and safer.

Continue into a small rift chamber from which a bedding on the right soon reaches the head of the fourth, 43m, pitch. This fine pitch lands on the broad ledge at the bottom of the descent from Bar Pot at the entry into the passage leading to SE Passage. This pitch can be unpleasantly wet so care must be taken with the rigging. A rebelay 8m down followed by two deviations avoids most of the wetness.

Continue as for Bar Pot to the Main Chamber of Gaping Gill.

Tackle:

	Rope length required	Bolts	Remarks
Pitch 1	25m	3	
Pitch 2	15m	1	2 threads.
Pitch 3	20m	3	
Handline for Cascade			Spike and thread.
Pitch 4	60m	6	Large thread at head of pitch.

Survey ref: Gaping Gill System including Ingleborough Cave, B.P.C., B.S.A., C.P.C., H.W.C.P.C., K.C.C., L.U.S.S., N.R.C.G., U.L.S.A., Y.R.C.
Bar Pot and Flood Entrance Pot, including Wade's Entrance and OBJ Hole, L.U.S.S.

GAPING GILL, Main Shaft   Grade 4/5

Grid Ref: SD 751727   O.S. Outdoor Leisure Series No 2, Yorkshire Dales – Western Area, 1:25,000.   Altitude: 396m   Depth: 95m

J. Birkwith reached the ledge that bears his name way back in 1848! The first complete descent was achieved by that well travelled Frenchman, E.A. Martel, who seemed to cave everywhere, in 1896.

Permission is required from the Ingleborough Estate Office, Clapham. During winch meets it will not be possible to do this route – except by winch! These are Whitsun and August Bank Holidays.

Parking in the car park at Clapham follow the route to Gaping Gill via the Ingleborough Trail. A small charge is payable for this scenic walk that passes by Ingleborough Cave and through the impressive Trow Gill to emerge on the moor. Twin stiles enable the wall to be crossed to see Bar Pot on the left, immediately after, in a large depression. Continue along the well marked path trending right to the fenced Gaping Gill with Fell Beck disappearing into a big black hole. Descend to the flat slabs at the far end of the fence.

WARNING: Fell Beck responds quickly to rainfall and during snow melt. A dry weather route.

A superb free hanging descent of 85m. Right of where the water is swallowed an exposed ledge is traversed to the left. Bolts above the ledge and a deviation low on the opposite ledge the mossy, damp corner is followed to a floorless rift. This is followed in an incredibly exposed position to a 'Y' hang. A totally breathtaking descent follows. Birkwith's Ledge is passed at –50m. Water hitting it sprays out, the amount depends on the volume of water tumbling down, as well as water spraying to the left issuing from Spout Tunnel on the Lateral Shaft route.

Tackle:
115m rope, 12 bolts.

Lateral Shaft – Dihedral Route   Grade 4/5

A huge block to the right of the flat slabs is passed behind to enter a short tunnel – Jib Tunnel. From the lip of the shaft a fine descent is made via 3 deviations, –6m, –25m, –30m, to keep away from the water spewing out from Spout Tunnel. A pendulum on to a large ledge some 50m down gives a superb view across to Birkbeck's Ledge. The second stage of the descent drops down behind a large jammed boulder into a rift via a deviation to another smaller ledge. Just below this a further short drop reaches an overhang. Just above the lip a rebelay in a dramatic position for the final, superb drop into what appears from above as a rather deep pool!

Tackle:
60m rope to first ledge, 10 bolts.
60m rope to floor of Main Chamber, 5 bolts.
Survey ref: Gaping Gill System including Ingleborough Cave, B.P.C., B.S.A., C.P.C., H.W.C.P.C., K.C.C., L.U.S.S., N.R.C.G., U.L.S.A., Y.R.C.

HURNEL MOSS POT   Grade 3

Grid Ref: SD 745724   O.S. Outdoor Leisure Series No 2, Yorkshire Dales – Western Area, 1:25,000.   Altitude: 419m   Length: 140m   Depth: 110m

The H.W.C.P.C. were the first to explore in 1970.

Permission is required from the Ingleborough Estate Office, Clapham.

Perhaps the easiest approach to the Pot is via Clapdale Lane from Clapham. Taking this rough track for about a mile to Clapdale Farm a steep path leads NW passing above Rayside Plantation to a stile and gate by some sheep pens. From here an obvious sink can be seen but if it is misty finding the Pot could be difficult! Walking on a bearing of 310 degrees magnetic from the sheep pens for 800m the Pot is the most southerly of the two large shakeholes. Some slumping has occurred in recent years of the hole near the entrance.

The entrance is low and square cut with a convenient thread above it for the back up to the first, 6m, pitch, which is quickly encountered. An awkward thrutchy take-off lands in a boulder floored chamber dropping down to Poseidon Pitch, one of the finest in the Dales. The collapse on the surface has affected this area – care. Keeping right follow the wall down past a flake where, after two 4m drops, a traverse out can be made across the shaft to a 'Y' hang. This drops down to an upward, outward sloping ledge some 25m lower, tapering towards the far end. Swing on to this ledge to a bolt traverse along the left hand wall and another 'Y' hang for the final 30m drop to land in a huge chamber floored with chaotic boulders and mud. The last 8m pitch is found at a hole between boulders dropping into a narrow trench. Scrambling down this reaches a pathetic sump. A pity after such a magnificent shaft.

Tackle:

	Rope length required	Bolts	Remarks
Pitch 1	15m	3	Large thread at entrance. Extend rope down boulder slope. Deviation at –2m.
Poseidon	90m	15	
Final pitch	20m	4	

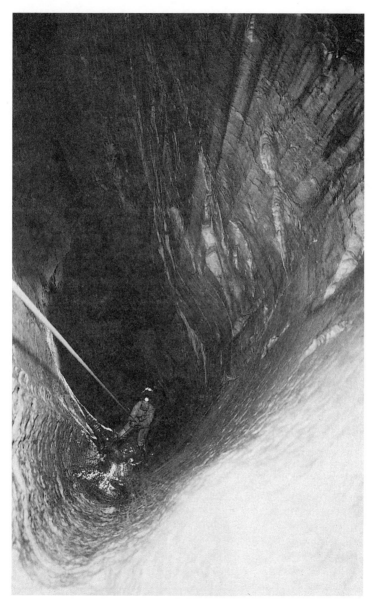

Looking down the fine Poseidon Pitch, Hurnell Moss Pot. Photo: Paul Deakin

50

STREAM PASSAGE POT

Grade 4

Grid Ref: SD 748725   O.S. Outdoor Leisure Series No 2, Yorkshire Dales – Western Area, 1:25,000.   Altitude: 415m
Length: 579m to Mud Pot Sump
Depth: 151m to Mud Pot Sump or 155m to Deep Well Sump

The N.P.C. explored this Pot in 1949.

Permission is required from the Ingleborough Estate Office, Clapham.

Approach as for Bar Pot and Wade's Entrance. The Pot is some 300m NW of Wade's Entrance, close to a prominent stream sink. The excavated entrance has been lined with oil drums.

A fine way into the Gaping Gill system. The 4m stack of oil drums need to be rigged from a loose scaffold pole to emerge into a tiny chamber from which another tiny chamber with a slot in the floor is reached. The slot, widest at floor level, leads straight onto the first, 6m pitch. A thread in the tiny second chamber provides a good back up.

Downstream from the chamber at the bottom of the pitch, a meandering walking passage reaches the second, 25m pitch. A thread a little way back from the lip of the pitch allows a traverse out above the shaft. Climb up and follow the roof to a 'Y' hang with a deviation about 13m down, on a calcite flow, keeping most of the spray away. Climbing up onto a ledge and fixing the rope with minimal slack allows those following to keep out of the spray entirely. A rift is traversed along the left wall at the level of the ledge to a 'Y' hang.

The pitch is dangerous if descended other than from here in wet conditions. Even with the traverse the pitch can still be wet so two deviations are required. One at −11m is hard to find but the other is easier at −18m as it is opposite a large debris covered ledge.

At the bottom a boulder floored rift has several holes in it which need to be scrambled over – care. At the far end the fourth, 26m, pitch drops down the side of some sharp flakes and lands in Stream Passage.

Through the waterfalls a large passage is reached which is followed briefly to enter the huge Stream Chamber. To the right here the lip of Mud Pot is passed into the dry galleries that lead to Sand Caverns and the route to Gaping Gill Main Chamber.

To reach the bottom of Stream Passage Pot (although seldom bothered with) is across Stream Chamber, round a large boulder and squeezing through more boulders to enter the bottom of Mud Pot. Scramble down through a boulder choke to regain stream and solid rock – albeit short – to the final 15m pitch at the bottom of which soon reaches a narrow sumped rift.

Tackle:

	Rope length required	Bolts	Remarks
Oil Drums and Pitch 1	25m	3	Scaffold pole usually in place for oil drums. Thread for pitch 1.
Pitch 2	40m	6	1 thread at start of traverse. Deviation at −13m. Fasten rope to bolt on ledge at bottom of pitch.

Pitch 3	50m	8	Tie rope to bolt on ledge. Deviations at −11m and −18m. Fasten rope at bottom of pitch.
Pitch 4	20m	4	
Mud pot	20m	3	

Survey ref: Gaping Gill System including Ingleborough Cave, B.P.C., B.S.A., C.P.C., H.W.C.P.C., K.C.C., L.U.S.S., N.R.C.G., U.L.S.A., Y.R.C.

Newby Moss Area

LONG KIN WEST   Grade 4

Grid Ref: SD 731724   O.S. Outdoor Leisure Series No 2, Yorkshire Dales - Western Area, 1:25,000.   Altitude: 451m   Depth: 168m

Explored by the Y.R.C in 1897! Extended by K.C.C in 1969 and 1989.
  Permission required from Ingleborough Estate Office, Clapham.

From Ingleton take the back road to Clapham. Just after the second turning for Cold Cotes a sharp turn off the road to the left leads to a grassy area, where cars may be parked, with a stile going over the wall. A track, which soon reduces to an indistinct path, is followed up the hill to a fork. Follow the right branch to where the path goes over the hole at its deepest point.

Descend beside the Bridge in a narrow rift which soon opens out. A ledge is reached after 35m from where the second half of the pitch is belayed. At the bottom a window opens onto the 2nd pitch which drops down shoring and loose boulders to enter a crawl in a shale bed. Crawling carefully along this (any dislodged stones will fall on people below!) the 3rd pitch is quickly reached. This is normally descended by traversing round the first hole and descending the succeeding drop for 10m to a rebelay from where the descent continues to a pool at the bottom of the pitch. Massive collapse at the bottom has prevented further extension.

Tackle:

	Rope length required	Bolts	Remarks
Entrance pitch	100m	7	Deviation -5m.
Pitch 2	10m	2	
Pitch 3	70m	4	Re-belay at window -15m.

White Scar Area

QUAKING POT   Grade 5

Grid Ref: SD 731740   O.S. Outdoor Leisure Series No 2, Yorkshire Dales - Western Area, 1:25,000.   Altitude: 436m   Length: 570m   Depth: 142m

Explored by the B.S.A. in 1942. Extension made by U.L.S.A. in 1964 and in 1973 by the P.C.C.

WARNING: A difficult and serious undertaking. Rescue from beyond The Crux is almost impossible.

Park at Skirwith just after leaving Ingleton on the Hawes road. Take care not to block the gate. Walk up the Public Footpath onto Fell Lane, a walled track. Walk up the track and pass Crina Bottom farm after 1500m. Continue up the incline until the ground levels off slightly at the top of the limestone then take the less worn track on the left. Shortly after this junction, look out for a large double shakehole on the right. Quaking Pot is in a shakehole on the opposite side of the path with a natural stone seat at the top and a limestone face at the bottom. The entrance is a small tube part-way down the shakehole.

A short crawl arrives at the first Pitch which is belayed from a rock bridge. This lands in a tight rift with the second pitch 7m further on. A long sling is required for a chockstone belay. At the bottom the passage enlarges. Take window in left wall and then along tight and winding passage to the third Pitch. This is split by a ledge where a rebelay then hangs free to the floor of a large chamber. The passage quickly returns to its former dimensions. Traverse in the roof and cross a 3m deep hole then continue traversing to the fourth pitch. This has a tight take-off and lands in a narrow stream passage which is best negotiated for most of the way at floor level.

The passage eventually closes down to the first of the three major squeezes, The Skydive. This is the 'easiest' of the three and it is a tight slot that drops you

White Scar Area

River Doe

to Ribblehead

Parking

Tatham
Wife
Hole

to Ingleton

White Scar
Cave

Quaking Pot

Crina Bottom

track

0   1 km

awkwardly into a wider rift. Coitus Corner, the second squeeze follows immediately. This is a tight left hand bend best tackled at floor level. Around the next corner, the third squeeze, The Crux, is reached. The Crux is a tight and technical section of passage approximately 3m long. Follow the widest part of the passage about 2m above the floor into a tight left hand bend, then drop down to the floor at an angle. (If you are particularly thin! then The Crux can be by-passed by squeezing down to floor level just before it.) The best way to move tackle is to push it through the slot to floor level prior to The Crux, then, after passing through The Crux, return upstream at floor level and drag the tackle through.

More tight streamway follows eventually reaching a small calcite covered chamber. The fifth pitch follows soon after. Continuing tight and awkward passage leads to sixth pitch followed by the seventh pitch. Both pitches have substantial rawlbolts in place.

The seventh pitch has a characteristic tight take-off and lands in a large chamber. The way on is with the water to the wet 'W-Bends' which is a duck through another awkward and narrow zig-zag passage into a chamber. From here take the 5m slippery climb up into Fly Crawl which is flat out over cobbles to the head of the Bridge Hall pitch, belayed to stals. Bridge Hall is a large breakdown cavern. Drop down the rubble heap to the greasy Fault Climb which needs a handline. This lands in the streamway and the final pitch is soon reached which drops into Gormenghast, a 30m long boulder choked chamber.

Tackle:

	Rope length required	Bolts	Remarks
Pitch 1			8m ladder, 1m wire belay, 15m lifeline.
Pitch 2			10m ladder, 6m belay, 20m lifeline.
Pitch 3	37m	6	
Pitch 4		1	8m ladder & .6m belay.
Pitch 5	10m	3	
Pitch 6	12m	3	
Pitch 7	20m	3	
Pitch 8 – Bridge Hall	10m		2 slings.
Pitch 9			20m handline.
Pitch 10	10m	1	Sling.

Survey ref: Quaking Pot, P.C.C. 1973, U.L.S.A. 1984

TATHAM WIFE HOLE   Grade 3

Grid Ref: SD 731747   O.S. Outdoor Leisure Series No 2, Yorkshire Dales – Western Area, 1:25,000.   Altitude: 440m   Length: 1,219m Depth: 155m

Explored initially by the E.P.C. in 1967 with subsequent extensions by U.L.S.A. in 1972.

Park at Granite Quarry Risings and follow an indistinct path up and left to the foot of the Scar. The path climbing up the Scar can be seen as you approach it. Cross the wall at the top and continue up onto the limestone pavement. Walk ESE for 750m to Tatham Wife Hole which lies under the slopes of Ingleborough at the end of Green Edge in the bottom of a large shakehole. A small stream enters the shakehole and immediately flows down the entrance.

Scramble down into stream passage and then a short climb down into Ogden's Chamber. Follow the twisting streamway down cascades until the first pitch is met.

The second pitch follows and then a lower passage leads to the third pitch. At the bottom is the Ramp, a wet sloping climb down, best roped. Crawl forward and then passage enlarges at a climb down to the Duck, which is short. (This can be avoided by a short but difficult climb, especially so on the return). Climb up then traverse forward to climb back down to stream in a large passage. Pass North Branch Inlet on the right and then low Well Inlet on the left. Continue forward to the fourth pitch. The passage below soon lowers to a long canal, with a duck part way along, which eventually arrives at the downstream sump.

Tackle:

	Rope length required	Eco hangers	Remarks
Entrance Pitch	10m	1	1 thread for climb down.
Pitches 1 & 2	45m	9	1 flake, 1 thread, deviation -3m pitch 1, deviation -3m pitch 2.
Pitch 3 & Ramp	30m	3	1 thread, chockstone belay at head of ramp.
Duck alternative	10m	3	·Bolts.
Pitch 4	20m	3	Deviation -4m.

Survey ref: Tatham Wife Hole, U.L.S.A.

WHITE SCAR CAVE   Grade 3/4

Grid Ref: SD 712745   O.S. Outdoor Leisure Series No 2, Yorkshire Dales – Western Area, 1:25,000.   Altitude: 259m   Length: 6,500m

Discovered and explored by C.F.D. Long in 1923. Extensions were made by T. Greenwood and the B.S.A., along with the H.W.C.P.C. in 1967 and K.C.C. in 1975. Sleepwalker Series explored by U.L.S.A. in 1970 and 1986. Battelfield Series explored by H.W.C.P.C. in 1971 with extensions being made in 1974 by U.L.S.A. and N.C.C.

Permission is required from the show cave owners. Access fee payable. Please do not change in the car park and make allowances for tourists already in the cave.

WARNING: In wet weather the choke after Big Bertha – the big boulder – becomes impassable.

From Ingelton take the road to Hawes (B6255) for 1 mile to where a sign indicates the White Scar Cave complex on the right. Park cars in the ample car park.

Enter and follow the Show Cave having first paid your entrance fee! Before the blasted tunnel leading up into the Battlefield climb over the barrier to enter the short First Lake. Upstream is the start of the 61m Long Stop Lake. It is deeper than First Lake but underwater ledges aid progress. The lake terminates at a massive boulder – Big Bertha.

The way through the boulder choke just beyond is by crawling in the water or slightly above. Do not climb up the choke as this enters the Battlefield and out of bounds to cavers. A large, quite spectacular streamway continues beyond the choke, through Swift's Lake – a short swim for most people succeeded by a fine passage having small cascades and potholes.

Easy walking on ledges reaches a tunnel bypass to a boulder choke. More traversing past the choke leads below the inlet to Sleepwalker Series (which is reached by an 18m climb up) and on to a short swim and further ledges above the stream. A greasy climb on the left leads into a very beautiful grotto with long straws – take care. The stream tumbles down cascades which are ascended into a lower wet passage soon reaching the sump after a couple of ducks.

Survey ref: White Scar Cave, H.W.C.P.C., L.U.C.C., U.L.S.A. and C.D.G.

Chapel-le-Dale Area

BLACK SHIVER POT   Grade 5

**Grid Ref: SD 737754   O.S. Outdoor Leisure Series No 2, Yorkshire Dales
– Western Area, 1:25,000.   Altitude: 408m   Length: 619m   Depth: 157m**

The cave was explored in 1967 by U.L.S.A. and extended by the C.D.G. in 1976.

The entrance is difficult to locate. Park cars in the lay-by above the Hill Inn and follow the footpath leading up Ingleborough. Eventually the huge depression of Braithwaite Wife Hole is passed and shortly after twin stiles lead over a wall. The path is then left behind to follow a shallow diagonal line across the fell to Meregill, recognisable by the trees that surround the entrance. Black Shiver is some 450m away. The shakehole has a small rock bridge above the short drop to a tiny stream flowing into a low bedding plane. If it is misty, walking on a bearing of 235 degrees from Meregill helps in locating the hole.

WARNING: The entrance passage sumps and there is flood debris on the roof of the upper streamway as well as the lower streamway. All the pitches quickly become impassable. Ensure the weather is settled before entering.

A really good trip having a lot of action in a short distance! A 4m drop leads straight away into a flat out crawl quickly leading to an awkward trench and then more easily to the first, 10m, pitch. This pitch is in two sections. The first 6m drop lands in a tiny chamber having a narrow exit leading on to the second shorter drop into a pool.

Hading Rift passage leads to the 9m Blood Pot. At the bottom a fault passage leads to the 5m Black Dub pitch which is awkward at the head and drops into a deep pool. There is an air of foreboding here. Keeping left of the pool a traverse can be rigged where a ledge 50cms below the water is quite useful!

A wet bedding follows and quickly reaches Thunder Pot, another short pitch of 6m followed immediately by Black Rift. This is a magnificent shaft well worth the effort of getting there. Following a short bedding crawl the Eagles Nest is reached from where the upper part of the shaft is rigged.

A 23m descent drops onto two massive boulders spanning the shaft. Descend between the boulders and after a deviation on the larger of the two, a tremendous 55m free drop reaches the floor of a huge rift soaring up into the darkness.

Downstream, Black Rift lowers and a low arch is passed into a fine streamway beyond. When a disgusting muddy slope is reached the stream leaves the rift to follow an awkward little streamway to the final 6m pitch which overlooks North Chamber. From the boulder strewn floor a clamber over boulders regains the stream and is followed to a 3m drop into a further passage with deepening water leading to the sump.

Chapel-le-Dale Area

Tackle:

	Rope length required	Bolts	Remarks
First pitch	25m	5	Thread at start of traverse out on right wall.
Blood Pot	15m	4	Thread in roof at head of pitch. Deviation midway down level with a ledge.
Black Dub	20m	5	Handline for traverse above the Dub!
Thunder Pot	20m	2	Flake and thread for traverse out.
Black Rift	90m	6	Can be split at the boulders (30m and 60m ropes). Deviation –5m. Deviation on larger boulder.
Last pitch	15m	2	Thread in passage before pitch.

A 10m rope is useful as a handline for the 3m drop.
Survey ref: Black Shiver Pot, U.L.S.A., 1989.

GREAT DOUK CAVE to MIDDLE WASHFOLD   Grade 1

Grid Ref: SD 747770   O.S. Outdoor Leisure Series No 2, Yorkshire Dales - Western Area, 1:25,000.   Altitude: 343m   Length: 914m

The first through trip was accomplished in 1934 by the N.C.F.C.

Park 250m NE of the Hill Inn. Walk back down to a stile onto the Public Footpath to Ingleborough. Follow this path over a further 2 stiles and then turn left. This track soon arrives at the scramble down into the large collapse of Great Douk.

A marvellous romp until the easy but damp crawls. A great beginners trip. Walk along the bottom of the collapse to where a small stream cascades from a passage 4m above. A simple but greasy 2m climb gains the passage and the stream is then followed. This is a walking sized passage and at one point passes under the skylight of Little Douk. Continue until the passage lowers to a crawl. Bear left at a junction and then climb into a roof passage. Another left turn then leads out onto the moor at Middle Washfold entrance.

MEREGILL HOLE   Grade 4

Grid Ref: SD 740757   O.S. Outdoor Leisure Series No 2, Yorkshire Dales – Western Area, 1:25,000.   Altitude: 396m   Length: 4,500m Depth: 165m

An epic and tremendous exploration by the Y.R.C. during 1908 – 12. Extended by U.L.S.A. during 1966/67.

WARNING: Meregill has a large catchment area with the run off being very quick. There are many signs of catastrophic flooding throughout the cave. Even in Aven Entrance there are signs of flooding half way up the walls!! A sobering thought.

Park cars in the lay-by above the Hill Inn and follow the footpath leading up Ingleborough. Eventually the huge depression of Braithwaite Wife Hole is passed and shortly after twin stiles lead over a wall. The path is then left behind to follow a shallow diagonal line across the fell to Meregill, recognisable by the trees that surround the entrance just beyond the wall. Aven Entrance is just before the wall in the west side of a shallow depression. There is a right angled bend just inside the entrance. Little Meregill is a miserably tight cave to the left of Aven Entrance.

A marvellous trip – one of the very best.

Aven Entrance is the most frequently used because the Mere only drops sufficiently during the 'dry' summer months and infrequently at other times. Round the right angled bend a short flat out crawl reaches the pitch head. This is awkward to rig but there is a thread in the roof of the crawl before the end and two bolts at the head of the pitch. This drops down via a deviation to the floor 15m below.

A short length of passage follows to where the stream cuts down. Here a traverse leads off around a corner to a tiny alcove overlooking the pitch. Part way down on the far side of the shaft is a deviation. From slightly above a broad ledge a rebelay can be reached to land clear (in normal water conditions) of the water.

A twisting stream passage continues down to the head of the third, 35m, pitch. This is generally very wet and is split by a large ledge some 15m down. Traversing up into the roof before the pitch (two chockstones overhead) jammed stones are reached. From this cramped position a direct descent can be made during dry conditions to the ledge where a rebelay reaches the floor of the shaft. However, it is possible to traverse out on bolts to a hang from which a short descent of 10m and further traverse reaches a rebelay. This crosses a ledge and down to another. Along this lower ledge a belay is found for the final short drop landing in the Canyon immediately by the fourth, 8m, pitch.

Although free climbable it is prudent to rig a traverse line out to a hang point – just in case! Following the stream, the floor of the Canyon contains some deep pools and some short cascades. Soon the fifth, 30m, pitch is reached. To keep out of the water it is better to start a high level traverse back from the pitch head to a constricted position in the rift from where the hang for the first part is rigged. A rebelay can be found on a ledge some 15m down the pitch. 10m below this a further rebelay in the roof of the widening rift will keep the party dry. Downstream there are two short 6m pitches each having a deep pool for the unwary at the bottom. The first one starts with a short traverse out to hang point, with a pendule at the bottom landing at the head of the second drop.

At the bottom of this Meregill Main Drain leads off in a marvellous walking passage for 500m. There is another 250m or so that is pretty miserable and hardly worth bothering with at the end. An inlet is passed – the Torrent – a 2.5m waterfall on the left wall, coming from Black Shiver Pot.

The Mere entrance provides an easier way in to the system but only when the Mere is down. From the clump of trees a descent is made to land by the entrance tunnel. This quickly leads to the bottom of Aven Entrance pitch. Only use this entrance when the weather is certain – it very quickly sumps!!

Tackle:

	Rope length required	Bolts	Remarks
Aven Entrance	20m	2	Deviation –6m.
			Thread in roof of entrance crawl.
Mere Entrance	20m	1	Belay to tree.
Pitch 2	35m	8	Deviation –12m.
Pitch 3	60m	9	
Pitch 4 – Canyon	20m	4	
Pitch 5	50m		Thread in roof for last rebelay.
Double climb down	30m	5	
Survey ref: Meregill Hole U.L.S.A.			

ROARING HOLE

Grade 3

Grid Ref: SD 742763   O.S. Outdoor Leisure Series No 2, Yorkshire Dales - Western Area, 1:25,000.   Altitude: 358m   Length: 4,600m including Meregill Hole   Depth: 134m

First explored by U.L.S.A. in 1968. Extensions were made by the N.P.C. in 1980 and by U.L.S.A. in 1990.

WARNING: Care must be taken descending all the chokes as they have been walled up and could become unstable. Water rises rapidly in wet conditions and the second and third boulder chokes become difficult to climb.

Take the path from above the Hill Inn to the prominent shakehole of Braithwaite Wife Hole. Roaring is to the west, in a shakehole with a tree and a lidded entrance at the bottom.

A classic trip through a series of boulder chokes, descending 130m on very little equipment.

Climb down the entrance shaft into the first chamber. Descend the walled steps and climb through the first boulder choke into a short passage to a second chamber. A short pitch reaches Bandstand Ledge followed by a traverse round the far side of the chamber to reach the boulder floor. Climb down through the second boulder choke into a stream passage which is followed into a muddy chamber and on to the third boulder choke.

This is the Morecambe Pier Choke and care must be taken when descending these walled boulders. Drop into the third significant chamber where a hole in the floor leads to a short passage into Slab Chamber. Descend to the bottom of this chamber and down through the fourth boulder choke into a stream passage. This passage is followed to the top of The Rift where on the left side of the passage a traverse (a 10m rope is useful) leads to a smaller rift. The third pitch follows and 15m further on is the free climbable fourth pitch into Sunset Boulevard, although a rope is useful for the return. Upstream the passage sumps but downstream is the final pitch into a sump pool and is not normally descended.

Tackle:

	Rope length required
Bandstand Pitch	8m ladder, 1.5m belay, 15m lifeline.
The Rift Traverse	10m
Pitch 3	8m ladder, 1.5m belay, 15m lifeline.
Pitch 4	10m handline.

Survey ref: N.P.C. Journal (1982)

SUNSET HOLE

Grade 3

Grid Ref: SD 742759   O.S. Outdoor Leisure Series No 2, Yorkshire Dales – Western Area, 1:25,000.   Altitude: 378m   Length: 900m   Depth: 86m

The Y.R.C. explored the hole in 1909, extensions were made in 1968 by the H.W.C.P.C. and 1988 by the N.C.C.

WARNING: Climbs are impassable in flood.

Park just up from the Hill Inn on the left then walk back down to a stile on the opposite side of the road. Approach as for Meregill Hole to the twin stiles. Over these and bear right for 100m to a patch of clints where wet and dry entrances to the system will be found.

Both entrances soon unite and the pleasant streamway continues until it reaches the top of a wet cascade. Another cascade soon follows and a handline on both of these makes the return a little easier. More gentle streamway eventually arrives at a third cascade which can be rigged on the left or traversed over to a climb down. 10m further on, step up onto a platform on the left which is the head of the main pitch. Numerous bolts allow a variety of hangs. The water sinks in the chamber below and at one time there was a connection to Braithwaite Wife Hole which lies just outside this chamber.

Tackle:
NOTE: The list below enables the Cascades to be passed in wet conditions. If treating the first two Cascades as handlines half the amount of rope is required.

	Rope length required	Bolts	Remarks
Cascade 1	14m	2	1 thread.
Cascade 2	16m	4	
Cascade 3	15m	2	1 thread.
Main Pitch	34m	3	Eco hangers.

East Kingsdale Area

BROWN HILL POT   Grade 4

Grid Ref: SD 714784   O.S. Outdoor Leisure Series No 2, Yorkshire Dales – Western Area, 1:25,000.   Altitude: 370m   Length: 610m   Depth: 112m

Explored by the N.C.C. in 1980.

Permission required from Braida Garth Farm.

Park in the small lay-by close to Yordas Cave. Climb over the wall via the stile and walk across the field to Kingsdale Beck. Follow the small tributary for 200m then climb up the fell side to the prominent tree beyond which there is a wall with a gap in it. Go through the gap and follow the shallow dry valley up to find the stream sink. 50m further, Heron Pot entrance is found on the right. Head south from here to a wall where Brown Hill Pot is found near the gate. An oil drum marks the entrance in a slumped shakehole.

Slide down the oil drums and squeeze into a rift passage which winds along to a small chamber. Climb high in the rift and thrutch forward to a sharp right hand bend. Drop down to the floor and follow the tight rift.

Gradually ascend the rift again to about half-height and so reach the first pitch. The first part can be free climbed but a rope is useful for the return. The pitch opens out and is followed by a short second pitch into a small chamber.

Proceed to the left in an easier rift passage on hands and knees. An easy traverse then leads to the Galerie pas Mur where a spectacular waterfall enters on the left. Continue traversing at the level of the ledge above the stream to a climb down to the stream. Follow the stream under fallen boulders until the rift widens out and a large flake boulder fills the passage. (An alternative is to continue the traverse above the stream and climb down this boulder. A rope is advisable).

From here a lower route leads over a 10m drop into a crawl to the head of the original Puits Ian Plant. However, at a higher level, a more obscure passage becomes a rift which enters the Puits Ian Plant 6m higher and is the usual SRT route. This magnificent shaft is split by a large ledge at –34m. The second part of the shaft requires a long pendulum to reach a deviation. The stream then flows

East Kingsdale Area

Yordas Wood

to Dent

Heron Pot (lower entrance)

Heron Pot

Brown Hill Pot

Kingsdale

Kingsdale Beck

Braida Garth

to Ingleton

Vesper Pot

King Pot

0   500 m

down Marmite Passage with short cascades and pools to the last pitch. This drops into a roomy chamber with a passage to the sump pool.

Tackle:

	Rope length required	Bolts
Pitch 1	20m	4
Pitch 2	20m	4
Puits Ian Plant	65m	7
Last Pitch	20m	4

Survey Ref: Brown Hill Pot, N.C.C.

HERON POT

Grade 3

Grid Ref: SD 714787   O.S. Outdoor Leisure Series No 2, Yorkshire Dales – Western Area, 1:25,000.   Altitude: 360m   Length: 1,097m Depth: 40m

Permission required from Braida Garth Farm.

Approach as for Brown Hill Pot. NOTE: after crossing over Kingsdale Beck follow the small tributary up to check the lower entrance BEFORE doing the through trip!

WARNING: The lower entrance/exit can become impassable in high water conditions, as do the pitches.

Slide down into small chamber. Way on is back under slide down to enter small passage. Follow this to junction and larger passage. A large inlet on the left is passed where the passage increases in size. After a considerable distance and a few formations two pitches follow in quick succession. These can be wet! The first one is awkward to reach the head, but a traverse to an alcove is helped by a number of ancient slings abandoned after pull through trips.

The second pitch starts off by a climb up to small ledge overlooking the chamber at the bottom. From the bottom of the second pitch a fine passage leads off. At a prominent right angled bend a 3m climb enters Phreatic Inlet. This reaches a small chamber and some fine formations.

Back in the main passage the stream cuts down with some small cascades to where a fallen block is crawled over. Just beyond this is the start of the long, wet and stony crawl to eventually emerge in daylight.

Tackle:

	Rope length required	Eco hangers
Pitch 1	20m	5
Pitch 2	25m	5

On pull through trips 1 x 25m rope is sufficient. BEWARE: the use of in-situ 'tat' is extremely dangerous.

Survey ref: Heron Pot, L.U.S.S.

KING POT

Grid Ref: SD 709776   O.S. Outdoor Leisure Series No 2, Yorkshire Dales – Western Area, 1:25,000.   Altitude: 378m   Length: 5,000.m Depth: 125m

First explored in 1954 by the R.R.C.P.C. with an extension being made in 1965/66 by the H.W.C.P.C. However, the main explorations were undertaken by the N.C.C. in 1978.

Permission is required from Braida Garth Farm.

WARNING: King Pot can be very tiring especially on the return. Loose boulders are a hazard in several places and lower parts of the cave are liable to flooding. The 8mm spits are the original ones placed during the exploration of the cave. Therefore treat all placements with suspicion and judgement is required to ascertain sound fixings. An accident beyond the Canyon would be very serious and rescue extremely difficult.

From the gate out onto the fell above Braida Garth Farm walk 250m diagonally to the right. The entrance is in a shakehole where the slope of the fell steepens.

At the bottom of the shakehole a 5m free climb down a narrow rift leads to a squeeze through a slot onto a ramp with a fixed knotted rope (care) which drops onto a ledge and the 9m first pitch. A few metres from the base of the pitch a partially hidden crawl over boulders is the way on. Scrambling up and along the narrow rift leads to a pit in the floor.

Fixed ropes (care) are in place for the traverse across the pit which leads to a short, awkward rift into a chamber and a slope down to a hole in boulders which is the head of the 10m second pitch.

A climb up over boulders and down into a canyon ends at a low bedding with the stream. Flat out crawling improves to hands and knees crawling into a fault chamber. Turning left soon degenerates into a twisting, tortuous rift to emerge after 40m over a 5m drop. A careful move to the right enables a climb down into the start of Queensway which begins bouldery before a climb down to the stream marks the start of a long section of fine meandering canyon. Lego Inlet is passed on the right and Squashed Chihuahua Inlet on the left. Continuing downstream past several boulder falls the canyon diminishes into a crawl in water, Canutes Canal. Beyond this is the 10m Emma's Pitch.

A twisting stream canyon follows to a boulder choke where a fixed knotted rope (care) marks a climb up. A well worn route through a hole in boulders and a squeeze past and climb down a large block leads to the steep ascent into King Henry Hall. To the right is the 11m Bloodaxe Pitch. This lands in another chamber from where the 9m Victoria Pitch lands back in the stream. At the bottom a slippery traverse avoids a short canal and soon leads to the large aven chamber, Kakemono Hall. A 150m crawl in the stream follows which eases as the 20m Elizabeth Pitch is reached.

Turning left under the arch at the bottom, a 3m climb up and back down a rock rib, Jane's Pitch, leads to a muddy crawl. The stream is regained and stooping passage gradually enlarges until a junction with a much larger phreatic passage is met. Unfortunately the way on is with the stream straight on into a 300m long crawl. The crawl ends abruptly 3m up the wall of the East Kingsdale Master Cave. Downstream the passage soon arrives at the terminal sump. The sump has been connected with the resurgence, Keld Head, on the opposite side of the valley – a dive of 3,050m which probably ranks as one of the greatest achievements in modern British caving.

The marvellous Colonnades in ___ made ___
photo: Paul Deakin

The Magnificent Main Chamber of Gaping Gill. Photo: Paul Deakin

The aerial take off at the head of pitch four in Gravel Pot. Photo: Paul Deakin

Tackle: King Pot is best done as a ladder and lifeline trip, however, an SRT guide follows.

	Rope length required	Bolts	Remarks
Entrance	15m		3 hangers plus natural belays per pitch.
First	13m		
Second	12m		
Emma's	17m		
Anne's	10m		
Bloodaxe	20m		
Victoria	12m		
Elizabeth	15m		
Jane's	15m		Plus sling. An assisted climb is necessary to rig this pitch.

Survey ref: King Pot, N.C.C.

VESPER POT   Grade 4

Grid Ref: SD 712776   O.S. Outdoor Leisure Series No 2, Yorkshire Dales – Western Area, 1:25,000.   Altitude: 381m   Length: 274m   Depth: 114m

The N.P.C. explored the cave in 1978.

Permission from Braida Garth Farm.

WARNING: Loose rock on the fourth and final pitches is a hazard. Care must be taken not to dislodge stones on to people below.

Park as for the caves of West Kingsdale near the track leading to Braida Garth Farm and walk to the farm where a vague path heads E climbing steeply up the hillside to a gate between two woods. The path continues to a second much smaller gate at the wall corner. Head due E across the boggy moor for approximately 400m to find a pile of stones. This can be reached a little more simply by following the wall for 200m or so to a rocky area. A sharp turn right here then enters a shallow dry valley to the SW. Vesper Pot is some 150m beyond the pile of stones by the stream sink.

An excavated entrance is in a small shakehole with a manhole. From the entrance an awkward, fairly tight, sideways crawl reaches a constricted bend entering a low streamway. This is followed, mainly on hands and knees, in a decorated passage. Beyond, past the main inlet on the right, the passage enlarges as it approaches the first pitch. The rigging of this is awkward and the take-off constricted but soon opens out.

From the base of the pitch continue along a tall but tortuous canyon at stream level to an 'eyehole' followed immediately by the second pitch. Rigging a traverse through the 'eyehole' a 7m drop lands on broad ledges. Continue across the rift to a hang for the third pitch on the opposite wall. This is drier and less tight.

The fine fourth pitch quickly follows and is rigged from two consecutive 'Y' hangs which gains horizontal distance over the inclined shaft. Halfway down the shaft a large thread is used for a deviation to avoid spray on the lower part.

The fifth pitch is reached by scrambling over loose boulders to a window which opens out into a huge transverse rift – the upper part of the Spectacle Pot chamber. From the ledge a long....reach reaches a 'Y' hang on the far side of the rift from where a very spectacular pitch drops to the bottom of The Great Rubble Heap via a rebelay half way down.

Tackle:

	Rope length required	Bolts	Remarks
Pitch 1	15m	2	
Pitches 2 & 3	35m	8	
Pitch 4	40m	5	Deviation at -15m.
Pitch 5	45m	3	

Survey ref: N.P.C.Journal (1979)

West Kingsdale Area

BULL POT, KINGSDALE   Grade 3

Grid Ref: SD 707787   O.S. Outdoor Leisure Series No 2, Yorkshire Dales – Western Area, 1:25,000.   Altitude: 355m   Length: 213m   Depth: 79m

First explored in 1899 with subsequent explorations in 1934 by the Y.R.C.

Park 1,200m beyond the Braida Garth track and strike up the hill towards some isolated trees. Climb up the scar and find a small stream which sinks just up from the entrance pitch.

At the bottom of the pitch a short passage leads to a traverse out to the second pitch. Swing onto a ledge 3m from the floor and descend the narrow slot in the floor, the third pitch. Traverse out to descend the fourth pitch and then follow the passage to a junction. Turn left. An awkward thrutch forward leads onto the final pitch. There is no way on from the bottom.

Tackle:

	Rope length required	Eco hangers	Remarks
Entrance pitch	20m	4	
Pitch 2	20m	4	1 thread.
Pitch 3	30m	3	
Pitch 4	30m	6	Deviation –4m.
Last pitch	30m	6	Sling for flake.

JINGLING POT   Grade 3

Grid Ref: SD 699784   O.S. Outdoor Leisure Series No 2, Yorkshire Dales – Western Area, 1:25,000.   Altitude: 378m   Length: 61m   Depth: 67m

The Main Shaft was bottomed by the Y.R.C. in 1926. The other passages at the bottom were found by the B.S.A. in 1969.

From the fourth gate on the left, beyond Braida Garth, follow the wall up to the Turbary Road track. Through the gate on the left and follow the track for approximately 200m, turn right to find Jingling Pot at the end of a beck, an obvious open shaft partly lined by rowan trees. The beck flows into the northern end of Jingling Cave but in very wet conditions overflows into the pot.

Use the trees N of the shaft to provide a free 'Y' hang. Use the Eco hanger in the streambed for a traverse line to the trees. A fine direct, free hanging descent to the bottom of the main shaft is made. A 6m traverse away from the shaft leads to the head of the final pitch. Cunningly placed Eco hangers provide a 'Y' hang for an 8m drop to a short passage. Further downward progress to a dig is possible by

West Kingsdale Area

Yourdas Wood

Bull Pot

to Dent

Kingsdale Beck

Jingling Pot

Kingsdale

Rowten Pot

Braida Garth

Simpson's Pot

Swinsto Hole

Parking

Valley Entrance

to Ingleton

Keld Head

0   1 km

following the hole in the floor immediately below the last pitch.

It is possible to rig a system of lateral shafts to the base of the main shaft for those wanting rigging experience by descending a short distance down the direct pitch before a pendule enters a window (80m rope and an extra 13 krabs Eco hangers).

Tackle:

	Rope length required	Eco hangers	Remarks
Main Pitch	60m	1	2 slings.
Last Pitch	12m	2	

ROWTEN POT   Grade 4

Grid Ref: SD 698780   O.S. Outdoor Leisure Series No 2, Yorkshire Dales – Western Area, 1:25,000.   Altitude: 363m   Length: 259m   Depth: 105m

Bottomed by the Y.R.C. in 1897! Frakes Series explored in 1965, 1973–1976 and again in 1980 by the C.D.G.

Prior permission not normally required but can be obtained from Fore Dales, Ingleton.

A fine trip. Rowten Pot is close to the Turbary Road having a classic open shaft as well as an 'eyehole'. Park near the track leading to Braida Garth Farm (NOT opposite it!). Go through the gate opposite the track and follow a path that passes in front of Valley Entrance. Strike diagonally across the hillside to reach the wall which is then followed to reach the Turbary Road just before a gate. Go through the gate and follow the rutted track until water is heard crashing down Rowten to the right.

Two large rawl bolts provide for an initial belay above the adjacent 'eyehole' and a descent is made to a rebelay after 3m. Continue down to the bridge that spans the shaft and make an exposed traverse across to the end of the muddy ledge.

A high 'Y' hang allows a 3m descent to a rebelay immediately above a rift leading back beneath the ledge. Swing into this hanging rift some 4m below the rebelay. Traverse across and slightly down using small footholds to a restricted position where it is possible to rig a 'Y' hang for the airy and spectacular 40m descent to the floor of the shaft.

The third pitch is found by keeping to the left above the huge boulders. Rigging from an alcove with a false floor of jammed boulders a 12m descent is made to reach a cross rift overlooking the streamway below the fourth pitch.

Rigging between the walls of the rift a further rebelay allows a good ledge to be reached and a high level bypass to the lower active pitches. By fixing a traverse line over the boulders and holes a 15m pitch is reached which drops down to the final chamber. A passage drops around to meet the stream at a deep pool beneath a waterfall pitch. This stream runs into two sumps and from the larger one it is possible to dive into the West Kingsdale Master Cave.

Tackle:

	Rope length required	Eco hangers	Remarks
Pitch 1 and Traverse across bridge	35m	9	
Rift and Pitch 2	55m	6	
Pitch 3, Traverse and last pitch	70m	14	Deviation 5m down last pitch.

Survey ref: West Kingsdale System, U.L.S.A.

SIMPSON'S POT   Grade 4

Grid Ref: SD 696779   O.S. Outdoor Leisure Series No 2, Yorkshire Dales – Western Area, 1:25,000.   Altitude: 376m   Length: 884m   Depth: 112m

First explorations in 1940 by the B.S.A and extended by U.L.S.A. in 1962.

Prior permission not normally required but can be obtained from Fore Dales, Ingleton.

Park near the track leading to Braida Garth Farm (NOT opposite it!). Go through the gate opposite the track and head directly up the hill. Once on the bench level, Turbary Road is reached. Turn right along this, and through a gate. Turn immediately left and continue for 120m. Simpson's lies in a small shakehole.

WARNING: In wet weather, the Blasted Hole sumps. Slit Pot and East Entrance Passage can flood badly. Kingsdale Master Cave can flood rapidly and severely to over 5m deep.

NOTE: Before a through trip the Roof Tunnel Pitch in Valley Entrance must be rigged.

Just inside the entrance, a narrow rift leads to a 60m crawl in water followed by a climb down into a taller passage and the top of the Five Steps. These climbable cascades are followed by a narrow rift along which the stream flows before falling down Bob's Pit, DO NOT DESCEND. Instead, crawl over it (roped for safety) into a larger fossil passage.

Two short climbs lead on, eventually reaching the first and second pitches, descended as one. Just around the corner is Storm Pot with the water from Bob's Pit entering from high above. At the bottom the passage ends at a deep pool. The way on is through a small hole, Blasted Hole, a simple duck which immediately opens out into waist deep water.

A traverse up to Carol Pot is quickly followed by Shuffle, Lake and Aven Pots, all separated by short passages. A squeeze after Aven Pot leads into the chamber at the top of Slit Pot. This can be very awkward for some! Narrow chests can pass through on the floor but those of a larger disposition must squeeze through at a higher level – care! The rope may snag on a flake half-way down. At the bottom of Slit Pot join Swinsto Hole just above it's last pitch.

An alternative to Slit Pot is the magnificent Great Aven Pitch which drops 41m, an easier option for the plumper caver! This starts before Aven Pot by ascending into the roof to enter a small chamber. At the far side of the chamber is a clump of slings, having dubious vintage. This is the belay for the Great Aven Pitch landing in a large chamber. At the bottom of this chamber descend an overhanging boulder

70

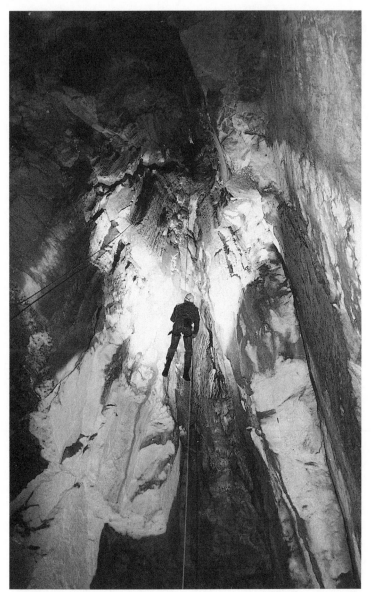

The spectacular free hanging descent of Great Aven Pitch, Simpson's Pot.
Photo: Paul Deakin

to reach the bottom of Swinsto's last pitch. A 90m rope is required for a pull through.

Swinsto Final Pitch, short and wet, drops into the boulder filled aven. Exit via East Entrance Passage which is a climb down under the wall to the left, of facing the pitch. A low but easy passage leads to a short dry section and then a flat out crawl in a deep pool to emerge at the Master Junction.

Ignore all the other passages and turn right to quickly arrive in Kingsdale Master Cave with a stream flowing from left to right. Go downstream through the unfortunately short, but magnificent Master Cave until it flows into the downstream sump. Climb up the Roof Tunnel pitch (which has already been rigged; see note above) and stoop along the Roof Tunnel to a 'T' junction. A left turn leads through short wet sections to a final crawl and an exit from the oil drum of Valley Entrance. Replace the lid.

Tackle:
1 x 30m ropes for all pitches up to Slit Pot
1 x 55m rope for Slit Pot
1 x 15m rope to pre-rig the Roof Tunnel pitch
A few extra slings will be useful
1 x 90m rope for Great Aven pitch
Survey ref: West Kingsdale System, U.L.S.A.

SWINSTO HOLE   Grade 4

Grid Ref: SD 694775   O.S. Outdoor Leisure Series No 2, Yorkshire Dales – Western Area, 1:25,000.   Altitude: 384m   Length: 914m   Depth: 131m

First explored by the Y.R.C., extended in 1930 by G.C. and 1962 by U.L.S.A.

Prior permission not normally required but can be obtained from Fore Dales, Ingleton.

Park near the track leading to Braida Garth Farm (NOT opposite it!) Go through the gate opposite the track and head directly up the hill. Once on the bench level, Turbary Road is reached. Turn left. After 75m there is a small (often dry) stream sink on the left. Turn right and follow the stream bed up, past a bigger sink, towards the hill. Swinsto lies just on the right side (true left bank) of the stream in some clints, just before the start of the first steep rise.

WARNING: In wet weather, Swinsto Long Crawl, East Entrance Passage and pitches flood badly. Kingsdale Master Cave can flood rapidly and severely to over 5m deep.

NOTE: The Roof Tunnel Pitch in Valley Entrance must be rigged for a safe exit.

Drop down the entrance into the stream and follow this to the 1st pitch. The stream flows into Swinsto Long Crawl, 300m of hands and knees crawling and then a lower section to the 2nd pitch. Short passage to 3rd pitch and again to 4th pitch. Descend this by a window on the right, at the head of the pitch, into a small chamber.

Ahead is the Main Pitch, descended in two drops via a large ledge. At the bottom stay with the stream until it disappears, then take dry passage to two pitches into Spout Chamber where the water reappears. A narrow rift with pools and cascades finally widens just before Swinsto Great Aven is reached with the last pitch of Simpson's Pot entering from above. Swinsto Final Pitch, short and wet, drops into the boulder filled aven. Continue as for Simpson's Pot.

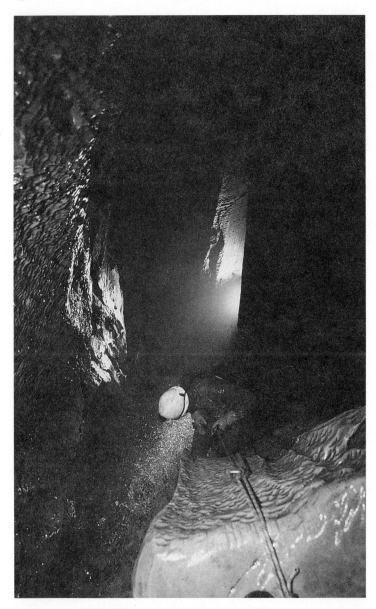

Abseiling down the Big Pitch in Swinsto Hole. Photo: Paul Deakin

Tackle:
2 x 30m ropes for all pitches in Swinsto Hole.
1 x 15m rope to pre-rig the Roof Tunnel pitch.
Survey ref: West Kingsdale System, U.L.S.A.

VALLEY ENTRANCE
Grade 3/4

**Grid Ref: SD 698774   O.S. Outdoor Leisure Series No 2, Yorkshire Dales
– Western Area, 1:25,000.   Altitude: 268m   Length: 4,000.m**

Explored by both U.L.S.A. and C.D.G. members in 1966.

Prior permission not normally required but can be obtained from Fore Dales, Ingleton.

Park near the track leading to Braida Garth Farm (NOT directly opposite it). Go through the gate directly opposite the track and follow the path to the right for 100m. The entrance is a lidded oildrum.

Replace the lid after entering and then crawl and stoop along the passage passing through a long pool. The roof lifts and easy walking arrives at a junction with a large passage on the right and a crawl straight on. Turn right and stoop along this passage until a 7m pitch is reached. Down this pitch is the West Kingsdale Master Cave.

The stream flows into the sump which reappears at Keld Head some 2,000m distant. Go upstream in a magnificent passage until the roof is at head height then turn left for 50m to the Master Junction. To the right is Rowten Passage, the arch straight ahead is Philosophers Crawl and the low watery bedding on the left is East Entrance Passage.

Rowten Passage: Climb over the pebble banks back into the main stream. Upstream, sections of chest/neck deep wading lead to the last of the downstream Rowten sumps.

Philosophers Crawl: Crawl forward to a junction, turn left and head upstream. Some flat out sections eventually lead to a climb out into Swinsto Great Aven.

East Entrance Passage: Crawl through the water for 10m then easier passage continues upstream to a climb up through boulders into Swinsto Great Aven.

Tackle:

	Rope length required	Bolts	Remarks
Roof Tunnel	15m	4	1 thread.
If using ladder		4	8m ladder, 15m lifeline.

Survey ref: West Kingsdale System, U.L.S.A.

Easegill

AYGILL CAVERNS
Grade 3

**Grid Ref: SD 663818   O.S. Outdoor Leisure Series No 2, Yorkshire Dales
– Western Area, 1:25,000.   Altitude: 302m   Length: 2,438m
Depth: 55m**

The N.S.G. entered the cave in 1965 with extensions being made in 1966 by H.W.C.P.C., 1965 by R.R.C.P.C. and 1971 by U.L.S.A.

Apply for permission from the Estate Office, Cowan Bridge.

EASEGILL

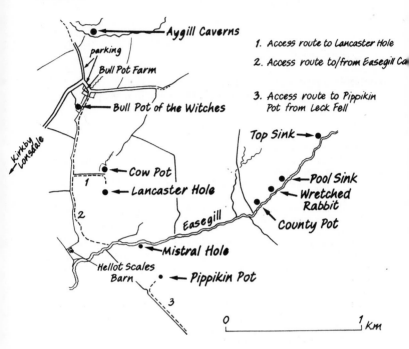

1. Access route to Lancaster Hole

2. Access route to/from Easegill Ca

3. Access route to Pippikin Pot from Leck Fell

A compact yet fascinating cave providing a memorable trip with the added bonus of being less crowded than much of the nearby Easegill system. The main route down provides lots of interest, not least the impressive terminal sumps, and also serves to identify the routes to the very worthwhile extremities of the system away from the hydrologically active passages.

On the true right bank of Aygill below a steep limestone outcrop and surrounded by an arc of stones, the entrance climb soon drops to a crawl. Following this for a short distance, the way on is via a well worn climb up to the left. This leads to a further descending crawl and narrow traverse over occasional small chockstones to the First Chamber.

Traverse Pitch is obvious across the chamber. Laddering can be avoided by an exposed traverse and a climb down for which a rope is recommended and normally in situ.

Under the ladder/climb, a damp slot leads to a crawl which enlarges and drops into a small chamber and the second pitch.

At the base of the pitch a series of cascades downstream follow, until the stream flows into a choked passage. Immediately to the right a dry crawl leads to a calcite ramp rising to a small chamber. Descending, the ramp opens into a stony crawl and a dry passage is followed leftwards to Sand Junction.

YORKSHIRE

Two routes are obvious above a mud slope to the right. The larger left hand passage is followed easily to a high chamber which becomes choked and wet to the right. Ahead, however, it leads to a descending crawl and the stream is rejoined in Middle Chamber identified by a small passage in the right wall and a steep choke to the left. Downstream is the obvious Wet Crawl which leads, after 20m, to a fine tunnel and the superb terminal sump. The water reappears in Bull Pot of the Witches.

Tackle:

Traverse Pitch	10m ladder, 25m lifeline. Belay to stake directly above pitch head. Lifeline belayed to boulders.
Pitch 2	10m ladder, 25m lifeline. Care with rigging. The thread on right wall is awkward to reach.

Survey ref: Lancaster/Easegill, published by Lyon Equipment/Inglesport

BULL POT OF THE WITCHES
Grade 3

Grid Ref: SD 662813   O.S. Outdoor Leisure Series No 2, Yorkshire Dales – Western Area, 1:25,000.   Altitude: 293m   Length: 2,400m

The Y.R.C. were the first to explore the cave with extensions being made by the B.S.A. in 1966/68 and R.R.C.P.C. in 1969. It was called Bull Pot of the Witches to distinguish it from Bull Pot in Kingsdale, not that witches had anything to do with it anyway. Just that Witches Cave is not that far away!

Please sign the blackboard at Bull Pot Farm (the R.R.C.P.C. hut) before starting your trip.

Cars need to be parked tidily at Bull Pot Farm. Go through the kissing gate just to the east of the farm and follow the track. This soon passes the tree lined shaft of the cave on the right. Go over the stile to find a metal stake in the ground.

Follow path to large ash tree and descend daylight shaft in two stages to the floor of the open pot. Waterfall enters from the north end. At the south end of the open pot take the lower of two passages. This leads, in 15m, to top of climb down. Although it is possible to free climb this it is better to treat it as a pitch.

At the bottom a rift passage leads via two climbs down to a junction. Turn right to follow a stream to a lower section of stream passage via a climb down on the right, to the top of a further climb down. Again, it is better to treat this as a pitch, although it is free climbable. Traverse across to the far side of the small shaft and descend in two very short drops to the floor. Flakes and a thread keep the rope and you out of the water! Drop down from base of pitch/climb a few metres to climb up into the higher of two holes to enter Long Gallery. (Stream continues to a climb down. Downstream to left sumps. Upstream, right, leads via a duck – a good one to do as a first experience – back into Long Gallery through a climb up 20m further on).

From the entry into Long Gallery going left ends in a choke or right reaches, after 20m, a small hole on the right of the passage. This leads to the stream and duck. Long Gallery continues to a lower section and stream to the right. Passage ends in choke where water emerges.

Tackle:

	Rope length required	Bolts	Remarks
Entrance Traverse/ Shaft	30m	3	Metal stake for backup, Long sling for tree.
Pitch 2	20m	4	
Pitch 3	15m		2 slings.

Survey ref: Lancaster/Easegill, published by Lyon Equipment/Inglesport.

COUNTY POT
Grade 3

Grid Ref: SD 675805   O.S. Outdoor Leisure Series No 2, Yorkshire Dales – Western Area, 1:25,000.   Altitude: 320m
Length & depth included in Lancaster/Easegill

Dug out in 1952 by the N.P.C and the R.R.C.P.C. It was extended in 1972 by M.U.S.S.

Club access is with R.R.C.P.C. permit from P Muckalt for weekend trips. For mid-week permits apply to T Bowering. Please sign the destination blackboard at Bull Pot Farm (the R.R.C.P.C. hut) before starting your trip.

WARNING: As with the other caves associated with the Easegill system parts of the lower cave flood to the roof.

Approach as for Lancaster Hole, but once over the stile continue to Hellot Scales Barn and into Easegill. Follow Easegill upstream passing the impressive Cow Dub to the right. Through the gate and cross the beck to the entrance about 100m ahead.

Climb carefully down the lidded shaft and slide through into the streamway. A tall, narrow passage leads down several climbs to the head of the first pitch. From the landing, a passage soon arrives at the climb down into Broadway, a square cut streamway and the first major junction.

Facing downstream, follow the right hand wall (i.e. The wall you've just climbed down!), round and up a slope to where a new streamway starts. This is Showerbath and water may or may not be falling out of the roof on the first section. Follow this down to a junction with another stream entering from the right. This is Confusion Corner and can be difficult to notice on the way out so take good note.

Carry on, past the higher passage on the right which leads to the Manchester By-pass (the flood escape route from Mainline Terminus, see below), and then down a short climb into Spout Hall. At the far end the stream runs into a hands and knees crawl for 30m and then suddenly opens out into a tall passage. On the right hand side and about 5m up in the wall is the opening of Poetic Justice, the link passage with the far reaches of the cave. To enter it, duck into a small hole in the wall and then thrutch up the hidden narrow chimney to the top. A short ladder may make it easier for the rest to follow.

Poetic Justice is a low bedding plane with a scoured stal floor and numerous filthy columns seeming to hold the roof up. At the end (it's only short!) a climb down and around to the left is the second pitch. From the bottom the passage leads down to the junction with Trident Streamway entering from the right. Follow the stream down until the passage becomes half filled with mudbanks. Crawl over these and arrive at Eureka Junction, the connection with the Main Drain which runs from right to left.

Upstream after a short distance, some huge boulders block the way. These can be passed with care via the route the stream takes or by a low bedding plane around their right hand side. On the far side is Stop Pot, a massive boulder slope rises to a short ladder into the High Level Route to Lancaster Hole.

Tackle:

Pitch 1	8m ladder, spreader, 3m belay sling, 17m lifeline.
Climb to Poetic Justice	Optional 4m ladder and 10m lifeline.
Pitch 2	8m ladder, spreader, 17m lifeline.

To be Eco bolted in Feb. 1997.

Manchester Bypass – Flood Escape Route

This is the least complicated flood escape route from the Stop Pot area to the upper reaches of County Pot.

On the High Level Route from Lancaster Hole to Stop Pot at the end of Monster Cavern keep right (left enters the low and wide passage that eventually leads to the ladder descent landing on the top of the huge boulder slope of Stop Pot). Scrambling and walking along the passage leads to a point where the floor suddenly rises and a shattered crawling passage is entered. Follow this up and right to a slot leading into Old English Chamber (straight ahead leads into Carrot Chamber).

A small and muddy hole to the left of Old English Chamber is entered into the initially low and narrow Spangle Passage. Short traverses in the roof and other obstacles which follow lead on to reach the start of a narrow descending rift. This ends above a 4m very slippery climb down onto the bouldery floor of Brown and Smelly Chamber. A handline is useful here.

Crawl out of the chamber to the left at the base of the climb quickly followed by a drop into a small and shattered passage. Rising over muddy boulders and to the right reaches the top of a 6m pitch. Ladder in place. (The pitch can be bypassed by slim cavers via Cono Crawl – a narrow rift that enters the chamber at the bottom of the pitch).

From the bottom of the pitch a short crawl reaches a short descent into a muddy fissure and into a low, cobbly crawl entered between two loose boulders. A low bedding chamber is reached. Climbing up and over large fallen boulders followed by a few metres of walking passage emerges in the active streamway of County Pot just upstream of Spout Hall.

Tackle:

Climb down into Brown and Smelly Chamber 10m handline. 15m lifeline for 6m pitch.

Survey ref: Lancaster/Easegill, published by Lyon Equipment/Inglesport.

COW POT   Grade 4

Grid Ref: SD 664808   O.S. Outdoor Leisure Series No 2, Yorkshire Dales – Western Area, 1:25,000.   Altitude: 305m   Length: 244m   Depth: 76m

Club access is with R.R.C.P.C. permit from P Muckalt for weekend trips. For mid-week permits apply to T Bowering. Please sign the destination blackboard at Bull Pot Farm (the R.R.C.P.C. hut) before starting your trip.

First explored by the Y.R.C. in 1899. Extended in 1948 by the N.P.C. and in 1969 by the B.S.A.

Cow Pot is approximately 100m N of Lancaster Hole in a walled enclosure entered via a stile. From Bull Pot Farm the approach is as for Lancaster Hole through the kissing gate to the left of the building onto the track past Bull Pot of The Witches. 500m further a gate is reached. Over the stile where a signpost points left to Cow Pot and Lancaster Hole. Follow the wall to the stile into the Cow Pot enclosure.

Whilst not suitable for a pull-through trip Cow Pot is an interesting way to reach the Easegill Main Drain and Montague East Passage. The main pitch being far more satisfying than Lancaster Hole.

The entrance pitch is from a rock platform best approached by following the path round to the right of the hole where hang lays over the lip of the rock at the top of the pitch. Rebelay 2m down and after a further 6m there is a deviation rigged from the opposite wall.

Several passages lead off from the base of the pitch offering entertainment for the inquisitive and optimistic. Up the slope to the S, is the route to Fall Pot, where a small lateral rift descends to the top of a short climb down into a small chamber. The rift and climb are constricted (a handline secured to a convenient natural thread is desirable for the return journey. At the time of writing there are separate fixed handlines in place for both the rift and the climb).

From the chamber, a hole at floor level emerges in a low passage. Right ends after a few metres, but to the left after crawling over cobbles and sand the height increases to permit walking in a twisting streamway with shallow pools. The passage soon opens out where the stream starts to cut down in the floor before falling into Fall Pot. Following the greasy ledge on the left leads to a substantial shale pillar which provides the anchorage point for the traverse line to the top of the main pitch. Two Eco hangers in the left hand side of the solution tube in the roof and one above the ledge on the other side enable the rift to be crossed without too much anxiety.

The Main Pitch is rigged from each side of the rift. 6m down there is a rebelay just above a natural rock bridge. About the same distance down again a deviation is rigged through holes in a rock flake. At the time of writing there is a fixed sling in place but self-sufficiency would require one sling threaded through the two closely adjacent holes in the flake or two slings for a more robust anchorage reaching from one hole to the edge of the flake. 11m below the first rebelay, there is a rebelay for the final 25m drop through the roof of Fall Pot Chamber with an impressive descent to land on the large blocks beside the climb down to the Main Drain.

Tackle:

	Rope length required	Eco hangers	Remarks
Entrance	30m	4	1 deviation.
Rift & climb	12m		
Traverse & Pitch	60m	8	Bollard at start of traverse, thread on traverse, 1 deviation.

Survey ref: Lancaster/Easegill, published by Lyon Equipment/Inglesport.

LANCASTER HOLE TO WRETCHED RABBIT, High Level Route   Grade 3

**Grid Refs: Lancaster Hole: SD 664807   Wretched Rabbit: SD 676806
O.S. Outdoor Leisure Series No 2, Yorkshire Dales – Western Area,
1:25,000.   Altitude: Lancaster Hole 294m   Wretched Rabbit 330m
Length: Total system exceeds 66,000m (Bull Pot of the Witches, Easegill
Caverns, Link Pot and Pippikin Pot).
Vertical range: Whole System, 137m**

Club access is with R.R.C.P.C. permit from P Muckalt for weekend trips. For mid-week permits apply to T Bowering. Please sign the destination blackboard at Bull Pot Farm (the R.R.C.P.C. hut) before starting your trip.

WARNING: In very wet conditions the Master Cave floods dramatically – at least to the floor of Fall Pot! A height of 20m above normal level.

Lancaster Hole was dug out by the B.S.A. in 1946. Many are the extensions that have been made, even today pieces are still being put together of this huge jigsaw – the longest system in Britain. The main clubs involved in these extensions were the R.R.C.P.C., N.P.C. and E.P.C. Wretched Rabbit passage had been known for a long time but the exit remained elusive until a barking dog was heard. Upon frantic digging from within, the exit was born. This event in 1984 dramatically changed people's attitudes to the system. Through trips were now possible with the minimum of gear. However, the iron ladders in Fall and Stake Pots were removed in September 1994 making a through trip much more serious. The traverse rope above the Craptrap was also removed at this time.

Cars need to be parked tidily at Bull Pot Farm. Go through the kissing gate just to the east of the building to follow a track. This soon passes the tree lined shaft of Bull Pot of the Witches on the right. 500m further a gate is reached. Over the stile where a signpost points left to Cow Pot and Lancaster Hole. Follow the wall, then bear right and down to a dry valley where the lidded hole is found in a small clump of limestone boulders.

The entrance shaft of 35m is narrow at the top but soon opens out and gives a fine free hanging descent to the rubble floor. A climb up, above a hole, of 1.5m gives access to a wide high rift. A short walk reaches the top of a slope down into Bridge Hall. (Part way down this slope is a small passage leading to the Graveyard. At the bottom of the slope in Bridge Hall a climb up on the left in a gully, followed by a traverse round a nose of rock enters a short lived, large passage to eventually reach the fine Colonnade Chamber).

The way on is to the right through a hole in boulders at bottom of the chamber. This is Kath's Way. Once through the boulders a low passage goes straight on – Bill Taylor's Passage.

Stooping and crawling leads to a showerbath on the left in an alcove. Larger passage continues to two boulders blocking the way on. These can be avoided by taking the mud slope to the right returning beyond the short obstacle. Alternatively an awkward manoeuvre over them or a damp crawl under to enter more walking passage to reach an awkward climb down over boulders – exposed.

Climb up into large passage – Montague West Passage. (Just before the awkward climb down a muddy slope going off to the right rejoins the main way shortly beyond the climb up). Follow the large passage on the left wall. A hole in the floor (the Craptrap) is soon reached. Passing this on the left is awkward and a slip would be fatal as the Main Drain is 25m below. It is better and much safer to gain the right hand wall to by-pass the hole. Beyond, return to the left hand wall and quickly reach Fall Pot. In situ hangers allow rigging for SRT (or an abseil pull through). Fasten the end of the rope to a large boulder to reach 2 Eco hangers for a 'Y' belay. Descend 8m to a rebelay. The bouldery and muddy floor of Fall Pot is reached after a further 6m drop.

Go under the huge fallen block and climb up to the right hand wall which is followed to an awkward muddy and slippery climb up jammed boulders or a devious route through them to emerge in Montague East Passage.

Scramble over muddy boulders to mud floored passage to a hole in the floor. Follow the left hand wall to Stake Pot. This is descended from a 'Y' hang for 6m to a rebelay where a 7m drop reaches the bottom of the pitch. Clamber up a muddy climb on the other side of the passage over muddy rock and follow the dry upper gallery over the boulders.

Soon Bob's Boss is reached with fine formations – care. At the end of the formations a slide down a slippery slope is followed by more boulder hopping on the right. These lead left to reach Painter's Palette – a fine formation. A rope in place assists a slippery climb up to more boulder scrambling to two large holes in quick succession – Scylla and Charybdis – which are passed on the right. Great care must be taken on the traverse around these as they drop into the streamway far below. Beyond these holes, gradually descend to a short climb down and go across to the left hand wall. The floor rises and a short hands and knees crawl enters a large passage. Keep to the right then take a muddy flat out crawl at roof level (down to the left is Oxbow Corner in the Main Drain). A triangular shaped passage on the left is entered and emerges in a stooping passage. This soon reaches a chamber with taped formations. Climb up past these to enter Oakes Cavern. Keep to the left in this huge passage and at the far end a draughting hole on the left is reached.

This is the entrance into The Minarets, a fine section of passages with good formations. These are connected by two very short, flat out crawls. At the far end a climb up a huge block enters the quiet and enormous Corne's Cavern. A central trench in the floor is the best way on and continues bouldery to Snail Cavern and on into Monster Cavern.

At the far end of Monster Cavern the large passage continues slightly right to Carrot Chamber, whilst further right leads to Manchester Bypass. A wide, low passage on the left leads to large slippery boulders that are climbed over, round and under to reach the head of a short climb down to the ladder dropping into Stop Pot.

From the foot of the ladder go down the huge boulder slope. Part way down a cairn is seen on the right in an obvious passage. This marks the entrance into Wretched Rabbit. A hole in the floor gives access to a crawl. Keeping to the left at a junction emerge in Four Ways Chamber after an awkward manoeuvre over a flat topped, jammed block. Take the hole under the block to reach a small streamway. Head upstream! A low crawl in the stream reaches a cross rift. Climb up to the right. After a short rift traverse enter a dry rift on the right where the stream goes left. Rejoin the stream a little further on and follow it to a cascade. Up this, then step right over the top of the waterfall and follow meanders to reach a very high rift and the fixed handlines that lead up to the exit crawl. Please replace the dustbin lid!

Tackle:

	Rope length required	Eco hangers	Remarks
Entrance Shaft	55m	2	Fasten rope to large surface boulder.
Fall Pot	25m	3	Tie rope end to boulder, via old ladder route.
Stake Pot	20m	4	

To be Eco bolted in Feb. 1997.

Survey ref: Lancaster/Easegill, published by Lyon Equipment/Inglesport.

LANCASTER HOLE, Main Drain   Grade 3

A marvellous stream passage, perhaps the finest in Yorkshire!

Follow the High Level Route to Craptrap. From here it is possible to descend directly into the Main Drain by quite a good, although somewhat muddy, 30m pitch. However, it is more usual to reach the Main Drain from the bottom of Fall Pot. Scrambling down to the lowest point a way through huge collapsed boulders leads into the Main Drain after an awkward step down – Care.

Downstream leads down a huge canyon passage to the sump passing two obvious passages on the right. The first one is Wilf Taylor's whilst the second, shortly after, at a sharp left hand bend and up a mud bank, is Waterfall.

Returning to the boulder pile beneath the climb up into Fall Pot the streamway continues upstream through pools, chutes and cascades to where a boulder pile blocks the way. Climbing out of the stream a way is easily found up through the boulders into Stake Pot before rejoining the streamway. Further marvellous streamway, in parts well decorated, leads eventually to a huge boulder collapse. It is possible to thread a way through the unstable collapse – care – to emerge at Oxbow Corner. From here climb diagonally left across the right wall to reach the High Level Route to Wretched Rabbit.

Tackle:

	Rope length required	Bolts	Remarks
Craptrap	45m	5	Large thread before traverse at floor level. Deviation at –3m. Rebelay at –10m.
Fall Pot	25m	3	Eco hangers. Tie rope end to boulder, via old ladder route.

Survey ref: Lancaster/Easegill, published by Lyon Equipment/Inglesport.

PIPPIKIN POT   Grade 4/5

Grid Ref: SD 667800   O.S. Outdoor Leisure Series No 2, Yorkshire Dales – Western Area, 1:25,000.   Altitude: 326m
Length: 6,600m total for cave   Depth: 113m

First descended in 1929 by the G.C. The main explorations, however, were undertaken in 1970 by the H.W.C.P.C.

A C.N.C.C. permit is required for this hole. This must be produced at Leck Fell House.

WARNING: Entrance series is tight and awkward.

A through trip to Mistral Hole via the Hall of the Ten and Dusty Junction. Most pitches have good 'pull through' points but take some spare slings along just in case.

Parking is usually permitted at Leck Fell House. Walk up to Leck Fell House and take the path through the gate. Cut across left to the next gate and then follow the wall down until a large shake hole is reached. Cut across the fell to the first dry valley and follow it upstream to where the stream sinks into some boulders. The entrance is an obvious hole on the left.

The 6m entrance pitch is immediate and requires a sling to be left in situ if the trip is to be a 'pull through' (this can be retrieved after the trip). The first pitch lands in a high chamber with the way on being through a crawl at floor level. Carefully traverse over Cellar Pot into the continuation of the crawl, which is quite restricted and opens up immediately into the roof of a small chamber 2m from the floor. This requires careful handling to avoid dropping out of the restriction head first. Climb through the window at the base of the chamber into a tight rift passage that is followed down past a few constrictions to the head of the 5m second pitch. A pull through can be rigged over the compression stemple in situ at the head of this pitch. The passage below follows the same constricted nature, through a further restriction to a wide shale band and the head of the 15m third pitch, rigged over a large bar stemple.

From the base of the third pitch the way on is down through a narrow slot into a very restricted squeeze. After a few metres the squeeze opens directly onto the top of a 5.5m climb. This can be tackled head first or feet first and has a compression stemple conveniently placed to act as a perch as you squeeze out of the constriction (a rope may be useful here for those who are not confident on climbs).

The 8m fourth pitch follows immediately and leads to a junction with the stream. Follow the stream down to the 3m fifth pitch, along a stooping passage to a 1.5m awkward climb down which is worse on the way up. The passage that follows is best done by traversing in the roof where there is more room and after about 46m the passage opens up into a high aven chamber with large blocks. The 4.5m sixth pitch is immediate and enters a large chamber after which is a junction with a high passage entering from the right.

Take the downstream passage which continues for quite a way as an easy walk in a narrow meandering passage, typical of the Lancaster/Easegill System, until the water flows under a low arch, the passage lowers and a boulder choke is encountered. The way on is up through the boulders into the Hall of the Ten and is best attempted at the far right of the boulder choke (take care, as some of the boulders are loose).

The Hall of the Ten is a huge sandy chamber and from now on the nature of the cave changes as the stream is left behind. Climb out of the chamber on the right into a low sandy passage at roof level and follow the obvious path through some small chambers linked by hands and knees crawls until the passage opens out into a wide low chamber with a cairn in the middle. This is Dusty Junction and the way on is down to the left (straight on is the passage that connects to Link Pot, whilst to the right leads to Red Wall Chamber).

From Dusty Junction the passage is fairly low and muddy until it opens out into a series of chambers and avens. Keep to the right wall and climb up a short mud bank into a very impressive large flat roofed chamber called the Hobbit. The exit is up the steep boulder pile at the end of the chamber to the start of a low crawl through boulders at roof level. A few metres in, a small chamber is entered and the start of the entrance crawl in Mistral Hole which is quite tight and awkward for large or long people. After a few corners the crawl pops out at the bottom of a deep wide fissure in the side of Easegill and an easy, though loose free climb up to the surface.

Tackle:
1 x 30m rope for pull-through,
1 x 30m rope as spare
Survey ref: Lancaster/Easegill, published by Lyon Equipment/Inglesport

POOL SINK   Grade 3

Grid Ref: SD 677807   O.S. Outdoor Leisure Series No 2, Yorkshire Dales – Western Area, 1:25,000.   Altitude: 332m
Length and depth included in the total for Lancaster/Easegill.

The P.P.S.G. explored the cave in 1956.

Club access is with R.R.C.P.C. permit from P Muckalt, for weekend trips. For mid-week permits apply to T Bowering. Please sign the destination blackboard at Bull Pot Farm (the R.R.C.P.C. hut) before starting your trip.

Approach as for County Pot. Some 400m further upstream Pool Sink, a rectangular shaped slot, is found on the left hand side of the beck next to a deep pool which is often dry! However, polished rock shelving surrounding the pool helps further to identify the cave.

Along with the other entrances to Lancaster/Easegill system exchange trips can be made although a thorough knowledge of the way is needed.

WARNING: As with the other caves associated with the Easegill system parts of the lower cave flood to the roof.

Pool Sink provides the most direct way into the further reaches of Easegill and can be very sporting. A squirm over boulders reaches a right-angled left hand bend in a smooth washed tube. This leads after a few metres to an awkward left/right dog-leg followed by a short bedding before the passage gradually increases to crawling and sideways stooping. Step down into a small chamber with water entering from the right.

Follow the water downstream in an easy crab-walk sized passage to reach the first pitch. The 20m pitch is started by a traverse to a 'Y' hang where the floor drops away. Land on a large ledge from where a small drop reaches a 'T' junction with the active steamway of Upper T-Piece Passage. There is a rebelay below the 'Y' hang for those wishing to stay dry at the bottom of the pitch but is difficult to reach.

Downstream the clean washed passage reaches the second pitch where the water drops down a steepening slot which is traversed over. A large pillar on the corner before the drop gives a good belay to start the traverse. Step up into an abandoned oxbow where around the next corner, low down on the left, is a small thread at the end of the traverse and 'Y' hang for the 10m descent. A 'Y' hang is found further out in the chamber, after a short traverse, for the third pitch. Land in a beautifully clean and tall, walking sized streamway. A short way down the curving passage the last pitch is reached – Jacob's Ladder. A long traverse across the drop and around the corner leads to a 'Y' hang.

At the bottom follow the water downstream in a large, tall passage – Lower T-Piece Passage – over large boulders. Just before the floor level closes climb up onto a ledge on the left and crawl until the stream below is crossed over into an old oxbow. This winds back to the stream again. Here, a descending traverse over 'bacon-slicer' shaped ledges lead down to the stream. This is quickly left after a short distance for another oxbow on the right.

The stream is joined again for a short distance until another oxbow on the right is followed by stooping and crawling to a squeeze past a block. Just beyond, another block is passed to where the passage is almost totally blocked by a huge boulder. A gap on the left can be climbed or a stoop through leads into a chamber. On the right the stream continues. Follow the water downstream in a lowering passage until a crawl on the right in a small bedding leads to the Main Stream Passage some 30m below Holbeck Junction.

Tackle:

	Rope length required	Eco hangers	Remarks
Pitch 1	25m	6	
Traverse			
Pitches 2 & 3	50m	7	Use rock pillar at start of traverse and thread along traverse on pitch 2.
Pitch 4	25m	6	

Survey ref: Lancaster/Easegill, published by Lyon Equipment/Inglesport.

GREATER EASEGILL TRAVERSE, Top Sink to Pippikin Pot   Grade 5

Grid Ref: SD 680811   O.S. Outdoor Leisure Series No 2, Yorkshire Dales – Western Area, 1:25,000.   Altitude: 349m
Length and depth included in the total for Lancaster/Easegill.

The first traverse was completed in 1978 by the B.I.C.C.

A C.N.C.C. permit is required for Pippikin and an R.R.C.P.C. permit for Top Sink.

Club access is with R.R.C.P.C. permit from P Muckalt, for weekend trips. For mid-week permits apply to T Bowering. Please sign the destination blackboard at Bull Pot Farm (the R.R.C.P.C. hut) before starting your trip and if doing an exchange please show C.N.C.C. permit at Leck Fell House.

WARNING: This is a long and serious trip. When the stream is running in Lower Easegill ALL the passages below the 88 foot pitch flood to the roof and the Wet Wallows become impassable in wet weather. Top Sink is also impassable in wet weather.

This is perhaps the greatest traverse in British caving. However, intimate knowledge of the route is required, especially around the Stake Pot series. Some sections have to be pre-rigged unless an exchange trip is done. This allows for all the ups and downs to be rigged in each direction. The easiest direction of doing this traverse is to descend Pippikin and exit via Top Sink, but the classic way is to enter via Top Sink. The Traverse can be shortened if desired as exits are possible at various points to which reference will be made. For example traverses can be made to (exits possible if pre-rigged), in downstream order, Pool Sink, Wretched Rabbit, County Pot, Link Pot, Mistral Hole and Lancaster hole.

Park at Bull Pot Farm and sign the destination blackboard. Follow the track to Hellot Scales barn then take the path that leads into Easegill. Follow Easegill upstream past the impressive Cow Dub and on to County Pot. Continue past Pool Sink and onto a level area where the gill has broadened. Top Sink is found on the left (true right) of the beck some 70m upstream of a sheep fold.

The description below is an outline only because some sections defy describing and we feel also that a blow by blow account is undesirable in this instance.

Climb down entrance into a narrow passage quickly passing a junction on the left. The floor of the passage cuts down and meanders to the 18m deep Walrus Pot. At the bottom the aptly named πr^2 passage doubles back beneath the pitch and an awkward series of bends reach an enlarging passage near the 5m Penknife Pitch. Below, Wisdom Tooth Passage enters from the left. Bradshaw's Passage continues, a long and winding hands and knees crawl to the highly complex Limerick Junction. Climbing up to the left and traversing along shelves a narrow rift is entered, suddenly enlarging at The Rock of Ages, a tremendous boulder seemingly hanging in space! Pass under this and enter Nagasaki Cavern which is followed as a series of climbs up and down over massive piles of collapsed and unstable boulders – CARE.

At the far end of the Cavern the route is channelled into a smaller chamber. A large meandering passage on to a short drop into a large unstable chamber – the Assembly Hall. (Near the point of entry a climb up leads into the now somewhat despoiled but still quite beautiful Easter Grotto – CARE).

A hole down through the boulder floor in the Assembly Hall leads down a climb to enter the off white White Way and Thackray's Passage which contains the main stream. Gradually the passage decreases to a hand and knees crawl where, up a rocky slope to the left and through a stalagmite grille, a larger passage is entered leading back to the stream. Easy walking now leads to Holbeck Junction and the exit out of Pool Sink.

Continue easily to Stop Pot (Wretched Rabbit goes off to the left. County Pot can be reached by threading a way through boulders just above the stream to enter the water beyond in a large passage. Continue down to Eureka Junction where County Pot goes off to the left. Wretched Rabbit can also be entered, to the left, a short distance up this passage reaching the route from Stop Pot at Four Ways Chamber).

From Stop Pot climb up the boulder slope to the top and ascend the iron ladder into the High Level route. Continue as for this route towards Stake Pot. (It is possible to continue to Lancaster Hole and exit if pre-rigged, to make a fine traverse).

Just before reaching Stake Pot, tucked away under the left (south) wall and behind a boulder, is the entrance to the Stake Pot series. This is the most complex section of the trip and prior knowledge is essential if time is not to be lost finding the correct route. The initial complex leads via Brew Chamber, a large dry tunnel, found beneath a damp climb down. A manhole near a bedding plane and slide down lead into the Long Gallery. Beneath here and downstream are shattered chambers and a choice of two routes uniting in Rat Pit Chamber. Crawling past formations and traversing reaches the head of the 88 foot pitch.

A fine decent leads to the lower stream system and the lowest part of the trip. Easy going for 22m reaches Wormway which is followed by easy hands and knees crawling ending at the impressive 24m high Echo Aven, the top of which signifies the end of the Stake Pot series and the start of the Link Pot passages. Go past a sharp bend to enter a canyon passage. Continue to a hole in the roof of the passage and enter Kamikaze Highway. Crawl through the dangerously poised boulders with great care to enter Hylton Hall which has tantalising daylight filtering down from the 15m Link Pot entrance shaft. It is possible to exit here (again if pre-rigged).

Marble Steps and Leck Fell

Gavel Pot

Rumbling Hole

Short Drop Cave

Leck Fell House

2

Lost Johns Cave

3 parking

4

1. Access path to Notts Pot
2. Access path to Gavel Pot
3. Access path to Short Drop Cave and Rumbling Hole
4. Access path to Lost John's
5. Access path to Pippikin Pot

5

1

Notts Pot

Ireby Fell Cavern

Marble Steps Pot

0   1 km

Large Pot

Water Pumping Station

to Masongill

A slit on the left wall of Hylton Hall enters a larger passage. Go straight ahead, ignoring left and right turns and pass a fine example of a false floor – Care – to Squid Junction. A low crawl to the left ends in an aven where it is possible to stand. Continue through the Wet Wallows and go on to a small chamber. Further crawling along a wide bedding eventually emerges at Dusty Junction. By turning right at the junction an exit can be made out of Mistral Hole, the last one before the struggle out of Pippikin, for those who are flagging. Going straight ahead at Dusty Junction through sandy tunnels reaches the Hall of the Ten in Pippikin Pot.

On the far side of the Hall of the Ten a hole through boulders reaches the Pippikin stream and once through the low arch follow the easy but narrow meandering passage to reach the large chamber at the bottom of the 6th pitch of Pippikin Pot. The rest is now uphill and considerable effort is required to reach the surface!

Tackle:

	Rope length required	Bolts	Remarks
Top Sink:			
Walrus Pot	30m	5	Eco hangers.
Penknife Pitch	15m	3	Eco hangers.
Stake Pot Series:			
88 foot pitch	30m	4	Natural belays.
Echo Aven	30m	4	Natural belays.
Pippikin Pot:			
Pitch 1	20m		For this and the following pitches
Pitch 2	10m		natural belays and stemples are used.
Pitch 3	25m		
Handline for			
rift climb	10m		
Pitch 4	15m		
Pitch 5	12m		
Pitch 6	20m		

N.B. Refer to tackle lists for Pool Sink, County Pot or Lancaster Hole if exiting one of these.

If exiting via Wretched Rabbit equipment only for Top Sink is required and a 45m rope is sufficient to enable a pull through trip to be made.

Link Pot needs a 20m rope and 2 bolts if coming out here.

Traversing to/from Mistral Hole requires that Stake Pot is pre-rigged along with the rigging of Top Sink.

Survey ref: Lancaster/Easegill, published by Lyon Equipment/Inglesport.

Marble Steps

LARGE POT   Grade 4

Grid Ref: SD 682768   O.S. Outdoor Leisure Series No 2, Yorkshire Dales – Western Area, 1:25,000.   Altitude: 402m   Length: 1,242m Depth: 122m

Explored by the N.P.C. in 1982. Connected to Rift Pot in 1984 by the E.P.C.

WARNING: The very awkward entrance series would make rescue almost impossible. An accident in the far reaches would be extremely serious indeed.

Park cars as for Marble Steps Pot and walk up Turbary Road to the stile. Instead of climbing over it continue up the rough track to the first bend. Leave the track at this point and go straight ahead for some 200m following the wall line. Large Pot is the left (W) of two shakeholes 6m apart (right is Little Pot). The entrance is covered by a metal lid.

The entrance pitch, although climbable with care, is best rigged from the scaffold pole. At the bottom a small hole enters a low crawl which must be entered feet first lying on your left hand side which soon reaches the second pitch. Narrow at the top the pitch soon opens out. A short drop at the bottom leads to the third pitch entering a chamber – Thornton Hall – at the bottom. Follow the passage downstream.

After a short distance a passage is seen on the left and is the way to Colossus and Rift Pot. (Downstream continues to a 24m pitch and the Red Herring Series). Along the left hand passage the Pit is soon reached. Descend the Pit by an easy climb and up the other side which has a fixed rope – CARE at the top. Follow the larger, partially silted passage – Secret Seven Passage. Part way along this passage is a sideways shuffle followed by an oxbow on the left. When the passages re-join Tinkle Inlet is off to the left.

Downstream, Secret Seven Passage ends at a high aven. Beyond is a short flat out crawl followed by a traverse to a right hand bend. Descend feet first to floor level. A short easier section leads to Calcite Corner. Go sharp right into a muddy tube. An awkward bend is passed from where alternate crawling and stooping – fine formations, care – lead to a rift ending at a squeeze. Muddy pools and slippery traverses continue to a crawl over calcite to reach Pumpkin Passage entering from the left.

Downstream, care is needed because 30m further is the magnificent 43m Colossus pitch edged with moonmilk. Belay well back from where a traverse is made out over the pitch. The calcite cascade descends the whole length of the pitch. Part way down a bedding full of formations is seen.

At the base of the pitch Necropolis is entered, a large chamber. South-east is low initially but soon enlarges to a calcite and sand choke. South-west leads towards Rift Pot and ends in a massive choke. Take the right hand side to just before it gets very low climb up to the side and over a boulder following the draught.

Beyond, is Eldon Extension entering a chamber. A very low, wet, flat out bedding with 10-15cms airspace continues for 6m to a climb up through the Mousehole to reach a passage entering Rift Pot.

Tackle:

	Rope length required	Bolts	Remarks
Pitch 1	15m		Belay to Scaffold pole.
Pitch 2	30m		Eye bolt at head of pitch.
Pitch 3	10m		Thread above pitch. Use as a handline.
Colossus	60m	4	Calcite block for back up at start of traverse.

Survey ref: Marble Steps Pot, Rift Pot, Low Douk Cave, Large Pot and Little Pot, N.C.C. Journal (The Caver) 1986.

MARBLE STEPS POT   Grade 3/4

Grid Ref: SD 680771   O.S. Outdoor Leisure Series No 2, Yorkshire Dales – Western Area, 1:25,000.   Altitude: 384m   Length: 1,113m Depth: 131m

Known for a long time, the cave was extended in 1966 by the G.S.S. and in 1978 by the N.C.C. Work continues at the bottom of the cave.

Permission required from Masongill Farm, Westhouse, Via Carnforth.

WARNING: All passages below Stink Pot are liable to severe and total flooding. Only descend in settled weather.

Turn off the main A65 Ingleton to Kirkby Lonsdale road to Masongill. Once through the village follow the lane to it's end by a water pumping station on the left. A green lane turns off to the right opposite this. Park cars tidily to one side so that neither is blocked. Walk up Turbury Road for about 500m to a stile that leads over the wall on the left. Walk up and across the hillside to the prominent clump of trees surrounding the entrance.

Follow the entrance gully down the right hand side, initially safegaurded by a handline, to a platform overlooking the less than vertical continuation of the Main Shaft. A series of hangs descends to the unstable floor of the Main Chamber. Cross this to it's upper end to enter the North-west Rift and a crawl between boulders to enter Lower Main Chamber. Altough the above is the most direct way of reaching Lower Main Chamber the following is much more impressive.

Descend the initial gully to the platform overlooking the Main Shaft. Traverse around the head of the gully, along the far wall to a window and large ledge. A 5m drop reaches the streamway coming from above. A vadose passage continues downstream to reach a 20m pitch into Main Chamber which is rigged from a floor slot above over the pitch. Dropping down alongside the waterfall an easy pendulum 15m down allows a ledge to be reached on a prominent buttress. A steep incline is descended via 2 deviations in the roof to gain a ledge above the final 10m drop into Lower Main Chamber.

A large passage leaves the chamber and a handline is used down a slippery climb over a floor trench to the bottom of the Great Aven. Follow the obvious rift – the 240 foot Rift – to a sharp bend. Here a traverse, at roof level, over a blind pit continues to the head of the 10m Stink Pot. Constricted at the top it soon opens out into a small chamber exiting above a deep fissure in the floor where the Intestines and Ninety routes lead off. Crossing the fissure (down leads into the Intestines) the passage shrinks as it nears the head of the fine 28m shaft of the Ninety. Two further pitches (10m and 7m) drop into a small streamway which ends almost immediately in constricted sumps.

Tackle:

	Rope length required	Bolts	Remarks
Entrance gully, Traverse and pitch	40m	10	
Pitch 2	60m	10	Belay to flake at head of pitch.
Handline	10m	1	For slippery climb.
Stink Pot	25m	5	Thread at head of pitch. Belay end of rope in passage beyond fissure.
The Ninety	35m	3	Belay to flake at head of pitch. Often unpleasantly wet!

90

Last pitches   30m   3   Belay to thread at head of pitch.
Survey ref: Marble Steps Pot, U.L.S.A., Marble Steps Pot, Rift Pot, Low Douk
Cave, Large Pot and Little Pot, N.C.C. Journal (The Caver) 1986.

Leck Fell

GAVEL POT   Grade 4

**Grid Ref: SD 666791   O.S. Outdoor Leisure Series No 2, Yorkshire Dales
– Western Area, 1:25,000.   Altitude: 323m   Length: 1,798m
Depth: 110m**

The C.P.C. and N.P.C. were the main explorers in 1970

A C.N.C.C. permit is required for this cave. This must be produced at Bank
House Farm (on the left at the first gate).

WARNING: The last two pitches respond quickly to rainfall and soon become
impassable. Take care when descending shored vertical shaft. It has collapsed in
the past.

A fine and underrated trip.

Park on Leck Fell at SD 670786 and follow access path down the hill on the far
side of a wall. Entrance is in the large, tree lined shakehole surrounded by a wood
fence with a stile at the SE corner. Climb over the stile and follow the fence round
keeping to the right. An obvious path in descended into with care the shakehole
reaching a natural bridge. The large open pot in to the right and a small passage to
the left.

Illogically the SRT way in is to take the left hand passage. Three bolts permit a
hang to land on the sloping and loose stony floor of a rift. (Down the slope leads
into Short Drop Cave via an exposed traverse and a further drop down via a short
7m pitch, 2 bolts at head, to reach the streamway).

The way on is up the slope to a short rift passage to emerge back into daylight
on the floor of Gavel Pot. (This can be reached by a short scramble down to the
right to a rock platform where a large metal stake gives access to the same point.
However, this is not recommended due to severe rope rub.)

Walk down the slope to two jammed boulders. Pass under these to reach the
12m second pitch. Although free climbable it is better to use a rope belayed to a
jammed scaffold pole to enter a small chamber. Beyond the chamber a descent
down shored walls enters more stable passage at the bottom which quickly
enlarges where some fine formations abound. After a short walking section
following water the passage lowers to a crawl on cobbles.

Larger passage follows and cuts down in a canyon past a tricky climb down to
the head of the 30m third pitch. (The tricky climb can be avoided by a dry oxbow to
the left). An awkward traverse out at the pitch head reaches two bolts for a 'Y'
hang. In all but normal conditions this pitch is very wet on the last 10m for the first
person down. Fastening the rope to a thread on a ledge 2m off the floor of the shaft
allows the rest of the team to descend more or less dry. A draughty spot!

Short section of canyon passage follows to the head of the last pitch. A fine
thread up on the right protects a traverse out to a bolt and short drop to a rebelay.
A deviation 6m down avoids most of the water. The fine sump pool is imediately on
arrival at bottom.

Tackle:

	Rope length required	Bolts	Remarks
Pitch 1	17m	3	Care on slope at bottom.
Pitch 2	15m		Belay rope to scaffold pole.
Pitch 3	55m	5	Flake up on right 5m before pitch head. Deviaiton at −15m. Fasten rope to thread on ledge 2m above floor of shaft.
Pitch 4	30m	2	Thread on right for traverse out to bolt, scaffold pole useful as foothold! Deviation −6m below re-belay.

Survey ref: The Leck Fell Systems drawn by Paul Hatherley 1983, based on compilation survey by A.C. Waltham 1970, published by B.C.R.A. originally done by L.U.C.C., U.L.S.A., H.W.C.P.C., C.D.G., G.C., N.C.C., C.P.C., M.U.S.S., N.P.C., B.C.C., C.P.G., along with others.

IREBY FELL CAVERN   Grade 3

Grid Ref: SD 673773   O.S. Outdoor Leisure Series No 2, Yorkshire Dales – Western Area, 1:25,000.   Altitude: 400m   Length: 4,600m + Depth: 128m

First explorations by the B.S.A. in 1949, extensions in 1964 by the C.D.G., 1966 by the R.R.C.P.C. and N.W.P.C., 1968 and 1975 by the N.C.C.

Approach as for Marble Steps Pot to the stile over the wall. Once over the stile head NW for the stile on the skyline. Over this and traverse round the fell to a massive dry stream sink near a wall. The entrance is at the bottom of the sink down a concrete pipe.

Traditional Route

Descend the steep boulder slope at the bottom of the pipe to the head of Ding Pitch. Descend direct from the small ledge on the right or traverse forward in damper conditions. Dong Pitch follows and the passage at the bottom descends steeply to the head of Bell Pitch. The bottom of this pitch can get very wet so traverse out to obtain a dry hang. Follow the passage to the climb down Pussy Pitch into a chamber with a hole in the wall at head height. Follow the stream at floor level if the crawl isn't blocked or climb into the hole and squeeze round the bends to emerge in the stream again. Hands and knees crawling passes an inlet on the right and also the climb up into the Glory Holes but soon lifts to walking height.

Some stal blockages force a short return to lying in the stream but the walking passage continues to a climb down to Well Pitch. Traverse onto the bridge and rig down the far side out of the water. A short passage then leads to Rope Pitch where the cave opens out into lofty avens.

The stooping tunnel which follows soon lifts and easy going leads to a step up into a dry passage after the stream disappears under the left wall. This dusty passage enters the side of Duke Street and a left turn here soon regains the stream. Stride down this classic tunnel six abreast until the sump is, unfortunately, reached.

Shadow Route

Part way down Ding Pitch swing off across the shaft to the left into a window. Descend 3m and traverse sideways along the narrow rift to emerge at a hanging belay in the next shaft. A pendulum 6m down this shaft reaches an arete. This overlooks the base of Dong Pitch to the right whilst to the left a superb circular shaft, initially sloping, is descended via a deviation just above the vertical section. Although most of this way down is dry the last section cannot be used as a wet weather alternative to Bell Pitch.

Tackle:

	Rope length required	Eco hangers	Remarks
Shadow Route	60m	14	1 deviation after obvious slope on last section.
Pussy Pitch	10m		1 thread.
Well Pitch	35m	7	
Rope Pitch	15m		2 threads.
Traditional Route:			
Ding & Dong	40m	8	Rig these two together.
Bell	25m	5	deviation.

Continue as for Shadow Route.

Survey refs: Ireby I U.L.S.A., Ireby II U.L.S.A.

LOST JOHN'S CAVE   Grade 3/4

Grid Ref: SD 670786   O.S. Outdoor Leisure Series No 2, Yorkshire Dales – Western Area, 1:25,000.   Altitude: 355m   Length: 4,800m Depth: 140m

The Old and New Roof Traverses were explored in 1928 by the Y.R.C. with the full descent of the Old Roof Traverse completed in 1935 by the N.C.F.C. The Master Cave was explored in 1928 by the Y.R.C. and extended by the B.S.A.

A C.N.C.C. permit is required for this cave. This must be produced at Bank House Farm (on left at the first gate).

Park on Leck Fell at SD 670786. Walk back down the road to a gate in the wall. Go through this and a dry stream sink is just ahead. This is the entrance.

Follow the passage in to a small stream and continue down passing an inlet on the left. A 4m climb down a cascade is reached. Above this can be seen the New Roof Traverse whilst down the cascade is the way to the Old Roof Traverse.

Old Roof Traverse   Grade 4

Continue from the bottom of the cascade until easy traverse ledges can be gained. These lead over a 6m cascade into a short passage ending at Hampstead Heath Pitch. The stream is soon regained and soon some more traverse ledges lead out over the top of Monastery pitch. In wetter conditions, swing into an oxbow after 3m for a drier hang. At the bottom a rift quickly arrives at Piscina Pitch. Follow the excellent stream way under low arches and round a deep pool to the head of Pinnacle Pot. This lands in Sink Chamber where the water enters some perched sumps to emerge at Battleaxe Streamway. The sumps are not free-diveable.

New Roof Traverse gives access to Dome and Centipede Routes.

Upstream from the 4m cascade, some ledges can be gained which give an easy traverse over the cascade and into a long abandoned passage. Along this are three holes in the floor, the first (No.1 Hole) being the start of Dome Route. By traversing over the holes, Centipede Route is gained.

Dome Route   Grade 3
From the bottom of No.1 Hole, Vestry pitch is soon reached and leads onto a traverse to the head of Cathedral pitch. At the bottom, the Crypt leads onto the head of Dome Pitch. 11m down Dome Pitch a deviation helps to gain a window to re-belay the final short drop entering a short passage leading to Dome Junction on Centipede Route via a short pitch.

Centipede Route   Grade 3
Over the holes the passage leads to Hammer Pot, Mud Pot and Centipede Pitch. At the bottom a rift goes down, via some slippery climbs, past Dome Junction on the left, to a climb round a blind pot - care - to Candle and Shistol pitches. The passage ends at a window with the Battleaxe Streamway 12m below. The Battleaxe Traverse goes left from the window and stays high until a stance is reached over Battleaxe Alternative pitch. (The original route descended Battleaxe Pitch to the stream and then followed it down the Wet Pitch.) At the bottom the stream is regained, then after 10m, a climb up on the right allows a dry hang down the final pitch. A short passage leads on to the impressive Groundsheet Junction.

This is the point that Lost John's enters the Leck Fell Master Cave. Upstream leads to Lost Pot and climbs up to Lyle Caverns. Downstream the Passage passes several inlets before arriving at the Long Pool after 1,200m. The Long Pool sumps in wet weather and is normally chest/neck deep wading. At the end of the pool is Deaths Head inlet and the Master Cave continues before lowering to the final sump.

Tackle:

	Rope length required	Bolts	Remarks
Old Roof Traverse:			
Hampstead Heath	10m	3	
Monastery	50m	10	
Piscina	15m	5	
Pinnacle Pot	45m	11	
Centipede Route:			
Hammer	10m	3	
Mud & Centipede	60m	7	
Candle & Shistol	30m	6	
Battleaxe Traverse &			
Battleaxe Alternative	65m	10	Deviation –15m.
Final Pitch	25m	5	
Dome Route:			
No. 1 hole	10m	1	1 thread.
Vestry	12m	2	1 thread.
Cathedral	30m	5	1 flake, deviation –11m just below Pulpit ledge.
Dome	28m	6	Deviation –11m.
Dome Junction	15m	2	1 thread.
Continue as Centipede Route.			

Survey ref: The Leck Fell Systems drawn by Paul Hatherley 1983, based on compilation survey by A.C. Waltham 1970, published by the B.C.R.A., originally done by L.U.C.C., U.L.S.A., H.W.C.P.C., C.D.G., G.C., N.C.C., C.P.C., M.U.S.S., N.P.C., B.C.C., C.P.G., along with others.

NOTTS POT

Grade 3

Grid Ref: SD 671778   O.S. Outdoor Leisure Series No 2, Yorkshire Dales – Western Area, 1:25,000.   Altitude: 370m   Length: 1,098m Depth: 127m

The first explorations were undertaken by the B.S.A. in 1946. Many ways down this cave have been sorted out. Adamson's Route was worked out in 1967 by U.L.S.A., BUSS Route by B.U.S.S. in 1970 and C.P.G. in 1976. Handshake Route was explored by L.U.S.S. in 1970 and B.U.S.S. in 1971 with a connection to Adamson's Route by the C.P.G. in 1977. Dubious Tactics Route had the lower section by U.L.S.A. in 1967 with the complete exploration being accomplished by the C.P.G. in 1977. Acrobat Series was explored by U.L.S.A. in 1967 with an extension being made by L.U.S.S. in 1970 and the Deprofundis Series being explored by L.U.S.S. in 1970.

A C.N.C.C. permit is required for this cave. This must be produced at Bank House Farm (on the left at first gate).

Situated on Leck Fell, park at the Lost Johns car park and walk back down the road. Through the gate across the road and then down the hill to the gate on the left beside the Shooters Hut. Go through the gate and head up the fell along the track which runs beside the wall. Continue until a dry valley runs down from the left. Cross the fence and follow the dry valley up until a large shakehole is reached.

There are many ways down the vertical network of shafts. The following description is, perhaps, the best and is known as Centre Route.

Short entrance pitch lands on boulders. Crawl forward with the water to an awkward 3m climb down to streamway. Follow this down to the 6m second pitch. This opens out at the bottom into 3-ways Chamber and the divergent middle section routes.

Under the far wall the 21m third pitch drops away. The fourth pitch, in three sections, follows (11m, 10m and 15m) and is descended to a pendulum over to a sharp arete. Continue down the far side to a small chamber, just above the stream trench, where the other routes join.

Scramble down to the stream and then take the obvious traverse above the fifth pitch. Traverse and climb up onto the flowstone blockage. Continue traversing to a floor slot and descend from here.

At the bottom an ascending traverse reaches an oxbow from where the dry sixth pitch descends, passing a large inlet and lands in a chamber. The water almost immediately falls down the last 5m pitch at the bottom of which is the sump pool.

Tackle:

	Rope length required	Eco hangers	Remarks
Entrance Pitch	20m	3	
Awkward Climb	10m	2	Rope useful for tired cavers and in wet weather.
Pitch 2	15m	2	1 thread belay.

Pitch 3	35m	2	2 deviations.
Pitch 4	55m	7	1 flake.
First traverse &			
Pitch 5	50m	8	1 sling.
Second traverse &			
Pitch 6	55m	6	1 sling.
Last Pitch	15m	3	

Survey ref: The Leck Fell Systems drawn by Paul Hatherley 1983, based on compilation survey by A.C. Waltham 1970, published by the B.C.R.A., originally done by L.U.C.C., U.L.S.A., H.W.C.P.C., C.D.G., G.C., N.C.C., C.P.C., M.U.S.S., N.P.C., B.C.C., C.P.G., along with others.

RUMBLING HOLE or Fairies Workshop   Grade 4

Grid Ref: SD 671791   O.S. Outdoor Leisure Series No 2, Yorkshire Dales – Western Area, 1:25,000.   Altitude: 350m   Length: 213m   Depth: 119m

Fully explored by Y.R.C. in 1932.

A C.N.C.C. permit is required for this cave. This must be produced at Bank House Farm (on left at the first gate).

Park as for Lost Johns Pot then go through the gate on the road and follow the wall down the fell for 100m. Turn right and head for the solitary tree, 250m across the fell where a fence surrounds the open shaft. This is just down the fell from Rumbling Sinks where an obvious stream goes underground.

Belay to fence posts and then to the tree. Rebelay to wall opposite and then drop down and round the corner to what can be an awkward hanging belay for the main drop. Continue down the gully at the bottom to the floor of the shaft. A rift passage leads on down several cascades and slowly becomes lower. A climb down leads to a wet drop ahead but a window on the right leads on to a parallel shaft in a narrow rift. This is split into two sections. The third pitch follows immediately and a short passage leads on to the last pitch. The passage downstream from the bottom of the pitch becomes wetter and more contorted until a set of nasty ducks connect with Rumbling Hole Inlet in Lost John's Cavern.

Tackle:

	Rope length required	Eco hangers	Remarks
Entrance Shaft	75m	10	1 fence post, 1 tree, 1 deviation near bottom of shaft.
2nd Pitch	40m	6	
3rd Pitch	30m	5	Thread deviation –15m.
Last Pitch	35m	3	1 flake.

Survey ref: The Leck Fell Systems drawn by Paul Hatherley 1983, based on compilation survey by A.C. Waltham 1970, published by the B.C.R.A., originally done by L.U.C.C., U.L.S.A., H.W.C.P.C., C.D.G., G.C., N.C.C., C.P.C., M.U.S.S., N.P.C., B.C.C., C.P.G., along with others.

SHORT DROP CAVE

Grade 2/3

Grid Ref: SD 670789   O.S. Outdoor Leisure Series No 2, Yorkshire Dales – Western Area, 1:25,000.   Altitude: 354m   Length: 2,408m Depth: 55m

First explored in 1898 by the Y.R.C. Extended in 1966 by U.L.S.A. and B.S.A.

A C.N.C.C. permit is required for this cave. This must be produced at Bank House Farm (on left at the first gate).

A fine cave.

From the car park walk down the hill on the far side of the wall by the side of some old wire enclosures to a shallow valley. The entrance is a small hole at the end of this valley some 250m from the road.

'Short drop' to small streamway. Upstream leads to Coal Hole entrance. Downstream gradually enlarges to a junction on the left – Rift Entrance. A low crawl to the right reaches a larger junction with the Main Inlet. Downstream the passage gradually increases in size. A short low section is avoidable by a dry oxbow to the right. A much larger and quite impressive passage continues and soon pass under an amazing boulder bridge.

Eventually a difficult climb down is reached. A ladder is useful here – especially for novices. Continue down in the fine well watered canyon to the top of the 8m second pitch. This leads down to the sump. However, a climb up shortly before this pitch and an exposed leftward traverse on a ledge reaches daylight in Gavel Pot. If the pitch in Gavel has been rigged beforehand a through trip is possible. (It is also possible to descend a 7m pitch down to the streamway from the alcove at the end of the traverse from Gavel Pot). If not then return the same way for twice the fun!

Tackle:

	Rope length required	Bolts	Remarks
Pitch 1	15m	1	8m ladder. Scaffold pole in place
Pitch 2	20m	1	8m ladder. Scaffold pole in place. Usually wet!
Gavel Pot Entrance	25m	4	Includes traverse to alcove beyond ledge, bolt above.
Pitch down to streamway	10m	2	

Survey ref: The Leck Fell Systems drawn by Paul Hatherley 1983, based on compilation survey by A.C. Waltham 1970, published by the B.C.R.A., originally done by L.U.C.C., U.L.S.A., H.W.C.P.C., C.D.G., G.C., N.C.C., C.P.C., M.U.S.S., N.P.C., B.C.C., C.P.G., along with others.

Columns in Ogof Ffynnon Ddu 2. Photo: Tony Baker

Upper Oxbow series Ogof Ffynnon Ddu 2. Photo: Tony Baker

Fountains Fell

HAMMER POT   Grade 5

**Grid Ref: SD 852697   O.S. Outdoor Leisure Series No 2, Yorkshire Dales
– Western Area, 1:25,000.   Altitude: 427m   Length: 1,036m
Depth: 90m**

Completely explored in 1957 by the N.P.C.

A C.N.C.C. Permit is required and must be shown at Rainscar House.

WARNING: Flooding is a serious problem both in and beyond Sludge Crawl. The
Master Cave often floods to over 3m in depth! A rise in water level of .3m will

certainly sump Sludge Crawl. The entrance rifts are tight so large cavers are better left on the surface.

Hammer Pot is found in a shallow valley containing a shakehole some 250m E of Magnetometer Pot and very close to the track coming from Rough Close. A small stream sinks at one end of the shakehole and the entrance is found at the other end under slabs.

A fine trip.

The entrance shaft of 2m is descended into a 1m high passage. Continue downstream in an awkward, low passage soon becoming higher. During the original explorations flakes were "hammered" off the wall along this passage! A climb down of 5m at the end of a traverse in the roof leads to a short walk to the first pitch. Stemple Rift follows. It too was forced by "hammer". Although easy at first the rift becomes progressively more difficult beyond a double bend.

A 3m drop where the rift narrows enters a wider section and the second pitch. The awkward take off is more difficult on the return trip! Showerbath Chamber is reached beyond a short crawl and down a climb where a handline is useful.

From the chamber a straight and easier rift leads to the fourth pitch which is broken by a ledge 5m down. A fairly long but easy stream passage follows to the fifth pitch which is in a wet fissure.

At the bottom an easy passage leads to a flat floored chamber after two climbs down. Sludge Crawl leads out of this chamber and lives up to it's name. Initially hands and knees crawling the passage lowers and the water deepens at a corner where an inlet enters from the left. Beyond a larger inlet the Out Fell Master Cave is met flowing from left to right.

Upstream quickly sumps. Downstream deep potholes in the floor need care. Eventually a 2m cascade is reached. At the bottom of the cascade is Tank Inlet on the left blocked by a stal pillar. Beyond a few bends is a fissure some 3m wide with water thundering down into a plunge pool far below. Pass this by stepping down on to a ledge .3m below the lip and move around the corner to the right (rope needed). This now reaches a parallel shaft 15m deep having a rather fine flow of calcite down the opposite wall.

Beyond the pitch the stream is followed across several more pools and down cascades to where the rift lowers into a bedding plane. The stream route is impossible but it can be bypassed to the left by a complex of oxbows to regain the shingled upstream. Again a bypass to the left is found. Boulders interspersed by solid sections reach the stream once more which quickly sumps.

N.B. Take careful note of the point of joining the stream each time for the way back to avoid some really nasty ducks in the attempt to find the way. The bouldery crawls are frequently blocked. Only those bent on reaching the bottom of the cave will explore further than the start of the bedding plane at the end of the rift!

Tackle:

This cave is best done on ladder.

Pitch 1	8m ladder, long belay and 15m lifeline.
Pitch 2	5m ladder, sling for stemple, 10m lifeline.
Pitch 3	10m rope for handline.
Pitch 4	16m ladder, long belay, 30m lifeline.
Pitch 5	10m ladder, long belay, 20m lifeline.
Last Pitch	16m ladder, long belay, 30m lifeline.

Survey ref: Hammer Pot, N.P.C.

MAGNETOMETER POT   Grade 3

**Grid Ref: SD 849697   O.S. Outdoor Leisure Series No 2, Yorkshire Dales
– Western Area, 1:25,000.   Altitude: 396m   Length: 4,600m
Depth: 91m**

First explored by the N.P.C. in 1957 with extensions being made in 1966, 1972–75 and 1978 by U.L.S.A.; 1973 by P.C.C. along with H.W.C.P.C.; 1980–81 by C.U.C.C.

Please ask for permission at Neals Ing Farm.

Walk up from Neals Ing Farm following the wall. Cross the wall at a gate and continue up the dry valley, past the ruined barn to the concrete pipes of the easily recognised entrance.

The concrete entrance pipes need to be rigged. Continue along the narrow rift and down some short climbs to holes in the floor which are Well Pitch. Step across into a body sized passage. This is short and leads into a low, wide and wet passage – Wet Crawl! It ends at a small chamber from where Dry Crawl continues for 100m to Styx Junction. Left leads down to the Styx Sump while right is the deepening canal of the River Styx. This becomes Easy Passage and emerges at Holes Junction where, on the left, these are obvious holes! On the right are stal littered shelves.

Take the obvious passage straight ahead which becomes a rift with easy traversing. Climb down 3m into Milestone Chamber and then continue traversing to a pitch into the large chamber of Caton Hall. The hole at the bottom of the boulder slope in Caton Hall is descended into Rough Crawl. Head downstream until the Labour Exchange goes off on the left. This crawl ends at a deep pool. The tight duck ahead can be bypassed on the right by a crawl into the Dole Queue. Downstream the Dole Queue enters the higher Benefit Passage which then leads on into increasing division of passages and sumps, of which the cave sports more than 20.

Tackle:

	Rope length required	Bolts	Remarks
Entrance pitch	15m	2	Belay to concrete pipe.
Caton Hall pitch	25m	3	Sling.

Survey refs: Magnetometer Pot U.L.S.A./P.C.C.

Penyght

HUNT POT   Grade 3

**Grid Ref: SD 826740   O.S. Outdoor Leisure Series No 2, Yorkshire Dales
– Western Area, 1:25,000.   Altitude: 152m   Length: 61m**

First explored in 1898 by the Y.R.C. and extended by B.S.A. in 1944. Shrapnel Pot at NW end of main rift was descended in 1965 by the N.P.C., a hole with many dangerous loose boulders.

A C.N.C.C. permit is required for this hole which must be shown at Holme Farm Campsite, Horton in Ribblesdale.

Follow the Pennine Way track from Horton in Ribblesdale towards Penyghent. After 1.5 miles go through the gate and turn right immediately to another gate,

Penyghent

Hull Pot

Little Hull Pot

Sell Gill Holes

Hunt Pot

Penyghent

to High Birkwith

New Houses

Penyghent Pot

to Ribblehead (B 6479)

River Ribble

Horton in Ribblesdale

B 6479

to Settle

0   1 km

often locked and a stile. (Straight on goes to Hull Pot). Through the gate or over the stile and follow the main track towards Penyghent. Hunt Pot is found 400m SE from the stile along a faint path leading to the hole after the track has levelled out. Descend into the depression, cross the stream, taking care with the slippery flat bedrock, to boulders. The descent follows the E side of the shaft.

A fine, classic shaft. A large thread 2m back from the lip and a bolt on the boulder nearest the lip are the belays at the pitch head. A rebelay is found, with in-situ hangers, 2m down. At –9m a deviation on the opposite wall allows a free hang to a large pool on a ledge 27m down. On the far side of the shaft 2 more in-situ hangers give a free hang to the base of the shaft 18m below. This part of the shaft is very unpleasant in more than normal water conditions and is impassable in high water. At the base of the shaft water sinks in the floor where most people terminate their trip. The cave continues up and down loose pitches but is not recommended.

Tackle:

	Rope length required	Bolts	Remarks
Main shaft	60m	6	Deviation at –9m.

Survey ref: Hunt Pot, U.L.S.A.

LITTLE HULL POT   Grade 4

Grid Ref: SD 821744   O.S. Outdoor Leisure Series No 2, Yorkshire Dales – Western Area, 1:25,000.   Altitude: 390m   Length: 1,097m Depth: 98m

First explored by members of the Y.R.C. in 1922 with extensions being made by the B.S.A. in 1939 and the C.D.G. in 1979.

WARNING: The pitches quickly become impassable in flood.

A C.N.C.C. permit is required for this cave.

Follow the Pennine Way track from Horton in Ribblesdale towards Penyghent. After 1.5 miles go through a gate. The path turns to the right to Penyghent and straight on to Hull Pot. Little Hull Pot is found in a shallow valley some 300m SW of a huge gash in the ground – Hull Pot – and 183m NW of the gate on a bearing of 320 degrees magnetic.

The low entrance enters a flat out section through shallow pools. Soon after the passage gains height and a fine canyon with small cascades reaches the first pitch. Swing across to a window on the far wall of the shaft a few metres down where a traverse along the left wall leads out into the shaft. There is a rebelay some 6m above the floor of the shaft to keep out of the heaviest splashes. A short length of passage follows to the second pitch which has a deep pool before it. It is better to rig this pitch by traversing out above the pitch head to a small window that has to be wriggled through to a very exposed stance overlooking the shaft. With the rope fixed to the far wall a magnificent descent of 33m is made to a stepped platform where flakes are used to rebelay the rope above the short gully dropping into the rift passage.

Continuing downstream a low wet crawl reaches the streamway beyond. It is possible, for the not so stout, to avoid the wet crawl by a very tight fissure on the right! The rift continues and is traversed at high level to reach a small shattered chamber overlooking the third pitch.

Rigging as high as possible the rope is diagonally hung to the opposite wall via 2 deviations. A sump at the bottom is avoided by climbing a very slippery and muddy chimney. This leads into a bedding plane crawl to emerge into a larger passage and in turn down to the terminal sump.

Tackle:

	Rope length required	Bolts	Remarks
First pitch	35m	8	
Second pitch	70m	6	Thread at head of pitch. 2 deviations −6m and −17m.
Third pitch	20m	2	2 deviations −5m and −8m.

Survey ref: Little Hull Pot, B.U.S.S.

PENYGHENT POT   Grade 5

Grid Ref: SD 829733   O.S. Outdoor Leisure Series No 2, Yorkshire Dales – Western Area, 1:25,000.   Altitude: 424m   Length: 5,200m Depth: 160m

Discovered by the N.P.C. in 1949 and largely explored by them between 1949–1954. Small extensions by B.P.C., C.D.G., H.W.C.P.C. and U.L.S.A.

A C.N.C.C. permit is required for this cave which must be shown at the Gamekeepers Cottage, Brackenbottom, Horton in Ribblesdale.

WARNING: The lower section of the cave fills to the roof in flood and other parts become impassable.

One of the great classic Yorkshire stream pots. Its' entertaining and sporting variety of passages has established it as probably the finest stream cave in the country.

Limited parking is available to the side of the narrow lane outside Brackenbottom Farm. From here, follow the road for a few metres to the N to gain a stile and obvious footpath leading up the hillside towards Penyghent. A sustained but gentle ascent eventually gains a series of wooden duckboards and the top fell wall, crossed via a double stile.

The track to the summit of Penyghent continues steeply ahead but for Penyghent Pot follow the wall to the left to gain a rusty iron gate. Through this, a faint track contours across the hillside towards the cave entrance some 500m away which is easily located in an obvious area of shakeholes approximately 70m E of the wall and a short distance beyond an old horse box and has a wooden lid.

Scramble down the shored up entrance – CARE – to gain a low wet crawl and a short stooping passage that ends at a 2m climb down into water. This is the start of the canal – the Pilgrim's Way – a 330m long wet crawl.

The canal is generally an easy hands and knees crawl in a passage averaging about 1m square. Eventually, after some 225m of monotonous but nevertheless easy progress, the passage begins to lower and widen into a short flat-out section over gravel which heralds the final part of the crawl.

Ahead, the enticing roar of water can be heard where the stream tumbles over a small cascade and into a short stooping canyon. After a few metres the canyon ends as the stream plunges into the void ahead. The main water is joined by a stream from the nearby Spike Pot Inlet to form the two waterfalls of the first pitch – Twin Falls.

The pitch head is well adorned with fossils and it is tackled using a metal bar jammed between some convenient ledges just below the roof (no bolt belays). The descent usually involves getting wet and the landing is in a thigh-deep pool whose outlet begins as a walking sized canyon. However, the roof soon lowers necessitating two short hands and knees crawls through water beyond which Easy Passage opens up into what is a rather awkward and prolonged stooping passage for taller cavers.

300m beyond the first pitch a water chute drops into a waist deep pool after which the passage enlarges to a comfortable walk before reaching the head of the short second pitch. Two bolts on the true right wall provide belays for the 4m descent into the chamber below where a drop through a narrow rift regains the stream.

Directly ahead is the 40m Big Pitch which is split into two (pitches 3 and 4). Under the left wall a bedding plane contains a small, bucket-like hollow, usually filled with a shallow pool, ends at the top of Pitch 3, a gaping rift. (If water is flowing down the pitch it is wise to retreat). By using a bolt high in the roof to the left traverse to a second bolt on the right. Descend 11m down a smooth and steeply inclined rift to a ledge and rebelay. Descend a further 7m down a narrower section of rift to land on a spacious ledge.

Drop 2m under the right wall by using a bolt on the floor to a narrow and airy ledge, the top of the fourth pitch. Bolt belays on opposite walls allow a free hang directly to the floor of a chamber. The chamber marks the start of the most appealing section of Penyghent Pot, the Rift.

Downstream in the chamber an obvious opening leads into a spacious rift. A short climb down into the water or a traverse at a slightly higher level soon gains the fifth pitch located immediately beyond a huge fallen boulder jammed in the rift. The pitch can be free climbed with care. However, it is safer to belay at the top of the fallen block.

At the bottom climb down a short cascade after which a short walk in the water ends when the stream sinks into the floor and a dry rift continues. Cross jammed boulders to avoid numerous holes in the floor. At the far end of the dry rift a hole leads to a slide down a smooth sloping block and a easy 5m climb that drops onto a small sandbank beside the stream. Follow this to a hands and knees bedding plane which has a heavily scalloped floor to the head of Pitch 6 – Coffin Pitch.

Step over the stream onto a dry ledge and then drop through a hole onto a coffin shaped block at the top of the pitch. Belay to a thread at shoulder height on the right. Again this pitch may be free climbed. At the bottom scramble down to regain the water which flows in a smooth clean washed rift. The stream quickly cuts down into a narrow trench.

A short but easy traverse just above the water reaches the top of pitch 7 – Flake Pitch. Belay directly to the top of the flake. Great CARE if free climbing. At the bottom the water crashes down a 7m trench in the floor which is traditionally the eighth pitch. This is usually free climbed by crossing over the trench and climbing over the back of a flake of rock where a natural staircase of footholds on the left provides a convenient means of descent (and ascent) to the floor.

Following the water the stream soon cuts down more steeply and progress is made by sliding down two rift climbs which are narrow at the top. A short climbable cascade heralds the end of the Rift where the water drops into Pool Chamber before flowing through a small wet section to emerge in Block Chamber.

At the far side of the chamber a hole behind an obvious large, cubic, block drops into a fine canyon quickly ending at a short but easily climbed cascade into a large circular pool. Here the stream slides over a small water chute before shooting out over the head of pitch 9 – Myers Leap. A single bolt high in the left wall and a couple of natural backups a few metres back near the outlet to the circular pool provide the belay for an 8m descent down the wall of a draughty spray lashed chamber landing in a broad but shallow pool. Beyond is a short hands and knees crawl leading into the Upper Main Stream Passage, an impressive walking size tunnel. This rather awkward passage has an abundance of elliptical milled potholes and submerged flakes of rock.

Two large openings on the right lead to Hunt Pot Inlet. Continuing downstream stumbling progress is made along a generally easy stream passage passing beneath three high avens and past a large dry oxbow on the right.

The stream continues to cut down over a series of small waterfalls and the top of a 2m cascade is soon reached. Above here an easy but exposed climb up the right wall leads to Eyrie Pot and the start of the invigorating Friday the 13th Series and Living Dead extensions. Continue to Pitch 10 – Niagara.

The pitch can be free climbed with care. However, prudence is the better part of falling off and a hand line is usually quite sufficient for the straight forward, if steep, 8m climb down onto a massive fallen block.

Immediately ahead is the rather wet eleventh pitch (nowadays used only by those determined to complete the traditional descent). The pitch is easily bypassed by scrambling down the left side of the block to gain a narrow rift and an easy slide down on to the floor of the continuing stream passage. Pass under the cascade of the pitch to enter a walking sized passage into a tall and impressive rift chamber.

At the far end of this chamber a hole drops down into the atmospheric Lower Main Stream Passage. Easy walking and stooping follow until the water drops over a small cascade and sinks into the ominous looking downstream sump a dark and gloomy elongated rift some 36m deep.

Tackle:

	Rope length required	Bolts	Remarks
Pitch 1–			
Twin Falls	12m		Belay to metal bar.
Pitch 2	10m	2	
Pitch 3 & 4	50m	6	
Pitch 5	15m		Belay to block.
Pitch 6–			
Coffin Pitch	20m		Thread belay.
Pitch 7–			
Flake Pitch	10m		Belay to top of Flake.
Pitch 8	15m		Handline.
Pitch 9–			
Myers Leap	12m	1	Backup with 2 natural belays.
Pitch 10–			
Niagara	12m		Natural belay.
Pitch 11	20m		Natural belay, easily bypassed.

N.B. Although many of the pitches can be free climbed in normal conditions, they would be impossible if much water was flowing.

Survey ref: Penyghent Pot, U.L.S.A.

SELL GILL HOLES

Grade 3

Grid Ref: SD 811743   O.S. Outdoor Leisure Series No 2, Yorkshire Dales – Western Area, 1:25,000.   Altitude: 347m   Length: 500m   Depth: 78m

The Y.R.C. were first to bottom the cave in 1897. Extensions were made by the C.P.C. in 1972 and 1977.

Permission from Holme Farm, Horton in Ribblesdale.

From the bridge in Horton, close to the Crown Hotel, follow the Pennine Way/ Ribble Way for approx. 1.25 miles to a gate. Through the gate the two entrances are found to either side of the track. DO NOT approach the caves from the houses of Newhouses.

A popular cave for both novice and the more experienced caver providing a good introduction to the delights of SRT rigging. The cave is mainly dry and as such is a good wet weather option. There are two entrances – wet and dry. The dry one to the left of the track and the wet to the right.

Dry Way

The surface hole of the Dry Way is cut by a shallow gully which needs to be rigged before the gully steepens. At the base of the entrance pitch scramble down over boulders to reach the head of the second pitch. Care with loose stones! There are many rigging points on both sides of the pitch so we will leave it to your own imagination to rig. The pitch lands in a large chamber.

Down-slope the third pitch drops over a large jammed boulder onto the pitch itself, again with many possibilities with the intricacies of rigging being left to you! Bear in mind that this pitch can become wet. If it is, look for a traverse out to the right around a corner! The pitch lands in a high rift passage which leads into (in wet weather) a spray lashed aven where the water from the Wet Way enters. A huge boulder filled chamber with mud banks indicates that this area floods. At the lowest part of the chamber the stream can be followed to where it ends in a miserable sump. There is copious mud hereabouts.

Wet Way

The stream cascades over short climbs – care with green, slimy rock at the start – to a stream canyon which is followed over a waterfall to the start of the vertical bit. In dry conditions it is possible to follow the water down in two pitches of 15m and 30m respectively. However, it is better to follow a parallel shaft reached 10m down the first section of the shaft through a small bedding plane crawl. To reach this crawl a roped traverse round the corner enters an oxbow which is taken to a hang point above a cascade. 6m down pendule across the wall to a bolt at the start of a very short crawl to reach a drop into a small alcove overlooking the parallel shaft. Descend this from a 'Y' hang to a rebelay some 15m down to join up with the Dry Way at the bottom.

Tackle:

	Rope length required	Eco hangers	Remarks
Dry Way:			
Entrance	20m	4	
Pitch 2	30m	6	
Pitch 3	30m	6	
Wet Way	90m	15	Two 45m ropes can be used. Split at the alcove.

Survey ref: Sell Gill Holes, C.P.C.

Birkwith

CALF HOLES TO BROWGILL

Grade 2

Grid Refs: Calf Holes: SD 804776   Browgill: SD 800777
O.S. Outdoor Leisure Series No 2, Yorkshire Dales – Western Area,
1:25,000.   Altitude: 357m   Length: 853m including Browgill Cave
Depth: 27m to Browgill entrance

WARNING: Floods dramatically due to gripping upstream of the cave.

Permission from High Birkwith Farm. A small access fee is payable.

By the bridge in Horton in Ribblesdale a minor road runs by the side of the River Ribble. Follow this to High Birkwith Farm. Go through the gate and up the rough track to a junction. Continue straight on passing Old Ing (the house not the cave!) on the right and park vehicles off the track before the gate. Go through the gate and turn left immediately to reach another gate after 300m. Over the wall via a stile is the entrance to Calf Holes where the stream sinks.

A really good beginners trip. Take the dry entrance on the left. An 11m pitch drops into a shallow pool at the bottom. Although it is possible to explore upstream, the way on is downstream in a roomy passage, passing two rifts to the left that lead into sumps. Where the passage becomes wide and cobbly with assorted fencing, poly bags and stakes a low passage on the left – Hainsworth's Passage – is soon encountered and followed through The Contortion to emerge into Browgill Cave.

Either follow the stream to a fine waterfall and descend this – whilst roped – in low water conditions to a large chamber at the base. Alternatively, a short distance down the streamway a tube on the right can be entered and followed to the head of a staircase which avoids the waterfall. Safety rope for novices, although a handline is often in place. Follow the rift until a large chamber is reached. Under a low arch reaches the streamway which is followed in a quickly enlarging passage to emerge into daylight at Browgill – care on slippery rock.

From Browgill walk uphill to a stile over a wall. Turn right along the track to pass Calf Holes and retrieve any gear that was left.

Tackle:

	Rope length required	Eco hangers	Remarks
Entrance Pitch	25m	5	Deviation –3m.
Waterfall	15m		Lifeline, thread belay to the right at top of fall.
Staircase	15m		Lifeline.

Survey ref: Calf Holes, Allonby and Beck.

BIRKWITH CAVE   Grade 2/3

Grid Ref: SD 804769, is found a short distance away in a plantation and makes a useful extension to the day. Permission as for Calf Holes.

OLD ING   Grade 2/3

Grid Ref: SD 807768, this cave again makes a good extension to the day out and is found by heading over the stile by the plantation and following the track to where it levels out. The easy walk in entrance is found a few metres from the track in a clump of nettles. Permission as for Calf Holes.

Great Whernside

DOW CAVE   Grade 2

Grid Ref: SD 983743   O.S. Outdoor Leisure Series No 30, Yorkshire Dales – Northern and Central Areas, 1:25,000.   Altitude: 320m Length: of trip: 450m (including Providence Pot 3,700m)

The first explorers are unknown but the C.P.C. extended the cave in 1953, 1956 and 1986

Permission from North Cote, Kilnsey.

Approach from Kettlewell following the road to Leyburn for about 2km to the start of a steep hill with a garage at bottom. Park here. A short way up the hill is a

GREAT WHERNSIDE

to Leyburn

Dow Cave

to Buckden

Providence Pot

Kettlewell

River Wharfe

to Conistone

to Kilnsey & Skipton

0 _____ 1 km

stile over a wall followed by another stile to a stone bridge. Go round to the right to cross a very slippery beck and up the obvious slope to the entrance at the top under the scar.

WARNING. Stream level rises considerably after prolonged heavy rain. Hobson's choice is best left alone.

Scramble down boulders to large a stream passage. This is followed by walking with occasional scrambles round fallen blocks leading to sandbanks with a deep canal on the left. A further section of large stream passage leads to The Treacle Mines, an area of mineral workings. Leave the stream by entering workings on the right, pass up through a dripping chamber and through an eye hole to rejoin the main stream passage.

A passage at shoulder height is a crawl to a descent and a junction, left passes an aven with a long crawl to emerge at the top of a climb down into a large chamber, the First Miners Chamber. Right from the junction rejoins the main stream passage.

Upstream leads to a short hands and knees crawl. At the end of the crawl, low in the right wall, is the tube like entrance to Dowbergill Passage. Continuing upstream the main cave leads into a large chamber, the First Miners Chamber, with the stream entering the chamber from between delicately poised boulders, Hobson's Choice. This is best left alone due to the uncertain stability of the choke!

Survey ref: Dow Cave, C.P.C.

DOWBERGILL PASSAGE, PROVIDENCE POT TO DOW CAVE   Grade 4

Providence Pot: Grid Ref: SD 992728   O.S. Outdoor Leisure Series No 30, Yorkshire Dales – Northern and Central Areas, 1:25,000. Altitude: 400m   Length: 3,700m   Depth: 30m

WARNING: Perhaps the most celebrated and notorious passage in Yorkshire. It remains a serious undertaking and the scene of many rescues. The innocuous straight line survey belies the many difficulties and at times route finding is totally frustrating within the confines of the 20m tall passage. Black telephone wires tend to confuse rather than help. It is, therefore, recommended that on first acquaintance cavers gain knowledge of both ends before contemplating a through trip. Usually traverses are undertaken from Providence Pot. It is advisable to have a car at the lay-by Park Rash (the car park for Dow Cave) to avoid the long walk back to Kettlewell.

From Kettlewell follow the faint path up Dowber Gill Beck for about 1.5 kms. A prominent lidded entrance is seen just before the fork in the stream. This is Providence Pot.

Carefully climb down the walled shaft to enter a 3m crawl. A small chamber is entered after a drop down followed by a short rift passage to enter the main passage. Continue through 54 Cavern to scramble through boulders. Keep right to reach an aven. An easy squeeze enters a slanting, muddy and bouldery passage which enter July Grotto.

Continuing reaches a 'T' junction. Go left to Terminal Chamber where a narrow tube goes up a calcite slope into the Blasted Crawl. This filthy wallow eventually reaches the Palace, a large chamber which is descended to an eyehole. Climb down the steep slope on the right into the aptly named Dungeon. Drop down the calcite boss into Depot Chamber, turn right into a crawl to enter Dowbergill Passage at Stalagmite Corner. If exiting via Providence Pot remember the point where the crawl emerges at Stalagmite Corner. It is easily missed. From Stalagmite Corner go downstream over rockfalls to enter an easy walking passage. A squeeze between boulders reaches Skittle Chamber from which some 250m of bouldery progress, including a short crawl in the stream, reaches a short traverse. After this a large boulder blockage is passed by a slit on the left before dropping through a window into the 3m x 5m passage of Bridge Cavern. This continues over a loose floor to The Bridge at the far end, a 2m arch of several hanging boulders. Pass under this and continue for a short distance to a boulder descent on the right which enters a chest deep canal, shortly followed by shallower water.

The narrow rift passage is followed for some 230m over several boulder obstacles to an oxbow. 90m further along the stream a low crawl on the left enters a parallel passage. A short distance along here and the half way point is reached – 800 Yards Chamber. Climb up from here to a high traverse and continue along a smooth holdless section – Greg's Horror – to a false floor.

Descend to the stream and follow it easily to yet another boulder choke below Brew Chamber. Although it is possible to surmount the boulders by an exposed climb it is better to crawl through the choke 5m above the stream to reach a chimney which is descended to blocks. Continue down to a traverse which is crossed to boulders before dropping down to the stream.

Continue in the stream to an obvious slanting climb up to reach Gypsum Traverse. The waterway beyond the slanting climb is not recommended due to the tortuous nature of the passage. From Gypsum Traverse scramble down to a chamber and slide past a massive slab to Hardy's Horror, a short hand traverse dropping on to a boulder in a pool. A fine passage continues past an easy duck under a mass of flowstone.

The fine canal gradually lowers until a chute rises to enter Dow Cave. Exit by this cave by turning left and following the streamway to daylight. Follow the well marked path to the Lay-by and car at Park Rash.

N.B. Some of the climbs have in-situ ropes of dubious vintage – CARE.

Wharfedale

BIRKS FELL CAVE   Grade 4

Grid Ref: SD 931769   O.S. Outdoor Leisure Series No 30, Yorkshire Dales – Northern & Central Areas, 1:25,000.   Altitude: 362m Length: 3,600m   Depth: 142m

The Y.R.C. were the first to explore in 1932. Extensions by the B.P.C. in 1947 along with the C.P.C. during 1968–9 and 1973.

A C.N.C.C. Permit is required. This must be shown at Redmire Farm, on the way to the cave. Member clubs must call at Redmire Farm when going to and returning from the cave. It is important to park cars in the car park in Buckden.

WARNING: The canal and the wet bedding caves flood easily sealing off parts of the cave. Dangerous loose boulders at The Block, great care required.

From the Car Park in Buckden follow the road that goes up Langstrothdale towards Hawes. Cross over the River Wharfe and continue for 350m to a left turn leading to Redmire Farm. After visiting the farm continue up the track to a shallow valley to where the entrance is found just before a small waterfall 100m beyond and to the W of the wall. One of the best caving trips in Yorkshire including most of everything except large shafts.

The entrance hole on the left of the normally dry stream leads into an easy rift passage which is followed to reach a small chamber. A flat out crawl – the Bradford Crawl – leaves the chamber eventually easing at Tree Chamber. A short section of rift passage reaches a canal. At the end of this a keyhole on the right enters another, but shorter, flat out crawl – Connection Crawl – to enter a large passage.

Downstream, the main passage continues to the 9m first pitch. The stream passage continues into Slipped Floor Chamber with the way out being down The Dig, a 3m drop just before the end, to regain the stream. Shooting Box Aven is entered after a number of sporting cascades after which a fine canal passage reaches Aven 2. A rubble slope leaves the aven followed by a hole back to the stream – CARE unstable boulders!

The stream continues to 40 Years' Corner with some marvellous formations. On again with the water reaches the First Wet Bedding Cave which is followed by a climb up to the left in a rift into Dry Fault Chamber. A Climb down from here enters the Second Wet Bedding Cave. Just before the end of this a climb up on the right enters Moon Milk Cave.

WHARFEDALE

The stream is now below. With care a series of unstable boulder chambers reaches The Block and as its name implies is a huge boulder! Crawl under this and down the small hole below to regain the stream passage.

Continue downstream to Cascade Pitch and two further short drops. The narrow but high rift is followed at stream level through a duck under a chockstone. A climb up then enters Bridge Aven. Once again regain the stream to enter the Grand Gallery ending in Whitehall – CARE with the fine formations.

Take the main passage, on the left, out of Whitehall to follow a well decorated rift passage to the remarkable Elbow Bend. Beyond the bend a descending rift enters The Thrutch, a narrow rift to reach Shale Crawl. This damp section eventually reaches Shale Cavern out of which is the 15m Shale Pitch entering a tight rift. (Many parties stop at the top of the pitch.) Tiring traverses continue to reach a climbable pitch. Climb up again to enter a bedding plane crawl which is followed to the head of The Slimy Slit, a 6m pitch. The Sewer Series, a canal passage, continues to the sump.

Tackle:

Pitch 1	10m ladder, long belay and 20m lifeline.
Cascade Pitch	8m ladder. There is no natural belay nearby, bolt belay allows ladder to hang down in water, dangerous with much water flowing.
Shale Pitch	16m ladder, long belay and 25m lifeline.
Slimy Slit	8m ladder, long belay and 15m lifeline.

Survey ref: C.P.C. Journal 4 (3), 1969.

Langstrothdale

HAGG GILL POT   Grade 3

Grid Ref: SD 895793   O.S. Outdoor Leisure Series No 30, Yorkshire Dales – Northern & Central Areas, 1:25,000.   Altitude: 320m Length: 1,500m   Vertical range: 63m

Discovered and explored by the W.R.P.C. in 1988.

Please call at Raisgill Farm for permission or write BEFORE visiting the cave.

WARNING: Great care must be taken throughout the cave to protect the fragile formations. Severe damage has occurred already in the short time since its discovery. Many of the formations are in particularly vulnerable positions and for this reason (as well as the loose bits on the entrance pitch) it is not recommended to take novices into the system.

Park in Langstrothdale about 250m downstream of Deepdale Bridge or 1km upstream of Yockenthwaite Farm opposite Cow Garth Barn. Walk up the hillside along the wall to where the tiny stream issues from underneath it. Bear left for 75m into the shallow dry valley and follow it up to the obvious concreted entrance shaft.

Ladder 15m entrance pitch from scaffold tubes. A narrow section half way down is potentially loose and people should clear the bottom of the pitch while someone is on the ladder. The pitch opens out after the narrow section is passed.

There are two ways on from the foot of the pitch. Upstream, a twisting passage with occasional low sections, passes a fine flowstone pillar. Climb over large fallen blocks to rejoin the stream. Take care in the next section which has some fine helictites. The passage then enters a large breakdown chamber with various small passages leading off. Climb half way up the boulder slope to an obvious ledge and head left into a small passage where a stream emerges. Go through a short squeeze into a small chamber with a waterfall. Opposite the waterfall is a climb up into a beautiful straw chamber where extreme care must be taken to avoid further damage.

Downstream from the entrance pitch the passage descends through two chambers. An easy climb down flowstone leads to a larger streamway. Downstream from here quickly arrives at a sump. Follow the stream up passing several small cascades. The passage is generally narrow and occasional crawling is required. A large inlet enters on the right and this can be followed up to a sump.

Continue along the main stream. Where the section of stooping ends a large opening on the right enters a large fault chamber. At far end of the chamber the stream is regained where it flows from a high narrow rift. Crawl forward until the passage enlarges where it can then be followed at various levels over occasional fallen blocks. After some distance a blank wall is met with the stream entering from a low passage on the left. This passage quickly ends at a waterfall but it contains a long line of straws formed from a joint in its roof – the Thin White Line.

Tackle:
Entrance Pitch   5m ladder + 40m lifeline

Darnbrook Area

CHERRY TREE HOLE   Grade 4

Grid Ref: SD 881704   O.S. Outdoor Leisure Series No 10, Yorkshire Dales – Southern Area, 1:25,000.   Altitude: 467m   Length: 1,200m Depth: 41m

Explored 1960 by C.P.C. who also made extensions in 1971.

Permission is required from Darnbrook House. The route to the Pot is via a stone track starting mid-way between Darnbrook House and Thoragill Barn, leading up to a shooting box. Cars may be parked close to the bottom of the stone track. This is normally at the track at 894704 or where the Pennine Way crosses the road above Tennant Gill. The cave is not obvious until upon it. It is a large square sided shakehole right beside the sometimes indistinct track.

Climb down the shakehole with care finding the way on behind boulders on the N side. Ladder the first, 4m pitch, followed by a squeeze forward and climb round a hole in the floor up into the top of an egg-timer shaped passage. Crawl forward to a block across the passage and then turn left into Crossover Passage. Follow this passage to Main Junction where a stream runs from right to left.

Upstream is Far Stream Passage which is easy going in a fine passage to a

DARNBROOK

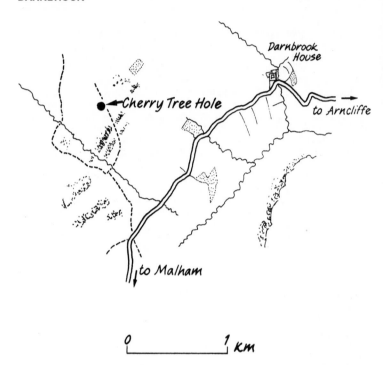

committing duck from where the Far North leads on.

Downstream at Main Junction is South Stream Passage which soon leads down into a long fault chamber. Beware of falling rocks! At the far end of the chamber, climb up and then crawl forward into a small chamber. The hole in the floor leads to the last, 9m pitch and then the downstream sump.

Tackle:

	Rope length required	Bolts	Remarks
Entrance shakehole			15m handline useful.
1st Pitch	10m	3	
Last Pitch	15m	3	

Survey ref: Cherry Tree Hole, C.P.C.

Penyghent Gill Area

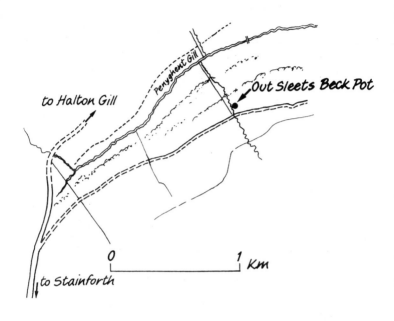

OUT SLEETS BECK POT   Grade 3

**Grid Ref: SD 868737   O.S. Outdoor Leisure Series No 2, Yorkshire Dales
– Western Area, 1:25,000.   Altitude: 405m   Length: 975m   Depth: 67m**

Explored by the B.S.A. in 1966.

Permission required from Manor Farm, Halton Gill.

WARNING: The entrance lies below stream level which is held back by a dam.
Ensure this is in good condition before entry and that the weather is settled.

Park cars at SD856729 off the track leading to Litton. Walk along the track
passing through two gates. Just before the third gate across the track a gate on
the left hand side of the track is seen. Follow the stream down for some 60m to
where the dam is seen.

The small entrance is found in the bank. Awkward climb down through hole
enters small but walking size passage which is followed to an awkward climb down
– handline useful – and crawl. Beyond the crawl small climbs reach the first pitch –
free climbable with care – into a small chamber beyond which is the main inlet
entering from the left. Downstream a fine passage with chutes and pools reaches
Cascade Pot. A dry descent is made from the roof. From the chamber at the foot of
the pitch a low crawl leads to a junction with a low and wet inlet on the left.

Further crawling eventually reaches walking passage and Deluge Pot. Again this can be rigged dry away from the water. From the bottom an easy walk soon reaches a canal with deep water and an awkward, tight squeeze to a duck with .3m of airspace. Beyond this, walking follows in a contorted rift passage to a climb down into Bridge Chamber and further climb down into the loose Shatter Passage. A big block at a sharp corner leads to the aptly named See-Saw Passage, alternatively crawling and walking. At the end the water flows into an impenetrable bedding.

Tackle:

	Rope length required	Bolts	Remarks
Awkward Climb	6m	1	Handline.
First pitch	6m		Handline, sling for belay.
Cascade Pot	25m	5	Large rawlbolt at head of pitch.
			1 thread part way along roof traverse.
Deluge Pot	23m	5	

Survey ref: Out Sleets Beck Pot, B.S.A. 6(42), 1968

Nidderdale

NEW GOYDEN POT   Grade 3

Grid Ref: SD 102754   O.S. Outdoor Leisure Series No 30, Yorkshire Dales – Northern and Central Areas, 1:25,000.   Altitude: 195m Length: 2,200m   Depth: 32m

Explored by the C.P.C. in 1956. Extensions in 1973/74 by U.L.S.A. and by the C.D.G. in the period 1980–82.

Permission is required from Limley Farm No 1 (nearest the road). It is most advisable to check the flood risk with Yorkshire Water's superintendent at Scar House reservoir.

WARNING: Total and complete flooding within a very short space of time.

Take the water authority road from Lofthouse to a layby just beyond Limley Farm. Park cars here. Please call at Limley Farm No 1 (on the right) before heading off towards the River Nidd. Follow the river bed downstream – DO NOT CROSS THE FIELDS – to New Goyden Pot some 500m south of Limley Farm.

A large river cave having a marvellous mainstream passage. Entrance is below a small cliff on the W bank of the river. Small entrance leads to the head of the first pitch via a traverse to a 'Y' hang. 2 deviations (threads) in opposite wall allow a free hang to the bottom. Tie end of rope to a bollard at the start of the second pitch and traverse out above it to a 'Y' hang and free descent into the marvellous mainstream passage. Downstream leads all too quickly to a sump but just before this, a large mud slope on the left leads through boulders into the aptly named Planetarium.

Tackle:

	Rope length required	Bolts	Remarks
Pitch 1	25m	4	Eco hangers, 2 slings for deviations just below head of pitch.
Pitch 2	20m	3	Eco hangers, tie end of rope to bollard for traverse.

Survey ref: The Goyden System, Y.U.R.T., U.L.S.A., C.U.C.C and C.D.G.

Nidderdale

Dentdale

IBBETH PERIL 1   Grade 3

Grid Ref: SD 741864   O.S. Outdoor Leisure Series No 2, Yorkshire Dales – Western Area, 1:25,000   Altitude: 181m   Length: 275m   Depth: 18m

Explored by the N.S.G. in 1967, and extended in 1992 by the D.H.S.S.
    WARNING: This cave should not be entered in wet weather. When the River Dee is in flood the entrance is completely submerged.
    From Dent drive up the valley on the N side. Pass Gibb's Hall and the turn-off to Broadfield House and then park in the large pull-in on the right hand side. A path leads back down the valley through the woods. After about 100m it is possible to cut down to the left to a climb down to the bottom end of the Ibbeth Peril plunge pool. Facing the waterfall, Ibbeth Peril 2 is in the oildrum low down on the left half way to the waterfall, whilst Ibbeth Peril 1 is in the dark opening in the face of the waterfall.

Carefully climb through any flood debris into a flat out crawl. Follow this into a small trench which rapidly gains height and drops into a small chamber. Take the passage out from this chamber to enter the back of quite a large cavern. At this end, classic anastomoses can be seen in the roof. The whole floor of the chamber is covered in large flat blocks that have fallen from the roof. Move round to the left to some excellent flowstone and calcite grottos. Now carefully climb across the blocks to the bottom end of the chamber.

An inlet enters from above on the right. Climb up into this beautifully formed phreatic passage. It can be followed up until it ends in a sump. Before climbing back down from this passage, admire the line of straws in the roof, marking the old continuation of this passage out into the chamber. Back in the chamber, stay at the bottom end but head to the other side. Behind the boulders is a way down into a vadose trench. At the end of this are two separate climbs down to sumps.

Survey ref: Ibbeth Peril, U.L.S.A./M.U.S.S.

Bibliography

Beck, H.M., Gaping Gill, Hale, 1984.

Brook, D., Davies, G.M., Long, M.H., Ryder, P.F., Northern Caves Vol 1 – Wharfedale and the North East, Dalesman, 1988.

Brook, A., Brook, D., Griffiths, J., Long, M.H., Northern Caves Vol 2 – The Three Peaks, Dalesman, 1996.

Brook, D., Davies, G.M., Long, M.H., Ryder, P.F., Northern Caves Vol 3 – The Three Counties System and the North West, Dalesman, 1994.

C.N.C.C. Eco – Resin rigging system, No 1. 1994, No 2. 1996.

Elliot, D., Lawson, D., SRT Rigging Guide, Lizard Speleo Systems, 1987.

Eyre, J. & Frankland, J., Race Against Time, Lyon Books, 1987.

Eyre, J., The Easegill System, B.C.R.A., 1989.

Gemmell, A. & Myers, J.O., Underground Adventure, Castle Cary Press, 1990 (Facsimile), Originally Dalesman, 1952.

Heap, D., Potholing: Beneath The Northen Pennines, Routledge and Kegan Paul, 1964.

Judson, D., Caving Practise and Equipmnet, B.C.R.A./Cordee, 1991.

Northern Caving – Handbook of the Council of Northern Caving Clubs, 1993 Edition.

Waltham, A.C., edited by, Limestones and Caves of North-West England, David & Charles, 1974.

DERBYSHIRE
by Iain Barker

Iain Barker has been exploring the caves of the Peak District for over half his life. A member and former chairman of a local club Iain has explored caves in Turkey, Scotland as well as the Peak District, often as a solo pioneer. His knowledge on the hydrology and speleogenesis of the Upper Dove area in particular is well recognised. Iain is a freelance writer and his caving related work has been published in all the major magazines.

INTRODUCTION

The Peak District is something of an anomaly when looked at alongside the other caving regions of the British Isles. The Southern and Welsh caves tend to have little vertical development but make amends with sheer length whilst the pots of the Yorkshire Dales, with one or two exceptions, go deep almost immediately. In the 'Peak' we have a cross section of the best of both, from the miles of walking passages of the Peak-Speedwell complex to the big pitches of Nettle Pot. This is apparent socially, as well as geologically; in the south are the Caving clubs, in the north are the Potholing clubs. In the Peak we have both. This mixture of cave types gives a choice of trips at both extremes of the scale. A decision taken over breakfast can decide if the rest of the day is to be spent wearing out your knees or your back!

It is arguable that of all the cave bearing areas in our country, the Peak District has been the most thoroughly searched for new passages. The history of cave hunting is deeply rooted here and the tenacity with which the prime motivators have worked in the quest for undiscovered passage is quite staggering.

USEFUL ADDRESSES

Eldon Pothole Club Secretary
K Bentham
11a George Mansions
Buxton SK17 6XW

D. A. Nixon
3 Rose Cottages
Litton
Buxton SK17 8QY
Send s.a.e.

J. S. Beck
Glebe Cottage
Eyam
Sheffield S30 1RB
Send s.a.e.

ACCOMMODATION

Technical Speleological Group HQ
The Chapel Works
Main Street
Castleton
Derbyshire

T.S.G. Secretary
Send SAE to Iain Barker
56 Thornbridge Crescent
Birley
Sheffield S12 3AE

Pindale Farm Outdoor Centre
Pindale Lane
Hope
nr Sheffield
Derbyshire S30 2RN

Orpheus Caving Club Cottages
Parsley Hay
Nr Monyash
Send SAE to Jenny Potts
3 Greenway
Hulland Ward
Ashbourne
Derbyshire DE6 3FE

TOURIST INFORMATION OFFICES

Old Market Hall
Bridge Street
Bakewell
Derbyshire DE4 1DS
Tel 01629 813227

The Crescent
Buxton
Derbyshire SK17 6BQ
Tel 01298 25106

The Pavillion
Matlock Bath
Derbyshire DE4 3NR
Tel 01629 55082

GEAR HIRE

Caving Supplies
19 London Road
Buxton
Derbyshire SK17 9PA
Tel 01298 71707

Hitch 'n' Hike
Bamford
nr Sheffield S30 2BH
Tel 01433 651013

CARLSWARK CAVERN   Grade 3

Grid Ref: Eyam Dale Shaft Entrance SK 218759   Gin Entrance SK 220758
O.S. Outdoor Leisure Series No 24, Peak District – The White Peak Area –
East Sheet, 1:25,000.   Altitude: Eyam Dale Shaft 196m, Gin Entrance
190m   Length: 2,268m   Depth: 31m approx.

Entered by the lead miners, the first recorded trip was in 1734. Later explorations
were by the B.S.A, John Beck and Dave Mellor. The last major discovery came in
1979 by John Beck and the T.S.G.

    The Eyam Dale Shaft lies on land belonging to the owner of The Hall at Eyam,
The Gin Entrance is on land owned by the trustees of the Chatsworth Estate. A
long tradition of well behaved climbing and caving in the area has led to a situation
of trust and there are no restrictions of access.

    WARNING: The nearest parking area to the Eyam Dale Shaft is the electricity
sub-station near the foot of the Eyam Dale. As this seems to have become a prime
spot for thieving from cars it is suggested that visiting cavers should park in the
large lay-by opposite the garage at the western edge of Stoney Middleton. Eyam
Dale Shaft is situated opposite the electricity sub-station a short distance up Eyam
Dale on the left of the road, up an earthy bank. A conspicuous path leads to the
entrance.

122

STONEY MIDDLETON AREA

1. Streaks Pot-top entrance – 2.-lower entrance
3. Carlswark-Eyam Dale Shaft 4. Carlswark-Gin entrance

0   1 Km

The 11m Eyam Dale Shaft can be abseiled and the rope pulled through IF you have someone in the party who knows the cave. If not, it is best rigged with ladders for escape.

At the foot of the shaft a short crawl leads northwards (behind you as you face the ladder), a low passage to the east should be ignored. A short way on, the entrance to Eyam Passage is passed on the right. Follow NW Passage which swings to the left and reduces to a crawl then hands and knees. Pass through an interesting left hand squeeze to reach a low junction; left leads into the Big Dig and John Smith's Passage whilst the main way on is to the right along Cockle Passage, through an easy duck, to the junction with Stalactite Passage. A few metres along this, Dynamite Passage enters on the left, with the way on straight ahead along the once well decorated Stalactite Passage, through Pearl Chamber, to a climb down into a rift. A mine level on the right leads to the upstream end of the sump. THIS SUMP IS OVER 27m LONG AND SHOULD NOT BE FREE DIVED. A tricky traverse over the rift leads to the short Aladdin's Crawl.

Retrace the route back to the junction with Eyam Passage. Enter Eyam Passage and follow it for a short distance to enter Noughts and Crosses Chamber, pass through this and continue along Eyam Passage passing Third Inlet, and further along, South Crawl, both of which enter from the right. Eyam Passage is mostly an awkward hands and knees height. Eventually, Oyster Chamber is gained. A difficult 9m climb down from a depression leads to the rather filthy Resurgence Entrance which floods dramatically in winter. Traverse over the depression and continue ahead. A sharp right turn emerges in the daylight rift of the Gin Entrance. An easy scramble up the far end leads to the surface. Walk down the rough track to the road and Stoney Middleton.

Tackle:
Eyam Dale Shaft
12m ladder, 18m lifeline, short spreader
OR:
18m abseil rope
Survey ref: Carlswark Cavern, E.P.C.

ELDON HOLE   Grade 3

Grid Ref: SK 116803   O.S. Outdoor Leisure Series No 24, Peak District – The White Peak Area – East Sheet 1:25,000.   Altitude: 415m
Depth: 82m

In the 16th Century a poor peasant was lowered into the depths and pulled back to the surface a white haired mumbling idiot. A descent in 1772 was a preamble to the more recent explorations by the aptly named Eldon Pothole Club.

Permission to descend from Mr H. Furness at Laneside Farm, on the eastern edge of Peak Forest (on left hand side of A623 when driving out of the village), small trespass fee.

WARNING: The short crawl which leads from the shaft bottom to the Main Chamber is occasionally blocked and always in a dangerous condition. Take care when negotiating this section.

Eldon Hole is Derbyshire's largest pothole, situated high on the southern slopes of Eldon Hill it is visible for miles around. The best route of approach is up Eldon Lane at the western end of the hamlet of Old Dam, Peak Forest. Cars are best parked on the grass at the end of the lane just past Sweetknoll House. From here an obvious path leads uphill, over a stile by a gate. Turn left along a track keeping a small copse on the left reaching the southern end of the perimeter fence surrounding the hole. Descents can be made down all four sides.

South End A good way down to practise your rigging. Belay rope to gate post and descend a short gully to a large metal hanger on left. Walk along ledge to further metal hanger and Eco hanger. Over the edge a deviation at –2m reaches a rebelay on an Eco hanger. Descend the gully/chimney via two more deviations to reach a small ledge and a 'Y' hang. Short descent to rebelay on single bolt. Half way down the next drop a deviation (not in place) on the opposite wall – above an overhang – enables a free hang to reach another rebelay for the final 10m descent to the floor of the shaft.

Note Over the years Eldon Hole has accumulated a plethora of bolt belays, threads and staples. It would be pointless to describe in more detail the various rigging possibilities.

At the bottom of the shaft there is occasionally a large snow plug even in summer. At the foot of the slope down is the entrance to a short but loose and dangerous crawl – take great care – entering the very impressive Main Chamber, requiring a powerful light to see the roof over 27m above. The floor of the chamber is a steep, unstable scree slope. At the northern end of the chamber a climb of 24m leads to the New Eldon Series, a short series of well decorated rifts. This is usually rigged with a pull-through system for SRT. Heading up-slope another climb on the left of 13m enters Damocles Rift, a well decorated chamber blocked with flowstone.

124

Looking down the 60-metre entrance pitch to Eldon Hole. Photo: Paul Deakin

Tackle:

	Rope length required	Bolts	Remarks
Main Shaft:			
South End	75m	4	3 deviations.
New Eldon Series:			14 krabs.

55m and 30m ropes required for the 24m and 13m climbs up. There are large fixed hangers at the head of the pitches with thin line to enable SRT rope to be pulled through the eye of the bolt and secured to a ground belay.

Survey ref: Eldon Hole, E.P.C.

GIANT'S HOLE (Round Trip)   Grade 3

Grid Ref: SK 119826   O.S. Outdoor Leisure Series No 1, Peak District – Dark Peak Area, 1:25,000.   Altitude: 373m   Length: 2,600m Depth: 93m approx

Entrance series was fully explored before the Second World War. In 1956 Les Salmon along with members of the B.S.A. reached Base Camp Chamber. In 1968 the entrance passage was artificially enlarged. Bill Whitehouse and friends gurgled their way through the Chamber of Horrors to link Giant's with Oxlow/Maskhill.

Permission from Mr Watson, Peakshill Farm. Trespass fee payable.

WARNING: Giant's is an active stream cave which should not be entered in flood or if the weather is doubtful. The 14m pitch into the Crabwalk is free-climbable if the party is experienced. Novices should be roped.

Giant's Hole is situated on land belonging to Peakshill Farm which is reached by following a track (carefully if you value your car) off the Castleton to Sparrowpit road, SW of the Winnats Pass. 100m before the farm is reached, the track crosses a shallow valley, usually containing a small stream. Cars can be parked here, but PLEASE visit the farm first to obtain permission. To find the entrance, head eastward along the shallow valley which is only a short way along on the right.

A large stream passage leads after 30m to the Blasted Passage, which in turn leads to Base Camp Chamber with the stream entering on the right. Walk downstream, passing the impressive Boss Aven to reach the head of Garlands Pot. This is a small 4.5m pitch suitable for both ladders and SRT. Many bolt belays exist, mainly on the left wall (when facing out) out of the water.

At the bottom of the pitch a rift opposite the waterfall is the entrance to the most famous passage in Derbyshire, the extended sick joke of the Crabwalk. This very high and narrow passage twists and turns until one feels as if they have been in it forever. After 410m the Crabwalk narrows for a short section to form The Vice. Passing this can entail a short wallow in the stream for all but the skinniest people. 8m further on is the free-climbable Razor Edge Cascade soon followed by the 3m deep Comic Act Cascade with iron ladder in-situ. Continuing along the Crabwalk, the aptly named Great Relief Passage is reached, sumping after 175m. 15m before this sump a passage on the right passes under a small waterfall to enter a small chamber, the Eating House.

On the left when entering the Eating House is a small passage which leads eventually to the Lower Syphon Complex and, ultimately, the East Canal. On the right when entering the Eating House is a 3m climb (chain or rope usually in-situ) leading via a short crawl to Maggin's Rift.

In Maggin's Rift a muddy passage on the right (almost opposite the entrance

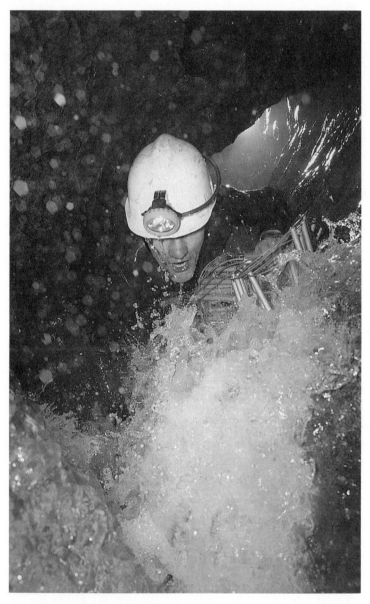

In the Crab Walk, Giant's Hole. Photo: Paul Deakin

crawl) leads into the North-East Swallet, a large, impressive passage containing a small stream. This is followed, free-climbing an 8m cascade 'en route', to a junction.

Left is Poached Egg Passage leading to the Giant's/Oxlow Connection. The way on is to the right along Letter Box Passage to Ghost Rift at the opposite end of which a depression in a slope of calcited pebbles leads to the tiny entrance to the Giant's Windpipe.

The Giant's Windpipe is an awkward, low crawl in water which has been known to become a duck; leading after a short, uncomfortable section to a junction. Handshake Crawl goes off to the left, the way on is to the right. Eventually, after several well decorated sections, this passage breaks out into the roof of the Crabwalk. An easy traverse along this roof passage leads to a thread belay on the right and several bolt belays in the roof. From here, either free-climb or abseil 14m into the upper reaches of the Crabwalk. Head upstream reaching the foot of Garlands Pot after around 40m.

Tackle:
Garlands Pot:
By ladder: 4.5m ladder, spreader, 12m lifeline, 3m belay, 4 karabiners/maillons for use with Eco hangers.
By SRT: 12m SRT rope, 4 karabiners/maillons for use with Eco hangers.
Upper Series/Crabwalk
30m abseil rope for novices (doubled)
Survey ref: Giant's Hole, E.P.C.

JAMES HALL OVER ENGINE MINE TO PEAK CAVERN   Grade 5

**Grid Ref: SK 135820   O.S. Outdoor Leisure Series No 1, Peak District –
Dark Peak Area 1:25,000.   Altitude: 426m
Length: 1.2km, including Peak/Speedwell 17km
Depth: 190m, including Peak/Speedwell 259m**

Digging started in December 1992 by Dave Nixon et al. The breakthrough into the main part of James Hall was made in December 1993. Further digging enabled the long sought breakthrough into Speedwell on August 5th 1995. Far Sump in Peak Cavern was reached after a protracted dig from the bottom of JH on July 15th 1996.

Access: Being part of the Peak/Speedwell system access is controlled by the B.C.R.A. Contact J.S.Beck or D.A.Nixon.

Situated on New Rake above Castleton, park at Rowter Farm (grid ref: SK 132822) and follow the path that runs east of the farm to a stile and continue for 150m where the entrance is found on the left on top of a small hillock.

The entrance series takes the form of a late 1700 lead mine beginning with a 50m pitch in the large Winding Shaft. Heading east a 400m Cartgate follows New Rake via many traverses – care – to the mined, second pitch called Bitch Pitch. At the bottom large natural passages are encountered typical of the Peak/Speedwell system.

A magnificent 80m natural pitch – Leviathan – is split into two and drops down directly above the Boulder Piles area of Speedwell Cavern. Caution needs to be exercised on this pitch in wet weather. A small, often wet, climbing shaft is found upslope from the bottom of the pitch. This leads down to the connection with

Speedwell Cavern. Continue downstream in the main Speedwell stream to the Bung. Through this usually very wet obstacle and continue to Egnaro Aven where a fixed ladder leads up to the long and very aptly named Colostomy Crawl. On through Fawlty Towers to Treasury and the exit via Peak Cavern.

Another route from the base of Leviathan leads via a crawl into the Far Sump Extensions of Peak Cavern, a series of large passages and caverns previously only accessible via the 400m long Far Sump.

Tackle:
All hangers are Eco.

	Rope length required	Remarks
Entrance Shaft	50m	Free hang
Bitch Pitch	50m	Traverse, 4 Deviations, 2 Rebelays.
Leviathan – part 1	40m	'Y' hang, 1 Deviation (permanent).
Leviathan – part 2	40m	Traverse, 2 Rebelays.

Survey ref: Peak/Speedwell, T.S.G. and James Hall Over Engine Mine, D.Nixon.

LATHKILL HEAD CAVE   Grade 5

Grid Ref: Resurgence SK 170658   Upper Entrance SK 167659
O.S. Outdoor Leisure Series No 24, Peak District – The White Peak Area – East Sheet 1:25,000.   Altitude: Resurgence 207m, Upper Entrance 248m
Length: 1,525m   Depth: 41m

The first limited explorations were undertaken by the old lead miners. At the beginning of this century Jimmy Puttrell pushed the cave to the chamber that bears his name. In the 1960's and 70's the E.P.C., S.U.S.S. and O.C.C. all made extensions. In 1990 the T.S.G. reached Lathkiller Hall and the Waiting Room. In 1991 the Upper Entrance was discovered.

WARNING: In normal weather the Tiger Passages are flooded and impassable. During wet weather the whole system floods and a considerable river issues from the Valley Entrance. The Lathkiller should be passed with extreme caution.

The Upper Entrance shaft is 20m deep. Fasten rope to lid and descend 6m to a stal and iron spike. A further 7m descent to a 'Y' hang for final free hang to the fine Waiting Room Natural thread Deviation at –2m. At the opposite end of the Waiting Room is a climb down through a choke and a short crawl which leads to the impressive Lathkiller Hall. From Lathkiller Hall the route is down through the boulder choke (The Lathkiller) to Handshake Chamber.

From Handshake Chamber two passages emanate; the left hand one leads to Gloop Canal and Iain Gasson's Passage, the way on is to the right along 146m of flat out crawling which is Tiger Three.

Tiger Three ends at a junction with the further end of Iain Gasson's Passage entering on the left. Keep to the right along the bedding plane crawl of Tiger Two for 61m to reach Fan Chamber and Bridge Chamber.

Continue along through these chambers to enter the 107m crawl of Tiger One, which enters Puttrell's Chamber with two passages. To the right is Mullen's Mistake. Turn left along a boulder strewn bedding plane to reach and climb Oval Pot.

45m after Oval Pot a junction is reached. Keep to the left and continue until a higher bedding plane on the right can be entered through a squeeze. This is wide

The bedding chambers, Ogof Ffynnon Ddu 2. Photo: Tony Baker

Flabbergasm Oxbow, Dan-Yr-Ogof. Photo: Tony Baker

LATHKILL DALE

and low and leads to an ascending route through boulders, The Spiral. Beyond The Spiral a short crawl enters the Rift Chamber.

From here an obvious bedding crawl leads after 61m to the large Resurgence Entrance.

Tackle:
33m SRT rope, plus 6 krabs and 3 slings for Upper Entrance Pitch.
Survey ref: Lathkill Head Cave, E.P.C.

MASKHILL MINE – GIANT'S HOLE EAST CANAL   Grade 5

**Grid Ref: SK 122821   O.S. Outdoor Leisure Series No 1, Peak District –
The Dark Peak Area, 1:25,000.   Altitude: 456m   Length: 897m approx
Depth: 211m**

Much natural passage was intersected by the early miners who first entered this mine around the 17th Century. They connected Maskhill to Oxlow during their excavations. Around the early 1960's the E.P.C. forced a way into the New Oxlow Series but most importantly the Oxlow/Giant's connection.

Permission from Oxlow House Farm on the Castleton to Sparrowpit road just west of Winnats Pass. A small fee will be charged. It is very important to do this. Access has been denied in the past due to irresponsible behaviour of some cavers.

WARNING: Many of the pitches have loose rock and caution should be exercised. Avoid touching stacked deads and old stemples.

From the farm, the road is followed in the direction of Sparrowpit (W) until just before the third gate on the left. It is possible to park here, but ensure your car is off the road! NOTE: Break-ins have occurred here, CARE! Here, a low section of wall and a wooden stile give access to a field. Follow a wall uphill for a short distance, then cross a stone stile and contour up the hillside to find the Oxlow entrance shaft where a plate points the way to Maskhill Mine. This is higher up the hill than Oxlow, 180m off to the right.

The 30m deep Entrance Pitch is covered with a steel lid and concrete surround, belay to rings on the lid and back up with a short scaffold bar. The Second Pitch of 15m follows immediately and leads to a natural passage where a short climb down and a steep slope bring one to the head of the Third Pitch. This is 11m deep and at the bottom a slope leads to the Fourth Pitch, the Murmuring Churn. DO NOT descend the 55m pitch as the whole place is tottering with deads. Descend 25m to a steep slope of 4m to the head of the Fifth Pitch of 8m. At the base is a walled shaft, descend this and traverse over a shaft in the floor to a 'bridge' where the Sixth Pitch of 43m is situated. At the head of the Sixth Pitch, looking out, below to the right can be seen the mined passage connecting Maskhill to Oxlow. This is 14m up the wall and is reached by carefully traversing across and down the right wall of the chamber selecting belays as needed. When the mined passage is reached the rope can be belayed to either a bolt or the in-situ staple.

Follow the mined passage and enter the West Chamber of Oxlow Cavern. Cross this immense chamber and pass under a low arch to enter the West-antechamber. On the right a 9m fixed iron ladder leads up to the New Oxlow Series. At the top of the ladder a short natural passage leads to a junction. Turn right, and follow the Pilgrim's Way, a hands and knees crawl as far as Mecca Aven ignoring any passages off. Just beyond Mecca Aven a passage on the left leads to the 20m high Water Rift where a crawl on the left meets a small stream. Head upstream up a low and occasionally very tight crawl to enter Oxlow Aven and the connection with Giant's Hole. This is the aptly named Chamber of Horrors, 222m of tight and nasty crawling with numerous ducks.

NOTE: If attempting the connection bear in mind that the owner of Giant's does not allow through trips. You must come back through! Be sure you can.

The connection brings one into Giant's Hole at Poached Egg Passage. This is followed for 40m to a junction. Left is Letter Box Passage leading to Ghost Rift; right is North East Swallet which is followed for 166m free-climbing down an 8m cascade on the way. At the end of the North East Swallet a short muddy passage leads into Maggin's Rift. Opposite the point of entry, a 3m climb down (rope or chain usually in-situ) lands in the Eating House. From here turn left to a junction, turn left again to another junction. Left leads back to the Eating House. Straight on leads to the North Rift. Turn right to gain an obvious high level roof traverse which leads to a passage above the sump. A passage soon leads to the Plughole, a 4m climb down which is free-climbable, handline in-situ. This lands in a chamber with a couple of feet of water. A passage continues a short way to reach the head of Geology Pot. This 12m pitch lands in a small chamber with a crawl to the stream, head downstream, descend a 4m cascade to reach the Far Curtain which in normal conditions is an aqueous crawl or duck. Shortly, a pitch of 2.5m, Spout Hall, is descended into a deep pool. Depending on water levels, scramble or swim the remaining distance to the East Canal. Reverse route for Exit!

Tackle:

	Rope length required	Bolts	Remarks
Maskhill:			
Pitch One	55m	5	3 re-belays, 2 deviations.

Pitch Two	15m	2	1 belay.
Pitch Three	25m	5	4 re-belays.
Pitch Four			
(Murmuring Churn)	45m	4	3 re-belays, 1 deviation.
Pitch Five	20m	2	1 re-belay.
	25m		4 re-belays.
Pitch Six	43m	7	7 re-belays, 1 deviation.

Giants Hole:			
Geology Pot	25m		2 belays.
Cascade	9m		1 belay.
Spout Hall	6m		1 belay.
Survey ref: Eldon Pothole Club.			

NETTLE POT

Grade 5

Crumble & Beza Pots   Grid Ref: SK 126819   O.S. Outdoor Leisure Series No 1, Peak District – The Dark Peak Area, 1:25,000. Altitude: 461m   Length: 650m   Depth: 180m

In 1934 the D.P.C. entered the pot. In the late 80's Frank Brown with members of the D.C.C. discovered Gour Passage through Freeze Squeeze and the impressive Derbyshire Hall. A 100m or so below, Ben Bentham with the T.S.G. and O.C.C. dug below Beza Pot reaching the deepest part of the cave at –177m.

Permission from Oxlow House Farm on the Castleton to Sparrowpit road just west of Winnats Pass. A small fee will be charged. It is very important to do this. Access has been denied in the past due to the irresponsible behaviour of some cavers.

Approach is the same as Maskhill Mine. Follow the road away from the farm in the direction of Sparrowpit. Park next to the third gate on the left near where a low section of wall and a wooden stile lead into the field. Ensure your car is off the road! NOTE: Break-ins have occurred here! Follow the right hand side of the wall uphill then cross over into the field on the left via a stone stile, contour the hill side, climbing steadily upwards until the Oxlow entrance is located. From here a direction finder points the way for the short remaining distance to Nettle.

Please adhere to these directions as the caves here have been closed before due to the actions of a few 'unofficial' trips.

WARNING: The area below Beza Pot is loose and can be confusing, take care here. Having an accident in the lower reaches of this cave would not be clever: rescue would be almost impossible

The 49m shaft is fitted with a steel lid, belay to the rings. The first 18m of the shaft is called the Narrows but is only tight in parts and should not present a problem to the caver of average build. There is a re-belay near the start of this section and a 'Y' hang about 10m below this. At the end of the Narrows is a small widening in the shaft, this is the Sentry Box where a re-belay is situated. At the foot of the shaft is a wide and low washed out lava bed, the Flats.

Ignoring the numerous choked shafts in the floor, turn east and descend the Grand Canyon pitch. At the foot of the Grand Canyon Pitch turn right (facing out from the wall) and traverse (roped) past the large hole in the floor to the far end of the chamber, passing the small entrance to Elizabeth Pitch. A short climb down

Paul Taylor in the Mucky Ducks, Peak Cavern. Photo: Tony Baker

leads to a bouldery chamber which has a small hole in the floor at its end, this is the head of Crumble Pot.

At the foot of Crumble Pot a climb up of 6m gives access to a tiny hole where the 4m Rope Pitch is descended to the head of Beza Pot. At the foot of the main pitch is a steep boulder slope which leads to the Shakes where the crawl connection to the foot of Elizabeth Shaft is located. Descend the boulder slope whilst still on rope.

Above the boulder slope, at the foot of Beza Pot is a crawl on the left which leads to a tight 15m pitch leading to the 9m deep, free-climbable Fin Pot. From here three crawls emanate; one leads to Bingo Pot, one to Eyes Down (the deepest part of the cave at −177m and the other leads to a chamber, Easy Pickings. Through Easy Pickings the Red River Passage continues, passing under several avens to end at a difficult downhill crawl, the Dratsab.

The descent of Elizabeth Shaft makes a fine, though much easier trip. From a 'Y' hang at the top of the shaft a fine 60m drop reaches the base and a, not to be recommended, really nasty crawl into the bottom of Beza Pot.

Tackle:

	Rope length required	Bolts	Remarks
Entrance Pitch (Narrows and Bottle Pitch)	61m	5	
Grand Canyon Pitch (inc. Traverse)	25m	3	
Crumble Pot	31m	3	Boulder backup
Rope Pitch	7m		
Beza Pot (inc. Shakes)	68m	3	Boulder backup
Rope Pitch (to Tin Pot)	15m		
Elizabeth Shaft	65m	2	Boulder belay by head of pitch.

Survey ref: E.P.C.

P8 (Jackpot)   Grade 3

Grid Ref: SK 107817   O.S. Outdoor Leisure Series No 1, Peak District – The Dark Peak Area, 1:25,000.   Altitude: 326m   Length: 1,018m Depth: 70m

Explored in 1964 by members of the B.S.A. Since then members of the C.D.G. have discovered 8 sumps and 600m of passage. In 1984 Ben Bentham discovered the curious Eldon Series above the Main Stream Passage.

Permission from Perryfoot Farm. A small trespass fee is payable. Please follow way-markers and do not climb walls etc.

WARNING: P8 is a very popular trip for novices and guided youth trips etc. However, when water levels are high such parties are strongly recommended to keep out!

The approach to P8 is through the gate just up the road from the parking area. Pass Gautries Hole, on the left in a clump of trees, and follow the obvious way-markers past Little Bull Pit to enter a large, irregular depression where a stream sinks. This is the entrance.

134

The stream sinks through a 2.5m free-climbable concrete lined shaft, to enter Cascade Chamber where a scramble over or under a couple of large boulders leads to the streamway. This is a fine, high, sporting passage which leads after a short distance to Idiot's Leap, a 2.5m climb down (rope often in-situ). The streamway continues, down several short water chutes to reach the head of the 8m First Pitch. This pitch can become impassable in wet weather.

At the foot of the pitch is a chamber with two routes on; the continuation of the streamway or a 3m climb up opposite the ladder into the Upper Series. The climb up enters a short hands and knees crawl which leads to a traverse along the roof tube above the streamway. Follow this until an eye hole with the top of an iron ladder protruding from it is reached. Descend the ladder into a chamber with the Second Waterfall Pitch entering high up on the right.

At the far end of the chamber turn left to pass through the narrow Gour Passage to enter another larger chamber, Mud Hall. Directly across Mud Hall a short passage leads to a 'T' junction with Main Stream Passage. Turn left (downstream) and traverse above the water until it is possible to climb down at an area of breakdown. Continue along Main Stream Passage, passing the entrance to the Eldon Series high up on the right and a short distance further an impressive flowstone cascade on the left. The final 30m of passage is a huge rift (T'owd Man's Rift) leading to Sump One.

Tackle:
Idiot's Leap 5m rope, 1 Ecohanger. First Pitch 8m ladder, 1.5m belay, 12m lifeline. 2 Ecohangers or use 3 Ecohangers for climb down.
Survey ref: P8 (Jackpot), E.P.C.

PEAK CAVERN   Grade 3 (Part Show)

(The Devil's Arse)   Grid Ref: SK 148825   O.S. Outdoor Leisure Series No 1, Peak District – The Dark Peak Area, 1:25,000.   Altitude: 188m Length: 8,900m (14,500m including Speedwell Cavern) Vertical range: 150m

The largest cave entrance in Britain. In the 18th Century a rope making factory was established in the entrance. Guided trips into Peak began in the 16th Century. At the end of the last Century Jimmy Puttrell explored as far as the Mucky Ducks. In 1949 the C.D.G. and the S.U.M.C. entered the main cave, and syphoned the Mucky Ducks. Wind Tunnel was entered in 1953 and was broken through 31 years later by Mark Wright and other T.S.G. members. In 1959 Moss Chamber was discovered where on the second visit after its discovery Neil Moss descended a tight vertical tube and got stuck. Despite a heroic rescue attempt he tragically died. Access was denied until 1962. Continuing discoveries were made by T.S.G. members and P. B. Smith. 1982 Far Sump was passed. Far Sump Extensions made in late 1980's by John Cordingley and friends. In 1984 Buster Wright of the T.S.G. climbed the impressive Victoria Aven and finally in 1991 the T.S.G broke through into the breathtaking White River Series.

Access on Sundays only, between November and March. Clubs must be BCRA members, individuals must sign an indemnity form and pay a small fee.

Apply to: Mr J Beck.

WARNING: Access to Peak Cavern is strictly controlled by the B.C.R.A. Visiting Clubs must be members of the B.C.R.A., whilst individuals must sign an indemnity

Castleton Area

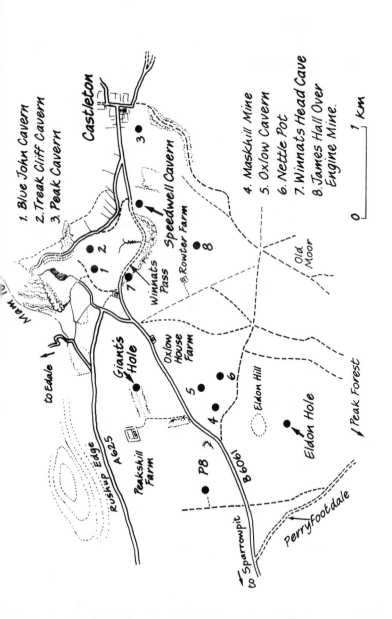

1. Blue John Cavern
2. Treak Cliff Cavern
3. Peak Cavern

4. Maskhill Mine
5. Oxlow Cavern
6. Nettle Pot
7. Winnats Head Cave
8. James Hall Over Engine Mine.

0   1 Km

Castleton

Speedwell Cavern

Winnats Pass

Rowter Farm

Old Moor

Mam Tor

to Edale

Giant's Hole

Oxlow House Farm

Eldon Hill

Eldon Hole

Peak Forest

Rushup Edge

A625

Peakshill Farm

B6061

P8

to Sparrowpit

Perryfootdale

form. If water levels are too high entry may be denied. In the unlikely event of a party being trapped in the cave (Lumbago Walk, near the entrance, sumps in wet weather), food, shelter and other essentials are stored in water tight containers at Picnic Dig (above and to the left of the second boulder pile before Far Sump). Please do not open the containers except in an emergency.

The short length of passage between Lake Sump and Ink Sump occasionally contains diesel fumes from the working on Dirtlow Rake, take care!

No cigarettes or carbide are allowed in the cave.

Peak Cavern is situated in the village of Castleton at the head of an impressive gorge.

The obvious path is followed through the show cave. Proceed through the Vestibule, to pass the inner gate and enter Lumbago Walk, a short stooping section of passage. This leads to two very large chambers; The Great Cave and Roger Rain's House (with waterfall entering from high in the roof).

Continue through Pluto's Dining Room to emerge at the top of a series of steps; the Devil's Staircase. Down these the stream is soon met. Continue upstream to reach a junction; to the left the stream from Buxton Water Sump spills over a low dam, to the right the main route continues, passing the debris cone from Victoria Aven to enter a series of wet passages and a short crawl. The main passage continues through the Mucky Ducks. These are a series of short, crouching wallows through water, a shadow of their former glory since the floor was dug out many years ago.

The Mucky Ducks give access to the large Upper Gallery. 150m along this, on the right, is a small passage emitting a trickle of water; this is Pickering's Passage leading to Moss Chamber, Toadstool Aven and Anniversary Hall.

The Upper Gallery continues for another 70m to another passage on the right, this is Treasury Passage, leading to the Speedwell Connection.

The main passage continues, eventually developing a deepening vadose trench until it abruptly finishes at the Surprise View. Surprise View is a 6m pitch at the head of which, on the right, is a passage leading into the Main Stream Inlet Series. Surprise View is rigged with an in-situ iron ladder; descend this to land in Main Stream Passage.

Downstream (left), gives over 300m of very fine, easy caving, to the upstream end of the Buxton Water Sump. Upstream from the foot of the ladder is the way on; after 170m Main Stream Passage turns to the left, on the right at this point (known as Squaw's Junction) is the waterfall entering from the Main Stream Inlet Series. Main Stream Passage continues upstream, passing Lake Passage on the left. This short passage, which occasionally necessitates swimming, leads to Lake Sump which can be by-passed on the right, but is an amusing, short, free-dive with a rope in-situ. This soon leads to Ink Sump which is NOT free-divable.

Return to Main Stream Passage. Continue upstream with the passage getting higher all the time; pass a fixed iron ladder-way, which leads up to the Maypole Inlet dig, and continue over a boulder pile. Picnic Dig (emergency dump) is up to the left. Main Stream Passage continues, regaining the stream, and passing over the final boulder pile to leave a short, easy, walking section to Far Sump, the limit for 'dry' cavers.

Survey ref: Peak/Speedwell System, T.S.G.

STREAKS POT (Through Trip, Saturday Pot)   Grade 4

Grid Refs: Upper Entrance SK 212759   Lower Entrance SK 214759
O.S. Outdoor Leisure Series No 24, Peak District – The White Peak Area –
East Sheet 1:25,000.   Altitude: Upper entrance 228m
Lower entrance 194m   Length: 777m   Depth: 41m

On New Years Day 1980, T.S.G. members noticed a possible dig. In June Tom Procter and Geoff Birtles passed Nervous Breakdown. It was explored from the Top Entrance. The Lower entrance was found a few weeks later on. Proctor climbed the impressive 30m Telescope Aven.

WARNING; High water levels in the cave can make the Nervous Breakdown a serious proposition, use your judgement. The Lower Entrance should be rigged with a short ladder or rope as some people have experienced considerable difficulty in exiting from the oil drums un-aided.

The Upper Entrance is situated at the foot of a small crag to the west, and higher, than the Lower Entrance.

The Lower Entrance is to be found about 4m above the road, on the right hand side, just before the first left hand bend when heading westwards from the junction with Eyam Dale.

The Upper Entrance is a short mined crawl which leads to the first pitch of 12m (belay ladder & lifeline to a handy tree near the entrance). 3m above the foot of the pitch is a passage leading to a shattered chamber containing a rift in the right hand corner; pass through this to an aven and climb down a narrow rift. This enters a short level section with rotten timbers holding the roof up, take care. A 9m free-climb leads to a muddy tube and the stream. At the stream, turn right (upstream), passing through either of the two sporting tubes from which it emerges. Soon a 'T' junction is reached; left is Main Stream Inlet, right becomes too low; the way on is straight ahead, through boulders (not obvious) to Alexander's Aven and a large crawl. The passage goes through a small breakdown chamber then reaches the base of the very large Telescope Aven. The passage continues (a short crawl off to the left leads to the Lu Blue Sump) getting larger then abruptly finishing at the West Choke which draughts enticingly.

Retrace route back to where Upper entrance reaches the streamway.

Continue downstream, almost immediately Nervous Breakdown is entered, a disordered jumble of large blocks through which the stream passes. Once through Nervous Breakdown the passage enlarges for a short while, then reduces to a crawl past an area of breakdown. A short distance further on a junction is reached; straight on (with the stream) becomes too low. The way on is to the right through a dry section of passage, passing Donkey Dong Inlet on the right. Pass through a small shattered chamber, a low squeeze and a flat out crawl – the Mousehole. This leads to a small chamber and the low entrance to Route 66, which is a dry, sand floored passage, which can carry a large volume of water in flood conditions.

Route 66 increases slightly in size after passing a small area of breakdown and (ignoring small side crawls) leads to a junction showing evidence of mining. Left leads to a muddy chamber, but the way on is to the right, slightly up-slope to another junction, left is a very tight, flat out crawl to a small chamber – the White House. Right, a short crawl in clean limestone soon leads to the constricted Lower Entrance oil drums.

Tackle:
Upper entrance: 12m ladder, 15m lifeline, very long belay.

Lower entrance: short ladder or rope.
Survey ref: Streaks Pot, T.S.G.

WINNATS HEAD CAVE
Grade 5

**Grid Ref: SK 131828   O.S. Outdoor Leisure Series No 1, Peak District –
Dark Peak Area 1:25,000.   Altitude: 404m   Length: 610m   Depth: 148m**

First and Main Chambers discovered in 1976 by O.C.C. and Ben Bentham. Fox Chamber entered by Ben Bentham and Chris Fox in 1978. In 1988 D.U.G. and the T.S.G. discovered a tortuous way through the boulder floor of Fox Chamber to emerge in another chamber containing a large sump pool. Further extensions were made soon after taking the cave to its present limit.

Permission from Winnats Head Farm. A small access fee will be charged.

WARNING: Winnats Head is a very loose system and the boulder choke through which the route to Cornwall Avenue passes is particularly so. Several tight squeezes exist in the second choke and to be rescued from beyond this point would be impossible.

Winnats Head is situated at the foot of a small rock scar on the south side of the road, just before the cattle grid at the top of the Winnats Pass, coming from the Castleton direction.

The entrance slopes downhill and soon reduces to a crawl which enters a small chamber, another sloping crawl leads to the large Main Chamber. Holes in the boulder floor can be descended with extreme caution (they periodically 'alter' themselves!) to emerge in the large passage of Cornwall Avenue. This leads down-slope to enter Fox Chamber, 20m high, 15m wide and 46m long.

The way on is through a hole in the boulder floor (not obvious), passing through a tight vertical squeeze to a 5m drop which lands in a small boulder chamber. From here a small passage leads to a boulder squeeze and entry to a large chamber with a 6m diameter sump pool. On the left is a 12m aquatic crawl (Down In The Sewer) leading to a high passage and an aven up which the route goes. This 12m pitch is usually rigged (1 re-belay, 1 deviation), and leads to a step over a parallel shaft, a couple of short free climbs and a short length of hands and knees passage which leads to a small aven with a stream entering from above. The water cascades over the lip of a 20m pitch (belay to eye-hole and bolt, possible re-belays on ledge away from water at −11 m).

The landing is in a chamber with a sloping floor which leads to the lip of the next pitch. This 14m pitch (bolt high up at pitch head, re-belay on opposite wall) is in a rift 3m wide and 8m long and lands at a sloping passage with a couple of short free-climbs to the lip of the last pitch of 14m (bolt at pitch head, re-belay on opposite wall). Descend this for 9m to reach wedged boulders with stream going down one side; way on is down the dry side for a further 5m. A small 5m long passage leads to the terminal sump.

Tackle:

	Rope length required	Bolts
Pitch 1	30m	3
Pitch 2	22m	2
Pitch 3	20m	2

Survey ref: Winnats Head Cave, E.P.C.

Bibliography

B.C.R.A. Transactions Vol 4, No 3, 1977 (Survey of Carlswark Cavern).
B.S.A. Cave Science, Vol 5, No 38, Les Salmon, 1965. (Survey of Giant's Hole).
Barker, I. Descent No 96, 1990.
Eldon Pothole Club Journal, Vol 9, No 2, 1979.
   Vol 9, No 4, 1984.
   Vol 9, No 5, 1986.
Ford, T. & Gill, D. Caves of the Peak District, Dalesman, 1992.
Ford, T. (Ed), Limestone and Caves of the Peak District, Geo Books, 1977.
Gasson, I. E.P.C. Journal, Vol 7 No 3 1970.
Lloyd & King, Philosophical Transactions of the Royal Society, Vol 61, 1780.
Lyre, The, (The Journal of the Orpheus Caving Club), No 5, September 1981.
O'Neill, P. 1987, Derbyshire Caving Associaiton Newsletter No 65.
Peak Rigging Guide, Crewe Caving and Potholing Club, 1995.
T.S.G. Journal No 14, 1993
T.S.G. Newsletter No 9, 1981, (survey of Streaks Pot)
Wright, Sheffield University Speleological Society Journal, 1971, Vol 2, No 1.

NORTH WALES
by Des Marshall

INTRODUCTION

The number of caves in North Wales is limited even though there are large areas of limestone, little of which is exposed. There are two distinct areas; one starting at Prestatyn on the north coast and continuing southwards to just beyond Oswestry. The other starting at Great Ormes Head, near Llandudno, continues south east, ending a couple of miles beyond Ruthin. Extensive mining in the area uncovered many caves, although mostly short, with some 140 speleological sites listed in the booklet 'The Caves of North Wales' by Tony Oldham.

ACCESS TO CAVES OF THE MINERA AREA

There is some very interesting caving to be had in the area but currently (Sept '93) the owner of Minera Quarry, Tarmac, are denying cavers access to Ogof Dydd Byraf and Ogof Llyn Ddu. Both of these have entrances in Minera Quarry. Similarly, Grosvenor Estates have stopped access to Ogof Llyn Parc and Park Western Shaft. Meanwhile, the N.W.C.C. are trying to secure access to all these caves.

Of note is Park Shaft. It has an entrance shaft of 105m followed by two further 21m shafts to a bottom level and boulder choke. This choke was broken through in 1984 into Ogof Llyn Parc, which is some 4 kilometres long, has a vertical range of over 115m and a large stream! There is a lot of cave here.

USEFUL ADDRESSES

For enquiries about the current access situation:
Tim Palmer
Ground Floor Flat
51 Victoria Street
Oswestry
Shropshire SY11 2BW

POACHERS' CAVE   Grade 2

Also known as Ogof Hen Ffynhonnau (Cave of the Old Spring) and Ogof o'r Herwheliwr.   Grid Ref: SJ 191655   O.S. Landranger Series No 116, Denbigh and Colwyn Bay 1:50,000.   Altitude: 146m   Length: 800m

WARNING: The cave is prone to severe and rapid flooding. Like Ogof Hesp Alyn this cave formerly acted as a resurgence for the underground channels of the River Alyn. It floods in a highly unpredictable manner. Although there are places where it may be possible to sit out a flood it may be weeks rather than days before the water subsides. If the surface river is swollen or discoloured DO NOT ENTER the cave.

From Mold take the A494 road towards Ruthin. At Cadole turn right towards Gwernaffield Y Waun and continue to the second cross roads (Hand Inn on the opposite side of the junction). Turn left here and go past Mold Golf club into

AREA MAP OF NORTH WALES

Pantymwyn. Go through the village around a sharp right hand bend (road junction to the left) following the sign to Cilcain, down a steep hill to a small car park just before the narrow Cilcain bridge. Walk back uphill to the first right hand bend where, by the chevron sign, a steep muddy path descends through the wood to the left to reach the River Alyn. DO NOT go through the caravan site. Continue along the river bank to reach the cave entrance, which is found under a small cliff on the right of the path. 6 minutes from the car.

The Northern Pennine Club started digging the site in June 1978 and a natural passage was found. Due to holidays, etc. they did not recommence digging until

September when they discovered that their dig had been pirated. The culprits were two members of the North Wales Caving Club, hence the name – Poachers' Cave.

Beyond the door an entrance crawl of 6m reaches a metal lid beneath which is a pitch of 5m. This is narrow at the top. (Continuing along, above the pitch head, enters a sadly vandalised, once pretty grotto). A ladder is hung from the in-situ hanger. There is also a good natural thread on the opposite wall. At the bottom of the pitch turn right (facing the ladder). (Turning left quickly leads to a dead end). 6m from the ladder a small hole on the left is found and going through this drops down into Old Springs Passage. This starts as a crawl on a solid rock floor bearing large scallop markings, which indicate an outward flow of water (as do the markings everywhere in the cave). The flat roof is deeply intersected asymptomatically, there being little of the thin limestone bed remaining to support it. Further along, the solid floor gives way to silt and at the side of the passage are mud banks, the remains of previous infill. These banks are present everywhere in the cave. From the roof hang a profusion of long, very thin tree routes, mud encrusted, eerie in the silence and swinging gently in the breeze. This first section of the cave appears very oppressive to some.

Soon the passage begins to gain height, becoming alternately of stooping and walking dimensions with the higher parts above the mud banks bearing some 'moonmilk'. The passage varies in cross-section from the traditional oval phreatic tube to triangular, as at Isosceles Passage.

Before long the passage intersects the Caleb Bell cross-course. Here the nature of the cave changes dramatically, the fault having been dissolved out of a high rift. There are chambers with excellent examples of cracked mud floors. One exit from the rift chamber – a climb up to the right – terminates in a circular shaft. The other exit – down to the left leads to a chamber with a sloping mud floor below an unhappy looking rock bridge. At the bottom of the slope there are two holes. On the right is a steeply sloping, extremely muddy tube ending in a vertical drop; the other, on the left is a clean, circular shaft (the downwards continuation of the shaft in the rift chamber). It is pointless descending either of these since their lower reaches can be gained with ease from the lower stream passage. However, there are 5 bolt sleeves at the top of the left hand hole for the 10m descent!

The way on from the holes in the floor is up a muddy slope into a mud floored phreatic tube leading, via a small chamber, to the top of a steep mud bank. At the bottom of the slope is a cavern sporting an active streamway. To the right the upstream passage is large, being 5m wide by 4m high in places, but to the left the water disappears amongst boulders to enter a more constricted, highly shattered region as it follows the fault down towards Ogof Hesp Alyn. It is possible to explore, via unsafe chambers to a point at the bottom of the holes encountered earlier and beyond, through muddy tubes to a rift. The upstream section from where the river is met continues in grand proportions for a while, but eventually the mud banks close in, the roof lowers and one is forced to crawl in water for a few metres in two places. (12mm of airspace has been noted and there is no doubt that in wet weather these would readily sump off). Beyond the low sections the roof rises quickly to around 4m and a few stalactites are seen. Before long a circular chamber, 15m in diameter by 11m high, is entered, containing, on the right, a huge stalagmite boss with accompanying flowstone cascade above. A flat section of roof on the left displays a profusion of fossil brachiopods.

There are two exits from the Main Chamber. To the left is a descending shattered rift which, in wet times, fills completely and from which a large amount of water flows to swell what is normally the main stream.

Across the chamber the main stream continues along a passage 3m x 3m, which contains some reasonable formations. The roof lowers to .5m at a point where the stream enters on the right. Here a slide up a muddy hole leads to a final, enormous shattered chamber, whose roof is suspended by as yet undiscovered forces! Tree roots are again seen, this time thick ones in the mud and traffic can be heard at Cilcain bridge!!

Tackle:
Entrance pitch – 5m ladder, 10m rope and long sling for thread.
Survey ref: Ogof o'r Herwheliwr (Poacher's Cave), N.P.C. Journal 1979

OGOF HESP ALYN (Cave of the Barren Alyn)   Grade 5

**Grid Ref: SJ 192655   O.S. Landranger Series No 116, Denbigh and
Colwyn Bay 1:50,000.   Altitude: 143m   Length: 1,372m   Depth: 98m**

WARNING: The cave is prone to severe and unpredictable flooding. Some sections could take up to two weeks to drain!! If the surface river is swollen or discoloured DO NOT ENTER the cave. Care is required with the fixed ropes.

Approach as for Poacher's Cave but continue downstream a further 200m to where an obvious path drops steeply down to the river on the left and a lidded entrance shaft.

Discovered in April 1973 by the N.W.C.C., this system is a classic example of a sub water table or phreatic cave and marks the original resurgence of water sinking from the River Alyn near Loggerheads. Extensions were made by W.C.C.in 1982 and G.C.C. in 1985.

An 8m entrance climb, best laddered, leads to a small chamber which is followed down to the left to the start of a low wet section. This shortly emerges in a chamber. Back to the left a large passage leads off to the NE from the chamber, whilst the main route is straight on via a couple of short climbs (one of which has a fixed rope on it) to a duck under a flake and a 'T' junction. Straight on is a funnel chamber and the Fieldmouse Series.

To the left at the 'T' junction, the passage eventually leads to the Sand Crawl (which may require digging out) and Dome Chamber. Climbing out of the chamber, negotiate a short crawl to ascend an 8m pitch (fixed rope in situ). This leads to a canal which is quite deep, but ledges ensure that you only get wet up to the chest! Exiting from the canal leads to a bedding and the start of the pitches. It is best to kit up here for these.

Using the rope, take the obvious exit from the chamber across to a fallen slab which is the head of the second pitch. This is 25m and best split into two sections. Two deviations where the rope goes over a lip 3m down enables a free hanging descent of 10m to be made. Another deviation here allows the rope to be guided around a corner to a ledge where a re-belay gives a free hang for the final 10m. The pitch is followed by a couple of short free climbs. These lead to the third pitch which is 6m. A short squeeze at the bottom of the pitch leads to a 'T' junction. To the left is the Worm Way, a crawl leading to a chamber which yields the deepest point in the cave. To the right is the fourth pitch of 10m. Belay well back from the head of the pitch to avoid sliding around in the mud. A convenient block at the head of the pitch provides the main belay. At the bottom (which is either a deep pool or a descending passage to a muddy chamber, depending on water levels) ascend the slope using the fixed rope. This leads through a muddy chamber to a

144

large passage with a short branch to the left. (This leads to a muddy climb down through boulders to a stream passage. When water levels are low this leads down stream to a squeeze into a chamber and another short pitch which lands in a pool.) Staight on at the junction leads to the 12m fifth pitch (belay to eyehole to the left of the pitch). At the bottom ascend the slope, using the rope in place. This leads to the sump chamber with sump one being perched at the top of a 6m climb. Sump one is normally the end of the trip but an 8m dive (not free divable) leads to a short section of passage and sump two, beyond which there is a further 400m of passage.

Tackle:

	Rope length required	Bolts	Remarks
Entrance shaft:			8m ladder, 16m rope, sling.
Pitch 2	37m	5	3 deviations.
Pitch 3	15m	3	
Pitch 4	20m	1	Fasten rope to block at head of pitch.
Pitch 5	16m		Thread.

Survey ref: Subterranean Courses of the River Alyn, including Ogof Hesp Alyn, North Wales, Transactions B.C.R.A. Vol.1 No 1, January 1974.

Bibliography

Appleton, P., Ogof Hesp Alyn, Caves & Caving, May 1984.
B.C.R.A. Transactions, Subterranean Courses of the River Alyn, including Ogof Hesp Alyn, Vol 1 No 1 January 1974.
Grosvenor Caving Club, Publication No 2, November 1982.
Kealy, L., The Caves of North Wales, C.C.P.C. Journal Volume 2.
Oldham, T., The Caves of North Wales, published by A. Oldham.

SOUTH WALES
by Donald Rust

INTRODUCTION

The main caving area in South Wales stretches along the breadth of the Brecon Beacons National Park and is most prominent in the upper Swansea Valley, Ystradfellte and the escarpment that overlooks Crickhowell. Several roads cut through the Brecon Beacons and give good access to the caving areas, noteably the A4067 in the Swansea Valley and the A465 through the Clydach Gorge.

The caves have developed long sporting streamways and have magnificent large passages but little vertical development although the deepest cave in the UK, Ogof Ffynnon Ddu in the Swansea Valley, can be traversed from top to bottom with little or no equipment.

Many smaller caves were entered for the first time by archaeologists in the 19th Century. The first recorded exploration into Dan yr Ogof in the Swansea Valley was by the Morgan brothers of Abercrave in 1912 when they entered the river entrance and explored to the Third Lake. But the main bulk of the explorations were after 1936 when cavers from Yorkshire and the Mendips extended their field of operation. Prominent figures stand out in those early days, namely Ernest Roberts and Gerard Platten. The entrance to Ogof Ffynnon Ddu was excavated after the Second World War and explorations of many new caves took a new pace. There are still large areas of limestone with no recorded cave, notably beyond Dan yr Ogof, behind Llygad Llwchwyr, west of the Llangatock Escarpment. I'm sure these will all, some day, reveal good and sporting caves.

The long caves described in this section such as Agen Allwedd and Ogof Ffynnon Ddu offer many classic trips. Included are some of the best providing interesting trips with minimal route finding problems. Also included are some caves that provide introductory trips and some of special interest. I hope you enjoy exploring these caves as much as I have over the last twenty years.

Accommodation in the area is plentiful, being the centre of a National Park, from B & B to holiday cottage lets, to caving club house accommodation.

USEFUL ADDRESSES

Mynydd Llangattock Cave
Management Access Committee
Lynne Bailey
5 Old Rectory Close
Maes-y-Gwartha
Gilwern
Gwent, NP7 0DZ
Please enclose s.a.e.

South Wales Caving Club
Permit Secretary
1-10 Powell Street
Penwyllt
Swansea Valley
Please enclose s.a.e.

Pete Francis
Kilvrough Manor
Parkhill
Gower
Please enclose s.a.e.

Elsie Little
Hennoyadd Villa
Hennoyadd Road
Abercrave
SA9 1UR
Please enclose s.a.e.

Tim Long
4 Brynllefrith Cottages
Llantrisant Road
Llantwit Fardre
Mid Glam, CF38 2HD
Please enclose s.a.e.

ACCOMMODATION

The Secretary
South Wales Caving Club
1-10 Powell Street
Penwyllt
Abercrave
Swansea Valley

Croydon Caving Club
The Secretary
Alan Ockenden
Rock Farm
Rock Lane
Chaldon
Surrey CR3 5BN
Tel 01883 345055

Chelsea Speleological Society
Arthur Millett
Tel 01873 810548

Westminster Speleological Society
Andy Sewell
Tel 0181 691 0497

Rhongyr Isaf
Penycae
Swansea Valley
SA9 1GB
Tel 01639 730518

TOURIST INFORMATION OFFICES

Cattle Market Car Park
Brecon
Powys LD3 9DA
Tel 01874 622485

Crickhowell
NP8 1AA
Tel 01873 812105

GEAR HIRE

Crickhowell Adventure Gear
1 High Street
Crickhowell
Powys NP8 1EW
Tel 01873 810020

Dragon Caving Gear
Bristol House
72/74 Heol Tawe
Abercrave
Swansea SA9 1XR
Tel 01639 730031

PUBS

Copper Beech
Abercrave
Swansea Valley

Bakerloo Straight, Dan-Yr-Ogof. Photo: Tony Baker

AGEN ALLWEDD

**Grid Ref: SO 187158   O.S. Outdoor Leisure Series No 13, Brecon
Beacons National Park – Eastern Area 1:25,000.   Altitude: 366m
Length: 32,700m   Vertical Range: 179m (-139m +40m)**

The cave has many circular routes and the largest continuous streamway in Britain. First explored by members of S.W.C.C. in 1946 with major extensions in 1957 by members of the H.C.C. The Grand Circle was connected by the E.P.C. in 1972. Extended by members of the C.S.S from 1982 to 1987, along with S.W.C.C. in 1984, and G.S.S. in 1987.

Permission from Mynydd Llangattock Cave Management Access Committee.

WARNING: In moderate flood Deep Water and The Narrows sump. In severe flood beware in Maytime, and Turkey Streamway is impassable in the narrow section near Northwest Junction and Second Boulder Choke sumps

Approach from Crickhowell, over the River Usk and turn right through Llangattock village. At the end of the village cross over the canal and follow the road around a left hand bend. Turn right after 200m and climb the steep hill to its top where the road levels out to the left. On the right is Whitewalls. Follow the road for another 500m to a car park slightly off the road. Thieves operate in this area. DO NOT park near Whitewalls as this causes a lot of aggravation from the locals!

Follow the tramroad round from Whitewalls past Eglwys Faen and over some scree to regain the path again. On the left is a small round gated entrance, near a sign warning of loose rocks. This is the Ogof Gam entrance which is always used. The original entrance which is now blocked, except for the passage of bats, is near the top of the small outcrop to the right of Ogof Gam. It has a classic keyhole shape, thus the Welsh 'Allwedd'.

The Grand Circle   Grade 4
Inside the gate it is possible to stand and sign the visitors book, then progress along a tall passage with sections of traversing or sideways walking to reach a short crawl to the two blasted ducks. These are normally no more than a puddle. Soon after this, the passage entering from the right is the original way in via Agen Allwedd entrance. From here easy going reaches a junction with a crawl low down on the left. Take the left which leads to a second junction after only a few metres. Right ends very quickly. The way on is left along a stooping passage. Another short passage is passed on the right. Then Stream Passage joins from the right, follow downstream in enlarged passage with boulder obstacles for almost its entire length. It passes a large side passage on the right, Queer Street. Shortly after this a choke straight ahead is reached. Climbing down through boulders at its start, a further climb down or crawl past Draught Passage on the right, rejoins the streamway. A short section of stream now leads to First Choke proper. A climb up at the end of the crawl in the choke, emerges in Baron's Chamber.

Over a few boulders in Baron's Chamber leads to the top of a slope overlooking the vast Main Passage. This passage runs for about 1,200m to end in North Wing. Walking along the passage over boulders an obvious passage on the right is reached at the base of a large mud slope. Take this crawl for a couple of metres to reach the Main Stream Passage. This is almost immediately joined by a stream on the right, emerging from Meander Passage. Continuing down Main Stream Passage, the way is littered with boulders for some considerable distance. When

Llangattock Escarpment and Clydach Gorge

Crickhowell

Llangattock

Whitewalls
Cottage

parking

Agen Allwedd

Ogof Darren
Cilau

1. Ogof Clogwyn
2. Ogof Craig a Ffynnon

A465

2

Clydach

Blackrock

River Clydach

to Brynmawr   A465

1

parking-
by disused
railway tunnels

0   1 Km

the going becomes easier an inlet is passed and soon afterwards the start of the Second Boulder Choke is met.

Second Boulder Choke has moved several times in the past so caution is needed (the last time was in late 1985). The first section of the choke is passed on the right to a tall passage leading to a junction. Normal route is straight ahead, down a 2m climb to a second 2.5m climb, which can be avoided by stepping round to the right into a rift going back to the choke and an easy descent to the stream. The stream is followed until boulders force a climb up into the bottom of Mud Rose Chamber. Route on is down through the boulders, (take heed of the notice) to the stream. A low section gives way to a large bouldery stream passage, until boulders force you up. This enters Keyhole Chamber where the stream can be regained either by a traverse on the right, to climb down through a hole or by a climb down at the start of the traverse. The Main Stream continues to have many boulder obstacles which slowly give way to an easy walking streamway. Roof lowers and water deepens a short distance before Northwest Junction is reached. Straight on, upstream is Turkey Streamway and the Inner and Outer Circle Routes.

Heading left, downstream from Northwest Junction, Cascade Passage joins from the right. The main stream continues on its 1 km route to Fourth Choke as a tall pleasant passage. This gradually becomes more muddy as it approaches Deep Water (only waist deep). This is followed by a turn into The Narrows, where traversing may avoid a wetting. This lower section sumps in flood. A short distance beyond on the right is Third Boulder Choke and straight on sumps. Enter the choke on the right and switch to the left via a letter box. This emerges at water level in a sandy streamway which has a huge cone to climb over before Fourth Boulder Choke is encountered. The way on is up through several squeezes to emerge in a small chamber, 13m higher. From here a crawl under a large block enters the solid Biza Passage. The crawling becomes easier as it develops a narrow trench. Turn right at the junction and through a couple of phreatic loops and past Sump Passage on the left. Soon after this a double rope climb down gains Main Stream.

At the bottom of the Biza climbs, upstream goes to Fifth Choke and downstream a waterfall is met immediately, a very loose traverse on the right can by-pass this. The streamway follows the line of a fault which becomes clearer as Quarry Corner is approached, with its huge blocks. Continue with the stream as it turns right and soon descends a second cascade. High Traverse Passage goes off on the left at a height of 8m downstream of this. A fixed rope now indicates its position more clearly. High Traverse is a route to Maytime, Priory Road and a short cut to Southern Stream Passage.

Downstream the passage slowly decreases in size until a low section with waist deep water is reached (this can sump quickly). The roof rises and on the left is Southern Stream Passage. Ahead the water deepens and swings through low airspace on the left before a respite just before Sump 1.

Head up Southern Stream Passage over a couple of boulder obstacles to an enlargement with a roof tube. Back over the stream is a short rope climb into Gothic Passage, a route to Maytime and Priory Road.

Continue walking upstream as the narrow passage widens until a 2m waterfall is met. Easy walking reaches a crawl and squeeze, this marks the start of the taxing section of wet crawls and boulder obstacles. The small second inlet is passed on the left and the going eases off. By the time first inlet is reached, the boulders are few and stooping brings you out between boulders into a larger passage. Ahead through a slot and over boulders for 60m reaches the bottom of the boulder cone at the junction with Main Passage.

On the way to the furthest parts of Dan-Yr-Ogof. Photo: Tony Baker

152

Right goes to the Cliffs of Dover and Aven Series. Climb up, and head left along the mud floored trunk passage. This passes several small side passages and the large Erse Passage on the left, before it descends a mud slope to its junction with Main Stream Passage again. The Grand Circle is complete.

Extended Grand Circle to Maytime, Sump 4   Grade 4
The route to Maytime may be accessed via High Traverse Passage in Lower Main Stream or via Gothic Passage in Southern Stream. From Lower Main Stream climb using the rope to a roped traverse to enter High Traverse. A simple walk passes a food dump before it lowers to a crawl into a wide sandy passage, Synchronicity, with its aven. To the right is Resurrection Passage. From Southern Stream climb up to Gothic Passage and continue to a junction. Left is to Priory Road but go right, through a low crawl to emerge near the aven in Synchronicity with Resurrection straight ahead.

Resurrection Passage begins as a sandy crawl but has sections of stooping. It then goes through and over a roof collapse to reach a walking sandy passage which develops a trench. This passage has many fine crystals on the floor so keep to the tape. This walking section lowers over a roof collapse to become a sand swim to a small aven. A second sand swim emerges in Reverberation Aven. The way on is through a 35m dig to enter a fault passage. A second choke which is loose leads to the top of a calcited ramp. The passage below has many fine formations and leads through a final dig to emerge in Maytime.

Maytime can FLOOD quickly and to a considerable depth. If the climb down to the water has not got a sand bank showing opposite take extreme caution. Right is upstream and leads through out of depth water to sump 3. Going downstream soon leads through waist deep water to the first cascade and trench. Continue downstream to another cascade and trench. The two cascades, although small can be impassable in minor flood. The trench gives way to easier walking past short passages to reach Sump 4. The sump has been dived through to Against All Odds Chamber after 297m at a maximum depth of 20m.

Outer Circle (clockwise)   Grade 4
From Northwest Junction (see beginning of description for Grand Circle) follow the stream through a narrow rift, climb through boulders and stal to reach an easy walking streamway. As the passage becomes taller a large roof passage can be seen above, Helictite Chamber. Turkey Stream continues past several other roof passages, Hedgehog Passage, Needle Passage, Calcite Gallery and Worker's Passage. Turkey Junction (Coal Cellar Junction) is then reached, this is where Coal Cellar Passage joins from the right and is one branch of the Outer Circle. The way on is up Turkey Streamway which can sometimes be missed if you are on autopilot!

Other passages are passed on the right, Shattered Passage and Phreatic Passage before Turkey Pool is met. This is a short section of deep water which can be traversed to a pleasant section of smaller phreatic tube. Continue upstream and climb up to enter Turkey Chamber. The way on is to rejoin the stream straight away but head up to the right and along, before dropping down to the stream at a bend to the right. The streamway continues large and within 100m a junction is reached with Hawkin's Horror. Turkey Streamway leads for some 600m to reach Sump 1 and 2, the route into the Remembrance Series.

Take Hawkin's Horror to emerge in a tall rift passage, Sand Caverns. Head left and the passage increases in size. A mud bank on the right is crossed after some 50m to reach Selenite Needle Passage. Sand Caverns continues for some 400m before choking.

Selenite Needle Passage is stooping for most of its length with the odd short crawl. After Spiral Passage on the right is reached it becomes walking, pass Western Avenue and Central Avenue on the left. Now with a small stream, Selenite Needle Passage joins Eastern Avenue at an oxbowed junction where the remains of an old rescue kit can be seen.

The Inner Circle can be done by turning left up over rocks to a stream which emerges from a choke some 200m away. Two thirds the way up this passage, a turn right passes through an area of roof breakdown to gain Inner Circle Chamber. Beyond this more breakdown is passed over to Bat Chamber and then a junction is met. To the right the passage becomes large as it rises up a ramp. At the top of this the way on looks huge as you look out over a massive junction. To the left the passage meanders to a flat roofed boulder choke. While straight on rises up another ramp to the Dome of St. Pauls. Down a ramp, into Scree Passage and more climbs and descents in this large passage until a junction is reached, Swiss Passage straight on and Midsummer Passage on the right. With Shamrock Passage acting as an oxbow to the junction. Head a short distance along Midsummer Passage to reach the other end of Eastern Avenue, with its stream joining from the right. Going back up this passage completes the Inner Circle.

A shorter Outer Circle can be done by heading right from Selenite Needle along Eastern Avenue to reach Midsummer Passage.

From the junction of Midsummer Passage and Eastern Avenue, head downstream over boulders and sand banks to reach a massive collapse which is passed by a crawl, low on the left. This regains the large passage but it soon lowers to crawling. After a flat-out section, walking passage is regained. Here the sound of water can just be heard coming from a tight rift behind a block on the right. This is the squeeze into the start of Coal Cellar Passage.

The squeeze drops sideways into a small stream passage. This starts with many boulder obstacles, crawling at low level for most of its first half. East Passage is passed on the right. As the passage becomes a tight sideways walk, there are two passages on the left. These both go into Stal Bridge Chamber, one at each end. Coal Cellar Passage now becomes easier but still has small areas of breakdown. A large stream joins from the left, this comes from Twin Aven Chamber. Continue downstream in walking passage for a short distance before Turkey Streamway is reached again. Thus the Outer Circle is completed.

Survey ref: Agen Allwedd, C.S.S., 1979.

BRIDGE CAVE   Grade 2

Grid Ref: SN 911140   O.S. Outdoor Leisure Series No 11, Brecon Beacons National Park – Central Area 1:25,000.   Altitude: 308m
Length: 311m

An ideal cave for beginners. Although known for a long time, the first record of any exploration was by T.S.J. Braithwaite in the 1930's. Members of the S.W.C.C. passed the boulder choke in 1947.

WARNING: The Main Passage floods in wet weather. Beware of loose rock to the right in the boulder choke.

Permission required from Blaen Nedd Isaf Farm, small access fee payable.

Approach as for Little Neath. From the parking area, climb the stile over the fence by the car park and follow the track down to the left for 10m to the obvious entrance.

The low entrance on the right leads after 50m to an easy boulder choke. Beware of the stacked and wedged boulders on the right. Drop down into the stream passage which is followed for 30m into the Main Passage which is followed downstream past West Passage on the right. The Bridge of rock over the stream signifies the end of the large Main Passage, the roof dips down and lowers to a crawl. After 30m the sump is reached.

Survey ref: Bridge Cave, U.B.S.S. 1970.

DAN YR OGOF

Grade 4/5

Grid Ref: SN 838160   O.S. Outdoor Leisure Series No 12, Brecon Beacons National Park – Western Area 1:25,000.   Altitude: 216m Length: 18,000.m approx

A classic cave of grand proportions with magnificent formations especially beyond the Long Crawl. First explored by the Morgan Brothers in 1912 with major extensions in 1937 by the Dragon Group, members of the C.D.G. and S.W.C.C. from 1964 to the present day.

A valid 3 year permit, complete with photograph can be obtained from Elsie Little. This is required to get the key from either Elsie Little or Dragon Caving Gear.

WARNING: The Lakes flood, sumping in one section, in wet weather. Flash floods can easily trap a party of cavers in the cave.

Approach along the A4067 north of Abercrave towards Sennybridge. Just north of Penycae is Craig Y Nos Castle and Country Park and shortly after, Dan Yr Ogof showcave complex which is marked on the map. Please change away from the tourists, preferably at the S.W.C.C. cottage at Penwyllt. Enter through the cavers entrance 50m inside the river entrance when the show cave door is closed.

Concrete steps lead down under the arch of Bridge Chamber in the show cave and a concrete path over Lake One ends on a sand bank. The passage is followed through Lake Two into Lake Three which, initially, is best passed following the left hand wall. Follow the cascading water into Lake Four which is exited on the right via a dry rift. A 3m climb up past a stal column leads through to a fossil passage. Pot Sump is immediately to the right, while to the left and around the corner a slope under a low roof leads to the base on an awkward 3m climb into Boulder Chamber. As an alternative to this climb squeeze down over boulders through the obvious low continuation and drop into a small chamber. Exit from here via a 2m climb on the right followed immediately via a scramble through boulders on the left to enter Boulder Chamber.

At the end of Boulder Chamber a right turn leads to Straw Chamber which is passed through on the left past a calcited boulder pile. To bypass a low crawl on the right, follow the left wall to what looks like a dead end. At the end a narrow passage can be entered on the right which joins up with the low crawl further on. Wind through the boulders on hands and knees until the roof rises, climb up a step and walk on into Shower Aven.

The passage beyond Shower Aven decreases in size to a crawl and winds around several bends to a flat out crawl through water, the Horse Trough, and the Long Crawl. Follow the passage for 50m until a polished squeeze on the left leads to a 2m chimney and the continuation of the crawl. A low tight bend follows and progress speeds up for smaller people who can now get on to their hands and knees. At the end of the crawl a climb down a hole on the left on polished holds for

Flabbergasm Oxbow, in Dan-Yr-Ogof. Photo: Tony Baker

4m leads to the top of the 7m pitch into Gerrard Platten Hall. The pitch has a fixed ladder maintained by the S.W.C.C. but no lifeline.

From G.P. Hall the way on is downstream (upstream soon chokes). After 50m the stream disappears down a large hole on the left, the entrance to the Lower Series, but continue on in the large passage to a pool. Circle around the pool on the left to avoid the crystal formations. The passage continues off to the left into Grand Canyon but a detour at this point is worthwhile. Traverse along the wall above the pool using a rope as an aid around the corner and climb up the slope into Flabbergasm Chasm, a fabulous array of fine straws delicately decorate this passage. There is a large drop at the end of Flabbergasm into the Grand Canyon and so a return via the pool is necessary.

Continue along the Grand Canyon until the roof begins to lower where care must be taken to avoid the straws. At a taped off area to the right a large black hole can be seen on the left. Climb up into the blackness and into Monk Hall. To the left is the exit of the Longer Crawl but the way on is to the right along the floor of a huge meandering passage and into Cloud Chamber, don't forget to look up to see the magnificent straws in the roof some 10m above your head. Follow the passage around a few bends to Cascade Aven. The water comes from Cascade Aven Series on the right. The way on is up an awkward 1.5m climb straight ahead which almost immediately leads to the beginning of the Green Canal. A crawl up on the left leads to Hanger Passage. Swim the initial part of the Green Canal (take care, its very cold, various floatation devices are usually found here) until the passage becomes wider and it is possible to touch the bottom. Further on the passage enters the larger Trench Way. To the left is the Abyss and entry into the Lower Series. To the right follow the passage until a fork is reached. The larger left passage leads to Surprise Chamber. Enter the smaller right passage, Go Slower Passage. Follow the obvious way on ignoring smaller passages on the right until, after a splash through water Bat Chamber is entered with its clean washed, sharp boulder slope coming in from the left. Follow the passage straight on at the bottom of the boulders into a large passage with a stream. Follow the stream to The Rising where the water issues out of a sump.

Climb the fixed ladder above The Rising and continue up the rift beyond to enter a window in the opposite wall near the top. Crawl through the passage, Windy Way until a climb down is reached. Here a difficult traverse down or 15m ladder pitch leads to the sandy floor of a tight rift. Continue along in the same direction to reach the head of the Great North Road pitch. This 15m pitch is rigged using the rawl bolts in place. A tight spot soon opens out for a free hang. The water at the bottom is the same as at The Rising.

The Great North Road is followed initially at floor level and when this becomes impassable, by climbing over the large breakdown boulders. A widening of the passage with a large flake on the right wall signifies the Pinnacle Chamber with the high level Pinnacle Series up an aven on the right wall. Continue along the Great North Road where a climb up through boulders enters the North Bypass. Alternatively a climb down boulders enters the Meanders. Both routes converge in the Meanders. Continuing, a short climb on the left enters The Mostest and eventually the passage is blocked, the North Aven, just a little way back on the right leads on.

Climb the North Aven and chimney above on the left and continue along the passage. The stream is rejoined on the left at the bottom of a boulder slope. Follow the direction of the water upstream to reach a junction, the Starting Gate. Right-Hand Series closes down after over 400m and Left-Hand Series continues further

Dan-Yr-Ogof. Photo: Paul Deakin

via large passage and breakdown on the floor to eventually reach Far North Choke. You can now look forward to the return journey.

Short Round Trip

The initial part of the cave into Gerrard Platten Hall and through to the far end of the Green Canal has already been described above. At the end of the Green Canal, at the junction with Trench Way turn left to the top of the Abyss, where the floor just drops away into darkness. Climb down and into a small chimney with the aid of an in-situ rope that is not maintained. Slide carefully down the chimney using the rope as a handline to exit at the bottom of the Abyss. Clamber across the floor of the chamber to a small slot in the left wall, the Camel's Back, over is slippy and under is tight, take your pick.

On the other side of the Camel's Back the dark and gloomy Thixotropic Passage leads to a water spout and after a small climb down, a small chamber off with a hole in the floor which leads to Mazeways (entry by non divers in low water condition only). Duck under the low roof on the left of the small chamber and stoop along the passage until a sharp left turn is followed by a 2m climb down a hole in the floor. This leads to Lake Ten. Skirt around the water on the right and follow the large walking size passage into Bakerloo Street, a large phreatic, clean washed tube to a four ways junction. Either go straight ahead to an awkward climb down or left around an oxbow and easier climbs to enter a stream with the sound of a waterfall to the left, the Washing Machine. Climb over a rock bridge above the level of the water and traverse around the left wall of the next pool. Follow the sloping passage up the sand bank and through a hole at the top on the right. Turn left and follow the passage over some gour pools and through four small lakes, not more than chest deep to the lip overlooking a large chamber. Traverse to the left and into a stooping passage for 10m to another chamber. Turn the corner on the left to a damp and awkward 3m climb up. Follow the water to the right and into a small chamber with another short step up and then into the much larger passage 50m downstream from Gerrard Platten Hall. Retrace your steps through the Long Crawl and back to the entrance.

Tackle:

Great North Road Pitch 15m ladder, 35m lifeline or 20m rope for SRT
Windy Way Traverse 15m lifeline (optional)
7m Lifeline for Gerrard Platten Hall (optional)
Survey ref: B.C.R.A. Transactions Vol.4, Nos 1/2 March, 1977.

LITTLE NEATH RIVER CAVE

Grade 4

Grid Ref: SN 911142   O.S. Outdoor Leisure Series No 11, Brecon Beacons National Park – Central Area 1:25,000.   Altitude: 304m Length: 7,855m

Explored in 1967 by C.D.G. and U.B.S.S. via Bridge Cave.

An active river cave with some splendid formations giving a fine sporting trip. It is very important to call at Blaen Nedd Isaf Farm, prior to going to the cave. A small access fee will be charged per person. Cavers must do this to ensure continued access.

Approach from Glyn Neath from the traffic lights on the A4109 road from Abercrave, turn E along the B4242. Turn left after 400m signposted Pont Nedd Fechan and Ystradfellte. Follow the road for 6 km and turn left onto a single track road (this is the second turning off the road, sign post Nedd Valley, 1 km after a BT telephone box on the right). Continue to the end where the road terminates at Blaen Nedd Isaf Farm. 400m before Blaen Nedd Isaf is a turning on the left down a steep hill. Park at the bottom of the hill. The entrance to Little Neath is reached by going over the bridge and turn right into the field. Follow the course of the river for 150m until just before the small cliff disappears on the far bank. Some of the river vanishes down a hole in the far bank and is often marked by an unsightly pile of plastic bags. It is also possible to approach from Hirwaun (see Porth Yr Ogof) via Ystradfellte and south towards Pont Nedd Fechan when the turning down the single track road is the first on the right 1.5km after the Ystradfellte Youth Hostel.

The low entrance takes a proportion of the Nedd Fechan water and is quite sporty. After several right angled turns a walking sized rift ends in a 1m waterfall and large plunge pool. Exit over boulders straight ahead leaving the stream temporarily. Regain the water and follow the splendid streamway for a few hundred metres occassionally using larger dry oxbows on the right.

The second large flowstone stal on the left leads to the Canal Bypass. This can be recognised as a 4m wide by 1.5m high rectangular shaped passage, the flowstone being cut away on the left. Follow the Nedd Fechan stream for a further 150m to reach the junction of the water from Bridge Cave on the right. A rescue dump can be seen on the sand bank. Please leave intact unless you are stuck.

Both streams merge and enter The Canal, a low wide bedding which is followed for 150m on hands and knees. Beware, this section becomes impassable in wet weather. At the end of The Canal the passage becomes very large. To the left is the entry into the Canal Bypass and to the right between impressive large boulders is the way on into Main Stream Passage. (Genisis Gallery and the Old World Series leaves the Main Passage high up on the right via a stony crawl).

Follow the main stream with the roof eventually almost reaching the floor to a duck (sump in wet weather) which can be bypassed via a roof tube. Continue along the now not so high passage until the sump bars any more progress on the right. To the left of the sump is a tricky muddy climb up into Gryn Fawr Passage the furthest point in the cave for non divers.

To return via the Canal Bypass leave the Main Stream Passage, straight ahead, with the water issuing from the canal on the left. The dry passage soon drops into a small stream beside a stal formation. Follow the water upstream past a waterfall inlet on the left until the stream comes out of a passage on the right and a dry passage leads straight ahead. (The stream comes from the North East Inlet series which is wet and crawly.) Follow the dry passage for 100m until a duck under a low arch on hands and knees. This soon becomes larger and drops back into the Nedd Fechan water at the flowstone. Follow the water upstream to emerge in daylight at the river edge.

Survey ref: Published by U.B.S.S. in 1973 as an extract from their proceedings.

LLETHRID SWALLET   Grade 3

Grid Ref: SS 531912   O.S. Landranger Series No 159, Swansea and Gower, 1:50,000.   Altitude: 43m   Length: 914m   Depth: 21m

A stream cave with a superb main chamber. First explored by Don Coase in 1949. Extended by the Taylors in 1953.

WARNING: Liable to severe flooding.

The cave is gated but keys are freely available from Pete Francis or the Secretary, S.W.C.C.

Following the B4271 road from Swansea, directly after dropping down from Fairwood Common past a left hand bend, a layby on the right provides suitable parking. From the lay-by, walk along the road down to Llethrid Bridge and go through the two gates before it on the left. Follow the track through the field, the entrance lies just inside the woods three quarters of the way along, to the right of the field. A stream sinks here but the entrance is to one side on the right.

Climb down immediately from the gate to a small chamber where the stream can be seen. Crossing the chamber and squeezing through boulders leads to the streamway itself where progress can be made by crawling, stooping and walking alternatively. In dry weather there may be no stream, making route finding more difficult, whereas in wet weather, crawls, in a few places, can sump easily. Two of the narrowest squeezes can be bypassed by climbing up a few metres directly before them, regaining the streamway immediately after again. Gradually the passage dimensions increase to walking size until the Ante Chamber is gained. A short, muddy climb (handline useful) leads left to the Main Chamber. Just at it's entrance, a left hand passage leads to the steeply sloping and well decorated Annex. Take care not to cross taped formations in the Main Chamber. A rising climb gives a dramatic view of the large chamber. Cross the floor, liberally coated with mud, where the roof drops to a set of large, unfortunately muddied, columns. Beyond them the floor rises steeply past a magnificent curtain, and at the uppermost corner, fine delicate helictites sprout from walls and ceiling.

From the columns a small bedding plane passage in the extreme right of the hall drops steeply away to the Camel's Hump, a large, mud covered boulder, over which care is needed on decent. Beyond this a short 3m drop leads to the mud encased Lower Stream Passage leading to the sump. It is not advisable to play around here as this is a lowland cave and the bodies of dead rats have been seen floating here.

An exit can be made skirting the Camel and following the large rift passage back to the Ante Chamber.

Survey ref: See – Oldham, T., The Caves of Gower, 1977

LLYGAD LLWCHWR

Grade 3

Grid Ref: SN 668178   O.S. Outdoor Leisure Series No 12, Brecon Beacons National Park – Western Area 1:25,000.   Altitude: 229m Length: 370m

First recorded exploration in 1841. Extended by C.D.G. 1960.

An active river cave which can be traversed from beginning to end along dry upper levels. A useful excursion for beginners. The water is pumped away from the resurgence to supply Llanelli. The cave has been known for a long time and has been used as a water supply for many years.

WARNING: The River Chambers flood considerably and contain deep water.

From Ystradgynlais in the Swansea Valley, follow the A4068 through Cwmtwrch to Brynamman. Turn left at the junction with the A4069 roundabout in Brynamman and follow the road for 100m round the bend to the right. Turn right at the next sharp bend to the left and follow the road up the hill and out of the village. Follow this road for several kilometres, always keeping right, to a cross roads, (left Ammanford, straight on Trapp) turn right for almost 2 kms and park before a gate

Difficult going in Peak Cavern. Photo: Paul Deakin

Fantastic formations in Otter Hole. Photo: Paul Deakin

across the road. On foot go through the gate and climb over the stile on the left. Walk across the field keeping the two rough mounds on the left to a gate/stile. Enter the next field and follow the line of the wall on your left to a track in the far corner leading to the right and above the resurgence. A stile after a further 20m gives access over the perimeter fence surrounding the stream.

Climb 2m up to the small entrance hole to the left of the resurgence. The passage takes several right angled bends until a high rift on the right can be entered. Climb into this and along passage which begins to increase in size to a comfortable walk. After a short step up over calcited rock and down a ramp on the far side, a hole in the left wall leads back and into the First River Chamber.

Back in the main passage, continue through a series of chambers connected by short passages to a right hand corner and a two-way junction. Both reach the same passage after a short drop. To the right leads to a small elongated chamber whilst left is the Main Passage leading to the end of the cave. From the elongated chamber a tight crawl at floor level can be followed through water (sumps in wet weather) to a left hand turn. Follow this through muddy tight passages to emerge in River Chamber Three.

The easiest way out is up a ramp to the left of the river just 3m away from emerging. This leads through an ascending crawl and a squeeze over a boulder to the Main Passage. A more exciting exit is to follow the water downstream past a high level entrance on the left to the pool before the sump at the end of the river chamber. Climb out of the water on a ledge to the right of the pool and walk along this ledge as it ascends around the far side of the pool and make a tricky move into the passage above. Follow this passage to the junction with the Main Passage.

A turn to the right soon brings you to River Chamber Four and the end of the cave. Turn left and after a pool of water a 2m climb into a high passage leads off straight ahead (the Main Passage and a dry route out again). A walking size passage leads off to the right onto a balcony overlooking River Chamber Two. This can be descended by an awkward climb on the left. Follow the deep water along magnificent streamway to the end where the water disappears through a 3m sump into River Chamber One.

A dry route through to River Chamber One can be found on the left hand wall as you come away from the sump. This ascends steeply and is quite low, past several squeezes to emerge high up on the wall above dry land in River Chamber One. This has an awkward exit and care should be taken. Alternatively, climb back out of River Chamber Two and wind your way back through the Main Passage to the entrance.

Tackle: A few slings and short lengths of rope would be useful as handlines on some of the climbs in and out of the river chambers.
Survey ref: Llygad Llwchwr, T.V.C.G., 1987.

OGOF CLOGWYN   Grade 1

Grid Ref: SO 212123   O.S. Outdoor Leisure Series No 13, Brecon Beacons National Park – Eastern Area 1:25,000.   Altitude: 244m Length: 165m

An easy cave for bigginers.
   Approach from Abergavenny along the A465 towards Ebbr Vale and Brynmawr for 7km and park in a lay-by/bus-stop on the left opposite the Drum and Monkey

Pub. Walk up the road for 100m and climb over the fence where a small path leads down the gorge. Cross over the river and follow the track to the left and up under the overhanging cliff. The resurgence is easily found at the base of the cliff. To the right of the main entrance is a tight keyhole entrance. Between the two and 6m higher is an even tighter entrance needing a ladder.

Follow the water around several sharp bends past magnificent phreatic shelving on the sides of the passage. Climb over some fallen blocks to turn a corner to the right and follow the stream to the sump. Above the fallen blocks climb into a high rift. Follow a high level crawl to eventually see daylight again or stay low to enter a small by-pass which leads back to the stream near the entrance.

OGOF CRAIG A FFYNNON   Grade 4

Grid Ref: SO 221128   O.S. Outdoor Leisure Series No 13, Brecon Beacons National Park – Eastern Area 1:25,000.   Altitude: 259m Length: 8,200m

A well protected cave with fine formations and excellent gours. Permission from John Parker or Jeff Hill, Grwp Ogofeidd Craig A Ffynnon, who both discovered the cave after a long dig and extended it to its present limit along with other members of G.O.C.A.F.

WARNING: The cave is liable to sump at Gasoline Alley.

Approach from Abergavenny along the A465. After the Gilwern roundabout follow the A465 for a further 2.5 kilometres and turn right. Follow the old road up the Clydach Gorge for 1.5 kilometres and park in the lime kilns 200m past the Rock and Fountain Inn. A walk up a gentle incline for about 250m reaches a normally dry flood channel crossing the path. This comes from the old Craig a Ffynnon dig. A few metres beyond, directly above the Rock and Fountain Inn, a 3m climb on the left gains the large entrance tube. It is also possible to approach from the top of the Clydach Gorge by turning onto the A4047 at the roundabout junction with the A465 and A467 at Brynmawr. From the A4047 take the first right along a residential street to the 'T' junction at the end. Turn right again and follow the old road down the Clydach Gorge. (A turning left just after the bridge over the Heads of the Valleys road leads to Llangattock and Whitewalls).

The entrance tube leads directly to the gate, an iron reinforced stone wall with a small steel gate set within it. The passage to the first chamber has been greatly modified over the years and is now a simple stoop to a once well decorated chamber. The passage continues through a second decorated chamber (Log Book ammo can may be in the chamber) to the First Choke. A short fixed ladder enters a large chamber. Tapes mark the routes over the mud banks, so please keep to them to help preserve the formations. They lead back to the stream and through a low crawl Gasoline Alley, which can sump in flood.

Soon after this a junction is reached, to the left through deep water is North West Inlet. Going right passes a sump (on the right) and leads to a broken pitch up to Second Choke. A short fixed ladder and a rope climbs the 7m pitch, the top section is exposed. A low crawl reaches the choke with the way up through starting at the hole. The small wet winding crawl works its way up through the choke to emerge at the top of a calcited slope in a large passage. This leads through short low sections, up over breakdown and becomes Travertine Passage, a huge passage with travertine dams across the floor with other formations dotted about. The passage leads up to and ends in The Hall Of The Mountain King and the Third Choke. On the right in the hall is a large passage but the way on is a flat-out crawl on the right of Third Choke.

This leads to Severn Tunnel after 250m, becoming stooping then walking to reach a right angled junction with three other routes leading off. Right is the main way on past a hole in the floor down Blaen Elin Streamway to enter another huge passage. To the right chokes, going left passes over rubble and then past a small hole in the left wall. This is the route into the Lower Series. Ahead a walk reaches Fourth Choke. Enter on the right and after a 2m drop a hole up on the left enters a small loose chamber with an exit via a small hole, up on its far side.

Once again, the huge passage is regained and followed to a junction. To the right leads to Fifth Boulder Choke after 200m. At the junction an 8m pitch on the left drops to join a streamway a few metres further on, Promised Land. To the left is a solid calcited choke with the Pagoda formation. Right the stream is followed until an oxbow has to be used. This has several boulder obstacles and eventually rejoins the stream, note this point for the return. Less obstacles bar the way as a high level oxbow on the right is passed. Eventually easy walking leads to a right angled bend to the right. The way becomes calcited and bouldery as the route passes through a chamber with avens. A squeeze through the boulders at the far side enters a rift passage to two high avens and a boulder choke which issues a stream. This is 40m to 50m from Busman's Holiday in Daren Cilau.

Tackle: 8m ladder for the Promised Land, plus 15m lifeline, use lifeline also to protect pitch by Second Choke.
Survey ref: Grwp Ogofeidd Craig a Ffynnon.

OGOF DAREN CILAU

Grid Ref: SO 205153   O.S. Outdoor Leisure Series No 13, Brecon Beacons National Park – Eastern Area 1:25,000.   Altitude: 399m Length: 26,200m approx   Vertical range: 216m (+3m -213m includes 22m deep sump)

A cave with a natural barrier to protect some fine crystal and calcite formations. Its huge passages and fine streamway cut all the way through the mountain. First entered in 1957 by the B.N.S.S.S. Major breakthrough and further explorations by Clive Gardener and members of the C.S.S. and the S.W.C.C. in 1984 and 1985, the R.S.C and the C.D.G. 1986 and 1987. Further smaller extentions continue to develop this fascinating system with a view to finding the elusive links with Agen Allwedd and Ogof Craig a Ffynnon.

WARNING: Entry or exit from the cave is difficult if the puddle in the entrance has frozen.

FLOODING: St. David's Streamway is impassable so the sump can't be viewed (not a great loss). Ankle Grinder By-Pass is impassable and its duck sumps.

Approach from Crickhowell, over the River Usk and turn right through Llangattock village. At the end of the village cross over the canal and follow the road around a left hand bend. Turn right after 200m and climb the steep hill to its top where the road levels out to the left. On the right is Whitewalls. Follow the road for another 500m to a car park slightly above the road. Thieves operate in this area.

From the car park at Llangattock, follow the track beyond the old lime kiln. A path between spoil heaps leads into the quarry. The entrance is situated at the

The Time Machine, Daren Cilau. Photo: Tony Baker

base of the quarry face, at the westerly (right hand) end, with Ogof Pen Eryr at the other end.

Entrance to the Terminal Sump   Grade 4

A flat-out crawl through a pool sets the scene for the 517m crawl. It starts as awkward crawling with occasional boulders to pass. The Vice is about 80m in and is a squeeze in a rift. Two main inlets are passed on the right. The going eases off and stooping is possible until a series of calcite squeezes are encountered. The last of these pops out into a larger passage. Go left via a short oxbow to a boulder chamber. The way out is up to the left, which emerges in the Old Rift Passage.

Right leads to the Old Main Chamber but the way on is straight across to a flat-out crawl into a downward choke (caution). The final drop lands on the top of a calcited ramp of boulders at the start of Jigsaw Passage. From here on in, many passages are taped, please keep inside them. Jigsaw is mainly walking but about half way along is a short squeeze, The Wriggle. Towards the end of Jigsaw, Misfit Passage is passed on the right.

Jigsaw then enters the Big Chamber Nowhere Near The Entrance in an area of large boulders. Ahead is a red ammo tin with the Log Book, please sign in.

After ascending a boulder pile, a crawl on the left enters Epocalypse Way, the route to White Company and the Antlers. To the right is the main part of Big Chamber with several passages leading off. At the top of the slope are two passages. The right-hand one, Man In The Roof, the left Eglwys Passage.

Take Eglwys Passage which passes over a short traverse and several low sections to a multi-way staggered junction, Fiveways Chamber. The smallest hole on the right leads to Valentines Chamber and the 1985 Extensions. All other ways are crawls, and choke quite quickly, except straight on which chokes after a few hundred metres.

The small hole leads to a drop and crawl up to emerge at the top of a large shale and boulder ramp into Valentines Chamber. The way on is at the lowest point in the chamber, where a tight squeeze down between boulders emerges at the top of a ramp in the roof of Preliminary Passage. Descend the ramp and a walk soon reaches the 20m fixed ladders up to Higher Things. Check the condition of the line and ladder before using them.

At the top, easy going meets a short climb down and then the 22m pitch into White Passage. A traverse round the right of the shaft is the bypass to the pitch. Check the ropes condition. The passage leads to a choke, but a flat-out crawl on the left leads to two rope climbs to enter White Passage, 50m downstream of where the 22m pitch enters.

Walking downstream to a cone of boulders marks Red River Passage entering on the right. Continuing down White Passage, its size continues to increase until it rises up a huge pile of rock to enter The Time Machine.

Head left and follow most of the length of this huge boulder strewn passage which extends for some 400m. After some distance the stream is seen running between the boulders. Soon afterwards on the left, an incline with a 2m climb goes to the Meeting Room which leads to Nameless Canyon and Half Mile Passage. Continue in the Time Machine as it narrows down with holes in the floor. Descend the last of these to the Bonsai Streamway.

Follow the stream over its boulder strewn path for a couple of hundred metres to meet a large stream entering from Crystal Inlet on the left. This junction can be misleading on the way back. Take note of it. In this stretch of passage is the Bonsai Tree, only a couple of inches tall and taped off.

About 100m after Crystal Inlet the stream reaches a cone of boulders beneath the Flyovers. The streamway now continues with fewer obstacles for over half a kilometre with many straws. The Bonsai ends where the water runs into a small rift with an obvious passage to its right, King's Road. If you have had to wade waist deep in the lower reaches of Bonsai, the cave is in flood and Ankle Grinder By Pass, beyond Rock Steady Cruise will be sumped off.

King's Road starts bouldery until the Hard Rock Cafe is reached. Near the Cafe, two passages lead off on the right, these unite and then continue as the Hard Rock Extensions, the route to the Restaurant and beyond.

King's Road continues as a pleasant passage with the occasional sound of the stream. After about half a kilometre the passage meets a large stream. Downstream, St. David's Streamway passes three strong springs in the right hand wall before the Terminal Sump is reached after around 50m. This sump has been dived through to Elm Hole in the Clydach Gorge after some 650m at a maximum depth of 22m.

Upstream passes an aqueous oxbow in the left wall before a short lake has to be swum to reach St. David's Sump after only 200m. Again this has been passed to reach the divers extensions, the original route to the Restaurant.

Hard Rock Cafe to Dweebland Grade 5+

From the Hard Rock Cafe take the oxbows on the right into The Rock Steady Cruise. This consists of an easy sandy passage with low sections. The more notable obstacles were sand sumps, Agrophobia Airbell and the Peace Pipe, but these have been dug out. Easy going continues to Brazil, a low chamber with a squeeze, Miami Vice to exit. A larger passage now continues and swings left to end at 12 O'Clock High, but straight on over a sandbank is Acupuncture Passage, the way into the Diver's Extensions.

Acupuncture starts with a short drop and a squeeze into a low crawl over sand and later, sharp crystallised rock. This reaches a pleasant sandy passage, with an obvious funnel in the floor, The Micron. This is now only a short climb down to reach Ankle Grinder Bypass. Going downstream quickly reaches the active Borrowed Boots Streamway, a point worth noting for the way back.

The way on is upstream for nearly half a kilometre with pots in the floor and stooping sections. The By-Pass ends after it enters a wet rift with a duck (this sumps in wet weather) to emerge in a large passage. Ahead a short climb reaches a junction with a sandy passage on the right. This has some good formations, The Icing On The Cake.

Straight on, boulders are crossed before a stream is seen running on the left. Soon after this the 5m fixed Jacob's Ladder is met. The water emerges from Seventh Hour Sump a short way upstream and is the last drinking water in the cave. Dehydration is a problem in the far reaches so don't waste the chance.

The ladder and a climb reach a large boulder floored chamber, La Plaza, the site of the Restaurant at the End of the Universe. A traverse back on the right is the route to the Blue-greenies and Pain-killer Passage. The way on towards the furthest reaches is via either of two exits on the left towards the back of the chamber. These unite and walking reaches two small climbs before it enters Cordillera Blanca Chamber.

The way on is to the right into a tall rift passage. A short climb and the Eyehole, now avoided at low level are passed before a short traverse arrives at the head of a 10m pitch. (A ladder and line is in place at present, but these aren't permanent).

The ladder lands in Big Chamber with an obvious passage leading via a couple of short crawls, to easy walking. The passage finally chokes with fill but a few metres before this on the right is a crawl to a parallel passage choked with boulders in both directions. In the far wall is a crawl to regain the large passage, Matchu Pitchu. This continues large to a boulder choke. To the left is a route under an aven to be joined by a smaller, less obvious passage which cuts across this hairpin bend some 20m back. The route on now passes under many avens to reach a wide low turn to the left into Trowser Filler, a sand dig. Straight on is a junction, right goes to Star Bar Chamber. Again, straight ahead is the way, through a crawl and small chambers. Easier going is reached and the Warren passed on the right, while ahead a flat out sand crawl enters Friday the Thirteenth. Easy going passes over boulders to a climb up into a chamber with an aven. Ahead, bouldery progress passes under avens and a high level passage. The route is now pleasant walking until it suddenly ends. A short climb on the right by-passes the blockage and progress is again easy. Friday the Thirteenth narrows and lowers to a sand crawl. This emerges at a boulder choke. Part way up this, on the left, is a small draughting hole.

This leads through a squeeze into Payoff Passage. Crawling and walking reaches a junction, right is Bad Bat Choke but turn left to enter Still Warthogs After All These Years. This is easier going, past a large passage entering on the right from DADES choke. Beyond this a crawl and walk reaches a fork. Go left along a rift to reach a squeeze up into a larger passage. Left is Spaderunner. Head right down a slope. Ahead leads to Sick Choke but a small hole on the left is the route into Dweebland.

The hole leads to a short drop and a tight crawl leads through into bouldery chamber, In-Betweeb. Continue to crawl on the right to reach a 4m climb down into Dweebland proper. To the left is Downdweeb which chokes after 80m. Head right in a larger passage to enter a chamber with the Archies leading off to the left. Ahead the passage continues to a fault. To the left this becomes loose but is only 20m from passages in Priory Road in Agen Allwedd.

Tackle:
10m ladder for Big Chamber.
20m lifeline for Big Chamber (Both in place at present).
Survey ref: Daren Cilau, C.S.S., 1988

OGOF DRAENAN   Grade 4

Grid Ref: SO 246117   O.S. Landranger Series No 161, Abergavenny and The Black Mountains, 1:50,000.   Altitude: 362m   Length: 55,000+m

First explored and surveyed by members of Morgannwg Caving Club, after extensive digging. Major extensions made by several other clubs active in the area.
Contact Tim Long for Access.
WARNING: Beyond A Choke streamway becomes serious after very heavy rain.
Ogof Draenen is one of the larger caves in Britain. The round trip should be treated as a serious undertaking.
When approaching from Blaenavon, take a left turn at Keeper's Pond. The first building on the right is the Lamb and Fox pub. Park opposite the pub on an area of concrete. Continue down the road and cross the stile immediately to the north of the Pwll Du Adventure Centre. Follow the fence down a steep slope to a small stream. Follow an obvious path to the entrance.

The entrance drops into a low crawl, beyond which a hole on the right leads down to a low, wet, bedding plane. Crawl through to emerge in a boulder choke. A squeeze down through the choke (Care) reaches the top of an 8m scaffolded shaft. Descend this to a small chamber. Straight on leads through tight rifts to the 30m Big Bang Pitch and the original Pitch Bypass, however, from the small chamber duck under the right wall into Spare Rib. Drop down a slot on the left and follow the inlet down a cascade to a point where the original Pitch Bypass joins in a chamber. A low passage on the right leads via a 5m climb to join the impressive main passage Beyond a Choke.

Turn right along the large passage and into the smaller Wonderbra Bypass on the left. After 250m descend a hole on the right which leads back to the main streamway just upstream of Tea Junction.

Turn left at Tea Junction along White Arch Passage for 500m to a choke. A crawl in the top right hand corner leads into the Lamb and Fox Chamber. Ascend the chamber on the right hand side up a boulder slope to reach Indiana Highway, a long series of traverses (care on exposed sections), to a junction. Right leads to The Canyon, but the way on is left and over boulders to a ledge above a trench. Left leads into Mega Drive North while right should be followed into Mega Drive. Continue down Mega Drive for some way to a sharp left bend immediately before Windy Junction.

Pass Windy Junction continuing along The Nunnery to the next turning on the right - Perseverance II, a crawl over cobbles. Straight ahead at the next junction leads to the 8m Balcony Pitch overlooking The Arms Park. At the bottom of the pitch the way on is left into The Players' Tunnel. A short distance down Player's Tunnel drop down through boulders on the left hand side. The passage continues 3m high and 8m wide via a choke to another impressive chamber with a perfectly flat roof - St David's Hall.

In the top left hand wall of the chamber a small hole leads into the complex Squirrel Rifts. The main passage through this area must be followed a long way past numerous side passages and junctions until a sharp right hand turn leads into a large chamber. To the left is the round trip connection which soon lowers to a stooping passage which soon enters the top of a rift. Traverse out and then drop down to reach a 5m climb down into a tight rift making the round trip connection to Haggish Basher One.

Continue straight ahead, ignoring the side passage to Life On Mars, into the Far Agent Blorenge streamway. Continue downstream for 500m in a large passage to a mud slope leading to a chamber. Follow the water on the right down a rift and on into Agent Blorenge.

Follow Agent Blorenge downstream to a waterfall. Descend this through a hole in the left wall dropping into The Sewer which is followed by some tight traversing in a rift, immediately leading to the top of two awkward climbs. Continue either through a duck or up a climb immediately before the duck into a small chamber. The water is then followed 400m down several cascades and waterfalls to the main Beyond a Choke streamway, just downstream of the chokes. Upstream leads back to Tea Junction and the way out.

Tackle:
8m Balcony Pitch is at present permanently rigged, please check prior to attempting the round trip.
Survey ref: Morgannwg Caving Club, 1995.

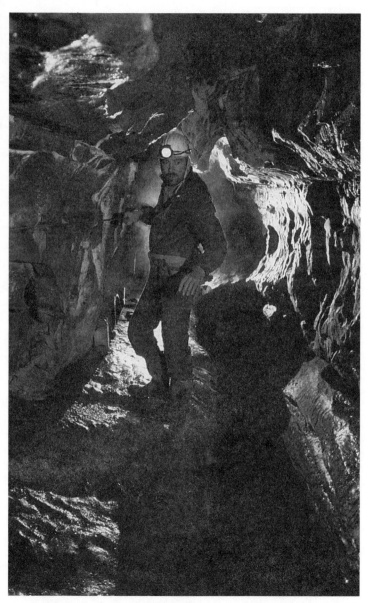

Gary Jones on the bolt traverse, Ogof Ffynnon Ddu 1. Photo: Tony Baker

OGOF FFYNNON DDU, I to II Through Trip   Grade 4

Grid Refs: Bottom Entrance: SN 848153   Top Entrance: SN 863158
O.S. Outdoor Leisure Series No 12, Brecons Beacons National Park –
Western Area 1:25,000.   Altitude: Bottom Entrance: 204m
Top Entrance: 432m   Length: 40,000m approx total for system
Vertical range: 308m

A complex series of dry and active passages on many levels and of great variety. There are many magnificent formations and perhaps the best streamway in Britain. Ogof Ffynnon Ddu I entrance was blasted in 1946 by members of the S.W.C.C. Divers discovered O.F.D.II in 1966 through Dip Sump Series. Other major extensions in the same year were the connection with Cwm Dwr and the discovery of O.F.D.III.

Access is controlled by the Cave Management Committee. Permission to enter the cave must be obtained by writing to the Permit Secretary, S.W.C.C. A leader system is in operation for access to Bottom Entrance.

WARNING: The Main Streamway floods in wet weather and quickly becomes impassable. Any trip that involves a traverse of the Main Stream should only be attempted in settled weather. Route finding is very difficult between Maypole to Top Entrance and Piccadilly to Cwm Dwr.

Approach from Abercrave along the A4067. Four kilometres north of Abercrave turn right, signposted Penwyllt. Follow the road, which ultimately leads to the South Wales Caving Club, around a sharp left hand bend. After 100m park in a layby on the left just after a turning to the left. Walk down the road behind the layby for 400m to Grithig Cottages (private property), into the yard in front of the house and through the gate opposite. Turn left, through another gate and follow the line of the fence to the left. Follow the path through bushes to the cave entrance.

Fixed ladders lead down the entrance shaft into a walkable passage. This is followed for 200m round several bends (ignoring the smaller side passages) to a steel ladder (up which leads to the Toast Rack). Go straight on, through Pluto's Bath, which leads to the main stream. Downstream soon sumps. Upstream the Main Stream is joined by the passage from the Toast Rack at The Step and continues for over 350m over 4 deep pots to a sump.

Turn left by the sump and follow the tall passage past high level connections to the Railton-Wild Series on the left, Lowe's Passage on the right (escape route in high water conditions) and Waterfall Series by a cascade and on into a large chamber blocked by huge boulders, Boulder Chamber.

Enter the bottom of the choke on the right and follow the solid wall to a 4m climb down into a small chamber above Hush Sump. Climb back into the boulders on the left and squeeze on the right over several boulders following a polished route generally upwards until open passage is reached. The sound of water can be heard from Dip Sump down a ramp on the right.

Walk up to the left and crawl into a small passage with a trickle of water flowing. The passage increases in size, past some fascinating mud formations on the right, to a junction after 100m. Turn right and squeeze down through a small hole to a flat out crawl and continue until the passage is large enough to stand up. Continue down the sloping passage for 10m and stoop through a hole in the left wall and crawl to a large chamber on the left.

Climb up the facing wall and traverse left to enter a passage at the top on the right. Walk and stoop along this passage for 100m until a 2m climb down into a

Swansea Valley Area

South Wales Caving Club

1. Ogof Ffynnon Ddu (Bottom entrance)
2. Cwm Dwr
3. Ogof Ffynnon Ddu (Top entrance)
4. Pant Mawr

A4067

Country Park

River Tawe

to Abercrave

Tunnel Cave

Pwll Dwfn

Cathedral Cave

Dan yr Ogof

0   1 Km

much larger passage. Right leads to Pot Sump but continuing left the passage immediately decreases in size to a crawl beyond a puddle. The crawl leads to a 1m climb up boulders. Continue following the left wall and climb up to the larger passage above and immediately down again. Continue straight on past a trickle on the left and take the next left at a crawl and down a 4m slippery climb. Walk up the slope and squeeze past a pile of boulders which have slipped down from the right. Crawl, following the left wall back up a slope to a chamber with small straws and a flat, sloping wall at one end.

Climb the slab on the right and post yourself through The Letter Box at the top. Turn immediately left and slide down to the bottom of the narrow rift. Crawl into the tube on the right and follow this down until the gravel floor is met. Various side passages lead off. Go straight across and then left at the next junction to a small puddle of water below a smooth polished low ramp on the left. Slide up the ramp and enter a crawl on the right after 4m. Follow this up-hill initially over some crushing bumps and climb down 30m at the end (rope in place of dubious vintage) into large passage again.

Take the passage down the slope and climb up 2m into a large continuation above. Follow the large passage for 200m through 3 pools of water to Piccadilly Circus, a junction with an enormous passage on the left (the way to Cwm Dwr) and a narrower, but still large, rift passage on the right, Flood Bypass, with a large boulder wedged between the walls above head height.

On the right, climb down 2m into Flood Bypass which leads to the Main Stream again and to The Confluence where the smaller Cwm Dwr stream joins from the left. Follow the Main Stream water under the low roof which soon rises again. The streamway is followed in large passage ranging from 1m to 3m wide and 5m to 80m high. Pass through River Chambers One and Two to an area of beautiful marbled walls, Marble Showers. (A spray of water from the right wall indicates the entrance to the upper series of Marble Showers.)

Follow the Main Stream for a long distance until a sump is reached. Just before this, climb out of the water on the left and into the Great Oxbow, a dry bypass. Re-enter the Main Stream down a short climb and follow the water again along the sporting streamway. A reflective indicator on the left marks the 3m climb into Maypole Inlet and the route through to Top Entrance. (The Main Stream continues via the Second Oxbow to Top Waterfall where the water issues out of an impenetrable bedding.)

Climb up 3m by the marker plate into Maypole Inlet. Another short climb is followed by a 5m fixed ladder, maintained by S.W.C.C. The meandering narrow passage is only wide enough in places to shuffle sideways. Follow this at water level, over or under several blockages until a climb directly up to the phreatic tube at the top of the rift. This climb is 20m before a junction and short waterfall. Carefully traverse along the top of the rift until a junction with a passage on the right can be entered. Walk along this passage to a major junction, The Crossroads, with large passages leading off to the left (to Selenite Tunnel and Edwards Short Cut) and straight ahead to Salubrious.

Squeeze past the large boulder on the right to enter Salubrious and follow the large passage with white mud on the floor until the small Salubrious Stream is met. The dry passage on the right after 10m leads to The Trident and The Judge, two large stal formations, and the way to The Knave. Back in the stream, follow the Salubrious Stream with a short climb of 2m, halfway, to bypass a waterfall. Continue upstream until the passage narrows considerably to 0.5 metre and then opens out into a small chamber with passages leading off left, ahead and an ascending rift to the right. Left leads to Arete Chamber, ahead into the Labyrinth but the way on is up to the right.

Climb into the ascending passage which rapidly gains height until overhanging boulders are reached. While standing under the largest boulder a small hole on the left can be seen at head height. Climb into this and spiral up and back on yourself until standing on the overhanging boulder. Continue ascending the steep passage to the top, Chasm Passage. Left leads to the Chasm, whereas right is followed over boulders to enter Gnome Passage at its highest point.

Follow the large passage to the right, walking away from Gnome Passage to a junction. Take the largest central passage to a 1m climb onto boulders and a left turn in a narrow rift. Follow this climbing over the boulders and staying high until forced down a 2m climb. Continue walking over the slippery boulders until a large chamber is entered with a drip coming out of the ceiling. There are several passages leading off. Follow the large passage to the right under the drip and continue straight on ignoring the side passages on the right which lead to Big Chamber Near The Entrance. The floor begins to rise and beyond a spoil heap is Top Entrance.

OGOF FFYNNON DDU II to CWM DWR, Through Trip   Grade 3

The area above the South Wales Caving Club is an S.S.S.I. and only cavers with permission to enter Ogof Ffynnon Ddu may leave the path to cross the moor. From the S.W.C.C. hut follow the path behind the building to the old tram road. Continue up the hill to the top of a cutting and turn right following another track. At the top of the next rise (100m) the entrance can be seen 10m away.

The large passage inside the entrance leads, past two large passages on the left leading to Big Chamber near the entrance, to a large chamber at the end with a drip coming in from the ceiling onto calcited boulders on the floor. To the right is White Arch Series. Turn left out of the chamber stepping down from boulders to a smaller passage and after 15m climb up 2m on the left and follow the passage into a tighter rift which ends at a 'T' junction. Turn right which soon leads to a chamber with a passage to the right, leading back to the entrance chamber, (a smaller passage does a 'U' turn to the left to Arete Chamber) and a large passage in the middle should be taken which leads to the top end of Gnome Passage.

Take the large passage on the left at the top end of Gnome Passage, Chasm Passage, past the Wedding Cake formation on the floor to the top of a slope disappearing down to the left. (Straight on leads to Chasm.) Climb down the slope to the top of a large drop under a definite passage leading off upwards in the facing wall (to Arete Chamber). The drop is bypassed by squeezing through the boulders on the right . Continue climbing down the narrow rift to appear in the Salubrious Streamway. The water comes from Arete Chamber.

Turn left and travel easily downstream. Eventually the water disappears through the boulders, just past a dry passage on the left which leads via the Trident and Judge formations to the Knave. An easy climb leaves the Salubrious Stream over a boulder pile and into a rift with white mud on the floor. This leads after two bends and an awkward squeeze past a large boulder, to the Crossroads. (Right leads to Selenite Tunnel, Shattered Pillar, the end of Edward's Short Cut, Midnight Passage and eventually to the high level through trip to Marble Showers.)

Climb up into the passage on the left at the Crossroads and follow this to a junction over a rift that disappears down below. Turn left and traverse a short distance high up before an easy descent of the rift can be made to the bottom and

Gary Nevitt at Piccadilly, Ogof Ffynnon Ddu 2. Photo: Tony Baker

the small stream. Follow the water over several blockages, sometimes walking sideways, to the top of a fixed ladder, maintained by S.W.C.C. Climb down this followed by a short free climb to a ledge that overlooks the Main Stream at Maypole Inlet. Upstream goes to Top Waterfall.

Follow the sporting Main Stream downstream for a considerable distance down to a marker plate on the left wall. Climb out of the stream at this point and into the Great Oxbow to bypass a sump. The dry passages soon regain the Main Stream beyond this obstruction. Continue again for a long way in the water to Marble Showers, a spectacular area of the cave. Beyond Marble Showers follow the water through River Chambers One and Two to a low arch at the end of which is the Confluence. The Cwm Dwr stream enters on the right which can be followed, as an alternative, to a point where a climb up enters the Smithy.

Continue to follow the Main Stream which soon disappears through small holes in the left wall. Follow the now dry Flood Bypass to its termination at a 2m climb, Piccadilly Circus. The chamber here takes on an impressive size, the passages on the left lead through to Ogof Ffynnon Ddu I whereas the route to Cwm Dwr follows the larger passage to the right which ascends steeply from the junction. A stream flows over the calcite floor. After 150m turn right at the first junction, up an awkward step and climb over a boulder pile. On the other side you can either turn left and then climb down into the Smithy or go straight ahead and enter the Smithy above the Cwm Dwr stream which can be heard at the bottom of a rift below (direct entry from the Confluence).

Take the first right out of the Smithy, the obvious route, and take the second left and then the first right up a climb and traverse 3m above the floor for 50m. Follow the obvious large passage until a calcite flow drops away to the left. Take the narrow rift on the right which enters the Big Shacks. Bear left and stay on the right of the passage to enter the Cwm Dwr Choke.

Follow the worn path through the choke going up and down until an exit can be made into the large passage on the other side. Follow the large passage through a stream and then across another stream to a climb up and continuation of Cwm Dwr Jama. A short while after climbing over a calcited pile of boulders protected by tape, a small hole in the floor, through well worn boulders, is the start of the Cwm Dwr Crawl.

Squeeze down feet first into the shallow water and then proceed head first through the initially wet passage. Continue along the flat out crawl until it breaks into a walking size passage bearing left. Follow this to a small chamber and exit via the low crawl on the left. Continue going uphill and after a short climb using a steel pole as an aid enter a larger passage at a 'T' junction. Turn left and walk to the bottom of the stempled climb on the right. Climb the rift to reach the bottom of the drain pipes which lead to the entrance gate. Walk out of the quarry to the S.W.C.C. hut.

OGOF FFYNNON DDU II to OGOF FFYNNON DDU III   Grade 4

From Top Entrance follow the route into Chasm Passage as described in the OFD II to Cwm Dwr description. Scramble down the slope that continues down to Salubrious, to a point where entry can be gained into a rising passage above the squeeze through the boulders. Climb carefully up the slippery climb into a walking, stooping passage past several fine stal formations to enter Arete Chamber above a short climb.

Either tackle the climb on the left or bridge it direct (handline useful). Follow the right hand wall into the rift passage opposite (the passage leaving Arete Chamber on the left leads into the lower Labyrinth and the passage that doubles back leads into Salubrious Streamway). The rift passage continues to a choke but enter a narrow meandering passage on the right just before the choke. Follow this, at one point on hands and knees, to enter a large passage at a 'T' junction. Make a note of this point for the return journey. Turn right and follow the sandy floor for a few metres, then bear right and take the first left along a short dog-leg to a 'T' junction. Right goes back to the Chasm whereas left is followed to the top of Poached Egg Climb. Continue climbing down over the boulders to gain the floor which is followed for about 20 metres before re-ascending to reach a junction. Left enters the Nyth Bran Series and Straw Gallery but the way on is to the right to quickly reach Bhowani Junction.

Left here follows Creek Alley into the Nyth Bran Series. Turn right to a short step down on calcited boulders to continue along the rift with a solid floor for 100m and over the Crevasse (~23m to Pendulum Passage below) on to boulders wedged in the rift. A few metres further leads to the top of an 8m pitch. Belay ladder or rope to bolt and boulders. It is possible to free climb this pitch by bridging but is very difficult. The large rift continues with a scramble up a boulder slope. Down a steep calcited slope the passage continues beyond a tight squeeze and 3m climb. Follow the rift at floor level climbing a pile of boulders that block the route to a 3m climb or awkward traverse to stay above blockages (handline useful). After a short distance a climb up under a boulder is followed by the Shambles, an area of loose rock on the left, that needs to be climbed over. Take Care! Round the corner, up a short step to climb calcited walls and boulders to the beginning of the Traverses. Utilize the large ledges maintaining height over the 25m drop below. The last section is the widest, 100m from the start. Climb up the boulder pile at the end and drop down the other side. Just before a choke drop down through a squeeze in the floor on the left above a 4m drop. Traverse along the rift a few metres to better holds to reach the floor. Follow the passage back under the squeeze to reach the squeezes into OFD III.

Follow the passage to the right, clambering down the boulders to a maypole bridge over the stream (downstream sumps after several hundred metres of streamway). Cross the maypole onto a platform and continue along the passage to an easier climb down to the water. Do not enter the streamway here but continue at the higher level following the left hand wall for another 200m until another easy slope gives access to the stream, remember this point for the return journey. This diversion bypasses two waterfalls that are impassable under wet conditions and are best approached from above with ropes anyway. Once in the stream, above the waterfalls, continue upstream ducking under low roofs and over boulder piles to a section with a low roof and ponded water. This area sumps in flood. The passage changes character completely here with a bed of rock blocking the passage. Climb onto the upper bed to keep dry and continue to a large chamber with grit boulders, Smith's Armoury.

Survey ref: Ogof Ffynnon Ddu, S.W.C.C.

PANT MAWR   Grade 3

**Grid Ref: SN 890161   O.S. Outdoor Leisure Series Nos. 11 & 12, Brecon
Beacons National Park – Western and Central Area 1:25,000.
Altitude: 436m   Length: 1,152m   Depth: 97m**

The cave was first explored in 1937 by the South Wales section of the W.C.C. An active stream passage which ends in a sump.

Permission must be obtained from the Permit Secretary of S.W.C.C.

From Penwyllt follow the path up the hill to the tram road at the back of the S.W.C.C. After 30 minutes walking this joins up with a forestry track. Follow the forestry track which passes 'The Byfre' (where the water to Ogof Ffynnon Ddu sinks) and contours around the side of the hill. 100m after the old quarry on the right, turn off the track and head up the hill to the right until the junction of two walls. Climb the gate and head down the hill again keeping the wall on the right. After 200m a track is reached follow this for another 200m where vehicle tracks lead off to the left through the heather. After 100m the perimeter fence is reached. Allow 60 minutes.

The 16m entrance shaft, rigged by bolts (or metal stakes behind the perimeter fence), leads into a large stream passage. Follow the water down stream until the boulders block the passage completely, the First Boulder Choke. A small hole under the right wall leads after several drops back to the water which quickly disappears under more boulders. Climb over these, under fine formations and through an oxbow in the right wall to bypass a steep climb. The passage descends quickly and gets larger. After 100m the roof appears to meet the bouldery floor. Climb up through a hole to enter the Great Hall. To the right is the Vestry. Continue down the Great Hall to meet the stream again which can be followed for some distance to narrower passage and the terminal sump.

Tackle:
15m handline from stakes to lip of shaft.
16m ladder, 40m lifeline, or 20m rope for SRT (ladder and lifeline are more usual here).
2 bolts (plus 1 bolt rebelay for SRT after 2m).
Survey ref: C.R.G. 1953.

PORTH YR OGOF   Grade 3

**Grid Ref: SN 928124   O.S. Outdoor Leisure Series No 11, Brecon
Beacons National Park – Central Area 1;25,000.   Altitude: 229m
Length: 2,220m**

First recorded exploration in 1804.

WARNING: The cave responds rapidly and catastrophically to rain, however, there are dry upper entrances. The resurgence pool is very dangerous. It has claimed many lives and should only be attempted in wet suits and by competant swimmers. Even then extra bouyancy is advisable.

From Hirwaun take the A4059 to Penderyn. Travel through Penderyn for a further 2 kms. Turn left to Ystradfellte taking the fork to the left after 2.5 kms. Take the next left after 1,000m which leads directly to the car park where the road reaches its lowest point. A National Parks parking attendant will charge a fee to guard the vehicles as thieves operate in this area.

Ystradfellte Area

Blaen nedd Isaf Farm
Little Neath River Cave
Bridge Cave

P.H.
parking
Ystradfellte

Porth yr Ogof

River Neath

River Mellte

river Hepste

to Pontneddfechan

to Hirwaun

0   1 km

A heavily used cave by centres and beginners.

The large impressive entrance, which takes the whole of the River Mellte, leads almost immediately to a deep canal leading off to the right from White Horse Pool. A swim through the canal can be bypassed through the Right Hand Series leading off immediately from the entrance chamber.

After the canal the river shallows as the Creek joins from the right at the Great Bedding. Follow the main river under the low roof to the first, and safest, exit through a collapsed entrance. There are warning signs here pointing out the dangers ahead if you follow the river and exit via the Resurgence.

From the Main Entrance, turn right and under an aven (15m). Many ways lead off to the right which give access to the Creek and the Maze with its many loops and squeezes, fascinating for groups of beginners. Keeping left gives access to the far end of the canal.

Also from the Main Entrance three passages lead off to the left to join the Upper Stream Passage both ends of which are sumped but an exit can be made before the upstream sump via Trademan's Entrance, an exciting finish to a beginners trip. Survey ref: U.B.S.S. & C.D.G. 1968–69.

PWLL DWFN   Grade 4

**Grid Ref: SN 834165   O.S. Outdoor Leisure Series No 12, Brecon
Beacons National Park – Western Area 1:25,000.   Altitude: 399m
Depth: 93m**

A classic vertical pot, unusual for South Wales. Discovered in 1946 with the first explorations taking place in 1947 by the S.W.C.C.

From the car park at the bottom of the hill leading up to Dan yr Ogof climb over a stile and follow a northerly track away from the Dan Yr Ogof complex. After 20m leave the track to follow a rising path on the left. Climb over another stile and, above some sheep pens, follow the path leading to the left up a gradual incline which is eventually bounded by a wall on the left. Follow the path until the wall turns left. Walk in the same direction as if the wall had continued and after 300m a shallow dry valley is entered. Keeping to the right walk 200m up the dry valley to an area where the valley opens out and a large boulder 1m x 1m can be seen. The cave entrance is very close to this boulder, a small hole in the ground.

Climb down the entrance hole for 3m to a short passage which leads to the first, 6m, pitch. Continue the rope to the top of the second pitch. Beware of the loose boulders at the top. The second, 16m, pitch is rigged on the right for a good hang.

A narrow rift on the right (good bolt on right before the rift for traverse line) leads after 3m directly to the head of the 8m third pitch which is descended from a 'Y'-hang. 4m above the floor of the chamber swing through a hole in the wall. A convenient boulder in the rift helps to provide a pull with the bottom of the rope tied around it for those following.

Slide down the steeply descending rift to the top of the 35m fourth pitch. A choice of bolts for a 'Y'-hang but re-belay after 2m for a free descent. Re-belay at 6m followed by two deviations at 12m and 22m.

At the bottom, climb down under the boulders on the left and scramble a short distance to the top of the fifth, 17m, pitch. A classic take-off for a free hang with a deviation after 2m, just above an overhang, to keep away from the dripping water. The short passage on the left leads almost immediately to the final pool of water.

Tackle:

Pitch	Rope length required	Bolts	Remarks
1 & 2	41m	7	
Pitch 3	16m	3	
Pitch 4	55m	7	Deviation 12m
			Deviation 22m
Pitch 5	21m	4	Deviation 2m

TOOTH CAVE

Grade 3

Grid Ref: SS 532911   O.S. Landranger Series No 159, Swansea and Gower, 1:50,000.   Altitude: 46m   Length: 1,525m   Depth: 9m

A long stream cave that is liable to severe flooding. First explored by John Harvey, Roy Morgan and Geoff Richards in 1961.

Special requirements for access are necessary due to the cave being on Forestry Commission land. Cavers must be members of the B.C.R.A. either as an individual or club. Cards must be shown when collecting the key from either Elsie Little or Pete Francis, Kilvrough Manor. A permit is required for the cave.

WARNING: The cave can flood under severe weather conditions and it is worth noting that parties visiting the further reaches of the cave can become trapped as it floods from behind and can back up to very high levels. It should not be entered in unsettled weather conditions.

The route to this cave is the same as that followed to Llethrid Swallet and both caves can be done in one day.

Follow the track through the field past Llethrid and past the gate marking the start of the forestry land in Green Cwm. A small meadow is seen immediately on the left. Half way along this the cave entrance is found just inside the woods behind it. It has a gate which at present is unlocked. Should it be locked, keys will be available from the same sources as for Llethrid Swallet.

An entrance crawl leads to a 5m pitch where a ladder is needed. This leads directly to Bone Chamber, a well decorated passage where the original explorers held an extensive and protracted archaeological dig revealing the funeral remains of at least eight Bronze Age humans. A steep rift leads on from here through an awkward squeeze, continuing on through crawls, which are a feature of this cave, until Razor Passage is met.

Razor Passage can be followed upstream for a 100m but the way on is downstream through some wide passages until a 3m drop occurs – the cave can sump here. Further crawling leads to the Elephants Legs, two prominent stal bosses. On through a bedding and the small Pebble Crawl leads eventually to the Main Stream Passage.

Heading right through a wide, low chamber leads to the upstream section, varying from an almost perfect 2m round phreatic tube, to a rough sided rift. A 4m pot leads to a rift where the clear water of the upstream sump is met.

Turning left at the junction a silty, gritty passage is followed until reaching a boulder choke. Aven Series lies above here though care is needed on climbing up through the boulders.

The main streamway continues on through the choke as a large passage. An intermittent sump can be found here, beyond which the cave continues as a large passage including some very decorated chambers, until, following some narrow rifts, the bottom sump is met.

The streamway water has been dye tested and found to come from Llethrid Swallet via the top sump which could trap cavers at the far end of the cave in flood conditions.

Survey ref: See – Oldham, A, The Caves of Gower, 1977

TUNNEL CAVE   Grade 4

Grid Ref: SN 838161 (Show cave entrance)   SN 836163 (Top entrance)
O.S. Outdoor Leisure Series No 12, Brecon Beacons National Park –
Western Area 1:25,000.   Altitude: 365m top entrance
Length: 2,135m   Depth: 100m

Please contact the Permit Secretary at S.W.C.C. for access.

WARNING: The gated caver's entrance sumps in wet conditions, check before doing a through trip from the top entrance.

Known for many years it was extended by exploring from the bottom up, to the present length by the S.W.C.C. in 1953. The top entrance was excavated in 1962.

From the car park at the bottom of the hill leading to Dan yr Ogof, climb over a stile and follow a northerly track away from the Dan yr Ogof complex. After 20m leave the track to follow a rising path on the left. Climb over another stile and, above some sheep pens, follow the path leading to the left up a gradual incline which is eventually bounded by a wall on the left. Follow the path until the wall turns left. Turn away from the wall to face N and climb 200m to the top of a slight knoll. The gated entrance is in a large concrete slab.

Belay to the scaffold pole and abseil to eye bolts at the head of the second pitch. Another abseil reaches a substantial wire traverse (cowstail useful). At the far end an abseil down the calcite slope enters a large chamber. Take the small passage opposite the slope to a 3m climb down into a small chamber. Under the boulder to a step up. Stay high in the rift to a 5m climb (rope for safety) down to a high chamber. Climb up on the outside of a chockstone on the left (tricky) followed by an awkward traverse right to a large high level rift passage.

Some 80m further, beyond a sloping climb down, step up into a passage and continue to a 3m climb down into a chamber with a passage going back to the left. Go straight on finding the best way in a tall rift. Continue traversing, climbing up and down, finding the easiest way passing another passage on the left to eventually reach a small inlet on the right. Go straight on, up and down in the rift, taking care, to eventually reach the locked gate and the show cave. An exit out of this is usually possible. Alternatively, almost at the end of the show cave, the cavers exit is on the left through a locked grill. The damp, small passage sumps in wet weather.

Tackle: 45m abseil rope.
Survey ref: Tunnel Cave, S.W.C.C. 1988.

Bibliography

Cambrian Caving Council (Cyngor Ogofeydd Cymreig) Handbook, 1993.
Ford, T.D., Editor, Limestone and Caves of South Wales, Cambridge University Press, 1989.

Oldham, T., The Caves of Gower, 1977.
S.W.C.C. Newsletter Numbers 7, 19, 33, 38, 42, 49, 56, 91, 10th and 21st Anniversary Publications.
Stratford, T., Caves of South Wales, Cordee, 1986, Fourth Edition 1995.
U.B.S.S. Proceedings, Vol 11 No 2 (1967).

MENDIP
by Andy Sparrow

Andy Sparrow has caved since 1971, started instructing in 1984 and obtained his CIC in 1988. He is currently registered as an assessor and trainer for the N.C.A. Local Cave Leader Scheme. He has published a book "A Mendip Caver's Ropework Guide" in 1991 and since then produced and directed a series of "Cave Safe" training videos. He has explored many new passages in the Mendip Area.

INTRODUCTION

Covering an area of 160 square kilometers the Mendips can claim to be one of the major caving areas in Britain. Mendip caves are found in a far closer relationship to each other and are within a few minutes walk from the nearest road. The main meeting point for cavers – both pre and post caving – in the area is the Hunter's Lodge Inn.

Although much archaeological work was undertaken in the 19th Century, caving truly began, as a recreational pastime, around 1900. Major explorations began in 1910 and continued apace right up until the Second World War with clubs such as the M.N.R.C., U.B.S.S., W.C.C. and the B.E.C. being predominent. One of the most prolific of all the cave explorers was H.E.Balch – dubbed "The Father of Mendip Caving". His name is synonymous with many of the caves which he explored by candlelight!! After the war in 1945 other clubs were established and became very active with much exploration – excavating – being undertaken. Even today discoveries are still being made.

Unlike other areas within the guide many of the caves described have locked gates. This is to comply with the landowners access conditions. Because these landowners felt that caving was dangerous a locked gate system – which also kept farm creatures at bay – administered by the Charterhouse Caving Committee was less of a risk to themselves when access was allowed. PLEASE adhere to these access procedures for each individual cave. It is most important to maintain a good rapport with the landowners to allow continued access to the caves.

USEFUL ADDRESSES

Council of Southern Caving Clubs
c/o Hunters Lodge Inn
Priddy
Somerset BA5 3AR

Wessex Cave Club
Upper Pitts
Priddy
Somerset BA5 3AX

Shepton Mallet Caving Club
Wells Road
Priddy
Somerset BA5 3AU

Bristol Exploration Club
The Belfry
Priddy
Somerset BA5 3AU

Mendip Caving Group
Nordrach
Blagdon
Somerset BS18 6XW

Cerberus Speleological Society
Larkshall
Fosse Road
Oakhill
Somerset BA3 5HZ

Charterhouse Caving Committee
11 West Street
Banwell
Avon

TOURIST INFORMATION OFFICES

The Gorge
Cheddar
Somerset BS27 3QE
Tel 01934 744071

Town Hall
Market Place
Wells
Somerset BA5 2RB
Tel 01749 672552

GEAR HIRE

Andy Sparrow
2 Pelting Road
Priddy
Wells
Somerset BA5 3BA
Tel 01749 677192

Bat Products
6 Tucker Street
Wells
Somerset BA5 2DZ
Tel 01749 676771

PUBS

Hunter's Lodge Inn, Priddy

Burrington Caves

The picturesque Burrington Combe offers a variety of caves within a relatively small area. Some of the systems are particularly suitable for novices, others much less so owing to their complexity and instability. There are no access restrictions.

GOATCHURCH CAVERN   Grade 2-3

Grid Ref: ST 476583   O.S. Landranger Series No 172 Bristol, Bath and surrounding area and 182 Weston-super-Mare & Bridgwater area, 1:50,000.   Altitude: 162m   Length: 750m   Depth: 55m

Archaeological exploration by William Beard 1830 and Boyd Dawkin 1860. Attempted to make it a show cave in 1900. Further exploration by U.B.S.S. in 1923–5.

The cave entrances are situated up the West Twin Brook Valley in the southern flank of the Combe. Follow the rough track from the road for 230m and scramble up the left side of the valley following the obvious path, passing firstly the Tradesman's Entrance, to the Main Entrance.

A highly popular and enjoyable system. The large Entrance Gallery (an abandoned show-cave) descends to a slide on the left into a lower, inclined passage leading back towards the second entrance. Routes to the right (last one, the Coal Chute, requires handline) lead down to the Boulder Chamber. Various routes then descend to Water Chamber where a passage to the right leads steeply down to the Drainpipe, a tubular crawl. Beyond, tight squeezes lead to terminal chambers.
Survey ref: M.C.G. 1959.

PIERRE'S POT   Grade 3-4

Grid Ref: ST 476583   O.S. Landranger Series No 172 Bristol, Bath and surrounding area and 182 Weston-super-Mare & Bridgwater area, 1:50,000.   Altitude: 129m   Length: 366m   Depth: 37m

Explored by the W.C.C. in 1983.

The pot is found a few metres to the east of the track up West Twin Brook valley and is hidden by bracken some 140m from the Combe road.

Entrance climb descends 7m in two stages (handline advised). Main passage, under rock bridge, traverses over a hole to reach a 5m upward climb leading to a step over a rift to enter a small chamber with superb moonmilk. Various routes passed on the right unite in the small chamber where a difficult vertical squeeze leads to the lower series. Upper series continues through a short tube to the final chamber where a phreatic switchback provides an entertaining round trip (for the slim).

Lower series begins with the notorious squeeze and descends through dig to a second squeeze. Beyond is a streamway which can be followed downstream, under a high aven, to a sump. Upstream, short but pleasant streamway passes a tight inlet rift leading to a sump. Dry passage ahead enlarges before reaching a

BURRINGTON COMBE AREA

1. Rod's Pot
2. Sidcot Swallet
3. Goatchurch Cavern
4. Pierre's Pot

tight squeeze. Easier going ends at a sump (an awkward 5m dive leads to a short extension and final sumps).

ROD'S POT
Grade 3

Grid Ref: ST 472584   O.S. Landranger Series No 172 Bristol, Bath and surrounding area and 182 Weston-super-Mare & Bridgwater area, 1:50,000.   Altitude: 174m   Length: 188m   Depth: 45m

Explored U.B.S.S. in 1944, small extension between 1988 and 1990.

130m below Burrington Cafe a narrow road ascends steeply above the Combe to the west. Soon the metalled road degenerates into a rough track and levels off along Mendip Lodge Wood. Park cars on the edge of open common land on the left of the track. Rod's Pot is the second of four fairly large depressions running NE-SW a few yards left of the track.

The small entrance leads through a smelly puddle to a slide down into a small chamber where care is required to avoid a deep rift in the floor. Two passages descend and unite at the 12m deep main pitch. The pitch is passed by a traverse to the right. Beyond, a narrow rift emerges at the head of a greasy climb down into the Main Chamber. A further descent through holes in the floor enters a steep bedding leading to a final 4m chimney (handline) and flooded dig.

Tackle:
Main Pitch 15m ladder, 30m lifeline, slings.
Survey ref: B.E.C. (1972). See – B.E.C. Caving Report No 17 (1973).

SIDCOT SWALLET
Grade 2-3

Grid Ref: ST 476583   O.S. Landranger Series No 172 Bristol, Bath and surrounding area and 182 Weston-super-Mare & Bridgwater area, 1:50,000.   Altitude: 149m   Length: 206m   Depth: 28m

Explored by Sidcot School Speleological Society in 1925

Approach for above but only go up West Twin Brook for 180m. A well marked path on the right leads to a clump of trees, a few metres above the main track, and the entrance.

Entrance slide leads down to wriggle into bedding chamber. Flat-out squeeze, the Tie Press, leads into the Boulder Chamber where a short descent enters Water Chamber. A vertical squeeze and short chimney is down Lobster Pot (5m handline or ladder) dropping into the final passage and flooded dig (passage over Lobster Pot leads to alternative very tight descent and chimney –15m handline essential). Survey ref: B.E.C. 1972.

Charterhouse Area

CHARTERHOUSE CAVE
Grade 3

Grid Ref: ST 477562   O.S. Landranger Series No 172 Bristol, Bath and surrounding area and 182 Weston-super-Mare & Bridgwater area, 1:50,000.   Altitude: 256m   Length: 427m   Depth: 69m

Explored by the W.C.C. in 1982.

CHEDDAR AND CHARTERHOUSE AREA

150m east of GB cave. Access controlled by C.C.C. All usual conditions apply but parties are limited to 3 persons and must be accompanied by an approved leader.

A stream passage, initially tight, leads to a very large decorated chamber. There are a few side passages containing more excellent formations.

From the gated entrance easy going quickly leads to the top of a vertical rift. An awkward descent leads to narrow passage and a tight squeeze to the right. Beyond, the passage enlarges briefly. Another low section is followed by a junction.

Ahead a short ascent through a hole leads up into the beautiful and spacious Midsummer Chamber. This terminates after 20m and the only visible continuation, Forbidden Passage, should not be entered.

To the right a small stream passage leads on through a low wet crawl, The Wallows. After a short drop the passage enlarges greatly and 30m further the large Splatter Chamber is entered. The chamber is dominated by a huge run-in slope of mud and boulders. A short distance further the passage divides.

The streamway descends to the left but a 3m climb ahead leads into the Citadel, a very large chamber. Numerous stalagmites are taped off. To the right a short climb enters Chiaroscuro Passage which passes more fine formations and terminates in a high rift.

The streamway also enters the Citadel and follows a deep gulley cut through sediments. The upper section of the chamber should not be approached from the streamway. At the lowest point of the Citadel the stream flows into a low wet crawl. From a small chamber beyond, the Grotto of the Singing Stal can be observed. The stream vanishes into a boulder choke which, despite much determined effort, remains the end of the cave.

Survey ref: W.C.C. & U.B.S.S., 1983 included in U.B.S.S. proceedings 17(1).

188

GB CAVERN   Grade 3

Grid Ref: ST 476563   O.S. Landranger Series No 172 Bristol, Bath and surrounding area and 182 Weston-super-Mare & Bridgwater area, 1:50,000.   Altitude: 253m   Length: 1,951m   Depth: 134m

Explored by the U.B.S.S. in 1939 with GB being the indicts of Messrs Goddad & Baker. Mud Passage was opened in 1948 but the most notable extension was the discovery of Ladder Dig Extensione in 1966.

Access is controlled by Charterhouse Caving Committee on behalf of Bristol Waterworks, the land owner. A C.C.C. permit is required by every person entering the cave. Minimum age 16 years. No novices or carbide. Application can be made to C.C.C. secretary, giving one month's notice, or by arrangement with key holding clubs – W.C.C., B.E.C., M.C.G., S.M.C.C., M.N.R.C., C.S.S., A.C.G.

WARNING: LADDER DIG SERIES CAN FLOOD! If water is ponding at the base of the climb into Ladder Dig, wait and monitor any rise in levels. It can overflow into the Ladder Dig passage and flood the crawls to the roof.

A spectacular, decorated, system on a grand scale. Progress through the cave is generally easy but caution is required in the Ladder Dig boulder ruckle.

The large entrance passage descends steeply to a junction. To the left is a short wet crawl leading to Mud Passage, the easiest route to the main cave. Ahead, past fine helictites, is a fixed ladder. The ladder leads to the Devil's Elbow route; certainly the more 'sporting' option presenting an ideal contrast to the bigger passages ahead.

Mud Passage leads down two short climbs to emerge suddenly into the Gorge. Devil's Elbow begins with a short crawl, followed by an upward chimney and stalagmite floored tube. A flowstone slope is descended to a small chamber where a passage to the left leads to the top of the Ten Foot Pot. An easy climb leads down to the Devil's Elbow itself; a partly flooded crawl which emerges high up in a boulder chamber after 10m.

A handline is advised for the climb down. A descending stream passage leads down two climbs before breaking out into the Gorge, a tremendous passage over 20m high and 10m wide. Up-dip leads to a very muddy area approaching close to the surface. Downstream passes Mud Passage and continues in fine style past huge stalagmite flows.

The passage becomes briefly lower and more tubular before reaching the Bridge and opening out into the vastness of the Main Chamber. Crossing the bridge the route follows a balcony along the right wall. Great stalactites frame the huge portal and a realm of blackness lies beyond. The sense of space here rivals any other vault under Britain. The enormity of the chamber usually distracts from the fine array of helictites sprouting from the wall behind the caver.

White Passage leads off impressively to the right and can be followed steeply up a boulder slope to a small hole on the left. The Loop leads off here and soon enters a chamber. Descending here with an inlet stream leads to easy and pleasant going. A short chimney down enters the Hall with a fine display of iron stained stalactites. Ahead is a large window into the Main Chamber providing a viewpoint from half way along its length and giving an excellent vantage point for the largest roof formations.

To the right in the Hall is the Oxbow; a high rift passage. This rejoins the Main Chamber by an awkward climb down, overhead are the most breathtaking displays of helictites. The Main Chamber soon encounters huge mud banks and a terminal choke, but a portal 5m above the floor leads to the

Ladder Dig Series.

Various tactics, from bolt ladders to human pyramids, can be employed to reach the ledge and anchor a 5m ladder and 15m lifeline. Crawling begins and leads to a decorated chamber before the roof lowers to a short wet squeeze. Excavation of the cobble floor may be required to admit larger cavers.

Beyond is the start of a massive boulder ruckle. The route ascends under huge jammed blocks. A hanging balcony of stalagmited boulders is reached by a tricky climb but provides a solid route up into the Great Chamber. The Great Chamber is a massive break-down feature with a domed roof. There are few stalactites but many excellent floor formations. Observe the marker tapes!

Back beneath the balcony a well worn route leads down against the solid wall and then horizontally passing more iron coloured formations. The route eventually emerges into the large Bat Passage. Some superb pure white formations are passed (with care!) before the passage changes character and degenerates into narrow rifts and various dig sites.

Returning to the Main Chamber and passing the climb down from the Oxbow leads to a 10m waterfall. This is climbed to the right onto a large ledge, and then to the left to reach easier ground. Looking back over the waterfall, three 15m flowstone cascades dominate the scene. A huge cluster of stalagmited boulders form the underside of a massive bee-hive formation; a truly impressive spot. Easy progress leads back under the Bridge towards the Gorge and the surface.

Tackle:

Ladder Dig Pitch 5m ladder, 15m rope, 2 x 8mm bolt hangers useful.
Survey ref: U.B.S.S., 1969. See – U.B.S.S. Proceedings 12(1)

LONGWOOD SWALLET   Grade 4

Grid Ref: ST 486557   O.S. Landranger Series No 172 Bristol, Bath and surrounding area and 182 Weston-super-Mare & Bridgwater area, 1:50,000.   Altitude: 213m   Length: 1,646m   Depth: 175m

Explored by the Sidcot School Speleological Society in 1944. Along with U.B.S.S. & W.C.C. Great Chamber was reached in 1945. August Hole opened by U.B.S.S. in 1947. Other extensions by M.C.G. between 1961–1972

Park cars at ST 488561 and follow muddy track across stream (not through Lower Farm). Path around field boundary leads to stile into Longwood Valley and blockhouse entrance near stream sink.

Access is controlled by Charterhouse Caving Committee on behalf of Bristol Waterworks, the land owner. A C.C.C. permit is required by every person entering the cave. Minimum age 16 years. No novices or carbide. Application can be made to C.C.C. secretary, (one month's notice required), or by arrangement with key holding clubs – W.C.C., B.E.C., M.C.G., S.M.C.C., M.N.R.C., C.S.S., A.C.G.

WARNING: Severe and rapid flooding occurs making many passages impassable and the entrance extremely serious. The cave should not be entered if any water is falling down the entrance chimney. The Wet Chimney, Sewer and sections of the August Streamway are dangerous in high water conditions.

A varied, sporting and highly enjoyable system. A narrow entrance series leads to two separate streamways that eventually join a third, major stream passage with fine formations.

The entrance chimney (10m) is easily free-climbed and descends to a small chamber. A low bedding plane is best descended head first to allow manoeuvres around an awkward bend. A letterbox squeeze follows and the passage enlarges briefly. A constricted passage continues down to the head of a 3m drop where care is required (10m double lifeline essential, 5m ladder advised).

The cave enlarges greatly as a second 3m climb is descended into a high rift passage. Turning right leads to a boulder chamber with water entering. A short climb and awkward crawl lead to the head of the Wet Chimney and a refreshing 5m descent. From the small chamber below, a wet crawl, the Sewer, can be followed and quickly leads to a junction with larger passage. The other direction offers a dry but very tight alternative leading to the same junction.

A pleasant canyon streamway now develops including some short climbs and traverses leading to the head of the 7m Swing Pitch. Traversing over the pitch reveals a chamber with good belays and well positioned bolts. A 10m ladder and 15m double lifeline are required. Below the pitch is a steeply descending chamber formed on a fault. (A passage to the right can be followed to an ascending bedding plane ending in a fine grotto). The water cascades down to enter a large horizontal passage below; the August Streamway.

Upstream in the August Streamway is an enlarging steeply ascending boulder gallery. This can be followed for some distance and assumes impressive proportions before choking very close to the surface. Downstream is a varied, decorated passage. Initial walking shrinks to crawling in the stream but is quickly followed by easier progress again. The passage changes to a deep canyon where a long traverse is required. This leads down to the lofty and impressive Tributary Chamber where the stream from Longwood Great Chamber enters via an impassable rift.

Downstream the passage lowers to more crawling and the water vanishes into a choke. A 5m chimney drops into Renold's Passage which gradually narrows to the head of a tight vertical rift. Below the rift is a long and very tight crawl leading to a short section of streamway and the final sump. This entire section can flood to the roof in wet weather and is best avoided.

From the chamber above Swing Pitch a short wriggle, Christmas Crawl, leads through into the Longwood Great Chamber. This large chamber leads down (over dangerous boulders) to a short streamway ending in a tight rift. A partial descent into the Great Chamber and cautious traverse lead to an impressive inlet waterfall. A climb up is followed by an easy but exposed traverse (20m lifeline) into the large obvious passage.

The route narrows and a short upward chimney is easily missed. The passage emerges into a high rift chamber under the full force of a powerful waterfall; the Showerbath. A high rift passage is followed up two short climbs until the bottom of the entrance series is met again below the 3m climbs.

Tackle:

Entrance Series: 3m drop, 5m ladder, 10m lifeline, slings.
Swing Pitch: 10m ladder, 15m lifeline, slings and 2 x 8 mm bolts.
Great Chamber:
Traverse: 15m rope.
Survey ref: M.C.G. 1961 and 1983

MANOR FARM SWALLET   Grade 3-4

Grid Ref: ST 498556   O.S. Landranger Series No 172 Bristol, Bath and surrounding area and 182 Weston-super-Mare & Bridgwater area, 1:50,000.   Altitude: 233m   Length: 1,067m   Depth: 151m

Originally dug at the stream sink between 1947 and 1960. U.B.S.S. started blasting the present entrance with N.H.A.S.A. carrying on in 1972 until they entered the cave and explored it in 1973.

Access controlled by the farmer at Manor Farm. Small goodwill fee charged. The cave is often closed during the period 1st June to 1st November.

A blasted entrance shaft and excavated passage emerges into a long, well decorated streamway. A fossil gallery bypasses a choke and descends steeply to the end of the cave.

WARNING: The streamway is hazardous in high water. Albert's Eye is liable to flood in extreme conditions. The stream is badly polluted and cuts are liable to turn septic. Gloves are advisable.

Entrance shaft is 14m deep. A blasted crawl leads (passing short working to right) to low chamber. September Rift follows, a narrow chimney 7m deep. This is free-climbable but laddering is advised. A larger passage beyond reaches the 1973 break-through point and the magnificent Curtain Chamber. Ahead is a 7m pitch (free-climbable with care) into a streamway. A taped path behind the curtain also leads to the streamway. To left is Inlet Series and a large chamber, to the right an entertaining bypass to Curtain Chamber pitch.

The streamway descends steeply past huge banks of eroded flowstone to end suddenly at Albert's Eye squeeze. A short wriggle leads to a fine chamber and on past false floors to 5m climb. A larger passage is met at a junction. Upstream is a 7m inlet waterfall above which is a long decorated passage (maypole required). Downstream large passage passes fine formations before narrowing at the Inclined Rift.

Beyond is a chamber and flowstone ramp on the left, ahead leads to streamway choke. Climbing the ramp reveals a black space between boulders. A short upward climb enters the impressive N.H.A.S.A. Gallery which is up to 10m wide and descends beneath a great flat bedding plane roof. The stream re-enters and the passage becomes obviously phreatic. A step down to the left leads through a wriggle to Florence's Bathtub and the final disappearance of the stream. Ahead the large muddy passage terminates in digs old and new.

Tackle:

Entrance	15m ladder, 30m lifeline, short slings.
September Rift	7m ladder, 15m lifeline, short sling.
Curtain Chamber	7m ladder, 20m lifeline, slings.

Survey ref: W.I.Stanton and B.E.C. 1974 published by U.B.S.S.

RHINO RIFT   Grade 3

Grid Ref: ST 485556   O.S. Landranger Series No 172 Bristol, Bath and surrounding area and 182 Weston-super-Mare & Bridgwater area, 1:50,000.   Altitude: 213m   Length: 274m   Depth: 144m

Explored by the W.C.C. sporadically between 1928 and 1961. In 1971 the bottom of the cave was reached after renewed efforts by the E.S.C.C. and W.C.C. from 1969.

Nhasa Gallery, Manor Farm Swallet. Photo: Tony Baker

Formations in Upper Flood Swallet. Photo: Paul Deakin

St Cuthbert's Swallet, Mendip. Photo: Tony Baker

Access controlled by C.C.C. See Longwood Swallet for details and location. Walking south past Longwood Swallet reaches a tributary valley on the right after 200m. The cave is located a short distance up the valley on the left and is reached by an obvious footpath.

WARNING: Beware of loose rocks, particularly on the Third Pitch.

An impressive vertical system with 3 airy pitches leading down to a narrow passage and final chamber.

The low entrance passage descends to a 'T' junction. Left closes down, but a stalagmite floored tube to the right emerges at the head of a steep calcite slope above the first pitch (30m). A thread belay around a stal column provides a traverse line belay at the head of the slope and a bolt traverse leads out along the left hand wall to a hang point.

An impressive descent between calcited walls drops 15m to a re-belay on a bulge of flowstone. Below the shaft enlarges and the descent lands on a slope overlooking the second pitch (15m). Rigging along the right hand wall gives an initial take-off which is quickly followed by a re-belay over the pitch. A spray of water is difficult to avoid in wet conditions.

The pitch lands on a steep rubble slope above the third pitch (20m). Great care is required here to avoid dislodging rocks onto those below. To the right are anchors for a traverse line descending to the pitch head. An initial descent past huge jammed boulders is followed down a solid wall in a large rift. A debris slope at the bottom leads down to a small hole amongst boulders.

The character of the cave changes abruptly as a vertical squeeze is followed by a small decorated passage. The passage continues down a short narrow chimney before enlarging at the head of the fourth pitch (7m). This begins as a narrow rift easily rigged to a thread directly overhead. The pitch widens and enters Fault Chamber which is dominated by an impressive aven. The fifth pitch is easily free-climbed to the left and descends to a boulder choke which marks the bottom of the cave.

Tackle:

	Rope length required	Bolts	Remarks
First Pitch	45m	6	
Second Pitch	30m	4	
Third Pitch	30m	4	
Fourth Pitch	10m		natural belay, slings.

Survey ref: W.C.C. 1971 published with W.C.C. Journal 12 (140).

TYNING'S BARROW SWALLET   Grade 3

Grid Ref: ST 471564   O.S. Landranger Series No 172 Bristol, Bath and surrounding area and 182 Weston-super-Mare & Bridgwater area, 1:50,000.   Altitude: 256m   Length: 1,219m   Depth: 132m

Explored by B.E.C. in 1977.

Access to the cave is controlled by Mr Reakes at Pine Lea, Green Ore, ST 580505. Small goodwill fee charged. The cave is 20m south of the stile across the field boundary in a shallow depression.

A long passage with a small stream drops gently down to a terminal choke. Various side passages provide additional interest.

194

Entrance shaft through concrete pipes leads to a letterbox squeeze at the head of a 7m pitch. Below, a spacious passage leads down to a triangular squeeze through a boulder choke. Narrower rift beyond is the site of the 1977 dig into main cave.

Low passage enlarges into a canyon passing a high rift on the right leading to the large Dragon Chamber after 60m. A second side passage, reached by a 3m climb, follows after 30m. This is Paton Place and by taking the second passage to the left another route to Dragon Chamber can be followed, allowing a short round trip.

The main passage continues under the Book, a jammed slab, to the Aardvark trap, a 3m deep hole across the passage, leading to a sump after 30m. Stepping over the hole and following the abandoned passage leads on through crawls and climbs for 100m, until the stream re-enters. The cave enlarges dramatically and descends steeply to the 3m Pyramid Pot.

The passage reduces to crawls and awkward manoeuvres are required to pass a flowstone obstruction. Narrow passage continues until a junction is met after 40m. To the right is Drunken Horse Inlet, 150m of varied streamway ending in an unstable boulder choke beneath the terminal Mountbatten Chamber. The main stream passage continues in unremarkable style for 100m before degenerating into a final narrow cobble-choked rift and dig.

Tackle:

Entrance pipes	5m ladder, 10m lifeline, short sling.
Second pitch	7m ladder useful, 15m lifeline, short sling (thread through hole in last pipe section).
Pyramid Pot	5m ladder, 15m lifeline, long slings.

Survey ref: B.E.C./G.S.G. 1977.

UPPER FLOOD SWALLET – also known as Blackmoor Flood Swallet
Grade 3

Grid Ref: ST 505557   O.S. Landranger Series No 182 Weston-super-Mare and Bridgwater area, 1:50,000.   Altitude: 237m   Length: 610m Depth: 40m

Explored by M.C.G. in 1968 & 1985.

Access is controlled by the M.C.G. Write or call at M.C.G. Hut. 4 weeks notice required. No carbide or novices.

A long partly excavated passage leads to a superbly decorated streamway. Low wet extensions lead to a final choke.

Entrance is a 4m climb down through concrete pipes. Below, a short descent enters a larger passage with elegant drystone walling. To the left are short upstream extensions, to the right the passage lowers before a small decorated chamber. Easy crawling continues for 100m, passing a second chamber, until a short duck is reached.

Beyond is the beautiful Midnight Chamber and the main stream entering from the right. Over 100m of superbly decorated streamway follows. Progress must be made with extreme care (mainly by crawling in the stream) to avoid damage to the delicate roof formations. The streamway terminates at a low bedding but a climb overhead leads to a short crawl followed by larger passage.

A duck follows after 15m and, after a short tight crawl, a junction with streamway. Upstream is tight inlet system. Downstream, a low wet passage enlarges at the Red

Room, a spacious chamber followed by the terminal boulder choke.
Survey ref: M.C.G. 1986.

Priddy Area

1. Eastwater Cavern
2. St. Cuthbert's Swallet
3. Swildon's Hole
A. W.C.C. hut
B. B.E.C. hut
C. S.M.C.C. hut

EASTWATER CAVERN   Grade 4

**Grid Ref: ST 538506   O.S. Landranger Series Nos 182 Weston-super-Mare & Bridgwater area, 183 Yeovil and Frome, 1:50,000.   Altitude: 238m
Length: 2,743m   Depth: 158m**

Explored by the Wells Natural History & Archaeological Society between 1902 and
1906. In 1910 M.N.R.C. explored Primrose Path and in 1933 finally reached Harris'

Chamber. J.Ifold entered 'his' series in 1951. Dolphin Pot was opened in 1940 by the W.C.C. and after frustrated efforts finally descended Primrose Pot in 1950. Small extensions made by W.C.C. and B.C.S.S. in 1954.

Access to the cave is controlled by landowner at Eastwater farm (300m NE of cave). Small goodwill fee charged.

WARNING: Entrance boulders – do not deviate from the marked route; some areas of the ruckle are extremely dangerous.

A strenuous and demanding system with distinctive Mendip bedding planes and trenches. Almost devoid of formations but strong on atmosphere, particularly in the lower section.

The entrance climb leads down to a wriggle through boulders often well watered by the stream. **In wet conditions entry and exit from the cave can be impossible**. The entrance ruckle spirals down for 20m amongst huge boulders. The main route, as marked by a guide wire, is well worn and relatively stable. Do not deviate from the marked route; some areas of the ruckle are extremely dangerous.

A short climb enters solid passage at the head of the 380 Foot Way. The way on is not down the obvious route but through a small opening on the left, which enters an extensive inclined bedding plane. Sliding down in a trench reaches the Upper Traverse. Progress is now horizontal across the polished inclined bedding (which is notorious for devouring dropped equipment!). After 10m of entertaining traversing the passage constricts to an awkward crawl over chockstones before emerging at a 'T' junction with a steeply dipping trench passage.

The way is downwards, as an easy slide until the passage constricts and dog-legs through Hallelujah Hole. Beyond, is the deep but narrow trench of Primrose Path. Followed to its conclusion this leads to the notoriously difficult squeeze at the head of Primrose Pot, which drops 55m in three pitches.

But the way on is to the left, through a small opening at roof level, 10m after Hallelujah Hole. This is the Lower Traverse, another inclined bedding giving more difficult progress until it emerges suddenly in the side of the First Rift Chamber – a blessed indication that the worst struggles are over.

Turning left and dropping into a rift passage reveals another descending rift branching to the right. This enters a small boulder chamber at the head of the First Vertical. The pitch reaches an obvious passage at -10m but continues down-wards, narrowing to a choke. The passage leads through a short constriction and climb down to a narrow rift that emerges at the head of the Second Vertical.

The Second Vertical is usually descended to -10m where a traverse and climb bypass the remaining pitch. SRT users may prefer to bottom the full pitch and follow a short tight crawl to rejoin the main route. The traverse below the ladder should be lifelined. A steep climb descends to an easier gradient before a final, awkward step down into a rift chamber with a small inlet waterfall.

Following the water leads to the 13 Pots. Here, an impressive steeply inclined bedding is deeply incised by a stream trench. A fine sculpted passage results, dropping in a series of entertaining climbs alternating with small pools. The Pots lead down into a small sandy chamber and the stream vanishes into the short Terminal Rift. Obvious small tubes lead off from the chamber to the delights of the Mud Escalator and the modest formations of Beechen Series.

The large up-dip passage is the Muddy Oxbow which ascends steeply and provides another (easier in this direction) route back to the Second Vertical.

Back up the Verticals an alternative route can be followed through the Upper Series. Turning right (away from the First Rift Chamber) leads through the 'S' bend to the Crossroads. A tube on the right leads to Dolphin Pot and a 10m Pitch. Beyond is Ifold's Series and the extremely extensive and strenuous West End Series. The down-dip route below Dolphin Pitch is Harris' Passage which descends steeply to a pitch. This is bypassed to the left and enters the Second Vertical by a bold step.

At the Crossroads the up-dip route is the start of the canyon which can be followed as a narrow trench to the left or a wide polished bedding to the right. Both routes combine as the trench enlarges and ascends steeply assuming an attractive canyon-like section. The passage terminates at the start of a tubular crawl which leads into the large but very unstable Boulder Chamber; this is best avoided.

Directly overhead the crawl is Baker's Chimney, a 6m climb beginning as a wide straddle and then narrowing into a rift. This emerges into the floor of a low passage. Down-dip quickly meets a larger trench with a chamber to the left. A narrow rift descends from here back to the top of the Canyon providing an alternative to Baker's Chimney. Down-dip from this chamber descends to the end of the Upper Traverse providing one route out of the cave.

A quick route from Baker's Chimney is open to thin cavers. The other direction from the top of the Chimney leads into a small chamber with a bedding plane descending under a wedged slab. The passage leads down to a tight squeeze. This is best done feet first, face down, moving to the left until a small trench is reached. An easy slide descends to the start of the Upper Traverse. The Boulder Ruckle is reached through a hole on the right.

Tackle:-

First Vertical	20m SRT rope backed up in chamber, one bolt over the pitch.
or Ladder	10m ladder to 8mm bolt, 20m lifeline, 5m rigging rope.
Second Vertical	30m SRT rope, natural back-up and short traverse along left wall to hang bolts (3 x 8mm bolts).
or ladder	10m ladder, 20m lifeline, short rigging rope or slings.

Survey ref: W.C.C. 1952–54.

PRIDDY GREEN SINK to SWILDON'S IV   Grade 4

Grid Ref: ST 527511   O.S. Landranger Series No 182 Weston-super-Mare and Bridgewater area, No 183 Yeovil and Frome, 1:50,000.
Alt:238m   Length: 260m (to IV)   Depth: 134m

Originally dug and blasted by a consortium of Mendip clubs from 1959–64. Finally connected to Cowsh Avens after prolonged blasting by B.E.C. during 1995–96. Cowsh Avens were climbed and blasted sporadically between 1958–74.

WARNING: A tight, awkward and committing series of crawls lead to the slimy and exposed pitches of Cowsh Avens. Beware of flash floods, loose boulders and Weil's Disease from the polluted stream. A collector's item. Rescue of a badly injured caver from Cowsh Avens or the streamway would only be practicable via Sumps 3, 2 and 1.

The cave is situated at the end of Priddy Green opposite the old fountain. Park as for Swildon's Hole and if doing the through trip pay at Manor Farm as usual. A key for the sink is avilable from local clubs who may charge a small fee. ENSURE LID IS LOCKED AND PULLED SHUT BEHIND YOU – IT CAN BE OPENED FROM THE INSIDE.

The 6m entrance shaft drops into 50m of polluted, low streamway ending in a cow dung sump. The way on is a crawl halfway along on the left into the roomy RAF Aven, where a descending crawl is followed through an unstable chamber to reach a 6m deep, free climbable rift after 25m. A further 10m descending crawl reaches a junction. Left leads to four free climbs and further cow dung sump of Virgin Series.

Straight ahead is the connection route – 55m of 'sporting' grovelling where at least one squeeze should be attempted feet first by the faint at heart. This is Barrel Series. At the 20m high Stone Bat Aven a left turn under a cemented pole leads after15m to the final tight and vertical 2m descent into Swildon's Hole.

The way on is through a short crawl on the right and a 5m free climb – rope useful. A further crawl reaches the Priddy Green stream entering from the choked Shit Sump and flowing through the next short crawl (beware flooding) to the 7m deep El Krapiton. A tube 2m above the floor leads to an 8m climb down to the head of the 16m deep Main's Aven (DO NOT descend). The correct route is along the roomy 25m long Ken's Crawl to the 17m Bladder Pot, 10m Boss Pot, 4m Little Pot, a steeply descending passage and the final 12m Cowsh Aven leading to the Swildon's IV streamway just upstream of Sump 4.

From here a choice of routes is offered to Swildon's Entrance – all involving an ascent of 'The 20' which the explorer has had the foresight to ladder in advance.

Tackle:
Either one 40m or preferably two 20m ropes tied together for the longer pitches allow for a double rope abseil. All relevant pitches are equipped with Eco hangers and in extremis can be free climbed by a skilled climber. Helmet mounted batteries are a blessing in the tighter sections.

SAINT CUTHBERT'S SWALLET   Grade 4

Grid Ref: ST 543505   O.S. Landranger Series No 182 Weston-super-Mare & Bridgwater area, No 183 Yeovil and Frome, 1:50,000.
Altitude: 73m   Length: 6,800m   Depth: 45m

Explored by the B.E.C. in 1953 after many attempts from 1944. Sump 1 was reached in 1956. Many discoveries followed from 1957 to 1970. Currently exploration continues.

The cave is located 50m from the B.E.C. hostel (The Belfry). All trips must be accompanied by a B.E.C. approved leader. Parties are limited to 5 persons. No novices or carbide. Apply to the Caving Secretary, giving six weeks notice.

An extremely extensive and complex system offering an enormous variety of scenery and sporting obstacles.

The entrance shaft descends 5m through concrete pipes to enter a low passage. After a few metres a climb descends to the head of the Entrance Rift. This is a narrow vertical chimney 10m deep. Descent of the rift is easy, but the return climb is awkward and strenuous. Below, a short wriggle through boulders leads to a 7m fixed ladder descent into the spray-lashed Arete Chamber.

A short drop and easy passage emerges at the head of the 18m Pulpit Pitch. A impressive wet descent lands in a high rift passage which drops steeply to Gour Passage Pitch (7m). Downstream the passage becomes more tubular and descends a series of short climbs to the head of the Waterchute. This 7m climb is less difficult than it appears and leads on to more spacious streamway which emerges suddenly into the large Traverse Chamber.

Entrance Rift, St Cuthbert's Swallet Mendip. Photo: Tony Baker

An inlet waterfall sprays down from above while ahead the roof lowers at the Choke; a flat out wet crawl. The Choke is (mercifully) short and walking streamway resumes. Numerous passages and openings lead off towards the upper series and a short low section can be bypassed by a concealed oxbow. Rapid progress is halted at Stalagmite Pitch where the water vanishes into a fissure. A short chimney followed by a wet wallow provides one route, a steep handline descent another.

Both combine in a short section of gour pooled passage which terminates at Sewer Passage; an inclined muddy bedding. The roof rises again at Plantation Junction and a large passage continues to a stalagmite barrier blocking the passage. Climbing over this leads to Beehive Chamber with it's huge deposits of flowstone. A second climb up aided by a chain emerges into the incredible Gour Hall. This lofty vault is dominated by the Great Gour which is over 5m high.

Descending the gour slope leads down to Gour Rift and easy progress to a dam built across the passage. Beyond here the streamway lowers to crawling before reaching the excavated Sump 1. This is now a 5m duck leading into Cuthbert's 2; 200m of stonking passage terminating at Sump 2. Despite herculean efforts this remains, obstinately, the end of the cave.

Returning to Plantation Junction and turning right leads to steeply ascending bedding plane emerging into the Rabbit Warren. A short slippery descent passes banks of mud formations resembling bunches of grapes. A maze of muddy tubes incised into the bedding continue up into the Railway Tunnel. A short excursion en route reveals an exquisite row of stalactites; the Fingers.

The Railway Tunnel is a superb 5m phreatic tube boasting some tremendous curtains and terminating in the superb Cascade Chamber with it's great stalagmites and tremendous white cascade. Following a crawl along a small tube, Strike Passage soon emerges in a large chamber. From here Curtain Chamber is easily reached. This is a huge rift chamber over 30m high with an incredible display of calcite draperies – probably the finest in Britain.

The route ascends steeply now up a chaotic boulder slope. More fine formations are passed on the left as the large Boulder Chamber is entered. The way out lies past a vast fallen boulder, Kanchenjunga, and follows a large passage past a traverse and upward chimney into Pillar Chamber. A short descent gains Upper Mud Hall and a fixed ladder leading up into the Wire Rift.

Wire Rift is narrow and awkward. A traverse over Waterfall Pitch is followed by difficult progress until wider passage is met at the base of the Ledge Pitches. Fixed ladders lead up these short ascents and back up into Arete Chamber. A final (and often epic) struggle up the Entrance Rift awaits.

Tackle:

Entrance rift   10m ladder, 20m lifeline.
Pulpit pitch   20m ladder, 30m lifeline.
Survey ref: B.E.C. 1991 (see Bibliography)

SWILDON'S HOLE – short round trip   Grade 4

Grid Ref: ST 531513   O.S. Landranger Series No 182 Weston-super-Mare and Bridgwater area, No 183 Yeovil and Frome, 1:50,000.
Altitude: 237m   Length: 9,144m   Depth: 167m

Entered and explored by Wells Natural History & Archaeological Society in 1901. The 40 foot and 20 foot pot were passed in 1914. In 1921 combined M.N.R.C.

and U.B.S.S. reached Sump 1 being passed in 1936 by J.Sheppard and G.Balcombe with Balcombe passing Sump 2. Since 1936 new passages were discovered yearly most prominent being C.D.G., I.C.D.G., M.N.R.C., S.M.C.C., S.V.C.C., S.W.E.T.C.C., W.C.C. and W.S.G.

Access controlled by the farmer, Manor Farm, Priddy Green. Small goodwill fee charged. Park cars on Priddy Green (avoiding grass whenever possible) and PLEASE always use the changing barn provided. Walking towards the church leads to a stile after 50m and footpath to cave entrance.

Mendip's longest and most popular cave system. The main streamway is over a mile long and broken up into 12 sections by a series of sumps. Extensive high level passages provide sump bypasses and a selection of varied separate trips. The Short Round Trip provides a sporting and satisfying introduction to the ramifications of the system.

The cave is liable to flooding. Negotiating the streamway is difficult and strenuous under wet conditions.

The cave begins with a complex area of interconnecting wet and dry passages. All routes converge in the Water Chamber which is easily identified by a huge fallen boulder. The streamway continues as a high rift descending to a 4m climb (handline useful in wet conditions) to the bottom of the Old Forty Foot Pot. An impressive and well decorated passage leads on easily to a 6m pitch; the Twenty.

The Twenty is easily rigged from natural and bolt belays. Beyond, the passage lowers to a short wet crawl before emerging at the Shrine, a large flowstone formation. A high canyon passage continues to the Double Pots where amusing manoeuvres avoid the traditional Mendip baptism. Beyond the stream flows into the narrow Inclined Rift but a traverse leads up into Barnes Loop, a superbly decorated oxbow. A short awkward climb drops back into the streamway again.

The main stream passage assumes impressive dimensions and cascades down a series of water chutes. About 50m downstream of Barnes Loop is a 'V' shaped cleft reached by a 5m climb. This leads up into Tratman's Temple a finely decorated chamber. An obvious route along a tubular passage leads up to the sad remains of Balch's Forbidden Grotto and a tortuous crawl and squeeze through the Blasted Boss. Beyond is Saint Paul's Series.

After wading through a long pool a walking size passage leads easily down to the First Mud Sump (do not attempt to bail or free-dive; the passage is long and heavily silted. 100m of passage has been explored beyond.) The way on is a rising tube to the left. The obvious well worn route should be followed which is mostly hands and knees crawling over calcite floors. Two short drops gain an enlarging passage which leads to the Mud Sump.

The Mud Sump is now a short duck which is often bailed down to provide a reasonable airspace. Do not attempt to free-dive as the sump can be over 10m long if the drain hole is blocked. Beyond is Paradise Regained, an extensive and complex series of passages. The obvious route follows a high rift to a junction with a larger passage after 30m. Turning right the way leads up a short climb into an imposing chamber overlooking a deep rift – Shatter Pot.

Shatter Pot is the heart of the Swildon's network and passages radiate in several directions. A climb leads to the South East Inlets, Swyne Puke (a round trip emerging from the hole high above Shatter Pot), Renaissance and the strenuous and remote extremities of New Renaissance. Down the Pot is Shatter Series, Paschendale and the Damp Link connection with Swildon's 6.

The Round Trip passes Shatter Pot, continues down a short tube, and crosses into a second tube. Follow this tube down through a low arch to the bottom of the

Greasy Chimney. This is easily confused with a more obvious climb to the left. A short struggle up the Chimney (handline useful) leads to a descending tube and traverse. Ahead, a narrow rift is followed until tubes on the left lead along a low passage (with pool) to a junction.

To the left a short passage leads to Fault Chamber with it's high aven. A smaller descending hole leads down to Watergate and an aqueous connection to Swildon's 4. Ahead is the start of a long meandering muddy passage. This is mostly spacious and has several entertaining mud slides. Progress is rapid for the next 150m until a deep canyon breaches the floor and progress is only possible by traversing. Descending into the canyon leads into Blue Pencil Passage.

Blue Pencil Passage leads down into the Swildon's 4 streamway and makes a very worthwhile excursion. The route is narrow and awkward and great care is required at a 5m free climb. Below the climb the passage should be entered feet first and followed around an awkward right angle bend. 10m further it emerges suddenly 4m up in the wall of a large stream passage. A fixed chain aids the climb down but great care is still required. Swildon's 4 is entered about half way along it's length. Upstream the passage is wide and arched and terminates at Sump 3 (over 10m long). Downstream is a magnificent sculpted stream canyon leading to the odious Cowsh Aven and the 5m long Sump 4 . Beyond the sump the streamway continues through 7 further sumps to the silted, impassable Sump 12.

The traverse over Blue Pencil Passage leads to the first of The Double Troubles; ducks that often require bailing to provide an airspace. The first Trouble will need to be lowered at least 20cms if full to the brim. Free diving should not be attempted. Beyond is Trouble Series and after 10m the Second Trouble which usually has adequate airspace. A narrow rift leads past a stalagmite boss to a small chamber and the next Trouble; a 3m duck that often needs bailing. This emerges in Doomed Grotto (a sadly appropriate name) which is followed by easier passage.

A short step up to the left leads into Glistening Gallery with it's fine curtains. Progress along the Gallery is halted by a tight inclined squeeze which is the crux point for big cavers. Past the squeeze a final duck leads into a series of descending muddy slides. Displaced water runs off into a hole on the left which should be followed down to the Landing and a rope slide down into the Swildon's 2 streamway. Missing the hole leads into Vicarage Passage and after 60m the head of Vicarage Pot.

Downstream in Swildon's 2 leads through Creep 2 and Duck 2 to the 7m Sump 2 (beyond are two flooded bell chambers before Sump 3). Upstream an easy walk leads to a short cobbly crawl (Creep 1), past a passage on the left into the Black Hole Series, through Duck 1, and then to Sump 1. This is only about 1m long and is easily passed using the fixed guideline.

Back in Swildon's 1 a boulder strewn gallery leads back to the stream canyon passing back under Tratman's Temple and the completion of the Round Trip.

Tackle:
The Twenty 7m ladder, 15m lifeline, slings
Survey ref: W.C.C. (et al) 1993.

THRUPE LANE SWALLET
Grade 4

Grid Ref: ST 604457   O.S. Landranger Series No 183 Yeovil and Frome, 1:50,000.   Altitude: 189m   Length: 1,067m   Depth: 117m

Explored by ATLAS in 1974. New Atlas explored by Andy Sparrow and Steve Ellis. High Atlas by A. Sparrow, S. Ellis and members of ATLAS.

A sporting system with a variety of pitches including the awesome, 58m Atlas Pot. Recent exploration has connected the upper levels of this magnificent shaft to the Railway Series providing several new spectacular descents and allowing exchange trips with the old system.

The cave is adjacent to the road and parking is available in the obvious lay-by. Please make a courtesy call on Mr & Mrs Butt at the cottage opposite the cave entrance. Small goodwill fee payable.

WARNING: The cave is liable to severe and sudden flooding. Do not descend the cave if water is ponding in the depression or flowing at the base of the entrance pitch. There is much loose rock in upper Atlas Pot to endanger those below; extreme care is required!

The 8m entrance pitch leads directly to a junction. Straight on (through an old gate) is a narrow descending rift, the Ferret Run leading to the old system. To the right a crawl floored by the remains of a wooden railway is the start of Railway Series and the connection with New Atlas.

The Old System

The Ferret Run is narrow and awkward and leads to two 5m climbs (handline useful on the second). Below the second climb, a narrow rift leads to Slit Pot but the main way doubles back and descends to the head of Perseverance Pot, 15m.

THRUPE LANE AREA

This is narrow at the top but soon widens to easier dimensions. Below is the sometimes aqueous (and odious) Cowsh Crawl. This emerges into spacious passage and an inlet waterfall that cascades into Bridge Rift. Bridge Rift leads down to the wet Avalanche Pot, 12m, and sump.

Climbing up the inlet leads up in to the large Butt's Chamber. Ascending the boulder floor leads to a short tube on the left into Marble Chamber where a descent through boulders drops into the attractive Marble Streamway. This meanders pleasantly down to Atlas Pot. Here the stream vanishes into a huge shaft beneath a massive aven. The direct descent is very wet, 20m, and should be avoided.

To the right is Ridged Boulder which overlooks the alternative, dry, Lateral Pitch, 17m. The climb onto the boulder should be rigged with a traverse line or lifelined. Another alternative is to the left where a short traverse is rigged to the head of the 8m Ledge Pitch. This descends to the Atlas Ledge where a muddy passage leads down to the circular Slither Pot, 20m. A low draughting crawl rejoins the streamway beyond Atlas Pot.

From the base of Lateral Pitch a wet descent leads down to a narrow rift passage. The low crawl from Slither Pot enters under the left wall. Downstream quickly leads to a choke. This can be bypassed with difficulty but a final choke soon follows.

New Atlas

Railway Series begins with a descending crawl and a short descent into a small passage followed by a wet squeeze. Immediately beyond the squeeze a climb up leads to an inclined rift and squeeze over a boulder. Beyond is a crawl to the right leading to the top of Chimney Pot, 10m. A fixed handline aids the descent into a narrow rift passage. The descending route constricts to a small awkward tube emerging directly into High Atlas and a pitch of 58m. WARNING: Any loose rock dislodged will fall through this hole into Atlas Pot. The other direction leads to a 7m pitch and climb down into Wuthering Heights, a rift chamber.

An obvious hole is the head of Lateral Aven, 40m. Another climb leads down (with traverse line) to a huge jammed boulder wedged over New Atlas Direct, 50m. Lateral Aven can be descended to Ridged Boulder to allow an exchange trip. New Atlas Direct is very wet on the lower half. An alternative is to descend 30m and swing over to the Atlas Ledge and Slither Pot.

Tackle:

	Rope length required	Bolts	Remarks
Entrance	15m	3	
Perseverance	20m	3	
Lateral Pitch	30m	6	Includes traverse.
Ledge Pitch	15m	2	
Slither Pot	30m	6	
HIGH ATLAS:			
Full descent	70m	5	
		6	Eco hangers, 2 deviations.
To Atlas Ledge	50m		1 deviation.
Wuthering Heights	20m	2	Eco hangers
Lateral Aven	35m	2	To Lateral pitch.
Lateral Aven	50m	4	To bottom.

New Atlas Direct	60m	2	Eco hangers, plus 1 bolt, 1 deviation.
NEW ATLAS DIRECT: To Atlas Ledge	45m	2	Eco hangers, Bottom anchor.
To Old Atlas	40m	2	Eco hangers, Bottom anchor required.

Survey ref: New Atlas – Descent No. 108 pp 26-7.

Stoke Lane Area

STOKE LANE SLOCKER   Grade 4

Grid Ref: ST 668474   O.S. Landranger Series No 183 Yeovil and Frome, 1:50,000.   Altitude: 171m   Length: 2,134m   Depth: 18m

Explored by P. Browne in 1947

No known access restrictions at the present time.

A long stream passage with much crawling leads to a short sump and a series of large well decorated chambers.

WARNING: The cave is liable to sudden flooding. The water is polluted and cases of Weil's Disease have resulted.

The Cave is best approached from Stoke St. Michael and is located 730m to the NE. Follow the road east from the village and take the first turning to the left for 800m. Park cars neatly on the grassy verge before Cook's Wood Quarry. From the southern boundary of the quarry a stile gives access to a small wood and a path down to the valley floor. Walk up the valley (towards Cook's Farm) to where the stream sinks. The dry entrance is 10m to the right of the sink.

Stoke 1

The low wet entrance tube leads to hands and knees crawl in the stream. A low wet section can be bypassed by a complex overhead route. Beyond is the Pebble Crawl, over 30m of low passage to a junction with the main stream. After 40m of low wet crawling the stream vanishes and the dry Tributary Passage must be followed to the left. A route through boulders to the right, leads through the Corkscrew and into Browne's Passage.

Browne's Passage is 40m long and passes an awkward constriction, the Nutmeg Grater, before emerging in Cairn Chamber. A flooded rift is followed for 10m to an apparent dead end. Feeling under the water reveals a low arch and airspace beyond. Ducking through is easy but the return dive requires much more care – the airspace is small and by diving too far the caver can be caught under a submerged shelf.

Stoke 2

The main stream enters from an inlet system on the right which can be followed for some distance in very dry conditions. Ahead a low tube emerges into an attractive scalloped streamway. A boulder slope leading up into the main chamber is passed before the roof lowers again. The stream cuts down several short cascades and spacious passage continues until two boulder ruckles are met. The second emerges into Pool Chamber and Sump 2.

A long boulder slope in Pool Chamber leads up into the impressive Bone Chamber which is over 30m long and 15m high. The chamber was named when human and animal bones were found together with ash and charcoal in the centre of the chamber – do not damage the remaining deposits!

Crawls lead on into the Throne Room, a large well decorated chamber with a Queen Victoria look-alike stalagmite. To the left a 3m climb leads up towards the Traverse Grotto, from where an exposed but easy traverse (lifeline required) and descent drops into the large Main Chamber.

Moving across the top of the Main Chamber leads to a descent into CB Chamber from which a narrow passage rejoins the streamway at the changing room, a short way downstream of sump 1.

Stoke 3 – 8 is only accessible to divers.

Bibliography

Irwin, D.J. and Jarrett, A., Mendip Undergroup.
Irwin, D.J. et al. St. Cuthbert's Swallet. B.E.C. 1991. Includes survey, photos and maps.
Price, G. Editor, Limestones and Caves of the Mendip Hills, David & Charles.

DEVON
by Dr. Peter Glanvill

Peter Glanvill has been interested in caves from an early age and started caving in 1966, also a scuba diver, the two hobbies were combined and he is a qualified cave diver. He has caved in most areas in Britain as well as France, Morocco and Iran. He combines his love of caving with photography and nowadays spends his time digging for new caves in Devon. He is the Devon regional correspondent for Descent magazine.

INTRODUCTION

Devon caves are unique in Britain. There is no well defined range of limestone hills, there are virtually no vadose caves and almost all have been exposed by quarrying. The geology of the region accounts for these characteristics.

Devonian limestone in which the caves lie is some of the oldest in Britain. The beds have consequently been shattered and disrupted by tectonic activity to produce scattered blocks throughout the county, many only metres wide but sometimes kilometres long. The location of the limestone dictates the presence of the caves rather than the volume of limestone. For example the limestone terrace in the vicinity of the River Dart has allowed the formation of the extensive Baker's Pit/Reed's Cave system in a small area of limestone. In other parts of Devon quite large blocks of limestone seem to have no associated major cave systems. Devon is a heavily farmed well-populated county and nearly all the caves described are on private land with controlled access.

All the caves are near major roads and 3 are marked on OS maps of the area.

USEFUL ADDRESSES

Afton Red Rift
Bill Tolfree
6 Ledsgrove
Ipplepen
Devon
Tel 01803 812582
(is prepared to advise on
contacts for access in cases of
difficulty. He does not have keys.)

Peter Waite
17 The Mint
Exeter
Devon
Tel 01392 56438

John Hooper
34 Richmond Road
Staines
Middlesex TW18 2AB

Wilfred Joint
93 Oaklands Park
Buckfastleigh
Devon
Tel 01364 43612

William Pengelly Cave Studies Trust
Higher Kiln Quarry
Russetts Lane
Buckfastleigh
Devon

208

ACCOMMODATION

Devon Speleological Society
Colin Pearce
2 Vine Close
St Leonards
Exeter EX2 4EX
Courtlands Centre
Kingsbridge
Devon TQ7 4BN
Tel 01548 550227

D.S.S. Hut Warden
Moorstone Barn
Marchington
Chagford
Devon

TOURIST INFORMATION OFFICE

The Plains
Totnes
Devon TQ9 5EJ
Tel 01803 863168

AFTON RED RIFT

AFTON RED RIFT   Grade 2

**Grid Ref: SX 838632   O.S. Landranger Series No 202, Torbay & South
Dartmoor, 1:50,000.   Altitude: 115m   Length: 400m   Depth: 30m**

Although not a long cave Afton Red Rift offers a sporting round trip passing a still well decorated chamber. This may be because the cave is off the beaten track and access is restricted. It has the reputation of causing some panicky moments to university clubs who have it as an easy option for 'freshers' trips. First explored by the Devon Speleological Society 1947.

For access, write to Peter Waite for key. There is likely to be a charge and deposit. Please note that on some Saturdays in the winter months the cave is closed.

WARNING: Slippery traverse – dangerous for novices.

The best approach is from Newton Abbot via the A381. The cave is marked on the map and is an obvious gash in the face of a disused quarry.

Beyond the gate the cave develops as a traverse along a 6m deep rift. This widens at an awkward corner where the ledges prove slippery before firmer ground is reached. After a narrow section the passage terminates abruptly in a climb down into Flower Chamber (handline useful for novices). In the right hand wall a slot leads into the short Lighthouse Series. The main route continues as a rift eventually debouching in the richly red Cascade Chamber that descends to a mud choke. Two routes exit from the chamber; one is the Upper Series, a series of ascending crawls and low chambers containing some nice crystals while the other route develops into yet another rift.

A chamber is reached (Mud Hall) with a hole in the roof on the left that can be reached by a very awkward climb. The passage beyond leads to a small streamway that has been intermittently dug. The main rift continues eventually becoming too tight but before it does so there is an obvious hole in the right hand wall. This is the chemically enlarged Watkin's Squeeze that provides an entertaining uphill struggle into the base of a high rift. An easy climb enters the entrance passage at the awkward bend completing the round trip.

Please take care to protect the formations – they are rarely as unsullied in Devon.

Survey currently out of print.

BAKER'S PIT   Grade 3

**Grid Ref: SX 742664   O.S. Landranger Series No 202, Torbay and South
Dartmoor, 1:50,000.   Altitude: 80m   Length: 2,500m (approx)
Depth: 23m**

Discovered in 1847 by quarrying only a few metres from the (recently burnt out) church on the hill top dominating Buckfastleigh, this cave system has the distinction of being the longest known in Devon. The only recent find is the kilometre long Plymouth extension discovered by the P.C.G. in 1968. Various small discoveries have been made since and in the 1970's the nearby Bullycleaves quarry breached the lower series creating another entrance (not usable except in rescues). The abandoned quarry containing Baker's Pit was used as a rubbish tip until, by the mid 1970's, it had been filled to the brim, grassed over and a concrete shaft driven through the rubbish to link with an older but also semi-artificial entrance, the original having been choked very early in the tip's genesis.

There is no 'top to bottom' route in the cave, so the route described is one that will take in all the main features of the cave while avoiding unnecessary backtracking. A copy of the survey is useful but not essential. A proper survey of the Plymouth extension has still not been published.

Keys can be obtained for access by contacting Peter Waite, a small fee and deposit may be payable. Bill Tolfree may be able to advise as well (see arrangements for Afton Red Rift)

The entrance lies about 100m due south of the church and is best approached by the lane that winds up from Kiln Quarry (William Pengelly Field Centre). A locked grill covers a 16m deep shaft lined by concrete rings. No tackle is required, rungs are embedded in the concrete. A stoop through a low door at the base enters the cave proper.

A short crawl enters the first large chamber. On the left a short passage leads to the original rubbish choked entrance. Across the top of the chamber along the bedding is the way on and then left down a meandering crawl to the entrance of a dripping stal decorated rift. To the right is a route to an impassable link with Reed's Cave.

Swildon's Rift opens onto a large bouldery passage. Left it diminishes and progress is over and along slabs to a slippery 2m descent. The low route then doubles back and emerges in the wall of Boulder Hall extension. Keeping right over the slabs the crawl opens out into the tent roofed start of Crystal Corridor, a roomy phreatic tube. Beware the pool, it is deeper than you think. Note the micro-gours and ribbon curtains below a trickle from the roof. Beyond, the roof lowers temporarily then rises. A passage to the right is the entrance to Crawl and Rift series (location of two major rescues). Straight on ducks under the wall into more walking sized passage descending to a final chamber. On the right near the end a cat crawl emerges at a curious porthole 2m above the floor. The way out is a crawl on the left that emerges back in Crystal Corridor.

Leave Crystal Corridor by the inward route – passages on left of pool lead to the well-decorated Chapel. Carry straight across Boulder Hall Extension and a meandering route between a sloping right hand wall and slabs on the left leads to a large flake tilted across a rift (Martin's Garden) beyond which a few metres of sideways walking leads to a junction. Ignore the down-slope tube and take the shoulder height squeeze on the right into Two John's Tunnel. This emerges in Glorious Devon Series.

Glorious Devon Series is a multi-level series of boulder chambers sloping up to scree cones below the graveyard. Left from Two John's Tunnel is a chamber that ascends to the flat out squeeze into Whitsun Chamber. Straight across the chamber is a route to Red Chamber where a prominent wall of fine red crystals can be seen. Before Red Chamber a hole in the wall is the main way on.

The hole opens onto a 5m deep rift crossed by a straddle on stal ledges – the Crystal Leap – onto a mud slope. Descend the obvious pot (roof height here is 15m!) and follow the roomy Great Rift. 20m on a small stream enters from under the left wall. Soon after the passage opens at Stream Chamber that is dotted with pits and slippery boulders. On the left at the start is an enlargement – Judge's Chamber – where a roof tunnel, the Drain, comes in from Boulder Hall Extension.

Stream Chamber ends where the stream sinks – a climb on the left leads to Lower Stream Series and the lower entrance. Avoid visiting this area in winter – hibernating bats.

The way on is found on the left hand side of Stream Chamber at an obvious inlet. Easy going ends at a waterfall. Above it a squeeze/climb up fissures in the roof is the normal route into the Plymouth Extension. The rift above enters a low horizontal tube ending at a deep rift in the floor and a cross roads. This enlargement and the bedding passage beyond are known as Plymouth Chamber. The Plymouth Extension can be confusing for route finding. Essentially cross the bedding until a point is reached where the cave ascends up dip. More precisely, cross the rift, turn right to reach a curtain and pillar cluster, beyond which, on the left, a route of crawls and squeezes leads to the base of Platform Chamber, a big multi-level chamber which can be reached at one end by a climb into a corkscrew tube and at the other by a crawl past some pristine clear stals.

Facing the climb up into Platform Chamber and going right along the bedding leads an ascending crawl which enters to a well-decorated grotto. Leave Plymouth Extension by the same route unless you don't mind some interesting route finding!

When leaving the system reverse your route to the pot then ascend the obvious Dutch Oven Tunnel to the right that emerges at Two John's Tunnel. Beyond Martin's Garden turn left down into Drain Chamber where a small streamway

BUCKFASTLEIGH AREA

1. Baker's Pit
2. Reeds Cave
3. Pridhamsleigh Cavern

0   1 km

enters. An interesting convoluted upstream route emerges in Boulder Chamber that opens after a scramble over boulders into the First Chamber. An easy walk up the chamber takes one to the entrance at the top on the right. Be warned, if you are going to get lost anywhere, First Chamber on the way out is the place most people become disorientated. It may be worth taking a peek at its layout on the way in to avoid this occurring.

Formations in the cave are plentiful but frequently muddy – please those which aren't unsullied.

A survey is available from John Hooper, (does not have the Plymouth extension on it).

PRIDHAMSLEIGH CAVERN   Grade 2

Grid Ref: SX 748679   O.S. Landranger Series No 202 Torbay and South Dartmoor, 1:50,000.   Altitude: 60m   Length: 1,100m

WARNING: Slippery mud, deep pools.

This complex phreatic maze lies within a mile of the Baker's Pit system. Discovered by quarrying in the last century it has become the premier site for outdoor activity groups in Devon and as such has suffered considerably.

Prid, as it is locally known, poses some interesting route finding problems and any description of a classic trip is somewhat arbitrary. What I have described is the most convenient route to the caves main feature The Lake. I have then selected an outward route that takes in some of the other points of interest in the system.

To reach the cave turn off the A38 dual carriage way at Buckfastleigh, go over it and then take the old main road which runs parallel to the dual carriageway. Take the first turning right that leads over the A38 to Pridhamsleigh Farm. An unusual stone dovecote will be seen on the left just past the bridge. Park on the left opposite the farm, visitors MUST call at the farm. A small charge is made to cross his land to the cave. Remember to close the gates and don't leave litter about. After the trip muddy gear can be washed in the stream on the far side of the motorway.

A track leads past some cattle sheds to a muddy path above the dual carriageway. The gaping entrance to Pridhamsleigh Cavern cannot be missed! Although there are obvious cave passages at opposite ends of the entrance chamber the way on is a low muddy grovel often in cattle slurry right in the centre. It opens immediately into walking size passage.

To begin the route is clear with few branches. However, beyond a step in the floor over the excavated Lobster Pot and a short stooping wade, Crystal Chamber is reached. The overhanging flowstone cascade on the right hand wall can be seen to be severely vandalised – a fate that has affected virtually all accessible stal in the system. The main way on is obvious but inspection of the chamber will reveal other routes that should be ignored.

Slippery flowstone leads to a portly, boulder blocked window in the left wall that opens into the large Bishop's Chamber. A trench in the mud floor is the residue from an unfruitful archaeological excavation. Passing through the curious circular hole in the roof on the right leads up to a bedding series – the Attics.

At the far end of the chamber confusion reigns. There are 3 obvious routes. The Mud Staircase ascends to the Attics while to the left is another route leading to a large steeply descending blind tube known as the Bear Pit. Straight on and down is the main route. The route is obvious for a while owing to the fact that large quantities of mud have been removed from the floor here over recent years creating a deep trench winding through a pendant festooned bedding plane. This debouches in standing passage where again there is a bewildering parting of the ways.

To the left is an almost vertical sheer climb known as the Slide adjacent to which is another less steep and stepped climb (the Coal Chute) above a figure of eight shaped hole in the floor (the Coal Hole) which drops into the Cellars, a lower series often flooded in winter months. Yet another floor level squeeze beyond the Coal Hole also connects with the Cellars.

The climb leads to a small chamber and a descending crawl over boulders into a much larger standing sized passage/chamber known as Junction Chamber. Forward the passage breaks up into the Little Maze passing yet another route down to the Cellars before a window opens onto the impressive Pit.

Fortunately the Pit is only 3m deep with an easy traverse round the side to arrive by a massive block of fallen flowstone. A short climb drops into an imposing descending tunnel the Grand Gallery that enlarges rapidly passing the route from the Cellars on the right until at a corner the Lake is encountered.

The Lake, a deep green 20m long pool stretches into the gloom. From here the cave is only accessible to divers. Several other passages in Pridhamsleigh reach the water table and on exit it is possible to visit them without retracing ones' steps.

Left of the diving platform a short climb and traverse leads to a short network of tubes ending in a chamber known as Mystery Pool. A short free-divable sump in low water leads under one wall into a short continuation and another, yet to be fully explored, sump. In high water one of the main routes into Mystery Pool may be sumped so beware.

Back at Junction Chamber a crawl following the right hand wall, the Bypass, leads to a drop into a rift. A short distance along this rift another climb up and a low crawl to the right drops through a hole into a tunnel which debouches at the far side of the Bear Pit and can be followed into the Deep Well which has been dived and gets too tight. An interesting traverse (or swim) across the Well leads to an interesting passage ending in another flooded rift. Carring on instead of descending the above mentioned hole one eventually emerges in the roof of Crystal Chamber.

An alternative route from Junction Chamber is to take the first left on entering the Bypass and crawl into the Attics from which an obvious and slithery descent can be made down the Mud Staircase back to Bishop's Chamber.

There are many other passages and devious routes in Prid that can be explored if time allows.

Fifty to hundred metres back along the track before one reaches Prid there is a hole in the bank. This is the entrance to Dogholes a short 300 metre system extended in the late '70's by the P.C.G. The cave although horribly desecrated still contains attractive formations in its inner reaches. Visitors are advised to explore this cave before or instead of Pridhamsleigh to avoid further mud damage to the crystal floors and formations.

Survey ref: published in Cave Science Vol. 5 No 34, October 1963.

REED'S CAVE Grade 2

Grid Ref: SX 742664   O.S. Landranger Series No 202, Torbay and South Dartmoor, 1:50,000.   Altitude: 60m   Length: 900m   Depth: 15m

First explored in 1939 by D.S.S. members Edgar Reed and Wilfred Joint.

Although Reed's Cave and Baker's Pit are connected, the link was blocked some years ago to protect the superior and unspoilt formations in Reed's. It has remained un-vandalised having been discovered within the last 60 years and has always been gated. Its prominent entrance is in an old quarry belonging to the Devon Wildlife Trust. Several other short caves lie in the quarry – noteworthy is the famous palaeontological site, Joint Mitnor Cave. Some have grilles to protect bat colonies.

There is a leader system operating for this cave. Contact Wilfred Joint or apply to William Pengelly Cave Studies Trust. No access during the bat hibernation season i.e. late September to late April/early May.

A step ladder (!) is used to reach the locked entrance gate. From here a walking sized passage gradually dwindles to a low crawl ending in a squeeze up through a false floor (originally opened with a car jack). A careful scramble over a stal bank past some spectacular curtains enters Easter Chamber, one of the largest chambers in the system. On the opposite side to the entrance are several tunnels that unite and end in a grotto containing one of the most remarkable stalactite formations in Britain – the Little Man. This fractured re-cemented stal pillar uncannily resembles a man wearing a top hat.

In Easter Chamber a climb into the roof to the left of the curtains while facing them, leads into the complex network of tubes and squeezes known as the Upper Series. Another short series lies under the floor of Easter Chamber.

Tackle: Step ladder for entrance.
Survey ref: see Baker's Pit.

Bibliography

Old D.S.S. Journals – available from J. Hooper, 34 Richmond Road, Staines, Middlesex.
Old P.C.G. Journals – A. Neill, 25 Lipton Road, St. Judes, Plymouth, Devon PL4 8PL.
Oldham, T., Caves of Devon, 1972.

FOREST OF DEAN and WYE VALLEY
by Des Marshall

ACCOMMODATION

A good campsite can be found at Christchurch, grid ref SO 566129.

SLAUGHTER STREAM CAVE   Grade 3

Grid Ref: SO 582137   O.S. Outdoor Leisure Series No 14, Wye Valley and Forest of Dean, 1:25,000.   Altitude: 145m   Length: 6,600m+ Vertical Range: 100m

The first digs started in the 1950's and continued sporadically since. The big breakthroughs were made in April and December 1990 by the JAGA Group (the initials of the 4 original explorers), reaching firstly Mouse Aven and then breaking through the choke leading to Balcony Chamber. Major discoveries both down-stream and upstream were made in January to May 1991. Exploration still continues to find more passages.

Access to the cave is administered by the R.F.D.C.C. on behalf of the landowner. Trips are allowed only at weekends. To arrange a trip contact Andy Clark, Sunshade Cottage, Lower Redbrook, Nr. Monmouth, NP5 4LZ. No carbide is allowed into the cave. Parking space is very limited 2 cars only at the small pull in by the gate at SO 580138. The maximum party size is 6 experienced cavers.

From Symonds Yat follow the B4432 to the 5 Ways at Christchurch. Turn right on to the B4228 and immediately turn left. After 500m turn left again into The Lonk. Continue along this narrow road, down a steep hill to signs denoting the Dog and Muffler pub to the right (a good watering hole!). Keep following the road to roadside houses on the left as the road rises. Park tidily to the right on the grass verge before the gate.

The cave is found by going over the stile by the gate and crossing the field to the trees where a stile leads over a barbed wire fence to the path that leads to the entrance – Wet Sink – the site of the original explorations. Descending fixed ladders reaches the locked gate. A squeeze beyond leads to a further fixed ladder descent to the floor of Mouse Aven. Directly under the pitch a choke is passed which has been shored by scaffolding – CARE. A climb down at the far end leads to the top of the 3m pitch into Balcony Chamber, followed immediately by a fine 12m pitch dropping to the floor of another aven. Climb down to a tiny trickle of water which is followed through some low damp crawls to the main Slaughter Stream at Cross Junction. Downstream, walking size passage leads to Sump 1. 100m upstream of this a crawl off to the right over sand enters the Dryslade Series to bypass the sump. The crawl quickly enlarges to walking in a dry passage to reach a dry, taped off mud sump. Pass this to the right to a junction. Right is Coal Seam Passage and links into The Chunnel in the upstream series. (Going back via Coal Seam passage makes a fine 3 hour trip). Left eventually rejoins the stream immediately beyond sump 2. Shortly before rejoining the streamway a short climb on the left leads to further climbs to enter the remarkable lengthy rift of Pirate Passage. The streamway continues in a 15m high passage. Due to the many waterworn features the passage has been named the Sculpture Trail. After two deep pools at a right angled bend a passage leads off to the left, Echo Passage.

Continuing downstream the roof lowers and eventually the stream disappears into sump 3. A sandy crawl to the right here soon enters larger passage and continues past a series of drops to reach Kuwait Passage with jet black walls adorned with helictites. A long way further on a climb down at Razor Pot leads to a rift at the end of which is Lights Out Chamber. Here the character of the cave changes. A series of tight rifts reaches a small stream ending at a static sump – sump 4, the end of the cave for non-divers.

Back at the point of entry to the main stream at Cross Junction going upstream a well decorated streamway leads to an obvious passage on the left, this can be followed with great care to an inlet through a loose boulder choke. To the right a narrow crawl reaches a large, high chamber with formations in the roof. The stream enters from the right but a climb up to the left reaches a fossil streamway. Crawl through a choke on the right leading into dry passages known as The Graveyard. A taped path leads through The Graveyard (passing bones which gave the passage it's name) and some formations known as the Gnome Garden. A mud floored passage continues to a junction. Going left enters a large passage called The Chunnel which enlarges even more until it is some 10m wide and 5m high.

Some distance on an obvious passage on the right leads off to Kiln Passage which ends in a choke – care with some good formations.

70m from the junction with Kiln Passage, three low sandy areas – The Three Deserts – separated by breakdown are passed to emerge into yet more very dry walking passage. The Three Deserts extension is 1,053m long, mainly walking!

356m from the Chunnel, along the Three Deserts passage, a climb up loose rocks in an area of breakdown leads to a split in the passage. Left goes to animal tracks and dog's grave, whilst right enters the largest passage yet found in Slaughter Stream Cave – Flow Choke Passage – some 5m wide and 12m high. At the end of this passage a heavily calcited choke marks the end, 737m from the breakthrough.

In The Chunnel shortly after the junction with Kiln Passage, a drop down through boulders leads into Coal Seam Passage and eventually the streamway. (It is also possible to do a round trip in this direction).

Tackle:

	Rope length required	Bolts
Climb down and Balcony Chamber pitch	30m	5

Survey ref: WET SINK (Slaughter Stream Cave) Drawn by Paul Taylor 1995.

Bibliography

Descent Nos. 99, 100 – 102, 104, 105, 112 and 113.

WYE VALLEY

USEFUL ADDRESSES
  Otter Hole Access
  John Hutchinson
  4 Redwood Close
  Bulwark
  Chepstow
  Gwent

OTTER HOLE

Grade 5

Grid Ref: ST 525962   O.S. Outdoor Leisure Series No 14., Wye Valley and Forest of Dean, 1:25,000.   Altitude: 13m   Length: 3,200m Vertical Range: 40m

The entrance was dug out in September 1974 with 270m of passage explored in 2 days by the R.F.D.C.C. Subsequent exploration became a joint effort between the R.F.D.C.C. and G.S.S., as well as a phantom digger from the B.E.C. Entry in to the Extension was achieved at the end of December 1975, with the fantastic Hall of Thirty being reached in January 1976. The end of the cave was reached in the same year as well as the magnificent Crystal Balls Passage. Exploration continues at the end of Tunnels Left. The various sumps have all been dived by members of the C.D.G. but nothing has been found.

Access is vested in the R.F.D.C.C. and G.S.S. with a leader system in operation. All requests for a trip must be addressed to John Hutchinson.

WARNING: The entrance series is impassable when tides are 14.7m or greater, as well as during a spell of wet weather. Access beyond the tidal sump is only passable 3 hours either side of low tide. Copious sea mud occupies the whole of the entrance series as well as a short distance beyond the tidal sump. Arrowsmith's Tide Tables are indispensable when arranging a trip and are available from local booksellers. Occasionally people have been ill after a trip in the cave from unknown sources so take care with cuts.

Situated on the west bank of the River Wye the cave is best approached from the Forestry Commission car park, 1km NE of St, Arvans, on the A466 Chepstow to Monmouth road. A good track leads S from the car park through the wood but becomes less defined as it descends towards the river bank. The entrance is beneath a small cliff just above the river bank.

A fantastic cave perhaps the most beautifully decorated in Britain!

Just inside the entrance is the locked gate. Immediately beyond is a 3m drop into the extremely muddy continuation crawl. Follow the black P.V.C. pipe to the lowest point in the bedding planes. Stooping passage continues and a not too obvious way to the right. Sliding, grovelling and climbing in the sloppy filth larger passage is eventually reached with some mud encrusted formations! As the Tidal Sump is approached the mud gets sloppier and deeper. If you have got it right knee deep mud descends to the sump and the arch through which the main stream of Otter Hole flows out. A small eye-hole above the arch stays open a little longer through which it is possible to pass. Horrendously slippery boulders are grovelled over to a 5m fixed iron ladder into the First Boulder Choke. Easy squeezes pass this to a slippery, squalid climb down to the stream, now in a rift passage. A short traverse and a few boulder obstacles reach a boulder hall. The stream goes off left while to the right dry bedding planes reach the Second Boulder Choke. A tight and quite awkward chimney leads up from the right of the choke to enter a bouldery rift passage. This ascends to the top of a boulder slope (the site of the old 7m ladder pitch) leading back down to the stream to reach Sump 2 after 120m. Some 60m after rejoining the stream a turn to the right ascends a rift via a series of climbs and squeezes to end above the streamway in the Extension in a 4m x 2m passage. Crystal Balls Passage goes off to the right whilst the main route is left.

Suddenly the passage enlarges at some large stalagmites and bosses, followed quickly by the stupendous Hall of Thirty. The way out of the Hall of Thirty is a

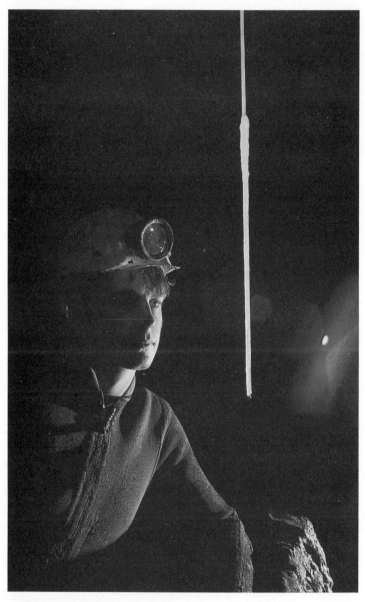

Otter Hole Wye Valley. *Photo: Tony Baker*

downward slot into the continuing passage. The wealth and splendour of the formations in the continuing passage is unequalled in Britain. Please keep to the taped path. Eventually Camp 1 is reached where there is a source of fresh water entering from the roof. Continuing, further magnificent formations are passed to reach Tunnels Junction. The, initially, bouldery Tunnels Left reaches the end of the cave at a boulder choke after a sandy hand and knees crawl. Tunnels Right is a smaller passage and care must be taken not to damage the delicate straws that abound. The passage ends at a pool choked with flaky calcite.

Survey ref: Otter Hole obtainable from John Hutchinson at the above address.

Bibliography

B.C.R.A. Transactions Vol 6 No 4, December 1979 (includes survey).
Stratford, T., Caves of South Wales, Cordee.
Arrowsmith, K.W., Tide Tables for Bristol and Bristol Channel Ports.

IRELAND – COUNTY FERMANAGH
by Tim Fogg

Tim Fogg starting caving in 1970 in Fermanagh and apart from 4 years in the 70's spent working in the Antarctic he has been caving ever since. He is a veteran of 15 caving expeditions including 4 to China, 3 to Mulu, Sarawak, 2 to Irian Jaya and he has caved extensively in Europe. He moved to Fermanagh 15 years ago to teach in outdoor education and is now the Director of an industrial rope access company. Tim holds the Cave Instructors Certificate and is actively involved in training cavers and the Irish Cave Rescue Organisation.

INTRODUCTION

A glance at the geological map of Ireland should gladden the heart of any cave enthusiast, for it shows a central basin of Carboniferous Limestone underlying almost half the country. The best caves are concentrated in the uplands of the Burren in County Clare and in those parts of Counties Sligo, Leitrim, Cavan and Fermanagh flanking the Arigna Coalfields.

In County Sligo the caves have formed in the youngest part of the strongly chertified Upper Limestone known locally as the Dartry Limestone. Concealed in the wild expanses of open bog are many rifts and potholes, including the 142m-deep Carrowmore Pot in the Geevagh Area, until recently the deepest known in Ireland.

The more extensive caves of County Fermanagh, are developed in the clean, massive 'reef' facies of the Dartry Limestone, whose structure encourages the development of systems similar in profile to those of the Yorkshire Dales.

The Fermanagh caves are situated in two main areas SW of the county town of Enniskillen, along the northern edges of Tullybrack and Cuilcagh mountains. Tullybrack is noted for its classic potholes leading into great horizontal systems (Reyfad and Noon's Hole) while Cuilcagh is best known for its dendritic river caves (Marble Arch System and the Prod's Pot/Cascade system).

A wet suit is very advisable for the caves described.

GENERAL ACCESS AND CONSERVATION

Local cavers should be contacted for information on the present state of access in the area. The situation with land owners is volatile and we rely on their good will.

Carbide has not been banned by the Irish caving community but ALL CARBIDE WASTE MUST BE CARRIED OUT OF THE CAVE.

Surveys for these caves can be found in 'Caves of Fermanagh and Cavan' and they can also be obtained from Gaby Burns through the Speleological Union of Ireland.

USEFUL ADDRESSES

Speleological Union of Ireland
c/o A.F.A.S., House of Sport
Longmile Road, Walkinstown
Dublin 12
Tel 01 509845

RESCUE

Cave rescue in the area is organised by the Irish Cave Rescue Organisation and there are four Fermanagh Wardens who can be contacted through the Marble Arch Show Cave (01365 348855), Gortatole Outdoor Education Centre (01365 348888) or in an emergency the police (999). However, I.C.R.O. only has two hundred people on the call out list and they are spread all over Ireland. The reaction time to a full rescue is inevitably slow and visiting cavers should recognise the self-help nature of caving in Ireland.

CASCADES / PROD'S   Grade 5

Grid Ref: 136337   O.S. of N Ireland Sheet 26, Lough Allen 1:50,000.
Altitude: 220m   Length: 4,100m   Depth: 94m

Prod's Pot was first discovered by the Reyfad Group 1970 whilst Farr and Morris explored Cascades after diving downstream from Prod's Pot in 1974. The resurgence was subsequently entered by Phillips, Drew and Ball in 1976.

WARNING: This system takes a finite amount of water, the overflow going to Marble Arch. However, because of the low entrance series high water could enforce a long stay. There is an I.C.R.O. depot on the upstream side of the ducks into the entrance series. The collapse areas in the main passage have mainly large rocking/loose boulders and great care must be taken.

The system drains the area to the east of the Marble Arch System, in fact it takes water from the same river off Cuilcagh Mountain as the Pollasumera Branch of Marble Arch. There are two entrances to the system, Prod's Pot and Cascade resurgence. The resurgence cave is characterised by its progression from the thinly bedded, lower shaley limestones up into the thick Dartry beds.

Cascade Resurgence to Sump 6

The entrance to the system is located some 15m up the slope from the resurgence but squeezing down through boulders the stream is quickly joined. Progress upstream is confusing as the water winds and splits many times through the joints and thin beds. Two or three routes are possible in a number of places including the final obstacle, ducks or a tight boulder choke, before the bigger passages. The route on from the depot follows the stream but soon, collapses force the route over the top through boulders. Back at water level very pleasant caving in the fine active Brandywine Streamway eventually ends in sump 8. The 180m bypass to sump 8 and 7 is just downstream on the right (looking downstream). This passage with its delicate calcite and mud formations enters the impressive Creatures End Chamber, in the roof of which are a couple of big avens. The Leprechaun Crawl back to the stream is the obvious way on. About another 150m of great streamway and sump 6 is encountered.

MARBLE ARCH   Grade 4

Grid Ref: 122345   O.S. of N. Ireland Sheet 26, Lough Allen 1:50,000.
Altitude: 150m   Length: 6,500m   Depth: 50m Approx.

The first explorations were by Martel and Jamieson reaching Pool Chamber in 1895 and the Yorkshire Ramblers discovered Skreen Hill One in 1936.

Cavers must call at the show cave building where they will be asked to read the

Marble Arch and Prod's/Cascade System

Prod's Pot County Fermanagh. *Photo: Tony Baker*

'Code of Conduct' and give details of their intended trip. Cavers should only use the undeveloped entrances to the cave and not the tourist entrances. Out of show cave business hours cavers should put details of the trip on a note through the letter box of the reception building.

WARNING: The water levels in some areas of the cave are controlled to a certain degree by the Caves Flood Management Systems and advice should be sought from the cave staff if rain is forecasted.

There are three main sinks just beyond the Namurian Limestone contact: Pollasumera, Monastir and Sruh Croppa. Entry to the system is gained by a number of wet or dry entrances just above the rising where the 3 streams emerge as the River Cladagh at the contact with the underlying thinly bedded Glencar Limestone at the 'Marble Arch' itself.

In 1985 the Wet Entrance and Skreen Hill 1 were adapted as a magnificent tourist cave, fulfilling a suggestion made by Martel in his book 'Irlande et Cavernes Anglaises', published nearly a hundred years earlier.

The Slit Entrance via the Show Cave to Legnabrocky Way.

The Slit Entrance to the system is just inside the National Nature Reserve where the tourist path leads from the reception building. The open rift is 5m to the left of the path. There is an awkward 3m climb to descend from daylight into the Great Boulder Chamber and a handline tied to a tree on the surface is advised. Descending to the lowest point in the Chamber and turning right to squeeze through boulders brings the show cave lights into view. This is Pool Chamber where the traditional way on to Skreen Hill 1 lies up the collapse boulders on the left through the Fly Over. However, the Show Cave path follows a man made tunnel over the pool to emerge in New Chamber which is the fossil route and present flood overflow for the river ahead. For 350m the Show Cave path runs upstream along superb river passage to the tourist's 'Journeys End'. Just ahead lies a lake and sump. The sump bypass is on the left and is reached by wading across the lake. A climb up through a calcited boulder choke leads to the Organ Chamber and a short crawl to the keyhole shaped Crab Passage is the way on. Spiralling down to a static pool the passage dimensions start to increase and the river is regained in Skreen Hill 2. To the left, upstream, is the 25m long sump to Skreen Hill 3 and right the sump just bypassed. At this sump the obvious Legnabrocky inlet joins the main flow. Legnabrocky Way starts as a small stream passage with a floor of rounded boulders and continues in crawls and wet rifts to a muddy chamber. Exit from this chamber is a low wet passage (the Wet Wiggle) which can sump in extreme conditions. The cave now becomes a series of bouldery, muddy chambers linked by low crawls and rift passages with an abundance of calcite formations. At Giants Hall the dimensions are impressive, 60m long, 30m high and 15m wide. Descending out of this cavern and passing the Mexican Way Inlet on the right the terminal sand chamber is soon reached. Charcoal layers in the sands mark the forest clearances on Cuilcagh Mountain 800 years ago.

A good finale to this trip is to continue on the Show Cave path to the Junction jetty where the three rivers merge and follow upstream to the Grand Gallery. If the deep water (wet suit needed) of the ducks is braved an exit can be made via Lower Cradle.

Tackle: 15m handline for Slit Entrance.

NOON'S HOLE / ARCH CAVE SYSTEM   Grade 5

**Grid Ref: 094483   O.S. of N. Ireland Sheet 17, Lower Lough Erne
1:50,000.   Altitude: 230m   Length: 3,500m   Depth: 108m**

First exploration. The Yorkshire Ramblers bottomed the shaft in 1912. However, the first person down the pot was Dominic Noon, an informer who in 1826 was cast into its supposedly bottomless depths as punishment for his treachery.

Contact local cavers for information on the current access situation.

WARNING: Fed by a small stream draining off upland bog it reacts quickly to rainfall. The first pitch becomes very wet (impassable) and the pitches below very draughty and moderately wet. The After Noon Series sumps off in various places. There is an I.C.R.O. depot at the junction between Crucifixion Crawl and High Noon but in extreme conditions this has been washed away!

The Noon's Arch System carries one major stream from the sink down the shaft of Noon's via a sump to Arch 2 and on to the Arch 1 resurgence via a further two sumps. However, it is possible to bypass the first sump from Noon's to Arch 2 through the Afternoon and High Noon Series.

Noon's to Arch 2

Noon's Hole lies just to the west and down slope from the track in a tree filled hollow. The best rigging points are in the gully on the opposite side of the pot from the waterfall. The 97m shaft is split by a series of ledges with the main water only flowing down the daylight 25m. From the small chamber at the bottom of the shaft a narrow rift leads instantly to a deep pool and 50m further on to a 'T' junction. The first sump is right, downstream, but left leads through pools, rifts and crawls to a static sump. Just before the sump and up a short climb is the tight entrance to Crucifixion Crawl. 10m of crawl ends with exiting up through the floor in High Noon. Following High Noon's Right past awkward boulder blockages and with the High Noon's inlet water occasionally audible below, the caving slowly becomes more pleasant until Artie's Chamber. Here a wade through the Canal leads on. As the noise of water falling into the High Noon's sump is heard a passage on the left goes up delicate flowstone to a gour pool. Trending right in the pool leads to a boulder choke and through this is Chamber Passage. The connection with Arch 2 is hard to find in this mass of collapsed boulders. From the entrance to the Chamber trend down slope to gain the right wall at its lowest point where a slot between the wall and a boulder can be descended to a pool. Squeezing left along the wall it becomes necessary to lie in the water and contour (left) round a right angle bend. Released from this, a short scramble through boulders emerges into the Dry Oxbow of Arch 2.

This splendid passage has lakes, avens, formations and a couple of awkward boulder chokes. Traversing the 900m to the downstream sump the passage increases in size to a steady 9m x 9m. This is a classic trip.

Tackle: 105m SRT rope, 14 hangers
Survey ref: Irish Speleology Volume 3, No 2 1985.

Noon's/Arch and Reyfad Systems

REYFAD / POLLTULLYBRACK / POLLNACROM   Grade 5

Grid Ref: 089469   O.S. of N Ireland sheet 17, Lower Lough Erne, 1:50,000.   Altitude: 300m   Length: 6,700m   Depth: 179m

The Yorkshire Ramblers entered the Main Chamber in 1960.

Access by agreement with the land-owner. Contact local cavers for advice. At present the landowner is refusing all cavers and walkers access to his land. Pirating will result in the physical closure of the entrances.

WARNING: All surface drainage in the area of Reyfad Pot has been channelled to it by man made irrigation ditches. Rainfall makes the shaft unpleasant and heavy rainfall makes it impassable.

The three entrances to the system, Reyfad Pot, Pollnacrom and Polltullybrack lie high on the northeast slopes of Tullybrack mountain in depressions on the open bog-land. There are five streams in the system and three have been positively dye traced to the Carrickbeg Rising.

Reyfad Pot to the Main Aven

Entering the Reyfad Pot an 8m pit, formed along a fault, leads through a small window into the sensational but slightly loose 60m main shaft. At the boulder constriction at the bottom of this pitch the rope is rebelayed and continuing emerges in the roof of a magnificent passage with a 24m abseil to the floor, this passage, the main trunk route, measures in places over 15m x 15m with the Reyfad stream flowing south along it. The route to the Main Aven goes N, upstream, leaving the spacious passage for the confines of a canyon with intermittent boulder chokes. Some 200m after entering the canyon the passage direction swings from N to SE. At this point climbing up above the stream an area of very fine and varied formations is found. Continuing in the active vadose trench through a deep wade, a small inlet enters the narrow rift from Rory's Aven and a short climb up a waterfall leads to the bottom of the Main Aven. In all but the driest conditions this is a dramatic spray filled place with the stream falling 53m from the Polltullybrack inlet. A through trip is possible in dry weather entering Polltullybrack and crawling flat out for 400m to a duck and the head of the Aven.

Returning to the Reyfad entrance shaft a trip would not be complete without a short excursion downstream over mountainous sand banks and boulders to the Camp Site. From here climbing up and squeezing along the gap, between roof and infill, difficult route finding allows the Reyfad stream to be regained in the Aghnahoo Extension. The route towards Pollnacrom follows the main passage past the Camp Site via the North West Inlet.

Tackle: 100m SRT rope (or 15m, 65m & 45m), 10 hangers.
Survey ref: Irish Speleology Vol 3, No 2, 1985.

Bibliography

Coleman, Caves of Ireland, 1965.
Llwyd Jones, Gareth, Caves of Fermanagh and Cavan.
Irish Speleology, Journal of the Speleological Union of Ireland.

County Clare – Map Areas

Map 1 Faunarooska and Pollballiny
Map 2 Polldubh
Map 3 Poll Na Gree and Poll Na gCeim
Map 4 Coolagh River Cave
Map 5 Doolin River Cave
Map 6 Poulnagollum and Poulelva
Map 7 Cullaun Caves

IRELAND – COUNTY CLARE
by Colin Bunce and Brian Lillis

Colin Bunce began caving in 1977 in England with the Croydon Caving Club and the Aberystwyth University Caving Club. He made his first visit to The Burren in 1979 moving to the area in 1984. Colin was involved in the discovery of Poll na gCeim and extensions to Cullaun One. He is a great believer of the further cave potential in The Burren. At present Colin works as an outdoor pursuits instructor and lives in Ennis.

Brian Lillis B.A., H.Dip.Ed. Brian first starting caving in 1969 while at University College Galway. In 1976 he formed the Limerick and Mid West Caving Clubs. Previously secretary of the S.U.I. Brian set up Kilshanny Caving & Outdoor Pursuits Centre in 1984. Currently Brian is senior geography teacher at Villiers Secondary School in Limerick and lives near Ennis.

INTRODUCTION

The Burren is a unique area in Britain and Ireland – 200 square miles with large area of bare limestone pavements. There are some 63 miles of explored cave with a classic tall narrow meandering canyon shape often continuing for long distance. Most of the early exploration work was by U.B.S.S. There is little vertical development, pitches tend to be short so ladders and lifeline are most suitable. Most of the caves are susceptible to rapid and complete flooding and stream levels can rise very quickly during rain falls but will usually drop again equally quickly.

There are very few access problems. Of the caves included only Fergus River Cave and Doolin River Cave have special requirements. Please help ensure this situation is maintained by talking to the locals, avoiding damage to the stone walls and replacing any covers over cave entrances.

Directions to the cave are all described from Lisdoonvarna with mileage taken from a car trip meter.

USEFUL ADDRESSES

S.U.I Librarian
c/o A.F.A.S. House of Sport
Longmile Road
Dublin 12

Burren Holiday Hostel
Lisdoonvarna
County Clare
Tel: 00 353 65 74300
Fax: 00 353 65 74490

University of Bristol
Speleological Society
University Road
Bristol BS8 1SP

ACCOMMODATION

There are no caving huts in the area but there are a number of independent hostels:
Doolin Tel 065 74006

230

Lisdoonvarna Tel 065 74300
Fanore Tel 065 76134

Camping is available at Doolin and Fanore.
Details of self-catering cottages are available from the Irish Tourist Board.

PUBS

O'Connors and McGanns in Doolin
Roadside Tavern in Lisdoonvarna
O'Donoghues in Fanore
Hylands Hotel in Ballyvaughan

RESCUE

The Irish Cave Rescue Organisation provides a rescue service and can be reached by dialling 999. However it is important to realise there maybe a considerable time delay before a response can be made as there are only a handful of local cavers in the area, and other cavers will have to travel from other parts of Ireland. For this reason all cavers should carry food and equipment to keep them warm in the event of an accident.

MAPS

Irish Ordnance Survey – 1/2 inch to one mile – sheet 14 Galway Bay.
Irish Ordnance Survey – 1:50,000 Sheet No 51, The Burren.
Map of the Uplands of County Clare – Tim Robinson – ISBN 0950400211.

COOLAGH RIVER CAVE   Grade 5

**Grid Ref: Polldonough M126014   Grid Ref: Polldonough S M124010
Irish O.S. Sheet No 51, The Burren, 1:50,000
Altitude: Polldonough 172m, Polldonough N 183m, Polldonough S 168m,
Polldonough W 178m.   Length: 5,300m   Depth: 72m**

Partially explored in 1936–37 by the Y.R.C. Further explorations by the U.B.S.S. in 1949–51.

The cave is very popular due to the impressive main streamway. However, the cave has a large catchment area and can respond very quickly to rain, the bedding planes will quickly sump and the cave has been known to fill completely!

Refer to Map 4. From Lisdoonvarna go north on the Ballyvaughan road N67 for 0.9 miles to Kilmoon. Turn left at junction 0515 and follow this road for 1.1 miles to a left turn. A further 1.1 miles reaches a cross roads, just before this on the right is the Polldonough Swallet, the exit point for the route described here. The entry point is Polldonough South Swallet, found by turning left at the cross roads. After 0.2 miles park on the verge. Enter the field on the left of the road by the gate. Straight across the field for 100m to reach the river. The entrance is a wide bedding plane taking the river.

The river is followed for 100m through a series of crawls and canals. (Entrance B9a avoids this section but is at present blocked). The passage gradually enlarges and develops an hourglass shape with an upper and lower level known as Double

COOLAGH RIVER CAVE

Passage. Traverse along the upper level on greasy ledges. This is probably the best place to sit out a flood and a rescue dump has been positioned here. After passing some large wedged blocks the traverse ends at Column Chamber. Here an awkward 3m climb down lands on a mud floor with several passages leading off. Opposite Double Passage a short mud slide leads to a low bedding plane. After 20m this enters Gour Passage. To the left the passage soon becomes walking size and a pleasant canyon leads to a 6m pitch into the main streamway. To avoid using tackle and so having to return by the same route it is possible to enter the main streamway by another route.

Turning right at the junction with Gour Passage follow the largest passage towards the sound of the river through a bedding passage until a dry canyon passage is reached. This joins a small canyon passage with the stream from the Polldonough Swallet. Turn downstream to the second bedding cave where there are pools of water in the low wide passage. The route is obvious when travelling in this direction and should be noted for the return. The second bedding cave leads directly to the upper main streamway. Upstream to the left leads to an upper

Fighting it out with the Coolagh River Cave, County Clare: *Photo Paul Deakin*

bedding cave with no continuation, downstream leads past tributaries first on the left and then the right. The passage increases in size as the floor starts to drop down first at a small waterfall and then Balcombe's Pot. The pot is a steep chute leading to a deep plunge pool which must be swum across. A handline may be useful in high water conditions. Just below Balcombe's Pot, Gour Passage enters at roof level.

The main streamway continues in impressive style down a series of cascades. At one point the passage at stream level reduces to stooping height due to an upper level oxbow. The oxbow connects with the stream entering from Polldonough North before rejoining the main streamway. The Polldonough North passage is 1,500m long with the route following the stream for most of this distance and includes several ducks. There is one major inlet from the left when going upstream. It is difficult to find the exit point when travelling upstream as it is at roof level and offset from the main passage.

Continuing down the main streamway the gradient lessens and there is a deep pool with a gravel floor. Beyond this is a breakdown section where it is necessary to climb over large blocks, initially on the right. This leads to a junction. To the left is mud branch – a short muddy passage rising steeply to the blocked swallet of Pollclabber. To the right the terminal rift passage leads to the final bedding cave which sumps after 30m.

To complete the through trip return up the main streamway past Balcombe's Pot and take the second inlet on the left into the second bedding plane. Follow the water upstream as the passage develops into a small canyon. In one section the stream follows a very low bedding and a number of routes via almost dry oxbows are possible. The main oxbow includes an awkward climb up the four foot pot but this can be avoided by other oxbows. The stream is soon regained and followed to the first bedding cave and following upstream in an easy canyon passage daylight is reached at Polldonough Swallet.

Tackle: Optional 8m ladder and 16m lifeline.
Survey ref: Caves of County Clare, U.B.S.S./C.Self.

CULLAUN ONE   Grade 4

Grid Ref: M182022 Irish O.S. Sheet No 51, The Burren, 1:50,000
Altitude: 218m   Length: 3150m

First explored in 1952 by U.B.S.S., this cave consists of an active and a fossil streamway, recent extensions now allow for a round trip. The lower passages are quite arduous and there is a risk of serious flooding in the passages below the first pitch.

Refer to Map 7. From Lisdoonvarna go north on the Ballyvaughan road N67 for 3.6 miles to junction 0832 where the forestry seen. Turn left and follow the track for 1 mile, a firebreak on the right between taller trees to the S and younger trees to the north follows the line of a low bank. 100m along this firebreak there is a depression on the left. On the far side is a second smaller depression filled with willow trees, which is the main entrance to Cullaun One.

The entrance is a 4m climb (a lifeline would be advisable for beginners but there are no belays except for the willow bushes). At the foot of the pitch the stream is reached by scrambling down over a couple of boulders. The route into the main section of the cave is by a sharp left turn to travel downstream. There are also

Cullaun Caves

some extensive passages upstream. Initial progress downstream involves scrambling over fallen blocks in the narrow passage. A climb is soon reached which does not require tackle and leads to a chamber. A further scramble over a long fallen block reaches the start of an easy pleasant streamway. There are a few small inlets, notably the 2 Pissers, but none are passable. There are numerous oxbows if the main passage becomes boring. After 500m the roof lowers to stooping height but this is offset by the presence of many formations. A second climb is reached, again no tackle is required, with a waist deep pool at the bottom. The streamway is followed past more formations until the roof suddenly lowers reducing the passage to a wet hands a knees crawl. This continues for 30m until it is blocked by a chert bridge, this is passed on the left by a low dry passage just above stream level which leads to a small chamber. The stream is again reached through boulders and quickly leads to the first pitch. This can be free climbed with care or rigged with a 10m ladder and lifeline although belays are hard to find. The pitch is in 2 stages with the second stage being in a narrow rift having a deep pool at the base, although it is possible to crawl around this. Follow the stream again into the Bastard Crawl a flat out crawl over sharp scallops for 20m until the roof rises in a rift with passages to the left and right. Extensions made by local cavers in 1986 and 1992 have made it possible for a round trip from here. This is described clockwise which is the easiest direction for route finding. There is, however, an awkward squeeze just before the end when travelling in this direction. As it is only 10m away it would be wise to check this for size first before continuing with the round trip.

The round trip follows the stream to the left in a low passage under an aven. The second pitch is soon reached, this is 2m and easily free climbed. Beyond here the passage is even lower crawling in the stream to reach the blind third pot after 30m. On the left just before the pitch and slightly above stream level is another passage. The stream is regained in a low canal which is followed for 100m to a small chamber. A hands and knees crawl continues and decreases to a flat out crawl leading to a rock fall. An obvious route up reaches an old fossil passage. Turning right quickly leads to a boulder choke. Left is initially walking size but the passage soon becomes too narrow, but can be bypassed on the right. The route continues through bedding planes until a boulder collapse is reached. This is passed at floor level on the left. After 30m it is possible to climb back up through boulders to rejoin the main passage. Much breakdown debris makes the next section awkward. A small inlet from the right cannot be followed far but after this keep to the right wall as the passage decreases in size and leads to a low wet crawl between chert ledges. Climb up between rocks to reach the previous end of the old streamway.

Follow the canyon or bedding passage for 50m to a pool where a passage enters from the right. Straight on leads to Gaffers Gulch old streamway, 500m of fossil passage with many loose boulders and some good formations. The way out is to climb into the right hand passage known as Queer Street. This is a low crawl for 50m until a narrow rift is seen crossing the roof of the passage. Squeeze up this and turn right to return to the end of Bastard Crawl.

Tackle:
Entrance   10m lifeline (optional).
2nd Climb   10m ladder and lifeline (optional).
Survey ref: Irish Speleology No 13. Caves of County Clare – U.B.S.S./C.Self.

CULLAUN TWO

Grade 3

Grid Ref: M182019 Irish O.S. Sheet No 51, The Burren, 1:50,000
Altitude: 210m   Length: 3,520m

First explored by the U.B.S.S. in 1952.

This is one of the easier and straight forward canyon type passage caves of Co. Clare. It is much used especially by beginners, scout groups, schools, etc. Nonetheless, it too can become impassable or at best very difficult beyond the first waterfall in very wet conditions. Also known as Bloody Guts from the iron oxide formation of dripstone in the cave. There are a number of optional tributary passages, some of which such as Year Passage and Old Streamway provide round trips.

Refer to Map 7. From Lisdoonvarna take the Ballyvaughan road to the third road junction going west. A distance of 3.6 miles. Turn left and go 0.7 miles to the edge of a forestry. A parking place should be found on the grassy margin on the left hand side of the road. Cross the road and follow the path or fire break for approx 200m. A sharp left over a small mud bank off the track brings one to the entrance.

The Main Route (Main Streamway)

At the entrance an easy descent leads down to a dry meandering passage. This is followed for about 250m to where a small waterfall is reached. Here the main flow of the water of the cave enters on the right. In very wet conditions the force of water at this point makes further progress difficult, as the cave narrows although higher, but this is rare.

About 100m downstream of the waterfall a small junction is reached where the water from Year Passage comes in to the right about 2m high. Here one can gain access to the lower end of the tributary passage which provides an alternative exit route. A detour of the first few hundred metres of this passage is recommended as this section contains some of the finest formations in the cave. (Great care must be taken so as not to damage the delicate formations at roof height).

In general some interesting straws can be seen along the mainstream at roof level and helictites on the walls. The most impressive of the formations is a grille of iron oxide, in a dripstone formation over a boulder type obstruction, effectively blocking the passage at head height. This is the Bloody Guts. Pass under the boulder in the water. The formation has lost a lot of its colour over the years from the number of people climbing over it – Care!

A further 100m or so downstream from this formation Pool Chamber is encountered. The water here is normally about waist high and fluctuates little. Just upstream of Pool Chamber an easy 3m climb gives access to the Old Streamway, thus providing an interesting alternative round trip back to the first waterfall. After the chamber a chert topped waterfall is reached and from here the character of the cave changes. It becomes lower and wider and there is some obstruction to the normal walking route with chert ledges or bridges that have to be climbed over and fallen slabs.

The final phase of the cave starts where it descends steeply to the head of a 10m pitch. It can be free climbed in dry weather conditions, though tackle is recommended. At the bottom of the pitch a sizeable chamber is entered. The stream flows into a sump which has been dived without conclusion.

Tackle: 10m ladder, long tethers and 20m lifeline.
Survey ref: Cullaun Two U.B.S.S.

CULLAUN FIVE

Grade 4

Grid Ref: C5 M182011, C5b M186008, C5d M187005
Irish O.S. Sheet No 51, The Burren, 1:50,000   Altitude: 190m
Length: 6,000m

Originally explored by two unknown men in 1952. More of the cave was found by the U.B.S.S. in 1953 and the C.P.C. in 1961.

First explored in 1953 by U.B.S.S. There have been no major extension to the cave.

This long system has a main streamway and several long tributaries. Some of the passage junctions are inconspicuous and there is a risk of being trapped in the far passages by floods.

Overall though this is a very enjoyable cave.

Refer to Map 7. From Lisdoonvarna go N on the Ballyvaughan road N67 for 3.6 miles to junction 0532 where the forest is first seen. Continue straight on for a further 0.3 miles to a gateway into the forest. Park here.

The entrance is 20m further along the main road on the north side, known as Poll-y-coe which means cave of the music from the sound of the stream.

This is the C5 entrance, an easy walk down leads to a low streamway. Downstream is 400m of low streamway with some minor inlets before a junction is reached. Left leads to a dry passage, Loop Way, which returns to the streamway just upstream from the C5 entrance. To the right the stream soon enters a low bedding plane which can be followed to Hunched Back Horror but consists of wet flat out crawls. The main route continues over muddy blocks to entrance C5b. (This can be reached by walking south from the main entrance for 100m to the edge of the forest, and following this W until a small collapse is seen immediately inside the fence)

From entrance C5b a short muddy crawl leads to a dry walking size canyon for another 400m to a 5m pitch. Anchors are available above the pitch. The passage below here soon meets the main streamway flowing from left to right. To the left is Hunched Back Horror which can be followed for 600m until the passage is blocked by stal. To the right the main streamway continues as a pleasant roomy canyon passing a high level passage on the right and then descends a short series of cascades. 150m further on a small, dry apparently insignificant passage on the left leads to the C5d entrance but contains a 5m pitch which would require pre-rigging, there are anchors in place. (C5d entrance is at the head of a small valley behind the cottage close to C5b entrance). After the junction the main streamway lowers in height to a bedding plane. For the next 100m the passage varies from hands and knees to flat out crawl and can flood to the roof in heavy rain. The passage height gradually increases and formations become abundant. There is an oxbow passage to the right of the main passage. After 400m the stream is lost in a low bedding on the left. The route on is by obvious oxbows to a sharp left turn. On the right here is the start of Red Carpet Passage several hundred metres of small canyon passage and breakdown chambers. A rescue dump is found at the start of this passage. Keeping to the left the main stream is soon regained in a low passage which enlarges before reaching Cascade Chamber. The floor of this chamber can be reached by keeping to the left hand wall. A very low wet crawl has been followed from here for 150m to a terminal boulder choke.

Tackle: 5m ladder and 12m lifeline
Survey ref: Caves of County Clare – U.B.S.S./C.Self.

DOOLIN RIVER CAVE (St Catherine's I to Fisherstreet Pot through trip) Grade 3

Grid Ref: St Catherine's I R096984, Fisherstreet Pot R096968
Irish O.S. Sheet No 51, The Burren, 1:50,000
Altitude: St Catherine's I 60m, Fisherstreet Pot 20m.
Length: of system: 10,500m   Length: of trip: 3,000.m approx.
Depth: of system: 55m   Depth: of trip: 40m

First explored in 1953 by the U.B.S.S. – perhaps their most spectacular discovery.

Doolin is easily one of the classic systems of Co. Clare with great variety. The through trip from St Catherine's I to Fisherstreet Pot represents a cross section of everything to be found in Clare caves; small pitches, wet bedding planes, large spacious chambers and well decorated sections.

Refer to Map 5. From Lisdoonvarna take the road to Doolin. About 1 mile on the Lisdoon side of Doolin Church a pair of imposing gate entrance pillars to Canavan's Farm will be seen on the right hand side of the road. Drive up the short drive to Canavan's Farm and make sure to obtain permission at the farmhouse. From the farmyard a small farm drive leads off for a distance of about 1,000m to an old building in ruins (a Nunnery). About 200m before the ruins on the left hand side of the drive a stream is seen sinking beside a large tree at the bottom of a slope, St Catherine's I.

Proceed as far as Doolin Church. Turn left at the 'T' Junction and pass the first village of Road Ford. Continue straight as far as a small crossroads approx 500m, straight past the cross roads for 100m. A circle of bushes and small trees can be seen in a field on the left hand side of the road. 50m from the road and surrounded by wire is Fisherstreet Pot.

NB. Doolin is a relatively easy cave. It is advisable after tackling to descend the Pot and check the level of the water in the final bedding cave. There is normally only a 30cms – 45cms air space and in wet weather this can easily close off temporarily!

Normally Fisherstreet Pot is tackled first before going to St Catherine's 1 to commence the through trip. This involves laddering or a 10m SRT pitch. If using a ladder, 13m is recommended as there is a steep slope leading to the head of the pitch proper. There is an overhanging tree inside the perimeter wire fence around the pot which may be used for belaying the ladder. Back up belay to the telegraph pole in the field beside the Pot.

St Catherine's I entrance begins with a wet crawl. A central channel in the centre of the crawl, makes it possible to avoid entering the water.

After 40m squeeze past a boulder collapse on the left to a dry meandering section. After this, a dry route, the old fossil streamway, goes off to the right and continues for more than 250m. Toward the end of the dry shelving, a drop down into the streamway to the left returns to the meandering canyon passage more typical of Clare, albeit on a restricted scale at an average height of 2m x 60cms wide.

Soon one reaches a point where the main stream goes off in a low tunnel. Once again a fossil passage to the right bypasses this difficulty. On following the fossil passage close to its end there is a small drop down between boulders to enter a canal. Dropping at an angle this canal is followed 15m to rejoin the main cave where it opens up again to largish proportions. It should be noted that recent hydrological changes apparently caused by the diversion of some of the water from Doolin Road Sink have made this canal quite tricky at times. Care should be

Ian Anderson in Doolin River Cave County Clare: Photo: Tony Baker

taken to check the water levels and flow before entering to the canal.

After rejoining the now larger passage, Smithy's Grotto is found up on the left hand side.

Soon after, the Doolin Road Sink tributary comes in under a low wide bedding on the left. 25m more downstream the way on is found by climbing up into the large dry oxbow passage – St Catherine's Oxbow. This passage offers walking over some 90m of wide shelving and boulders. Soon after drop down into another oxbow Smithy's Oxbow. This time the going is muddier and is of a different nature to the previous oxbow.

From here there is a climb down over boulders to enter the streamway once again. This is the big streamway that makes Doolin such a pleasurable trip.

300m further downstream the Doolin Dry Tributary comes in on the right. Further on the Great Oxbow goes up to the right. This is the normal route. Before the end of the oxbow where it returns to the stream again a climb up on the left gives access to the Great Oxbow Grotto.

Rejoin and follow the large canyon streamway to where the stream goes into a bedding plane cave which may be bypassed on the right. Beyond the bedding plane cave, Aran View tributary is soon reached on the right.

Further downstream enter another bedding plane soon assumes larger proportions.

This is the final stretch of the cave. One of the features to note is the Aille River Cascade entering from high up on the right. The cave now drops into a lower bed and reaches a height of 2m for a short distance before shrinking to 1m. In this final wet section the light from Fisherstreet Pot can be seen over to the left hand side.

On the right the stream continues down past the Pot, towards the sump. On the final section a shelf protruding waist high just below the water may be used as a guide to reach the Pot.

Tackle: 25m SRT rope or 13m ladder, long tether, 10m backup rope to pole, 30m lifeline.

Survey ref: Caves of County Clare – U.B.S.S./C.Self.

FAURNAROOSKA CAVE   Grade 3

Grid Ref: M142046 Irish O.S. Sheet No 51, The Burren, 1:50,000
Altitude: 264m   Length: 1,751m   Depth: 94m

First explored by the Y.R.C. in 1936. The R.A.F. Potholing Club found more cave in 1952. During 1957–58 the U.B.S.S. finished the exploration of the cave.

Refer to Map 1. From Lisdoonvarna proceed along the Ballyvaughan road as far as Kilmoon junction (0515) a distance of 0.9 miles. Turn left up the Kilmoon road to the triangle, 2.6 miles. From the triangle go along the Fanore road 1 mile to a sign for the Green road on the right. At this point there is a spectacular view of Galway Bay and the Aran Islands. Go 100m up this Green Road to a gate and a wall. 300m past the gate is a second wall leading to the top of the hill, 500m. The entrance is surrounded by posts and wire.

Faurnarooska 1 is the best entrance. There are other entrances upstream which are best avoided. Normally the cave does not flood easily. There are many good beautiful straws and abundant flowstone in this cave. Apart from the pitches, the cave is not particularly difficult.

Descend a steep canyon passage to a 'T' junction leading into the main

DOOLIN RIVER CAVE

streamway. It is important to remember this turn on the return journey. The water chutes make the return climbs challenging.

Dropping down a small waterfall enter a phreatic tunnel. Follow this to the right. After about 80m the Letter Box on the right hand side of the passage leads to the wet pitch. Through the Letter Box reaches a difficult 5m climb and open passage continues to the head of the 35m pitch. There are bolts in place for ladder or SRT at the pitch head. The bottom of the pitch ends abruptly in a narrow sump.

Continuing in the main passage the stream disappears on the right. This passage is known as the Dry Series, notable its mud and moonmilk. Traverse a large obstruction of moonmilk to a rift at roof level. Continue to traverse at roof level along ledges at the end carefully climb down to the bottom of the rift. This is a muddy but well decorated passage. The gradient now steepens where at a sharp left hand bend, the passage opens out over a small balcony at the head of the dry pitch. The pitch is 22m deep and there are bolts in place high up above the pitch head. From the bottom a short passage leads to a sump.

Tackle:

	Rope length required	Bolts	Remarks
Dry Pitch	23m	2	High natural belay.
Wet Pitch	23m	2	Rebelays from natural flakes.

A handline useful for the chutes in wet weather.
Survey ref: Faurnarooska Cave, U.B.S.S.

FERGUS RIVER CAVE   Grade 5

Grid Ref: R252922 Irish O.S. Sheet No 51, The Burren, 1:50,000
Altitude: 50m   Length: 2,300m   Vertical Range: 56m

WARNING: This is probably the most difficult cave described in this section and is particularly susceptible to flooding. It should only be attempted by experienced cavers and in settled conditions.

Refer to general location map. From Lisdoonvarna take the road to Kilfenora. Take the Corofin Road for 3 miles as far as Leamnagh Castle. After Leamnagh Castle a straight stretch of road for 1 mile reaches a sharp bend with a small road to the right. From the bend, approx. 200m on the right hand side of the road is a gate with a cattle grid. From the gate the path over the land is straight forward. Through two more gates and after a distance of approx. 250m the cave entrance is found at the base of a small cliff.

Access is a problem with this cave. The owner, Michael Killeen of Curraghyle, Corofin, has requested that cavers should first call at his house to sign a form indemnifying him for legal claims. Telephone (065) 37876.

This is one of the few resurgence caves in Co. Clare and as such is described going upstream. The cave should only be attempted in stable and dry weather conditions.

Because it is considered to be a relatively dangerous cave, it is visited by few groups. The cave contains many formations although there has been some damage recently.

The entrance is a rift with many large fallen rocks jammed in the floor. On the right hand side of the rift low down is a hole allowing entry into a low bedding chamber. At the upstream end of the bedding chamber continue into a small passage and from there into a low bedding passage until the cave appears to be at an end.

However, looking carefully in the roof a small hole allows a squeeze to be made into another bedding plane. Further low passages are followed until a respite is reached in Shingle Chamber. Before the chamber the 3 stalagmites are called the Skittles.

At the southern end of the chamber a small hole leads to White Aven, 10m high and well decorated.

At the northern end of Shingle Chamber under a low arch on the right pass several small side passages to Block Chamber – a chamber of massive fallen slabs. At the end, of Block Chamber on the left, a low arch leads over boulders to a large bedding chamber.

The most direct route from Block Chamber keeps to the right hand side. A climb down leads to a nasty crawl for 120m including several squeezes to a mud slope leading up into Acoustic Passage. Take note of the route here for the return. Acoustic Passage, under a flat wide bedding roof, reduces in height progressively to a crawl. Near the end are several holes on the right. These provide a choice of route (route finding is difficult because of the many other wet low lying passages which are impossible to enter) to reach Gurgle Chamber. Occasionally the gurgling sound of water below and between the boulders could warn of the need to retreat.

From the western or the left hand side of Gurgle Chamber the passage soon narrows where a stream runs across the passage from right to left and continues to the Stack Room where the main streamway is seen to come out of a pile of rocks. On the eastern side of the passage a bypass leads to the furthest point that is attainable under normal flow conditions.

The stream comes out from a sump and upstream on the right a static pool is found. However in dry conditions both the sump and the static pool dry out. Through the dried out static pool a low crawl leads for 30m to a very tight squeeze under a block on the right hand side of the passage.

At this point there are 2 choices the main route and, the aptly named, No Mercy Tributary. In the main route a bedding plane leads over fallen slabs to finally enter a large passage. After 75m a permanent static sump has been dived without conclusion.

Taking No Mercy Tributary passage, a crawl into a small inlet passage soon opens up into a large canyon and can be followed for 135m to the bottom of an aven.

An oxbow named Straw Oxbow is in the upper part of this passage. The aven provides an awkward 5m climb into No Mercy Hall. A handline is necessary here on this tricky, slippery and muddy climb.

No Mercy Hall is 30m long where at the northern end another awkward 15m climb in 2 stages leads to roof level where the final 75m passage of the cave divides into smaller passages with no obvious way forward at present. However, a strong draught emerges.

NB. The latter parts of this cave and at least from Gurgle Chamber, should only be attempted in very dry and stable weather conditions.

Tackle: 10m handline for No Mercy Hall.
Survey ref: Fergus River Cave, U.B.S.S.

KILCORNEY CAVE, Cave of the Wild Horses   Grade 3

Grid Ref: R223993   Irish O.S. Sheet No. 51, The Burren, 1:50,000
Altitude: 103m   Length: 865m   Depth: 40m

First recorded in 1736 the cave was surveyed in the 1960's and a major extension was made by U.B.S.S. in 1983. This cave is a rare example of a much older Burren cave and is very different from the shale edge stream caves containing some large phreatic passages and plenty of mud. It is uncertain how this cave responds to rainfall, but it can fill completely so should be avoided in unsettled weather.

Refer to general location map. From Lisdoonvarna go north on the Ballyvaughan road N67 for 4.9 miles to junction 0448. Turn right and drive 1.5 miles to a fork in the road, keep left and turn left again at the next junction after 0.4 miles. Follow this road down into a large depression and park beside the ruined church. The entrance is at the base of the cliff on the right.

Scramble over boulders to enter a comfortable sized passage to soon reach a junction. To the left a series of crawls leads to a narrow, blind 20m pitch. To the right, follow the main passage to a climb up boulders into the main aven. Climb down on the far side to enter a meandering tube 1m in diameter leading to pitch chamber. (A passage to the right soon becomes blocked). The pitch is 13m deep if rigged down through the boulders. A short traverse leads to anchors placed for a direct 16m hang both landing in a large muddy chamber where a short passage leads to a junction. (To the right a large passage can be followed for 50m to a 5m pitch below which a small passage is soon choked). To the left an easy passage is followed for 60m to another junction. This is Gour passage, left leads to a boulder choke, while to the right a triangular passage leads to a series of large deep gour dams which can dry out in good weather. The final dam is a 9m pitch which was first descended in 1983.

A large passage can be followed for 20m to a squeeze. Beyond here the passage is very muddy but contains some fine delicate gour pools. A small stream enters from the left after 40m. This stream is followed past mud banks until it sinks into the floor. On the right 5m before this a passage leads over boulders to a small chamber. A low wet crawl continues for 15m to a climb up to a higher passage which leads to a 2m climb down (handline useful) to the large frog passage. This passage is choked to the left but to the right continues for as a large passage for nearly 100m over mud and boulders to a mud sump.

Tackle:

Pitch 1	16m ladder, long tether and 35m lifeline.
Pitch 2	10m ladder and 20m lifeline.
2m climb	5m handline.

Survey ref: Proceedings U.B.S.S. Vol. 16(3), 1983.

POLLBALLINY   Grade 4

**Grid Ref: M141043   Irish O.S. Sheet No 51, The Burren, 1:50,000
Altitude: 253m   Length: 2,065m**

First explored by the Y.R.C. in 1936 to the second bedding plane which was thought to be a sump. This was passed in 1974 by U.B.S.S. members to find the impressive final passages.

The long crawls near the entrance make this a demanding cave but it is worth the effort to see the large passages at the end.

WARNING: Low passages in the cave would be impassable in high water. Avoid the cave during heavy rain.

Refer to Map 1. Go north from Lisdoonvarna on the Ballyvaughan road N67 to Kilmoon turn right at junction 0515. After 3.5 miles the road crosses a green road and it is possible to see down to the coast. Turn right onto the green road and park without blocking it. Go right at the first gate and follow a wall up the hill to the corner of the forest. Another turn right beside the forest follows the edge for 100m until a depression is seen just inside the forest.

An easy climb down the entrance enters a walking size canyon passage 0.5m wide. Upstream can be followed a short distance to the stream sink. Downstream the canyon narrows and the upper section is frequently blocked with flowstone forcing the way on at stream level. There are 2 small inlets from the left. Mostly hands and knees crawling in the stream follows for the next 350m until the stream enters a narrow chute and the canyon is regained leading to a short climb down. A slightly more comfortable sized canyon passage is now followed with some good formations until after 500m a chert band is seen in the walls. The roof becomes lower until it is necessary to crawl under the chert which now forms a complete false floor. This area is called the First Chert. Crawl over it before climbing back to stream level. After this the canyon regains height and walking is again possible for 400m to the Second Bedding Cave. For a time this was thought to be the end of the cave. In fact it is only a 20m long wet crawl leading to a 2m waterfall.

Immediately after this is the first boulder choke which is passed by climbing up on the left side to roof level. A short crawl then leads to a descending route through boulders via an awkward squeeze to regain the stream. Downstream passes more boulders to emerge in a large passage 10m high by 3m wide. This is followed for 50m before the water enters the Scalloped Bedding Plane on the left which can be

FAURNAROOSKA AND POLLBALLINY

followed, but, as the name suggests is an uncomfortable crawl for 75m. It can be bypassed by following the large passage for another 10m where a rift can be seen on the left. The large passage is blocked by boulders after 20m. An easy traverse in the rift leads to a series of muddy bedding planes through which several routes can be followed to reach the stream at the end of the scalloped bedding plane. Here there is a 3m climb down into another large passage. For the next 100m the passage enlarges until it is 10m square. Here the passage narrows abruptly at the first pitch. This is 6m deep and has anchors in place. After 10m the second pitch is reached, this is 4m deep and can be belayed from boulders. The passage is now 3m wide climb down between boulders and soon after this the terminal boulder choke is reached. This has been pushed extensively but without success and becomes more unstable further in.

Tackle:

Pitch 1   6m ladder, hanger, spreader and 15m lifeline.

Pitch 2   4m ladder, tether and 10m lifeline.
Survey ref: Caves of County Clare, U.B.S.S./C.Self.

POLL DUBH   Grade 4

Grid Ref: Poll Dubh North M138038, Poll Dubh South M136033
Irish O.S. Sheet No 51, The Burren, 1:50,000
Altitude: Poll Dubh North 244m   Poll Dubh South 236m
Length: 1,430m

The first recorded exploration was by the Y.R.C. in 1936–37, with the U.B.S.S.
beginning explorations in 1955 which they continued during 1964–65.
    Refer to Map 2. From the square in Lisdoonvarna take the Ballyvaughan road to

POLL DUBH

junction 0515, a distance of 0.9 miles. From here a sharp left turn up the Kilmoon road for a distance of 2.6 miles tales one to the Triangle. From the triangle proceed along the Fanore road .15 miles only, or counting the telegraph poles from the triangle between the 6th and 7th poles. Here there is a grassy margin where it is possible to park.

Enter over the fence/wall and follow the obvious fire break in the forestry to the second telegraph pole in the forestry. Take a sharp left here entering the trees and a well worn path with a series of timber palettes. Firstly pass B3a before reaching the more obvious depression of B3.

B1g is located on the surface by continuing along the main road from the car park until a small road going to the right is met. Follow this (Peat Cutters) road about 150m past the tree line and turn right into the forestry for approx 50m.

NB. Poll Dubh South is quite easy and a suitable cave for beginners. Poll Dubh North is marginally more difficult.

The cave is effectively in 2 parts, Poll Dubh North and Poll Dubh South.

The easiest point of access is through the B3 entrance to Poll Dubh South. The suggested through trip here is from the B3 entrance to the sump retracing ones steps as far as the junction with Poll Dubh North where the waterfall cascades down.

B3 is a bedding plane entrance beside a prominent waterfall. 10m from the bedding entrance it is easy to stand, after which the cave assumes comfortable proportions. It is a meandering passage with many loose rocks on the floor of the cave. One or two nice formations are worth noting particularly on the right hand side of the passage a small stalactite coated in dripping iron oxide.

120m from the entrance, the water from Poll Dubh North cascades down a 4m waterfall on the right. Just beyond the waterfall there is a point where it is possible to climb easily up behind it.

Continue below the waterfall along Poll Dubh South, in a narrow canyon with high level benches. Some small streams of water come down off the benches. Passage height is about 5m high by 1m to 2m wide over much of the distance. Eventually the stream goes under the floor and the passage becomes a dry oxbow.

Soon the roof level drops and the passage widens correspondingly. Enter a waist high pool of water with a protruding rock. Continue in shrinking passge by crouching and then crawling. The stream disappears away to the left in a small passage, requiring flat out crawling to continue for about 200m getting smaller and nastier all the while.

Returning as far as the waterfall and the junction with Poll Dubh North climb easily up the 4m climb to gain access to Poll Dubh North. The passage above the waterfall is about 2m high by less than 1m wide at first but rising gradually to 3m high. Some pleasing delicate formations are noticeable. After 150m a sharp turn to the left is followed. This passage is easy to miss. Continuing ahead the passage soon closes down, but is worth a visit for the very fine formations.

Take the turn on the left. A waist high protrusion of rock has to be passed over in order to make progress. Finally some crawling on the floor and scrambling over fallen boulders in a tight section of passage for 30m to exit B3a on the right.

There is a choice to exit here or to continue. This is a good point to exit if taking a group of beginners, for the next section of Poll Dubh North is more challenging.

Continuing under the B3a exit is the last and the longest section of the cave. The first part of the passage is crouching as the average height is less than 2m high. There are many small formations worth noting. Soon the passage increases to more than 2m in height and many small streams carve out little tiny passages about head level, forming small meanders, oxbows and benches. At about 400m from the B3a exit the passage height increases and a number of avens are encountered. The going is quite comfortable here with many of the sections bigger than anything encountered in Poll Dubh South. The last section requires traversing at high level.

The first point of exit is at B1g, where due to collapse a climb of some 4m or 5m up the side of the meander exits in the forest. Alternatively, continue the final 50m, again traversing at the higher level to exit at B1f where a short climb reaches the surface.

Survey ref: The Poll Dubh System, U.B.S.S.

POLL NA gCEIM   Grade 4

Grid Ref: M129034 Irish O.S. Sheet No 51, The Burren, 1:50,000
Altitude: 242m   Length: 60m (to sump one)
Depth: 75m (to sump one)

First explored in 1986 by local cavers this cave is unusual for the Burren as it contains a series of pitches. The pitches are all straight drops, spacious and usually dry which make this a very pleasant, if short SRT trip.

Refer to Map 3. From Lisdoonvarna, go N on the Ballyvaughan road N67 for 0.9 miles to Kilmoon. Turn right at junction number 0515 and follow this road for 2.6 miles through some forestry. On emerging from the forest the tarred road swings right and an un-surfaced road leads straight on. Follow this for 0.3 miles and take a left turn, park after 0.1 miles opposite a swallow hole on the right hand side. The entrance is in the field on the left hand side of the road covered by barrels and poles.

The entrance is a 6m pitch. There is a bolt directly at the pitch head and another on the pavement 2m N of the entrance. The foot of the pitch has loose rocks leading down into a narrow canyon passage, reacing the second pitch after 6m, this is also 6m deep. Bolts for a 'Y'-hang can be reached by a short traverse over the pitch head. The pitch lands in a chamber with good flowstone formations from a separate inlet, the main pitch opening out directly from this chamber. It is 31m deep and rigged from bolts on the left of the pitch head. There are also bolts for a deviation 1m down on the right. This pitch is spacious, well decorated and usually only has a trickle of water and lands on a large ledge where the cave changes direction to the S in a large rift. 4 pitches follow in quick succession 5m, 4m, 6m and 9m, all of which are bolted and can be rigged with a single 50m rope. A short rift leads on above the last pitch but quickly closes down. At the foot of the last pitch the stream volume is increased by an inlet from an aven the water from which flows down a series of climbs, the largest being 2m. With the last climb supporting a dam and associated pipe work used for draining sump 1, seen around the corner.

Sump 1 has been passed and leads to 3 more sumps (2 of which have been removed) in a horizontal passage before a second set of pitches is reached. These lead to a further sump before a large breakdown passage is reached.

Tackle: All pitches can be rigged with a single 50m rope using 14 bolts.
Survey ref: Irish Speleology, Vol. 4, No. 1

POLL NA GREE AND POLL NA gCEIM

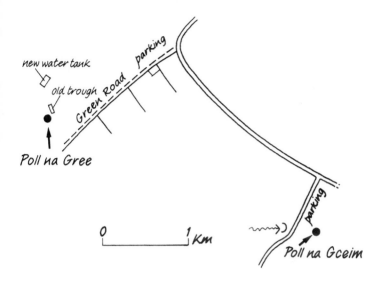

POLL NA GREE   Grade 2

Grid Ref: M122036 Irish O.S. Sheet No 51, The Burren, 1:50,000
Altitude: 235m   Length: 1,225m   Depth: 70m

First explored in 1955 by U.B.S.S.

The cave is essentially a single streamway. The most notable feature being the two impressive avens. There are no route finding problems and little risk of flooding except in very heavy rain, making this a short easy trip. There are no access problems.

Refer to Map 3. From Lisdoonvarna, go N on the Ballyvaughan road N67 for 0.9 miles to Kilmoon. Turn left at junction 0515 and follow this road for 2.6 miles through the forest. On emerging from the forestry the tarred road swings right and an un-surfaced road leads straight on. Follow this for 0.55 miles to a junction with a green road. Park here and walk S on the green road for 0.3 miles. A new concrete water tank can be seen 100m to the right of the road half way between the road and this water tank is an old trough beside a water pump which stands over the entrance rift.

An easy free climb into the rift leads to an obvious passage which descends a steep boulder slope. The passage continues over some short easy traverses and further climbs to the first aven. This is 40m high and connects with two other entrances (presently blocked). A slippery climb down enters a short passage leading to the second aven. Here a high level passage can be followed back to the first aven. The route on from the second aven is a low passage at floor level zig-zaging along the joint planes. The passage gradually becomes higher but remains narrow. 600m from the second aven a short inlet passage enters from the right and soon after this it is necessary to traverse up to roof level. At a sharp turn to the left another passage on the right leads to another well-decorated aven via a tight squeeze. The main passage continues as a traverse for a further 70m as the roof becomes lower and the passage wider. The passage divides and sumps in both directions, after some short muddy passages, one of which leads to a muddy rift from which exit is difficult. Both sumps are impenetrable.

Survey ref: Poulnagree, U.B.S.S., see also Cave Notes U.B.S.S. Proceedings Vol. 19(1), 1991.

POULNAGOLLUM / POULELVA   Grade 4

Grid Ref: Poulnagollum M162036, Poulelva M164023
Irish O.S. Sheet No 51, The Burren, 1:50,000
Altitude: Poulnagollum 225m   Poulelva 198m
Length: 2,285m (for through trip)   Depth: 100m approx.

The earliest documented exploration was in 1880. E.A. Baker and H.E. Kentish found new passages in 1912 with Baker returning in 1935. The Y.R.C. made several visits, notably in 1935, 1938–39, 1944 and 1948. Poulelva received attention in 1936 when the Y.R.C. made the first descent. New passages were found by the C.P.C. in 1952 and by the R.A.F. Potholing Club in 1956. The U.B.S.S. continued exploration in 1957, 1959 and 1967.

This is the most extensive cave system in Ireland (14 kms). The Poulnagollum / Poulelva through trip is normally a straightforward trip with perhaps some route finding as one approaches the Poulelva Pot. The Main Stream can be hazardous in wet conditions.

Refer to Map 6. From Lisdoonvarna take the Ballyvaughan road to the second junction on the left, 2.35 miles from Lisdoon where the road goes westwards toward Slieve Elva. From this junction stop after 1.6 miles in order to locate Poulelva. Having parked by the grass margin (there is not much room by the road) cross over the wall where some 100m from the road (on the right hand side) the edge of a limestone escarpment is met. From here a large clump of trees/bushes is obvious against an otherwise limestone background. A low wall surrounding the bushes hides the Pot. Continue along the road for another 0.8 miles from Poulelva (or 2.4 miles in all from the junction) where there is a space provided to park a car. The shaft of the original signpost and stepping stones over the wall point to the large funnel shaped depression – Poulnagollum.

The usual way to approach the through trip is to tackle Poulelva Pot first, then return to Poulnagollum Pot entrance. An exchange trip is also possible. When tackling Poulelva Pot there are a number of possibilities. There is also a bolt immediately below the overhang for re-belaying.

Poulnagollum.

Easily descend the Pot, characterised by its funnel shape and tree growing at the centre. A handline is necessary in wet weather. At the bottom of the pot there is a choice of two routes – one is to the right at the base of a limestone cliff through a small entrance giving access to the relatively dry Gunman's Cave. The alternative route to the right at the base of the same cliff gives access through a boulder choke to another smaller pot within the main pot leading to a stream passage. Most of the water enters the system here. Gunman's Route to the right goes through a series of lime encrusted pools to a small 4m pitch which can be free climbed on the right to join with the main route.

POULNAGOLLUM AND POULELVA

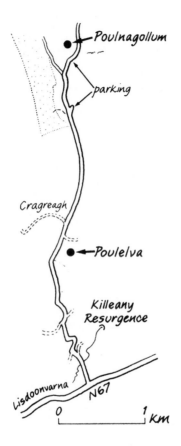

The Main Streamway.

Returning to the other entrance at the Pot, having gone through the boulder choke a series of wildly twisting meanders dropping all the time reaches the 4m pitch mentioned above. Follow the meandering main streamway, 8m high by 1m wide, to the Waterfall, set in an aven about 12m high. Continue down the meandering passage through Westrop's Chamber to the main junction At the main junction the water comes in on the left from a branch passage and continues to the right down towards Poulelva. Take note of this junction as it can easily be missed on the return journey upstream. Continue downstream, the typical section being an inverted 'T'. The base of the stream passage is now up to 5m wide in places and 20m high.

There are at least 2 levels to follow – stream level or the high meandering one which provides a useful alternative. In many places the collapse of whole beds of limestone rock have made a challenging series of pools and climbs but the route finding is straightforward. About 450m from the main junction the high and low ways meet. The obvious route forward leads to a rift which soon closes up. But, by retracing a few metres back before the climb into the rift the water flows underneath to the left to regain the streamway once again. 300m below the junction of the high/low ways, where the height of the streamway gets progressively lower, the stream from Cotter's Gallery enters on the left. The stream now flows off to the right into a low bedding plane crawl for 85m where a low chamber is reached. Here the stream disappears into another low crawl which soon sumps. To the left, however, the route continues and the roof gradually rises over the next 150m, the start of the Maze. A tunnel at roof height leads to a junction where the right hand route leads after a short crawl to Craven Canyon.

The canyon runs westwards for about 170m from this junction with an average height of 3m x 1m wide. Route finding is important, bear in mind that where possible turn right or W to move in the general direction of Poulelva. The canyon is crossed by several small streams from right to left. These can be ignored. At the end of the canyon a junction is reached and a low crawl to the left marks the Poulelva Streamway. Turning right the stream follows a tight bedding plane crawl. Soon the passage height increases to a climb up into a high rift. From here there are 2 possible routes to Poulelva – 1) at the foot of the rift a low crawl leads over shale debris to daylight at the northern end of the pothole. 2) climb up the W side of the rift that emerges behind a series of blocks that are on the E side of Poulelva Pot involving a 30m ascent.

Tackle: Poulelva – 40m SRT rope, 2 bolts with a backup to the tree.

Branch Passage Gallery Round Trip   Length: 2,810m

WARNING: In wet conditions leave tackle in place at the pitch and go to the main junction or beyond to check the water conditions in the wide main streamway passage.

Medium to difficult – low crawl at Muddy Link and awkward wet sections in the Main Passage.

In Poulnagollum – Poulelva cave system, Branch Passage forms a round trip within the main cave. The normal approach is from inside Gunman's Cave (Poulnagollum Pot), to take the small tributary passage on the left just inside the entrance called the Muddy Link. Initially 2m high x 1m wide the Muddy Link soon lowers. At the first junction turn right and enter a crawl about 45m long. Keep right past two side passages and eventually walk down a 5m bank into the large Branch Passage Gallery. Make a note of this point as it can be missed on the return or upstream way. Branch Passage is 8m high at this point, with the water coming from the left.

Following the stream in this high and narrow passage there are many deep pools and fallen slabs in the water. 800m below the Muddy Link a 35m canal has to be followed. It can be traversed or swam. Soon after this the stream leaves the rift through a hole on the right. Beyond this the overflow route is followed to the right through a waist deep pool. Soon the main feature of the round trip is found, a 7m pitch. Here a ladder bolted to permanent eyebolt or a rope is the usual method for an exchange trip. The group going upstream removing the ladder/rope on the way out. From here it is a relatively easy stretch of 200m to the main junction. Care should be taken not to miss the junction where the water from the main streamway enters under a low bedding on the right. The return journey is upstream along the main streamway – to Poulnagollum Pot.

Tackle: Ladder 8m, 10m lifeline or 10m SRT rope.
Survey ref: The Polldubh System, U.B.S.S.

Bibliography

Coleman, J.C., Caves of Ireland, Anvil Books, 1965.
Self, C., Caves of County Clare, U.B.S.S. 1981.
Tratman, E., Caves of NW County Clare, David & Charles, 1969.
Irish Speleology – Back issues from S.U.I.

INDEX

JOHN WAYNE
a giant shadow

By Carolyn McGivern

Sammon Publishing Ltd

Revised Edition by Sammon Publishing Ltd 2000

PO Box 3841
Bracknell
RG42 2YJ

1 2 3 4 5 6 7 8 9

ISBN 0–9540031–0–1

Printed and bound in Great Britain by
4edge Ltd, Hockley. www.4edge.co.uk

Cover artwork by: Pentacor Book Design

Cover photograph courtesy of
The Academy of Motion Picture Arts and Sciences

This book is dedicated to
Katie, Heather and Christopher

Author's Note

The perception of life that most of us share is, in large part, created by the producers, directors, and the stars of motion pictures. John Wayne was perhaps the most powerful of all the Hollywood players during the Golden Age, and hence his image continues to burn brightly today, some twenty years after his death.

But images are creations and John Wayne was mortal. This is the story of the man who lived in the shadow of the image. It is loosely based on transcripts of interviews he gave when he visited the United Kingdom together with the vast collection of material held in the British Film Institute Archive. Also extensively used were the oral histories of the Ronald L. Davis Archive, SMU, Dallas. Most important in providing an insight for me were the personal interviews conducted with friends and employees of John Wayne, particularly Captain Bert Minshall who skippered The Wild Goose for many years. When Bert told me, "There still isn't a day goes by that I don't think of Mr. Wayne," I knew I'd got behind the image.

All photographs are courtesy of The Academy of Motion Picture Arts & Sciences, Captain Bert Minshall or are from the Author's collection.

Foreword

John Wayne was a very intelligent man, in the sense that he knew the difference between melodrama and realité. He understood. And I loved him.

He was a great guy.

He didn't want me to make 1941. He said to me, "You're making a mockery of a very serious time ... and I read your script ... it's attempting to be a comedy ... I for one didn't laugh." He gave me such a bollicking about it.

We stayed friends although he was just disgusted that I would make what he thought was a very anti-American picture ...

I make movies that are important to me, but I think he would have loved *Saving Private Ryan*. I think he would have respected and honoured it.

The above text was authorised for inclusion in this book by
Steven Speilberg, Knight Commander of the British Empire.

I've always been Duke, Marion or John Wayne. If people say "John" ... Christ, I don't look round.

CHAPTER ONE

The Warrior

"It was my Dad who worked out the John Wayne walk. He held my hand and told me to put one foot in front of the other. That was walking. Do 'er the other way round and that's walking backwards! I must walk different from other people otherwise why keep mentioning it? But, God, I get hot when they say I wiggled my rear and that stuff."

On Christmas Eve 1978 a soft mist rolled in over Newport Bay from the Pacific toward the house on Bayshore Drive. Day was giving way to evening and already there was the sight of coloured lights being switched on in boats all over the harbour. Hooters and horns sounded. Men, women and children could be heard laughing loudly and calling to one another across the water.

Inside the house, a man sat very still behind his desk, head bowed in concentration as he scanned the pile of papers in front of him. Huge shoulders were slumped in a gesture of defeat and a symbol of recognition that ultimately fate had not been kind to him. They were barndoor shoulders belonging to a mountain of a man, shoulders instantly recognisable from any camera angle, as belonging to Hollywood's golden icon, John Wayne. He was scarcely aware of his surroundings and yet he shivered and shook his head as the air cooled around him. This was his favourite night of the year and his love of Christmas was childlike, almost unreasoned in the anticipation he felt as he waited for the next day to arrive. Tonight was different. The house was empty, quiet and cold … all the things he most hated … and he felt solitude wrapped round him, something almost tangible.

He enjoyed the hum of activity that usually accompanied the visits of his children and grandchildren. He liked to listen as they wandered in and out, usually with a pack of scampering dogs underfoot. He liked to hear Pat, his secretary and now companion, talking on the phone or typing at her desk in the far corner of his huge den. He preferred any noise at all to the deathly silence that was closing in tonight. "Deathly" was so cold. It crossed his mind to get up and put on a warmer shirt but somehow he didn't have the energy to get out of his chair and he remained sitting in the growing gloom. There was something infinitely sad about his eyes as thoughts of other, happier times crowded him. He knew he should have been standing tall and proud, as he always had, but tonight he felt lost, tired and restless. He shrugged as he tried to gather himself, but he simply couldn't bring the future into focus and instead he allowed his gaze to return to the papers on the desk. He had no interest in anything he saw there either. Reviews, films, Hollywood gossip, political intrigue, murders, none of it mattered anymore.

He was scared. He felt ill. He knew what was wrong and what was on the horizon even though he didn't want to look there. He hadn't mentioned his inner knowledge to anyone else yet. He could not give voice to fears that lay festering along with the dread disease he knew was back. Once he had battled cancer and won the shoot-out but he wasn't sure he could do it again. Too much had already happened to him, taking a heavy toll and sapping his legendary strength.

"Duke, are you in there?" Pat called. She had let herself in and run straight to his den, knowing where he would be and what he would be doing. He glanced up to see her bounce in through the doorway. Their eyes met and held for a split second before he looked away, careful not to let her see any trace of fear or any of his most private thoughts. The quick shift of his eyes was a familiar action now; no longer the steadfast, steely blue gaze of old, no more openness as he shielded himself from every aqaintance. When he had been making movies he had learned, in the hands of the best directors, to lay himself bare, to expose his emotions, but here in the real world, he couldn't let anyone close enough to touch his pain and so he was completely isolated and adrift with it ...

The first-born son of Molly and Clyde Morrison made an early entrance on May 26th 1907. The circumstances surrounding the birth of the mighty thirteen pounder, following a long and torturous delivery, indelibly coloured the way the new mother related to her offspring; she had resented her heavy and ugly pregnancy, hated the pain of labour, and detested the instant of birth which was fully a month premature. His arrival, only eight months after her marriage, led to much scandal and tongue-wagging in the sleepy mid-west town of Winterset, Iowa, and the socially conscious Molly blamed him for coming too soon. She felt deep shame and embarrassment, could hardly bear to look at him and was never comfortable with the howling infant from the moment he was forced into her unyielding arms. Molly, a waspish, sharp-tongued and generally unhappy woman, felt life had treated her harshly when she was presented with a tiny replica of Clyde, the husband she was already so bitterly disappointed with.

Although the baby was christened Marion Robert Morrison, his birth certificate read Robert Michael and for the first five years of his life he answered to the name Bobby. Molly underwent a change of heart, re-naming him Marion Mitchell after his paternal Grandfather, when her second son was born. He was told the new baby would now be called Robert and he would have to get used to his new name. Any child of five might be resentful and confused when a sibling rival entered his domain, but how much deeper was the trauma when that baby also stole his earliest identity. The newly-dubbed Marion was naturally hurt and offended and he stubbornly ignored anyone who used the severe name he now found himself saddled with, "My name made me a target for every bully in town. I was regularly taunted. They called me little girl — asked why my Mother dressed me in pants instead of skirts — did everything they could to make my life miserable."

Marion took many a school yard beating and frequently arrived home cut, bruised and with his clothes torn and dishevelled. The name was the target of course, but he was also singled out because he was skinny and already ludicrously tall. In those early years the shy, sensitive, gentle boy was too afraid to fight back and life was tough until he acquired a more dignified title and some boxing lessons at the age of nine. Every morning his faithful hound, a giant Airdale called Duke, followed him to school. Their daily journey took them past the neighbourhood fire station and the lonely boy often stopped to talk and to watch the men at work. One was particularly sympathetic and took him under his wing. He taught the youngster how to throw an effective punch, he also gave him the nickname "Little Duke" after the dog at his heels. Marion was delighted with it and from that time on, except when he signed legal documents, "Duke" was the only name he ever acknowledged, "I hated my given names. It didn't matter what I chose to call myself."

But back then young Duke had a lot more to cope with than the bullies who ridiculed him at school and his earliest memories were full of an anxiety rooted more deeply in the unhappy home life that affected every aspect of his development. He was unsure of his position there, insecure in the relationship he had with his bad tempered mother. Whilst he was the first to concede that Molly, more than anyone else, shaped and created the man he later became, he acknowledged his fear and admitted her unpredictable moods scared him right through to adulthood. On the other hand he also recognised her extraordinary sense of humour and was strangely attracted to her wit and brightness. Even as a child he grudgingly found the acidity of her tongue amusing, particularly when the sharpness was directed at someone else. He longed for her attention and always did his best to win her over. Nothing worked and when Bobby arrived their relationship deteriorated rapidly until she became almost frosty toward him.

Increasingly he turned toward his marshmallow-like father, Clyde, or "Doc" as he was known. Duke thought he shared much of his mother's personality, "I inherited too much from her. I got my own hot temper from her," but in fact he was more like Doc, an introverted man who was quietly spoken, soft and charming. Father and son were both serious, shy and retiring, kind and gentle and both faced stern criticism from Molly who was as hard as nails. Her attitude toward her son had a lot to do with the fact that he looked so much like his father and he couldn't help but remind her of Clyde's many weaknesses. Duke's own daughter later said that Molly heaped so much torment on him about it that he came to loathe any sign of softness in himself, "He was left deeply scarred. It was why he always acted so tough." He suspected himself, however, that whilst he shared his father's handsome looks and charm, he was in fact much more like her in the depths of his being and was completely motivated by the same drive and desire for success. He hoped he was not as nasty, mean or petty as she was, but still, he fought a life-long battle against any tendency toward those characteristics that he suspected lurking inside. Whenever he knew he had been unkind to someone he was tormented by feelings of guilt, and was always quick to beg forgiveness.

Duke was unflinchingly devoted to his father and stood squarely, in true John Wayne fashion, right at his side. His dad couldn't stand up to his mother so he tried to do it for him, instinctively, even then, the protector. Unfortunately he was also particularly ill-equipped to handle his mother's venom and whilst he was resolute in his determination he also became silent, withdrawn, sulky, angry, and all but uncontrollable. Highly strung, he suffered bouts of insomnia from his earliest childhood as a result of the continuous friction. He didn't understand what was happening but knew his mother was sorely dissatisfied with both him and his father. He remained forever trapped in it and, caught squarely between his parents, his tough stance was forced on him by his mother's indifference. Choosing sides caused him to feel great guilt and he spent much of his later life in atonement. He craved his mother's admiration, then and later, but she continued to snub him all her life. "I don't give a damn about him," were words the biggest film star in the world never got used to hearing and he rejected them, never giving up on his attempts to please her. Still she offered him no comfort and as a child he often curled up with big Duke, falling asleep in the dog basket, wrapped up next to the Airdale. He needed close physical contact all his life and when his mother rejected his childish advances Big Duke and Doc had to satisfy his craving. Duke later suspected his mother had been jealous of the close and warm relationship that existed between him and his father. He understood she was an unhappy person who best expressed that in acts of spite against him and his dad. He knew they should never have married and that they were completely incompatible. Their marriage, together with his own happiness, were things doomed from the start.

He hated thinking about those days and rarely mentioned them. When he did talk about his childhood he deliberately presented an incomplete picture, believing the truth somehow demeaned him, that it was his own failure that he never won his mother's love. Even Molly's parents, his Grandparents, felt sorrow and sympathy for his plight and they showered him with affection in compensation. Whilst his own mother could barely tolerate the sight of him others took to him easily and his Grandfather particularly appreciated his soft voice, twinkling intelligent eyes, his sense of the ridiculous and his raucous laughter. He often took him for long walks, weaving wonderful tales of the Wild West as they went. They grew close and Grandfather did his best to pacify the unhappy boy when he cried childish tears on his shoulder, "Marion, you've always been a wriggler, a fidgeter, always running, pacing and jumping around, you give your Mother no peace, you're full of undirected energy that none of us can keep up with. She doesn't know how to be with you, she can't cuddle you because you're never still for long enough." He decided when he was still a boy, crying about his loneliness to his Grandfather, that when he had children they would get all the love he had been starved of. Years later he fulfilled the promise and was often pictured holding his own kids close, he was rarely seen without one or other of them perched on his knee, their faces all full of beaming smiles.

But his Grandfather had been right. Marion couldn't keep still, he was driven by a restless energy that he could never contain. He felt uncomfortable with it but how much worse it must have been for his mother. She was tired, he never slept. As an infant he cried constantly, demanding her when all she wanted was to sleep and forget about him. She wanted him to leave her alone and finally had no option but to leave him alone. If his demands had been less constant she might have been better able to deal with them, as it was she gave up on him. He had arrived too early for comfort. He embarrassed her. He gave her no peace and she took no pleasure in him. As he grew out of infancy she was increasingly disturbed by his wriggling and fretting, especially on Sundays in church when he ran up and down the aisles, completely out of control. If he was afraid of her when she raised her voice it was also easy to see why she felt uncomfortable with him.

He often felt the need to escape and even as a five year old he frequently ran away from home. He took to jumping on passing rail cars, forcing Molly to make hysterical phone calls to friends and neighbours as she tried to track the little monster down. Many times he woke up on the floor of a train not knowing where he was or the havoc he had left behind. The good people of Winterset eventually became good at organising search parties for Duke and his dog, at tracing train destinations, and at completing the task of getting the spitfire home again, usually much against his furious wishes. The childish attempt to gain Molly's attention worked, although her reaction often brought stinging tears to his eyes. His time might have been better spent doing other, more normal things. Equally, it could have been the effort he put in here that stood him in such good stead later when he had to survive in a difficult and often hostile world. He couldn't win the affection of his mother, instead he acquired the happy knack of making others like him. He was forced to learn early, and though he and Molly were destined to remain poles apart, coming at life from opposite directions and forever clashing head on, it was a direct a result of her attitude toward him that he became so good in the art of charming the birds from the trees.

Soon after Bobby's birth Clyde became seriously ill with tuberculosis and Duke was afraid when he listened to his father struggle to breathe and heard his hacking cough. He hated listening to his parent's nightly arguments, fearing what they meant, but this was worse. He was terrified his father was going to die and he could not bear the thought of being left alone with his Mother. In fact, although Clyde didn't die, Marion was left alone as surely as if he had when his father set off for California in search of a hot, dry climate where his condition might improve and where he hoped his family might eventually settle. No one thought to tell Marion he was going, all he knew was that suddenly the only stable factor in his life had disappeared. Molly had considered him too young to understand why his father was leaving and Clyde had been too ill to argue the point. He had also been too weak to face the tantrum he knew would follow from his young son when he heard the news and he walked away from Winterset leaving the boy to pick up the pieces of his shattered life alone. He was devastated by the turn of events and was left running up and down the streets, frantically searching for his dad. Eventually he was found by a family friend who sat him down at the side of the road, wiped the tears away and tried to explain what his parents should have told him earlier. Duke clutched the man's hand tightly until they reached home but then he was left on the doorstep to go in and face Molly on his own. His Mother was waiting for him, her eyes hard. He looked at her and wished she would take hold of him, knowing she wouldn't. And, sure enough, she was unmoved by the plight of her aching son. He was torn apart, desperate and lonely, terrified that he would never see his father again. He needed something or somebody to cling onto. He found no comfort in her.

The next months saw no improvement in their relationship and Duke slid into a severe depression, becoming withdrawn, uncommunicative and sullen. Things didn't get any better until, in 1914, Clyde wrote to tell Molly he was feeling better and that she could bring the boys out West to join him. He had acquired some cheap land in the Mojave Desert from his Father and had built a small shack to house his family. He planned to grow corn in the desert and then move on to Los Angeles once his health improved. Marion was thrilled to find he was to be reunited with his father.

It didn't matter to him that the place his dad had chosen to homestead was the end of the world, or that a real Hell awaited the whole family; nothing mattered except being back with dad, joking, playing football, having his comfort to cling onto again. As soon as he saw him at the station he ran full tilt into his dad's arms, the aching forgotten, words tumbling out of his mouth as his Dad held him up high toward the sunshine.

When Molly and the boys alighted at Palmdale they were horrified to find nothing but desert as far as the eye could see, it was like something from a nightmare. Iowa had been fertile, prosperous and pretty, but all that was here was heat and grinding poverty in the middle of a desert. Molly hated the shack and even Duke recalled his new home as a "miserable little shanty," there was no gas, no electricity, no water, no telephones, no roads. The things he had taken for granted back in Iowa no longer existed for Marion but he felt tremendous exhilaration, "Imagine how it was for a boy from the plains to be set down in a land that had huge mountains looming along its western rim, stretching hundereds of miles. My horizons widened. So did my love and awe of my country." In Palmdale he was cut off from the rest of the world, and the hard life he faced there honed him for his destiny, where year after year he made movies in the arid lands that reflected the harshness of the old West, "We were real homesteaders and it was tough." He experienced all the difficulties the pioneers faced when his family settled there and when he acted the lonely cowboy roaming the wild frontier he well remembered how it felt. Back then he found himself in a land teeming with rabbits and snakes and he was as uncomfortable there as his Mother was.

His Dad gave him a job to keep him occupied and out of trouble. He had to shoot as many wild critters as he could, "The more I shot the more kept coming. The more Dad cleared the land the more rabbits and snakes appeared and the more I had to shoot." Later Hollywood gossips said he couldn't hit a barn door at ten paces, but in fact by the time he made his first movie he had already spent a lifetime around guns and knew the need to be both accurate and fast. He'd had to be good because he was terrified of the rattlers which seemed to be staring straight at him with eyes that bore into his soul. Still a poor sleeper, the little he now managed was marred by terrible reptilian nightmares.

Although he was scared he still helped his Dad, following him around, rifle at the ready. He picked corn until his hands bled at harvest time. He did everything in his power to make things work for his parents, for Bobby and for himself, driven by the fear that if he didn't work hard enough everything he cared about would come crashing down around his ears, that maybe his Father would disappear again with no warning. He did find a bonus in his effort; if he worked till he could hardly stand he was sometimes able to sleep a little more peacefully.

And his memories of Palmdale were not all bad. Things were rough but he had some fun too. He loved to be out in the fresh air and thrived in the hot, dry climate. His fair skin burned badly at first but then his body went brown, he toughened up, began to look like a real Westerner and the desert soon became his natural environment. He came into contact with horses for the first time. Again, the media later said he didn't like horses, but that wasn't really the case, he didn't dislike them, "No one taught me to ride. I could ride as soon as I could walk, but I didn't particularly enjoy horses the way some people do." He was always around them but explained that he thought of them as tools, always just an extension of his life, "I wouldn't make a pet of one. To me a horse is something you use on a farm or in a movie. They're big critters with a leg at each corner." And yet when he was caught off-guard gently stroking the horse he was about to ride in a film, whispering in its ear, he offered, "Isn't that lovely? The greatest vehicle of action in the world is the horse. Oh, a car has speed, but a horse has grace. The world can escape its problems on a horse, can ride back to the simple things." He understood the function and value of the horse back in Palmdale, but he came to appreciate it more when he later filled his own home with wonderful statues and pictures of horses.

Once the family settled in Marion had to go back to school. Lancaster Grammar lay four miles from the homestead and the road was not paved until 1921, long after the Morrisons had left the area. Whilst he was a pupil there he got up at five every morning to do his chores before trudging off on his eight mile round trip. Sometimes, when he was lucky, he was allowed to ride the older of the family's horses, Jenny, instead. The horse was skinny and some parents complained about him using the animal, saying he mistreated it, "Some nosey biddies accused me, a seven-year old, of not feeding or watering my horse. This was a lie." The complaint was taken seriously and investigated by the school, and although his name was eventually cleared, he was deeply embarrassed by the incident and matters were made worse when his new classmates dubbed him "Skinny" after the horse. He had been relieved when they dropped Marion but he was ashamed of his thin frame and his height and he found it hard being constantly reminded of it. His strange mid-western accent further ostracised him and again he was constantly picked on and ridiculed.

Though not everything in his life was bad he had few happy memories of Palmdale, "There were days when I was so hungry, I thought my stomach was glued to my backbone. If we wanted meat Dad had to go hunting. He used to say, "Marion, if you've just got one bullet you better bag two rabbits — one for your Mom and me and Bobby, and the other for you." Still, he rarely complained, his school friends never knew about his home life, and he never told his parents about the misery of school. In Palmdale he learned how to hide his feelings and he spent a lifetime carefully and quite deliberately not telling people how he felt. He kept his innermost troubles to himself, and ultimately he could hardly even admit them to himself. It became a big problem for him and everyone close to him, but those who were interested could always scan his movies, where every slight he had ever suffered was professionally portrayed, for the world to see.

Back then he made light of his fears, hurts and childhood difficulties, although the whole family was in serious trouble. Doc saw himself as a failure, Molly ferociously protected Bobby, who could never escape her attention, and Marion, naturally gregarious, loyal and in constant need of love was desperately lonely. Perhaps he remained unloved, but while the rest of his family stumbled and faltered, he learned how to cope. Surviving without any of the things he most needed was one of his greatest achievements. Palmdale was the place where, against all odds, Duke began laying down the rules that he lived the rest of his life by, where the John Wayne credo was born, "I will always keep my word. I will try always to be a gentleman. I will never insult anyone unintentionally. I will not look for trouble, but if it finds me I'll make sure I finish it." It was also where he started avoiding the trouble that dogged his early tracks. He kept his head down and got on with his life as everything crumbled around him and family life eroded away. Parents and brother faded into the distance as he grew stronger in his ability to cope. And though he was only a child, he had already discovered he had a natural talent for avoiding things he didn't want to face.

He developed the skills that later became useful in his career when he began to escape into a world of fantasy as he walked to and from school. He slaughtered countless imaginary bad guys, criminals and Indians never dreaming how his life would pan out. He often played the cowboy, outnumbered and heroic as he approached the rocks where Apache warriors were waiting to ambush him. He was brave as he held his breath and crept with the greatest stealth so they couldn't hear his approach. In his vivid imagination every Indian perished, and as he played the scene with all his heart and soul, shouting his joy when another hostile bit the dust, the thrill of it left him breathless. It had been so real to him that if John Ford, the famous director, had seen the boy at play he would have known for sure that Duke could act.

Marion had never seen a movie, but he had lived all his life with tales of the frontier. The stories he had heard so often at his Grandfather Brown's knee about the wagons travelling Westward, the train-robbers, Indians, stagecoaches, the gold rush, were real where he had been born back in Iowa. The frontier that John Wayne came to inhabit on celluloid existed for his Grandfather, and even for his Father, and he had relished it all those years before as he sought escape from his real life misery, shooting from the hip all the way.

His parent's marriage was at breaking point and they argued constantly, not caring how much they upset their two small boys. At night Marion tried to think about other things as he covered his head with a pillow in an effort to blot out the noise of their screaming. During the day he desperately sought peace and refuge from the misery that school bullies and his brother heaped on him. And Bobby had become a big problem. His mother insisted Duke took him everywhere he went, "He was always too little, and whenever he cried or was unhappy I was always to blame." He hated having to take him with him but he kept his mouth shut and let the kid tag along, life was easier that way, and Bobby continued to hang onto his big brother's shirt tails long after they reached adulthood. As children it troubled Marion deeply when Molly scolded him if his little brother came home with a scratch but seemed completely unmoved when he got hurt. She had not offered him a word of comfort when he nearly lost his thumb in a bicycle chain. The accident, so severe it hit the local papers, never raised a second glance from her, "You just look out for Bobby" she warned him, "I'll hold you responsible if anything happens to your brother." It had been tough and he wanted to ask, "What about me? Don't you care what happens to me?" He didn't bother, he knew the answer.

Children approaching adolescence are faced with a mass of seemingly overwhelming problems and uncertainties, but Marion had already, at an early age, faced and overcome that multitude of difficulties to emerge a headstrong, self-willed, and self-motivated youngster. By the age of nine he was already manifesting the resources that were to power his future career. He steadfastly refused to wallow in self pity, did his utmost to laugh at hardship, and even recognised the challenge in it. In 1916 when Clyde finally accepted defeat in the desert and moved the family on to Glendale, California, Marion was simply taking the next giant step along the path to stardom. He had learned to make the most of life in the circumstances of grinding poverty, now he was about to be offered some of life's rewards. He never looked back and, ever the optimist, he buried the horrors of Iowa and Palmdale and rarely spoke about them again.

When he first arrived in Glendale he had moved home and changed schools frequently, moving from the mid-west to the desert and on now to prosperous California. He had been regularly bullied both inside and outside his home, he was unsure of himself, almost neurotic and shy to the point of terror. He protected himself behind a detached facade and it was hardly surprising, considering the way he shielded himself, that the kids in his new school found him strange. They saw only an outsider who made no effort to join in, and he discovered that bullies existed everywhere. Fortunately one classmate, Pexy Eccles, found something to like in him and they became close friends. Marion spent as much time as he could at Pexy's home in a further effort to avoid his own and life began to settle down nicely in California. He was maturing in a quiet and unremarked way.

Both his parents wanted him to do well and they both invested time in his future, ensuring he was well-read, and equally well-mannered. They had long recognised that a major part of their son's problem was that he simply had too much energy and too little direction. He had difficulty settling to anything for long and bored easily. When they hit Glendale they devised a plan to keep their wayward boy out of trouble by ensuring he was occupied. He suddenly found he was expected to help contribute toward family finances. They needed him out making money but they also wanted to keep him busy and out of harm's way. It was a strange turn of events and he did everything he could, pleased to think they depended on him, unaware of their ulterior motives. He really didn't care about their motives either, he was just happy to be able to escape the whole family. He found welcome relief out at work, away from the raised voices that he so hated. He took as many odd jobs as he could, earning enough to pay his own way, to satisfy the demands his parents made and, at the same time, escaped the endless arguments. He also began attending numerous youth clubs for the same reason. Whilst he was out working or at scouts he was safely away from the sound of anger and also from the bane of his life, "The biggest trial of my young life was shepherding my little brother around. Wherever I went, Bob had to follow." Now he specifically chose groups he knew Bob couldn't go to and in such formal settings found the peace he had craved for so long.

However, a new problem presented itself at school, one that he had no idea how to manage and was almost too much for him to bear. To his horror, he found the teachers there liked him. He had buried himself in books in an attempt to escape his bleak reality for some time and he excelled in the resulting knowledge; that confirmed his place in class as teacher's pet. They smiled pityingly at trousers that were always too short, at shabby, threadbare clothes, and offered words of comfort when he got involved in a scrap. He did his best to avoid them and their pity. He wanted to be shorter and heavier. He wanted to feel normal. His height alone meant he could never disappear into the background of any situation, he was always there, plainly visible to teacher and bully alike and he was very self-conscious about something that was a distinct handicap to the stranger in town who longed to go un-noticed.

In the past he had never made much attempt to fight back when the bullies targeted him. He had no idea what was expected of him, and no understanding of why anyone would want to harm him. He hated conflict and did his utmost to avoid it. Word of course soon flew round Glendale that sissy Marion was easy game and anyone who thought they were tough could easily prove their point by attacking him. But things had changed. He had changed. He suddenly found the determination to stand up to the intimidation and provocation, to show everyone that he was much more than a skinny mid-western misfit. He had grown even taller and now possessed a pair of fists almost twice the size of those of his tormentors. At long last, with an inner sigh of relief, he recognised the time had arrived to put them and his boxing lessons to good use. He handed out a few short, sharp lessons. They did the trick and whilst he never started anything and continued trying to avoid fights, he finally discovered he could stand up for himself, and win.

He no longer considered himself a child and he decided to do something about his clothes, about the trousers that were always too short, about the threadbare shirt cuffs. He started getting up at four every morning to go to work before school. He saved his earnings until he had enough to buy the things he wanted and began going to school in the immaculate navy blue suit and fresh white shirt paid for by his own hard labour. Unlike the other boys in class he always wore a tie. The proud habit of dressing well was established then but became something he clung to later when he came to understand the worth of image. The clothes he wore became an important symbol of his own success and were a mark of his achievement. Success now became vital to him and he was so determined to do well that he started going to the local libraries where he devoured every book he could get his hands on. He remained a voracious reader all his life, scanning most new books and journals, always on the look out for stories that might make a good film. He had an exceptional memory that, together with his reading, ensured he continued to do well in school. He gave up worrying about being teacher's pet when he discovered he enjoyed studying for its own sake. He was like a sponge soaking up every piece of information that came his way and a friend remembered, "I never knew anyone so **interested** all the time." Staff were impressed with the rapid progress of their quiet, sensitive, likeable, intelligent and attentive boy who so rarely spoke. He would answer questions if called upon but never volunteered information and was never seen raising his hand in class. Later, when biographers questioned them, they described him as clean, tidy, well behaved … a good student … bright-eyed … neat, a nice boy. They were however worried that he often appeared ill, pale and bruised. For some time they suspected he was seriously ill but when they asked him about it, he mumbled, "I'm fine." He stubbornly refused to tell anyone about the punishing schedule he had set himself, both in the classroom and out on the street.

He was stronger now and his restless soul possessed amazing amounts of natural energy. He worked hard, went to school, to the library, played any sport on offer, rarely slept and always woke at four on the dot ready to start another action packed day. No demand was too great and he strove every minute of every day, helping his family out, working to clothe himself, studying and defending himself. He wanted to be the best at everything. He dedicated himself to that end and his unstinting effort gave him an edge and made him special. He was happier and his energy and ambition had found new focus but he continued to live with the legacy of being unwanted and unloved at home, bullied and brutalised outside it. Still, in California his in-bred mid-western "Scotch-Irish" Morrison values and work ethics were gradually transformed into the All-American ones that so typified him for the rest of his life as he emerged from the trauma of his childhood to become a complex combination of ancestral characteristics just waiting for the chance to shine.

He busied himself, doing everything he could in a natural but futile desire to please as he struggled to make everybody, particularly his mother, like him. By the age of twelve he was fending for himself, doing a paper-round in the morning and delivering prescriptions after school. Nothing was enough to please the ever-dissatisfied Molly who now told him he had to earn even more money to help support his brother's needs. Fortunately Duke was thriving on the effort and directing his energy into something worthwhile made him feel good about himself, invigorated, as he discovered he had an unusual ability to make money and a strength that none of his peers possessed. He never knew where the power came from. It was his natural gift, "I had to hustle all the time, I had to make it on my own, right from back then and support the others as well. I had to keep moving all the time."

As a result of his mother's acute embarrassment at relying on her twelve year old, at her absolute dependence on him, she became increasingly harsh toward him. No matter what he did or how hard he tried, Duke never heard a word of thanks from her. He expected none and later said, "Hell, times were hard then. I didn't mind if my folks needed my money. Dad would have given the shirt off his back to anyone who needed it." He shared none of his Mother's resentment toward his father's failures and the generosity of his spirit was part of his natural make-up. If Duke had money in his pocket he was willing to share it with anyone who needed it and a friend of the mature Duke, Iron Eyes Cody, said, "He was the hardest working man I ever knew. He was also the most immensely generous man, the softest touch in Hollywood." If that was true of Duke the film star, it was equally true of the boy who fell for any tale of woe and was always willing to lend a hand where he could.

Although he worked like a man and accepted all the responsibilities of adulthood, he also found some childish pleasure for the first time. The boy who had never had an opportunity to socialise with his peers discovered he made friends easily in the groups and sports clubs he joined. He particularly enjoyed himself when the neighbourhood boys took to playing his own favourite game, cowboys and Indians. By the purest luck he had arrived in the perfect place to play make-believe, the place for a future movie star to find his destiny. Duke began learning his craft right there out on the street with his new friends. He had lived all his life with the tales of the Wild West, in the desert he had developed the skills necessary to survive on the frontier, but he was now just a stone's throw from Hollywood and his future. His past made him what he was … the future awaited his arrival.

He became accustomed to seeing film crews at work as new studios sprang up all over his neighbourhood, "All the kids were movie conscious in our town," and because he was ever alert to the goings on around him, he absorbed everything. He stood spellbound, lost in wonder for hours, as he watched the stars and crews at work. Then, when he found his way into a theatre for the first time he was, like millions of others, amazed at the images that greeted his senses. He had always loved his books and been able to transfer himself into the stories he devoured. Movies made that even easier. When he went to see a movie his imagination took over and he started living out the adventures in his mind, "Some of us even played at making movies ourselves. We had actors, a director and a cameraman. We used a cigar box with holes punched in it for the camera." Going to the movie theatre became his big passion. He enjoyed all types of films and appreciated the full galaxy of stars and heroes. Two became his particular favourites; he was strangely attracted to the star of silent Westerns, Harry Carey, and he also idolised Douglas Fairbanks.

Although Carey and his family came to wield a big influence in Duke's blossoming career when they met later, back in Glendale it was Fairbanks who most affected the boy, mainly because of the incredible stunts he performed in his pictures. When he was later transformed into John Wayne, Duke said he knew every scene Fairbanks ever played, word for word, "Once, as a kid, when it was my chance to be the leading man, I tried to copy a Fairbanks stunt I'd seen. I jumped out of a second-storey window ... grabbed hold of a trellis and swung onto the vines growing there. I ruined a beautiful arbour. Stunt was a big success though ... my friends were real impressed. Another time I climbed onto a neighbour's roof and was holding onto the chimney when it gave way. I hurtled to the ground and the palm of my left hand still carries the scars ... that was a big success also." Young Duke was often to be seen swinging through trees or leaping from roofs with a huge grin on his face before hitting the ground. The pretend-movie crew rarely joined in the heroics, preferring to watch him splatter himself instead, marvelling at the thud he made as he landed at their feet. In fact he planned each stunt carefully, practised his new craft meticulously and had surprisingly few accidents. As he escaped into the movies, to his imaginary view of making them and into the world of the stuntman the pain of his reality dissolved away and Duke, lonely for so long, blossomed in the headily exciting atmosphere of Glendale, "Those were the happiest days of my life."

The theatre became his first love but wasn't his only escape and he continued to enjoy reading books of all kinds. He had been able to read before he started school, encouraged and helped by doting grandparents, and later became, "A confirmed and avid reader. I've loved reading all my life, I spent hours alone, lost in the libraries of California." In those libraries he discovered the novels of Zane Grey and the stories which carried him back, time and again, to the Wild West. In a library, sharing endless adventures with his stoic heroes, or in a theatre, watching a screen ablaze with them, Duke found he didn't need anybody else and for the boy who had always craved company he found welcome relief from his isolation. But whilst he might allow himself to retreat into a fantasy world, he could never live there. He was a realist, easily able to move from reality to fantasy and back again, to suit himself and his own needs. He allowed himself the respite of escape from time to time but his feet remained planted firmly on the ground. He always knew that however successful he was at hiding in his books and films, they could never provide real compensation for the emptiness and insecurity he had carried inside for so long.

He was growing up fast and had become more thoughtful, he was wise beyond his years, and now, as he established the habit of flitting between reality and fantasy he discovered that he was possessed of a wonderful gift himself, and though it was still unformed in Glendale he began developing it to suit his own needs. It was his natural gift, always there, and only loaned out later as he learned to act in the hands of John Ford and the other great directors. He suddenly recognised that a number of different characteristics made up his very complex persona. He didn't understand then who or what he was perhaps, but he knew he had a rare ability to separate aspects of his personality at will, so he could become a different character for each of the different people who inhabited his life. For his teachers he could be the serious, studious reader with a voracious appetite for knowledge, getting excellent marks in all subjects. His public persona was conservative, serious, mature, reserved and ever anxious to please. He was extremely successful in these presentations, but there were many other facets. Hidden deep was the soft, sensitive dreamer who existed in the theatres and libraries. For class mates and friends he became the daredevil, willing to undertake any stunt and to take on any physical risk, one later recalled, "Duke never showed any fear and some of his stunts were really wild." When he entered High School in 1921 he was already over six foot and, mainly because of his size, he was selected for the school football team. He excelled in his academic studies but now became increasingly involved with the football crowd and what he called, "The roughest gang of guys in Glendale High School." He never shared the complete person with anyone. He deliberately compartmentalised his life and allowed no overlap. With the footballers he was a typical teenager, drinking prohibition liquor and playing practical jokes, with them he shared his sense of humour, vile temper, and worse language.

There was one area of his sectarian life that he found some difficulty with. By the age of fourteen he was tall, limber, had piercing blue eyes and dark waving hair swept straight back from his face. He had the warm lop-sided grin and girls started following him around the basket-ball courts to watch, "The handsomest thing" they had seen. He was described at the time as, "So good looking he would stop traffic." One commented that his earliest films didn't do his looks justice, "He was unusually tall and rugged but he retained the shy, sensitive look. The films and photographs of that time never effectively showed his eyes, the colour of the Californian sky, a bright and vibrant blue, always full of fun, laughter and understanding. He was irresistible, gentle, warm, more tolerant than other boys, and he carried the vulnerable, haunted look even then." He noticed the girls but wasn't quite ready and he gave no sign that he was particularly interested. He left them bewildered by his polite indifference, shy wariness and impeccable manners. His mother had often screamed at Dad for flirting, no one was ever going to accuse him of that and he kept his distance from every girl who smiled coyly up at him. He worked at "keeping his distance," and though he was popular with them he remained uncomfortable and bashful in the presence of women for the rest of his life, never understanding what they wanted of him. After watching his parents and listening to their never-ending arguments, he took great care around people, never allowing anyone, male or female, to become too close, too soon, "Too much squawking at home left its legacy I guess." The girls went crazy for a date but they would have to wait a long time for him. When Marion became "Duke" he acquired a degree of confidence and self-belief that had enabled him to begin to emerge into a brave new world. He believed it had been the change of name that made the big difference in his life, "Until I got the dog's name I was Marion. As I spent many a night in the dog basket it seemed appropriate. I liked the sound of my new name." From then on the first thing out of his mouth when he met strangers was, "Just call me Duke." But having it didn't render him any less shy or uncertain in situations he didn't understand. One thing was certain, girls were a complete mystery, he kept his mouth shut around them and tried, for the time being at least, to steer a clear path to safety.

Everyone, in each of the very separate groups, seemed to respect him and enjoyed being with him. He continued making huge efforts to please and spent the rest of his life trying to keep his life tidily in its separate compartments. He juggled to keep everyone he was involved with happy. Round and round he went in ever decreasing circles, until the only people he ever really satisfied were the movie-going public, his fans. Over the years the gap between his public and private lives narrowed as he deliberately blurred the edges, but he always retained the separate units that were the structures of his life. When John Wayne's screen persona was at its height, the hell-raising, masculine and macho image who was polite but distant from women, socially liberal, but politically conservative, was an image instantly recognisable to those who had known him during the Glendale years.

Before he found stardom his most amazing exploits were performed on the football field as a member of the Glendale team of 1924–25. The team was acknowledged as something very special indeed and was talked about long after Duke left. Within the team he was ruthless. He had to win and was not prepared to give an inch on the field. It was where he discovered his stubborn streak and where others found that once he had made up his mind nothing could shift him from his path. Football taught him many valuable lessons, "It was the greatest equaliser I ever found. It was one of the few places where ability, and only ability counted, one on one, the best man won every time. Neither the colour of your skin, nor the size of your bank balance mattered." Duke was considered special in the setting of school football. Though he was still very thin and school photographs showed him with long curly hair, sensitive, gentle eyes, and almost poetic good looks, Duke was already six foot four and had the broad shoulders and narrow hips of the natural athlete. He was also a rugged player and opponents hated coming up against his tough, imposing figure. Duke was able to hide all his old anxieties behind a smiling demeanour in the completely masculine world of football. It was where he came fully to life and where he felt at ease.

He might have been relaxed there but at the same time he found he had new needs and, although he kept it close to his chest, he finally began to reciprocate the keen interest of the girls who dogged his every step. He was inexperienced and naïve perhaps, he couldn't talk about his feelings, but Duke was a hot-blooded male and eager to learn. He never openly romanced any of the girls as his more worldly-wise friends did, but all that meant was he was successful at keeping his romantic life separate from everything else. He had also made the discovery that was to change his life. Whilst America choked on its Prohibition laws, Duke found bootleg liquor. He loved it and the powerful affect it had on him. The shy youth found it liberating and he started drinking before going out dancing at the weekend and found himself suddenly able to fulfil his potential with those girls who thought him one of the most handsome men they had ever seen. He began to escort Polly Ann Young, sister of actress Loretta, to local dances and he recalled his first regular date fondly. In the scheme of great romances theirs actually didn't last very long, mainly because he always wanted to do an awful lot more than just dance with her. His shyness had prevented him even talking to girls for a long time, now he found it difficult to admit, even to himself, that he enjoyed their company. There was a catch. Without a drink he was still the tongue-tied child he'd always been, and before going dancing with Polly he had to drink … a lot. Polly was smug at first, out of all the girls he could have had she was the one he escorted, but eventually she was forced to sever the relationship, warned off by concerned parents who smelt the alcohol on his breath.

Still Duke was well and truly over his bashfulness. Now he took the greatest pleasure, "Picking up a certain type of gal on a Saturday night! I was already a serious drinker. That part of my life was no fit place for Polly. She wanted to dance, to be seen on my arm … But hell, Saturday nights were there to mix with the rough guys from Glendale and with girls who wanted to do more than dance." There was no place for Polly on Saturdays, and though he felt some regret at losing her, he was enjoying himself too much to worry.

Drinking allowed Duke to feel like the man he wanted to be. He knew he was lucky because it didn't seem to matter how much he consumed he never suffered as his friends did, either from hangovers or from lack of desire for those certain girls. He later admitted smilingly, "I did get backache from falling over so often." He was drinking heavily most weekends but kept his love of alcohol out of other areas of his life, though here maybe he was less successful with the now well-honed technique of compartmentalising. Even his teachers were aware of his drinking, "Owing to the life he led I was never surprised he fell asleep so often in class. I was always amazed that his grades never seemed to suffer and that he maintained the standards he set himself for academic excellence." He enjoyed drinking because it enabled him to talk easily to others and made him less self-conscious and the social aspects related to alcohol consumption drew him in deeper. He drank to excess and used the effect of alcohol for his own ends for the rest of his life, but he didn't let it take over his life. He wasn't alone in the discovery that liquor numbed the senses and most of his friends, both at school, and later in the film world were heavy drinkers. Many of them became sorry alcoholics whilst he somehow managed to avoid the crippling dependency that later decimated his inner circle of friends.

Whilst still in high school he joined the Stage Society as prop boy where he helped build sets, acquired lamps, tables or anything else that was needed. School productions were a source of never ending amusement to him. Once he was to ring a bell offstage to simulate the sound of a telephone that a boy on stage would answer. He didn't like him and deliberately "forgot" to put a phone out on the table. The audience roared with laughter at the red-faced star who had nothing to answer when the phone rang. Duke himself was convulsed with laughter at the success of his prank until his teacher caught up with him and gave him hell. He hung his head in shame and admitted that maybe it had not been so funny after all, anyway not worth the verbal beating he got for his effort. He never did anything like it again in front of that teacher but never lost his propensity for playing practical jokes either. He often landed in deep trouble as a result of boyish pranks, always worked out in the minutest detail so that they hit their targets like flaming arrows. But on that one occasion he took note. He was already on his way to becoming a professional, already willing to learn from his mistakes … an early hall-mark of someone cut out for greatness.

He had joined the Stage Society because it was another place he could escape to. He had no desire to act in any of the productions. Acting was his idea of sheer hell, "One thing you are never going to be is an actor."

He was happy arranging the props, he took his work seriously, and learned how important detail was to any production; if the job was done badly it affected everyone else involved. A happy coincidence or part of a planned journey as he later went on to become a first rate prop boy on the Hollywood movie lots? Anyway it was a happy coincidence for millions of film fans that the path of that particular young prop boy eventually led him into acting despite all his best efforts to avoid it.

As he entered his senior year he determined to get as far away from his warring parents as he could, as fast as he could. He was still running, breathless, when his parents finally divorced in 1929. Divorce was rare and he was filled with their shame and humiliation, but also, finally, with a sense of relief. His Father remarried and Duke acquired a step-mother and sister. He grew to be very fond of them both. His Mother moved to Long Beach with Bobby to start her new life. She also married again and Duke liked his stepfather. He rarely unburdened himself to anyone and both Doc and Molly were filed away separately, deeply. They had affected every aspect of his life yet were now kept separate within it. He hardly ever mentioned them again. Neither they, nor the pain they caused him were permitted to intrude into his public life which was developing very nicely.

He was thriving, doing so well at everything he touched in Glendale, particularly in the state-record-setting football team, that the University of Southern California now offered him a coveted football scholarship. Although the boy born in the mid-West and raised in the desert had never been to sea, indeed had hardly ever seen it, Duke had long maintained a secret dream of joining the navy. The dream was firmly rooted in the exciting sea-faring adventures he had enjoyed reading and had heard at his grandfather's knee. He had never mentioned his plans to another soul, but much of his outstanding achievement at school had been specifically aimed at winning a place at Annapolis, the naval school. When the time came he was not accepted although his name was held for some time on their reserve list. He was heartbroken, "Not making it into the navy was one of the biggest disappointments of my life. Deep in my heart I was always a sailor. I loved the sea ... never tired of it." For weeks after his rejection he was quiet, withdrawn and moody. He believed all his effort at school had been wasted. Anyone else offered a scholarship at prestigious USC might have been overjoyed, Duke only tasted dejection and humiliation.

Although he was depressed his Mom had been planning a career in law for her smart boy for some time. USC had its renowned law school and the football scholarship would enable him to study at one of the best schools in the country. The black cloud began to lift; if he couldn't join the Navy, perhaps he could finally do something to please her. He stopped sulking but later admitted that winning a football scholarship hardly thrilled him and rejection by Annapolis rankled for a long time, "I guess I never really got over it."

He had no option now but to settle down to football and law and he went away full of determination to succeed. He started his freshman year in September 1925 at the University of Southern California as a member of the Sigma Chi house, enrolled as a pre-law student. He was surprised to find himself a big shot right from the start. USC was a private and very expensive institution. Its members came from the families of the most prominent leaders in California. At the age of eighteen he arrived at college with a few dollars in his pocket and one suitcase containing his every possession. A friend recalled he had one suit, some shirts and ties, one jumper, some socks, underwear, and one extra pair of trousers. Still, no one at Sigma Chi seemed aware of the disparity and he was accepted into their elevated ranks straight away. By that time although he was physically huge he no longer felt like a freak, he was particularly ambitious and tenacious, and the fellows at Sigma Chi seemed to recognise his outstanding qualities. He was embraced and well-liked by his fraternity brothers.

His scholarship paid tuition fees and provided him with one meal a day. Unlike the other boys he had to pay for everything else himself, there were no rich parents paving his way. He was hustling, playing football, studying law, feeding and clothing himself but the athletic department wanted him so badly they found him the work that would support him through the coming years. This may have been normal practice at other schools but Duke, initially working in the local telephone exchange, was very much in the minority at USC.

Traditionally freshman year was one of torment and, like the rest of the year's intake, Duke suffered at the hands of older students. He cleaned shoes, washed cars and ran errands. On one more serious occasion, when he had offended a senior, he was tied up, had a sack put over his head and was thrown into the communal, large and deep bath which was full of iced water. He nearly drowned after being plunged into the freezing water three or four times in the practice known as "tubbing." The custom was eventually banned following the death of a student but Duke went through the ritual a number of times during his years at college. He once filled his mouth with ketchup before being thrown into the bath, and as he was pushed under, he spat it out. He hoped his tormentors would think he was bleeding and pull him out quickly. Initially it did the trick, he was dragged to the surface and the sack was torn off. All would have been well if he hadn't started laughing in the face of his tormentors. He was tubbed again with renewed vigour. Fellow Freshman, Pexy Eccles, Duke's old friend from Glendale, was his room mate and Duke involved him in so many pranks that he was regularly tubbed himself! Although they were both frequently beaten up for forgetting to call seniors "Sir," Duke's life settled into an acceptable rhythm and he loved college life, "It was all fun for me." He was able to relax away from the stress of family life, surrounded by other young men, all like him, intent on having a good time. There was no pressure to try to please anyone or to be someone he wasn't. At eighteen years of age, for the first time, he found value in himself as his fellow students applauded his special gifts. The rich play-boys, who were only at college to while away a few years until they went to work in their Father's businesses, cared about him and liked having him around. The person they saw had enormous power even then and of course they respected the multi-talented Duke. He was a first rate chess and card player, he was attractive, could make people laugh and was fun to be with, he could drink with the best of them and his athletic ability made him a star football player. All in all he was considered to be an acceptably good companion, even though his brothers found he had a hot and wild nature and was always ready to fight like a demon for the things he believed in. His temper became legendary amongst them although his outbursts never lasted long. He exploded when crossed but was just as likely to throw a bear-like arm around the shoulders of his target in a gesture of reconciliation, smiling and begging forgiveness. He invested a lot of himself in Sigma Chi but there was also rich payback for his effort; naturally gracious, he was now rubbing shoulders with members of America's highest society. He acquired polish, finesse and absorbed some of the confidence and charisma that seeped from their pores.

He lived in a world of men but still found himself surrounded by girls. He enjoyed their company and liked what was on offer though he was still painfully shy, never a natural womaniser, and too deeply scarred by his mother to be completely at ease with them. The girls at USC were wildly attracted by his old-fashioned manners, and they loved his natural hesitancy. He was rarely left alone and he and Pexy often double dated.

He still kept his life in neat and tidy compartments but gradually, inevitably, there was increasing tension between his "good boy" persona and the laughing, hard drinking, hell-raiser he became at Sigma Chi. He found value in both but personally felt more at ease with his new role. He was increasingly relieved to be able to leave behind the good boy his mother had raised. She had never seen value in anything he had tried to do, but even now he was free to choose his own path, he remained driven onwards, probably he reflected, by her inherent will and determination.

As a member of the USC Trojan freshman football team Duke was a big success. Each afternoon consisted of gruelling training sessions under the tutelage of Coach Howard Jones, a man puritanical in his approach to the game. He spelt the rules out, "No smoking, no liquor, and no women … absolutely no women," and Duke knew what was expected of him on the field. He loved every minute he spent there, even though he couldn't, in all honesty, say he lived according to Coach Jones' code. In return for the pleasure football gave him he received broken bones, sprained tendons and torn muscle; it didn't matter because he was in his natural element. Duke idolised his coach, the personification of honesty and decency, and Jones was equally attracted by the skills of the gifted footballer, taking a deep interest in his life. He offered the direction Duke had so desperately needed from his parents and was one of many who recognised how special the youngster was. Duke himself was so naïve he didn't realise how strange it was for people like the football coach to pay such close attention to a student. Whilst he never understood his own charisma, so evident even as a teenager, he did enjoy its rewards. He was never happier than when people warmed to him, he needed to be surrounded by human warmth, craved company, and inevitably, without knowing how or why, people were drawn to him, seeing "something" in the sky blue eyes of the tall, shy boy.

Tickets for USC Trojan matches were at a premium during those years, interest in the all-conquering team ran high, and the cash-strapped young Duke could have sold his allocation on for fifty dollars a pair, as most of his richer team mates did. He gave his to his Dad, despite the fact he could hardly afford to eat and survived training and match days on his one free meal a day. He knew his father wouldn't have taken them if he had known their value and he wanted him there at the games. It gave him the greatest pleasure to see his proud Dad as he cheered the team on to its phenomenal successes. And Clyde supported in good company. Everyone in town wanted to see the matches. Tom Mix, the great western film star, was another loyal and dedicated fan who begged for tickets. Coach Jones did a deal and, in exchange for a box for the season, the star provided summer jobs for some of the players. Fate was again smiling on Duke when he was sent over to the Fox Film Lot that summer. Movies about college football were popular at the time and the producers often used members of college teams as extras. Duke began earning good money in front of the camera but no one at college ever heard him say he had any desire to go into films, his only interest was making enough to buy the food to satisfy his enormous appetite.

Mix spotted Duke immediately, told him he had a future in movies, promised him a bigger role in his next film and told him he wanted him to start work as his personal trainer! It was too good to be true. Unfortunately, the ever-naïve Duke believed everything he was told and took Mix at his word. The film star proved to be less honourable than the football player and when Duke duly reported for work he found himself assigned to a gang moving props around the set. This was his wonderful job, there was nothing more, and he retained the bitterness he tasted then long after summer was through. Mix had got him work, as promised, but not in the movies, not as a trainer, and he never even looked in Duke's direction again. Always so easily hurt with his fragile sense of dignity, he confessed to feeling wounded but added, "It was bread and butter to me and I guess I had no feeling for the business then ... Just the same, I was mad as hell with Mix."

But Fate took a firm hand in all that followed and the mythological journey was about to begin in earnest. Up to now Duke had been no more than a bit player in a normal world inhabited by mere mortals. He had not led a perfect nor exemplary life, he had been far from happy, his achievements might have been extraordinary, but he was just a boy, having the same experiences any other might until the heroe's legendary adventure engulfed him when he was discovered by the man who became his life long mentor. Halfway through the summer of 1928 he reported to the set of *Mother MacCree* where he was assigned to the film being directed by John Ford. Duke, the young vacation worker, knew his movies, and had spent long hours in the theatres of California, deeply enthralled in the director's work which had already played a big part in his young life. Ford's films had provided much of the bedrock of his childish dreams of escape. Now, he was excited and awed at the thought of working alongside a man he considered a hero.

Yet it was Ford who ended up the more enthralled. Duke went to the set, full of eager anticipation, and found a replica of an Irish village, complete with chickens, ducks and geese. His task was to keep the poultry in some sort of order and await direction. When Ford shouted, he was to release them from their pens and when he shouted "Right" he was somehow to get them all back in again. He was handed a pole to help in the rounding up operation. On Ford's first signal Duke opened the gates and whacked at the birds, encouraging them out of the pen. Ford required another take and back the birds were shepherded. "Action," out he pushed them again, another take and another. And so his day went, chasing the poultry up and down. The chickens and ducks hid under the cottages, the geese attacked him and pecked at his legs ferociously, honking and annoying the director. Duke was flustered but refused to give in and he hustled the birds all day. Unfortunately, he wasn't fast enough to please Ford, who called, "Action" every time he got the geese rounded up. After a few days of the same, he was frustrated and anger was simmering the day Ford chose to notice him.

The director was tall, strong, scruffy, energetic and ultimately in control of everything going on around him and Duke recalled, "He reminded me of an angry eagle." He was only just hanging on to his temper himself when Ford approached him in an inauspicious start to the legend.

"Hey, you, Morrison." ... "Yes sir?"

"Are you one of those USC football boys?" ... "Yes sir."

"What's your position?" ... "Running guard."

"Please assume your position." ...

He did as he was told, crouching down, mystified, his palms on the floor and one knee down, in classic football stance, head up, back straight. Ford lunged at him and, without warning, kicked his hands out from under him sending him crashing, face down, into the dirt. It hurt and Duke had not seen the funny side of it, and he got his revenge as soon as he managed to stand up. He offered to try again. This time he ran straight at the older man and, in a flying tackle, kneed him squarely in the chest. When Ford fell into the dust a hush came over the set, but he only laughed as he got up and slowly brushed himself down. No other man would have dared to do that to him. He didn't know Duke wouldn't have dared either if he hadn't been so angry. After the incident he commented dryly, "I really liked the big kid's style. He wasn't like the others guys, just hanging around. You could always see he was working toward something. I immediately invited him to lunch." It was a dramatic beginning to the relationship between an unknown prop boy and a legendary film director, the stuff films might be made of, and the beginning of the story in which Duke was lifted and transformed, by a wave of Ford's magical wand, into the realms of superstardom. On that day he was ashamed of himself and shocked to realise he had knocked his idol over but all Ford said was, "Let's get back to work" with a knowing look on his face. Duke believed Ford was a genius and from that moment on he worshipped him. He saw a tough, durable character, able to take the knocks, get up and get on with life and at that time Ford appeared to be exactly the type of man he wanted to be himself. At the very moment he felt so unsure of his own family a strong, father figure had miraculously turned up. Their lives became entwined and a bond was forged then that tied their destinies together, linking their successes and failures right through Hollywood's most glorious years.

Even though he idolised Ford, Duke understood, from that first meeting, that the director enjoyed humiliating people. It was only the first of many incidents where Ford tormented him causing his wild anger to flare, but he never again reacted as he had done on that day. He had been surprised that Ford hadn't thrown him off the set, he was more surprised to find himself involved in a strange, but lasting, friendship, "It has been the most profound relationship of my life. Were it not for John Ford's belief in me as an actor, I would still be playing cowboy sheriffs in third rate westerns." However it was also a relationship that never altered much from that of master and pupil, neither ever seeming to want it to become anything more. There were long periods when they were prickly toward each other, but Ford also admitted, "He is the son I would have liked to have, he is my favourite boy."

Later, recalling that day and the golden years that followed, Duke said, "I watched the way he handled people, the way he managed to get the best his actors had to give in every damned scene. I'd never seen a genius at work before, but I knew I was seeing one now. The man was a great artist, a perfectionist, and I wanted to be like him. He was like a rapier darting in and out, getting what he wanted, when he wanted it. I think he could have been anything he wanted to be, especially in the military field. Jack could handle personalities. He was also the finest editor I've ever seen. When Dudley Nichols was doing *Stagecoach* he'd make him write a scene five or six times till Nichols was just about drenched. And then he'd find three lines out of the three scenes. He knew how to draw lines out that gave character and progress the story at the same time. I wanted to be as good as he was."

Just as he had absorbed polish from his rich friends at college, he now seemed to soak up and take on many of Ford's characteristics. He hoped some of the genius would rub off on him. At Fox he was given ample opportunity to observe, learn and become close to the great man. The one Ford characteristic he steadfastly refused to draw on was his pleasure in belittling others, it was a part of the director that made Duke squirm in embarrassment. He accepted that was how the old man was and allowed him to have his fun, "The man was a genius, and that was all there was to it as far as I was concerned, nothing else mattered."

Their meeting might have been pre-ordained, coinciding precisely as it did with the talking picture revolution. Ford's career had been established in the era of silent film, but now he was actively searching out actors with good voices to feed into the new sensation. Duke, the vacation worker, had startled his every sense. Even as he picked himself up after Duke's flying tackle he noticed something that intrigued him.

He saw the skinny frame alright, spotted the exceptional good looks certainly, but the director's eye also caught the vulnerability that could not be hidden. He knew instantly that the camera would pick it up. He watched him closely after the initial confrontation and noticed it was always there, in wonderfully expressive eyes, around the sensitive mouth, and that his whole body reflected it. He was young and extremely awkward, not in his body movement which was fluid and almost feline then, but in his very being. Ford sensed an overwhelming discomfort and the director was, as ever, precise in his perception. But so much more important to Ford right then was the voice, obviously the most important attribute at the advent of the talkie. As soon as the director heard the rich, deep, expressive voice he was tremendously affected. He stored all the information about Duke in his film director's mind. He needed no screen tests and it didn't even matter to him if he could act or not, "He was clumsy around me but I could tell the big dumb oaf had something special. I believed I was going to be able to use him but right then he was too skinny and too pretty to do much with. I offered him bit parts from time to time so I could keep an eye on him."

Duke was given a small part in *Hangman's House* as an Irish peasant found guilty of a murder he hadn't committed. He had to stand with bowed head in the witness box as the judge told him, "You shall hang by the neck until dead." It should have been easy enough, but something tickled Duke's sense of the ridiculous and he started giggling during the first take. By the second and third he was laughing helplessly. This was a sight directors eventually had to get used to, but Ford was not one of them and he screamed in rage, ordering him off the set, "And don't bother coming back, you dumb oaf!"

Duke couldn't remember what he had been laughing at, all that stayed with him was the sense of overwhelming humiliation as he trudged away. As he sat in the dressing room dejectedly getting out of costume, he felt complete despondency and looked pretty much as he should have done for the shot that Ford had set up. When the angry assistant director came to find him he saw the white face and the tightly clenched jaw, "Don't worry Duke, just lie low for a while. Put your shirt back on. Come back out with me. But keep quiet."

"I don't think I'd better."

But he did get back into costume and wandered toward the set. He stood waiting, hardly daring to breathe until Ford relented. The experienced director had, of course, known exactly what he had done to the untrained Duke and he hoped his rugged handling would pull a performance out of him. And sure enough, when he next stood with head bowed in the dock it was full of the vision of Ford ranting at him. There was no more laughter and instead the magical cameras of John Ford caught a great and very real sense of fear and a quivering cheek muscle. The director was pleased with the effect his tantrum had created. "Right. Print it."

What they achieved together on set that day was pure accident. Duke sensed no sudden desire or ability to act, his reaction simply looked good on film. Ford told him years later that it had been as he was laughing in the dock that he knew for sure that he had something vital, unprofessional, adolescent and unformed, not acting ability certainly, but something profound that the camera picked up. By chance he had discovered Duke's innermost self was effortlessly revealed in the glare of the arc lights.

In the summer he started working at Fox, he returned from college to his parental home and received a severe shock to the system. He arrived in Glendale on the first day of the vacation eager to tell everyone about his job. He knocked at the front door and called out loudly when no one answered. He went to the house next door and was told his parents no longer lived there and that another family had moved in some weeks before! Neither his mother nor father had bothered to tell him they had finally separated. He was nineteen. He had no home, no family, nowhere to go, and no idea what to do. He was hardly surprised his parents had split but he was devastated by the disappearance of everyone and everything he knew. Even worse was the fact that no one had thought about where he was going to go that night. He had seen his Dad only days before, yet he hadn't told him he had no home to go back to, and he had been allowed to arrive back on the doorstep completely unprepared for what met him. When he thought about it he supposed it was not really surprising his Dad hadn't had the courage to warn him, nor that his Mother hadn't cared enough to, "I guess they each thought the other had told me. Well, it sure was a shock I can tell you. I ran down to Pexy's house, and was fortunate enough to find him home."

Pexy's parents were deeply moved by the plight of their son's homeless friend and they allowed him to sleep in a room over their garage all that summer. It took Duke several days to locate his own family and he decided not to move in with either parent, preferring the peace of Pexy's refuge instead. And it turned out to be a good summer, despite its horrific start. He managed very easily without his screaming mother and he wasn't expected to take his brother everywhere either. He liked his friend's family who allowed him the freedom to do anything he wanted. In fact Pexy's parents had no reason to worry about their young workaholic guest, he gave them no trouble and spent most of his time on the Fox lot. When he wasn't working he was down at the beach. He had no money but that didn't prevent him body-surfing or hanging out there with friends. He was a real water baby and could usually be found at Balboa, swimming, surfing, drinking, and later, dancing the nights away.

It had been at a Thanksgiving dance at the Balboa Inn that friends fixed him a blind date with the wealthy Carmen Saenz. Her father was consul for the Dominican Republic and her mother was French. After the dance he walked Carmen back to her beach side home and was introduced to Carmen's younger sister, Josephine and her date for that evening. The four of them liked each other and went out together later for supper. They sat around talking and drinking coffee. Duke was strangely drawn to Josephine and vividly recalled catching her eye frequently as they chatted. The hot-blooded Duke also possessed a highly romantic nature and on that magical night fell hopelessly in love with, "The most beautiful girl I had ever seen." She was tiny, delicate, and he thought, perfectly formed. She had white skin and jet black hair smoothed back from a perfect face. She had the deepest, most enormous black eyes, framed by the longest, thickest lashes, "I felt as if a hypnotist had put me in a trance. I stared at her all night. She was aristocratic, serene, and I was lost." Carmen finally lifted the trance-like state he had fallen into, asking, "Duke, are you going to put the sugar in, or not." He had no idea how long he had been sitting with the spoon hovering above his drink, "I was so lost in admiration that I put it straight in my mouth, rather than into the coffee. I felt just like Jack's big dumb oaf alright." Not knowing what else to do he chewed the sugar and Josie laughed as he crunched the granules. She liked him.

Once more fate took a hand and Josie became his date for the rest of the evening. Relationships in those days were casual and there was no problem about changing partners mid-evening, "I walked toward the water's edge with her. Later we strolled along the pier, we stood real close, gazing out to sea. I vividly remember the ocean and the sky. I was full of feelings I hadn't known before … I was real sentimental about Josie. That never changed." He couldn't remember saying more than two words to her all that evening, "But as I opened the car door for her later, my hand brushed against her arm as she stepped out." Years later he still felt the shiver of excitement run right through him, "It was the first time it had happened to me, but I knew I was in love. It was just like in the movies. But I wish someone had told me how much it would hurt. They never tell you in those movies how much it hurts. They don't tell you it hurts from the start and I guess it never stops. But it's still a beautiful feeling to have. We started to keep company and she was my steady girl, and it was beautiful. But it hurt a lot. Why don't they warn you how much it hurts?"

At the very first chance Duke had, he rushed straight back to Balboa, excited at the thought of seeing her again, determined to talk to her more this time, hopeful that he wouldn't appear so stupidly naïve. They went to the beach where Josie sat in the sun, pleased to discover he had a tanned, muscular body to go with his beautiful face. She watched him as he spent the afternoon showing off in the element that was all his own and where he knew he appeared to best advantage. Usually the waves were just right for surfing at Balboa, breaking comfortably into four foot of water. Only occasionally did they become violent and unpredictable. He seemed to be at least a mile out to sea as he waited for a big wave. Eventually he threw himself into a cascading roller, and raced in toward the beach with the wave. He was in control and holding his flat body position in the torrent of foaming water. His heart thumped in his chest until the second of truth arrived. It was vital not to get dragged into the underside of the wave. Once that happened the surfer was no longer in control and he got sucked back out to sea like a piece of driftwood. And he lost it, right there in front of the girl he so badly wanted to impress. His body had rarely let him down before, he had no idea what went wrong, but this time he was well and truly beaten and, as he was pulled into the underbelly of the wave, he became all flailing arms and legs. His muscular power was no help and he was eventually deposited stomach down, straight onto the unforgiving beach, "I felt like I'd been shot out of a cannon. I could only lie completely still, winded, unable to catch my breath. Jesus, I hurt." Josie and some surfers ran to his rescue and started pumping water out of him until he vomited, right there in front of his aristocrat! The dazed confusion left him, "I knew my right shoulder was badly smashed up. I was surprised I was alive at all. I could hardly move my neck or arm, I felt just awful." He felt particularly bad because he couldn't hide the pain he was in before the fussing girl. He took no pleasure in her obvious concern for his well-being. He was deeply embarrassed and ashamed of himself. By the next morning he felt worse.

The shoulder was swollen and he was forced to go to the doctor who diagnosed torn and separated shoulder muscles. The pain-wracked Duke was informed they would take several months to heal. He could not use his right hand or arm for anything and the only way his shoulder would heal was with rest and immobilisation, "I couldn't believe what doc was saying. Oh, sure, I could eat and write with my left hand but what about football?"

"No more football this season son."

It was catastrophic, "But I just have to play Doc." No football meant no scholarship, meant no food, meant going back to a home that no longer existed for him. "There was simply no way I could accept the doctor's diagnosis or treatment. I kept it to myself. Told no one at college, especially Coach Jones. I practised every afternoon, using my right shoulder the best I could, but the pain was excruciating. I tried to play like nothing had happened. I even tried to tackle with my left shoulder. Coach went crazy … called me a damned coward in front of my team mates. He wanted to know why I was afraid to block. Then I got demoted. I was fitted a special shoulder harness so I could train. That was how I played all the rest of that year, Jeeesus …"

He carried on until one day as he practised tackling against a dummy the slowly healing shoulder muscles tore apart again in an injury so severe he had no option but to confess to Coach Jones, who was glad to finally know what was going on, to know he hadn't been wrong about Duke. He felt sorry for the blistering he had given him about being a coward and knew not many of his players would have attempted to tackle with an injury like Duke's. In an effort to compensate he didn't release him from the team and allowed him to keep his scholarship. However, he did loose training privileges, including the all-important free meal a day! Life was a complete disaster and Coach Jones could do no more for him.

His courtship of the beautiful Josephine was proving long, arduous and as usual for Duke nerve-wracking, "She had a way of saying "no" that was like an invitation." Whether she invited him or not he doggedly pursued her all summer despite his injury and the fact that he had no money. He never dated anyone else, nor did he chase "those certain kinds of girls" anymore. Pexy remembered the courtship as "stormy" and felt sorry for his room mate's problems which he rarely seemed able to escape, but which he unflinchingly met head on with an endurance that amazed him. Generally the difficulties were caused by Josie's jealousy. Duke rarely then gave her cause to be suspicious but she taunted him for looking at other girls and he was unable then, or later, to convince her of his devotion. And the taunts stung because they were the same ones his mother had thrown at his dad, because they had no foundation, and because he was the most loyal of souls. Still, he also recognised that, "In the end Josie paid a high price for loving me too. Neither of us got out of it whole. Ours wasn't a one way love."

Pexy discovered that Duke started selling his blood at the local blood bank and that he had, in fact, occasionally been doing it during training. He immediately understood why he sometimes looked so pale and tired. Duke now sold so much blood that he was eventually banned by the blood bank and even barred from entering the building. Feeding himself was a huge problem as he stared at failure once again, "I was never started on the team again. The only real food I got was earned because of my place on the team. I was angry but more than anything right then, I was just goddammed hungry."

It was a practical problem that Duke anticipated being able to sort out once he was fit again. He tried to hang on and for another term managed to live on money borrowed from friends. But finally, and despite every determined effort, he realised he couldn't even repay the money he had already borrowed. He had to accept he wasn't only finished in football but at college too. He had a term's worth of debt and didn't want to start another. He made one of the hardest decisions of his life, "I didn't have any money — son of a bitch! My shoulder was hurting so I figured, what the hell, I'll lay out this year and catch up on some money … I got so interested in pictures that I never went back. I got work with Pappy Ford as a prop man and was so intrigued by him that I decided to strive to be a director, like him. I worked with him as often as I could just so I could get more experience." The explanation sounded simple, straightforward, it was how he liked to present his life, but it hadn't been like that at the time. It was a devastating blow that he was slow to recover from.

Pexy, though still member of Sigma Chi, was now living at home with his parents. He still attended the fraternity house for social gatherings and one evening he drove up to find Duke sitting on the porch with a box containing everything he owned in his hands. Duke confessed, "I don't know what to do. I can't pay my bills, and I can't live here anymore."

"When he finally got the word, I guess he was too proud to ask for help. He didn't even call me, which he could have, and he didn't have the faintest idea what he was going to do or where he was going to go. It was just coincidence that I passed when I did."

Pexy was so upset to see his friend like that, that even before asking his parents, he offered Duke his old room over the garage and drove him and his box straight home. Pexy's parents had known Duke since childhood. He had always spent a lot of time at their house, escaping the horrors of his own. They had known him so long that he was still Marion to them. They remembered him always towering above their son and their other friends, but as the most gentle and decent boy. They, like Pexy, had a soft spot for the laughing boy he had always been and for the charming, sincere and considerate young man he had become. He had stayed above their garage when his parents split, and now they told him he could stay there again for as long as he wanted or needed.

Duke wanted to do what he had always done in times of trouble, run away. He had no idea how to tell his Dad that he had left USC, "Worse than that was the thought of telling Josie." Although he was soon back at work and making reasonable money at the studio he confessed, "It was a

hell of a problem. I hoped she'd accept I was no longer a college boy …
I was a man making my own way in the world." He hated confrontation,
and right then, even as a man making his own way, he felt a strong urge
to run from it, the need almost as strong as when, at five, he had jumped
on the passing railcars.

He had suddenly learned at USC that he was just a scholarship boy
surrounded by money, and that he was accepted at Sigma Chi because of
his prowess on the football field. As far as a career in law was concerned,
he'd never had any real future. Lacking the contacts in the outside world
so vital to a career in law, he could never have gone far. Though brighter
than the other students and despite working harder than any of them, he
would have ended up working for them in their father's firms. Even if he
could somehow pay the rest of his way through school, he now knew he
would end up writing briefs in a back-room for people who weren't as
smart as he was. On consideration his leaving was not such a disaster, it
just seemed like it at the time, "I didn't figure I'd amount to much then."

He was undecided about his future. If he could win his scholarship
back he could go back to his studies, but he was no longer sure that was
his best option. Friends on the lot said, "Duke just lit up when he talked
football," but his shoulder took over a year to heal and by then he'd
accepted he wasn't such a special player and he suspected he'd never
make it back onto the first string. He had missed so much training and
lost too much ground to other, better, faster players. He could surf, swim,
ride and take part in all the other sports he loved but he could no longer
pay his way playing football. Years later whilst making a film about
football where he played the part of a coach himself he badly injured the
same shoulder causing long term and far reaching damage. As far back as
he could remember that shoulder had hurt and the movement of his right
arm been severely restricted. Whenever he fell off a horse in some stunt
he inevitably landed on it, when he got hit in a staged fight it was always
that shoulder that took the full brunt of the blow. He believed fellow
actors had an ability to find it, like homing pigeons drawn to a loft.

All in all then, just another rotten year. His indecision about the
coming ones left him irritable and he began loosing interest in what was
going on around him. He started drinking heavily, even by his standards,
as he tried to drown his sorrows in whiskey. He brooded, was depressed
and felt tired. All he wanted was to be with Josie, but even when he was
with her, all was not well. She told him she loved him, but it didn't seem
like it to him. Too often she did what her parents told her to do rather
than what he wanted. He was all too aware they didn't approve of their
Catholic, church-going daughter dating him. In part he even agreed with

them; he had no career prospects, no social status and no future. He was not Catholic, and worst of all, his parents were separated. Dr and Mrs Saenz conceded that he was handsome, dashing even. He dressed well, was polite, courteous, well spoken, very gentle and they understood why Josephine had fallen in love with such a nice boy. Still, they believed she would get over her crush and whilst they didn't stop her seeing him, knowing it would only make matters worse, they repeatedly pointed out his faults, belabouring the issue of the amount he drank. He was allowed to see her twice a week, but her parents made sure she also met other men. Duke was left in no doubt, they considered him a most ineligible suitor for their daughter.

Anyone who knew him at all understood that saying "No" was like waving a red flag at a bull. He may have seemed shy, polite and reticent, but above everything he was a fighter. Being told he was unwelcome in their home only served to make him all the more determined to slug it out for the prize and he stubbornly refused to accept "No" from Dr Saenz. He arranged to see Josie as often as he could. He may have been crushed by what had happened at college, but once he recognised the challenge he could not resist lifting himself for the fight in prospect.

They were tough times for Duke. He loved, respected and longed for Josie, but she also enraged him as no one else in his life ever did and at her hands he openly wept tears of bitter rejection, "She frustrated and confused me, but I could never have given my heart so completely had I not respected her." And so they carried on, Duke increasingly frustrated, cursing the fate that had led him to Josie and to the beach on the day that cost him his future, and Josie sympathising with his urgent needs, unable to satisfy them.

He had lost football, law and was still unable to get Josie. He had decided not to go back to college, he no longer felt part of that set up, excluded from the camaraderie he had known before and at this point in the life of the man who was to become the epitome of machismo there was dark poetry. He spent many depressed hours pouring over the tribulations of Shelley, Byron and the other romantics who wrote of the hopelessness of love. Duke even tried his own hand at writing.

He and Josie argued all the time and Duke, who could not abide raised voices, was goaded into them by the strength of his feelings for her. It had been during one of their many heated exchanges that he finally blurted out that he had left college and was earning forty dollars a week at Fox Studios. He told her that should be enough for them to live on if she would marry him right then. Needless to say, when he asked her, he knew she wouldn't even consider it and that her parents would never willingly allow her to marry him. Even though he had known what the answer would be, he was still angry when she told him, "You know I can't."

In 1928 he moved out of Pexy's garage to rent a room nearer her home. He continued dating her despite every obstacle thrown in his path. He was, however, already suffering the bouts of depression that later swamped his life. He became discouraged and didn't know how to get what he wanted. He had been fighting stubbornly, building up his savings, hustling for extra work, and had started doing some stunt work. By the standards of the times he was earning good money, easily enough to support a wife. But he was also, like his father, always lending money to friends, and the savings he put together seemed to pour through his fingers.

In a sudden fit of despair he decided he'd never be able to make enough to win Josie and he told her it was over, "Josie, I just can't take anymore." They both cried but when he took her home that night he didn't let her out of the car and his hand didn't brush her arm. There was no kiss. Her father had won and Duke's resistance over, he finally gave up. His life changed and nothing would ever be the same again. Like his father, grandfather and great grandfather Duke decided to go west in search of a brighter future. He was running again; not forging a way forward as they had, but running away from a hopeless past. He went to San Francisco where he planned to find work on any ship in port. He loved stories of the sea and longed to be a sailor, now he saw his chance to live the life of adventurer. He sold everything he owned, including the car he had scratched around for, all his sports equipment, his books and his few clothes. He had started at USC with one case of belongings, now he was setting off on his own, with nothing. Things could only get better from here on in.

He planned having a wild time in a city where those "certain sort of girls" were readily available and where he could get Josie out of his system. He went after them with a vengeance, seeking revenge. He took everything he so badly needed and said, "I hoped I would never again feel guilty for having those needs!" But in San Francisco Duke discovered that was not the way things worked for him and he was left strangely unsatisfied. No matter how many women chased him he was only ever interested in one girl at a time and although it was uncomfortable, he found he had to be just a little bit in love before he could accept any of the offers that continued flooding in. For only a very short time he tasted the exotic delicacies on offer in San Francisco. He didn't enjoy himself or have the fun he'd anticipated, "It was like stumbling around in the dark and then suddenly being blinded by a flash of lightning for a brief moment. Most of the time I felt lost in the dark, I just wanted to be with Josie." The only time he escaped her was when he passed out after a heavy drinking session. So he saw the sights, drank and partied, felt empty and alone, guilty and dirty in turn.

Desperate to escape America and Josie's haunting influence, he scoured the port for work. There was nothing to be found. He was hiding in dreams, enthralled by the romance of his misery and frustration. He was twenty and even more reckless now than he had been as a child and he decided if he couldn't get work, stowing away on a passing cruise ship might be a good adventure, at least it would be romantic. After checking out the destinations of some of the ships, he chose one sailing for Hawaii. Not caring about the consequences of his actions he walked up the gang plank and began mingling with other passengers. No one took any notice of him and a wild sense of excitement filled him as he ambled around, smiling and shaking hands with everyone he came across, "Course, really I shoulda' felt foreboding and doom ... shoulda' remembered my earlier attempts at running away. Nothing I ever did then worked out like I expected."

He had the clothes he stood in, a toothbrush, a comb, and some loose change in his pocket, "I was finished with the past ... said all my farewells ... when I looked out to sea I was searching for a future ... I was hungry for happiness. I wandered round trying to look like I belonged, talking to passengers. I was looking for a place to settle, to hide, somewhere to sleep. It always looked so easy in the movies."

In spite of his yearning to be a sailor this was actually the first time he'd ever been to sea. He felt completely alone on the ship in the middle of the ocean and he was both excited and frightened. He liked the sensation that man was only a very small and ultimately unimportant entity in the scheme of things, it scaled his problems down, made them less traumatic, perhaps they didn't even really matter at all. Life went on, regardless of anything he did or didn't do. Later that was the very reason he was drawn back again and again to the sea. His dramatic soul gazed out at the sight before him and in a symbolic, cinematic touch, he threw his loose change, all that was left to him of his old life, into the ocean. He wanted to start his new life completely uncluttered and he turned away from the rail to continue his search for a convenient hiding place. He crept stealthily in and out of the public rooms, looked for a life boat to climb into, searched for a coil of rope to curl up in. The lifeboats were too high, he could find no ropes, and when he went into the public rooms he began to be aware of the smell of food and the fact that he now had no money. He hadn't eaten before boarding and was, as ever, hungry. For Duke there was hunger and there was starvation, and even before the first night was over he was starving. Things would get a lot worse, but that night, despite the discomfort, it was all just part of the adventure, "My whole life was on the line, so to hell with dinner, a man should be hungry when he sets out to establish himself."

By the next morning a growling and empty stomach caused him to doubt the philosophy. Whenever he told the story in the years that followed he made light of it; hunger was a feeling he had known in some degree most of his life. But it wasn't funny to him then, and although the adventure may have been good in the telling, even now he wished he had not been so stupid when he was twenty.

Things didn't go the way he had expected when he first set off and he found out he lacked the basic instincts of the adventurer. He paced up and down outside every cabin on every deck looking for any scrap of food and found nothing. He craved a drink. He was on a ship full of bars and legal drink and he couldn't get one. One evening he joined three men in a game of cards and he had winning hand after winning hand, "If I had been playing for money I would have won hundreds of dollars. Never before or since have I had such a run of luck. The bastards didn't want to stop for dinner and they weren't even buying drinks."

Eventually he was discovered by a steward who turned him over to the captain. He was handcuffed and taken to a room below decks where he was held prisoner, after being fed stale sandwiches left by the card players, until being transferred to another ship going back to San Francisco. There he was handed over to the Harbour police who arrested him. He spent the day in jail before finally gathering the courage to ring John Ford who organised a speedy release and a ticket back to Los Angeles.

Duke no longer knew where home was but it seemed that forces, elemental and strong, carried him back to Hollywood where he had appointments to keep. He had still no plan for the future but knew that, whatever the cost, however much it hurt, he wanted to spend it with Josie. He rushed straight to Balboa to tell her he loved her and couldn't live without her. He told her he was going back to Fox where he would earn enough to support her. He was no longer a boy, and whilst his voyage had been a childishly petulant act, it was also a turning point in his life. He could not go back to being a college boy, struggling to earn a crust when he was already able to earn a man's wage, "That was the time I really took a different view of pictures. I enjoyed the work and, because of my friendship with George O'Brien, the leading man at Fox, I felt I belonged on the lot. For the first time I knew that was where my future lay." It seemed to Josie and her parents that nothing had changed. Duke knew, everything had. From now on, though she held a place in his heart, she would have to share what he had to give with Hollywood. He wanted her, but he wanted a career in the movies too, he already needed it as much as he needed her.

In spring 1929 he was assigned to work on another Ford film, *Salute*, a story about naval cadets being shot at Annapolis. Duke jumped at the chance of seeing the school he had longed to go to as a cadet himself. He was also thrilled that Ford had offered him another chance. In fact the director was taking a keen interest in the developing career of odd-jobber Morrison and over the next years he began testing Duke in ways imperceptible to outsiders. He belittled him, befriended him, gave him extra responsibility, took it away again. Whatever was happening in Ford's complex mind, Duke obviously, but unknowingly, passed all the tests. Ford had already begun telling people about Duke's potential in front of the camera but perhaps even he didn't understand the power of their fast developing relationship. Many later suggested Ford was homosexual. If he was he was never open about it. He certainly feared intimacy, mistrusted love, and preferred the comfort of celibacy. He undoubtedly found the young Duke very attractive, seeing him with an artist's eye, but if such attraction was homosexual in its connotations, Duke remained blissfully unaware of it. Both were always happiest in the company of men, possibly for different historic reasons. That didn't make either of them homosexual and Ford's behaviour toward Duke was never, at any time, of an overtly sexual nature. If the director suspected homosexuality in himself he controlled his feelings, firmly repressing any sign of what he considered to be weakness in his character. Even at nineteen, and despite the frequent child-like lapses, Duke appeared everything a man should be and Ford could never have made any sexual approach toward this epitome of maleness. Duke's heterosexuality was beyond doubt, and whilst the reasons for Ford's interest in him remain open to conjecture, their relationship was certainly special, strong and unusual. In fact Ford himself went some way to explaining why he promoted the prop boy into one of the permanent members of his Stock Company, confirming that he had seen something deep inside Duke at a very early age, "I guess you could call it star power."

For the next three years Duke remained a property man at Fox and he loved his work, setting the artefacts for scenes, arranging the other objects that actors carried to suggest personality, and helping to create the background for action sequences. He was highly regarded for his talent at the studio. He worked hard, was keen and interested in everything going on around him and he developed a great insight into the world of making films right there. The knowledge he gained stood him in good stead later when he turned to acting, and later still when he moved into directing his own productions, he admitted, "My mind, both as an actor and director, was conditioned by the work I did in my youth. I read somewhere that it took a certain minor talent to write, direct, produce or star in a movie, but that it took genius to be a good prop man. That made me, in some minor way, a genius too." He learned the movie industry from the bottom up and received an education he could not have got anywhere else but on the Hollywood back lots.

He learned the importance of detail serving an apprenticeship behind the cameras, whilst his contemporaries and future colleagues rarely gave a thought to such trivia as they struggled to learn their lines and positions. To Duke, detail was the vital element in a good production and he never lost the sense of precision he acquired then. He remained the same artist all his working life, maintaining near infallible judgement in the handling of props for the next fifty years, "When I read a script I needed to know why a character did a certain thing, there had to be a point of action for me; when a character threw a cigarette butt into a flower pot I wanted to know what brand of cigarette it was, was there a cigarette case in evidence? I had to know what kind of pot the flowers were in, what type of flowers were they? Were they on a table?" His endless questions drove directors and producers mad at the time; he was fanatical about having things perfect, but his perseverance later made all the difference to John Wayne movies.

Even when he eventually stepped in front of the camera himself he still got excited about lighting and prop set-ups, and he often barked out orders to independent crews, "Take that one to the side … and please bring me that chair to sit on, bring that stone elephant over … yeah … that'll do it." And the crews seemed unable to resist his infectious enthusiasm as they jumped to carry out his instructions. Sometimes, if he suddenly realised he wasn't in charge, he looked up, embarrassed, laughed and apologised, "Oh … sorry," before getting straight back to business as usual a few moments later. He loved every second he spent working with cameras and film crews. He could be over-generous with his advice perhaps, but anyone who took the trouble to listen learned valuable lessons from the master prop man.

His eye for detail was so precise that whenever he chose gifts for friends or relatives he unfailingly knew what would suit who, and which size would fit them. He surprised people with gifts from all over the world, and many of his friends received the very ornament to perfectly compliment their decor. His enthusiasm for getting things right made him a great prop man, it also meant people often found a package on their doorstep containing the very thing they had been looking for! He never tired of "getting things right" and even at the end of his career he could be found twirling his six shooter or rifle off screen with the enthusiasm of a child playing with a toy, still practising because he needed to perform perfectly.

He started in props but became just as interested in every aspect of film making, going to enormous lengths to learn everything he could about each craft involved in the industry. He spent every spare moment he could at the lot, working from sun-up to sunset, soaking up the knowledge that sustained his career through the next fifty years. There were no unions in Hollywood then and he moved freely from one trade to another. He became a decent carpenter as he helped build sets, he rigged lighting, carted and arranged furniture and got to know everything that went on behind the scenes. He developed an uncanny ability to visualise what a scene was going to look like long before it was shot and later in his career he rarely needed to look at the daily rushes to know what had been filmed the day before.

He enjoyed being around everyone involved in the movie industry and he responded to their boundless energy; they all led frantic lives as they struggled to meet demanding schedules. Their existence was abnormal, they spent most of the day in a fantasy land, surrounded by the producers of dreams and they compensated for their long hours of work in the bars around the studio at the end of each day. At the studio and in the bars Duke found a family atmosphere that held an obvious appeal. Everyone, involved in any capacity at Fox, knew everyone else, from the boss down to the prop boy and Duke felt more at home there than he had ever felt anywhere else. The instant he walked onto the lot at the crack of dawn he was relaxed, content, settled and focused. Much was demanded and expected of him, but that exactly suited his own needs and for the first time in his life he felt in control of his destiny. He had a regular job and many friends. He particularly enjoyed the company of George O'Brien who was already a big star but liked all the same things he did; talking, laughing and drinking. Because of their close friendship Duke felt he belonged and had found his place in the world.

He looked back fondly to the time when he was just an ordinary man, successful in his chosen field, earning good money, and lucky enough to have found a girl he loved. Life was pleasant and simple and for the first time he began to visualise a bright future. He took on still more work earning another fifty dollars a day as an extra as he tried to save enough to persuade Josie to marry him. The directors at the studio found his pleasant face photogenic, but failed to notice the star power; they knew he was different but they didn't know how, why or where he fitted into the scheme of things. Ford alone recognised that the sensitive, painfully shy boy radiated before a camera, became luminous, and seemed to glow, "The camera never missed Wayne. It had something to do with inner honesty." To him the nothing, walk-on part of the peasant boy of *Hangman's*

House had been everything. Ford had seen a "movie face" that conveyed an innocence which had nothing to do with youth. There was an openness about him that even later, when he played men of great violence, still shone through; it was effortless but it made his acts of cruelty on screen somehow less degrading than they might otherwise have appeared. Nothing that ever happened to him, not all the physical suffering in his later life, not the dissipation, not the effects of fighting with his whole heart and soul for his place in Hollywood, not his intense dedication to his profession, nor the overwhelming sorrows of his personal life ever took away the innocence or the honesty from the screen performance. At the start of the adventure he had no idea what he possessed, but finally even he understood that it was the underlying self that filmgoers loved and paid their money to see. And he offered himself to the fans, "I don't work for the producers ... I don't work for the studios ... and I don't work for the critics ... I work for the audience. They pay my salary ... I always give the best of myself so that people aren't disappointed in me." He had always been grateful to Ford for teaching him such values right at the start.

He had been propping Submarine for Ford when he inadvertently became a stuntman, allowing himself to get roped in for the extra cash that Coach offered. The film, later released as Men Without Women, was about a submarine trapped on the sea bed following an underwater explosion. Duke's first task on the film was to produce air bubbles from the sinking sub. The scene was being shot round Catalina Island and the sea was particularly rough. Day after day Duke worked a hand pump to produce the required bubbles. Two stuntmen were to dive into the sea and emerge where the bubbles were coming up, supposedly having escaped from the stricken sub through the torpedo bays. But each day the men decided the sea was too rough to attempt the stunt. Ford was desperately trying to keep the picture within budget, and he contemplated scrapping the scene and shooting something on the lot instead. He called a break while he decided what to do. Duke didn't hear the call and kept pumping for all he was worth. When Ford finally spotted him still furiously working away at the hand pump he fell about laughing, but suddenly wondered if Duke would risk getting in the choppy sea.

"Duke?"

"Yessir," he stopped pumping.

"Hit the god-damned water." He did the stunt work no questions asked, he always did everything Coach told him to do, no questions asked, trusting him implicitly. He made six dives that day into the dangerous waters before Coach was satisfied with the footage. When he later signed his work sheet Duke was horrified to find he had only been credited seven dollars and fifty cents bonus instead of the four hundred and fifty he was expecting for doing the stunt! The studio explained that he was employed as a prop man and that was what they paid him as.

"So what's this seven dollars and fifty cents? What the hell's that for?"

They explained it was a bonus for his extra effort, "I'd nearly killed myself … risked my neck on a stunt that no one else had the guts to do, and all I got was a bonus!" He couldn't do anything about it but he carried the bitterness of that day around with him for a long time and was still fuming about the incident in the 1970's. Whenever he told the story the anger poured out afresh; whilst magnanimous in most areas of his life, he also carried Wayne-sized grudges.

But he had discovered he was a good stunt man after all and decided that was what he was meant to be. He had enjoyed all the work he did at Fox, but now set his heart on becoming the best stuntman that ever lived. He was fit and muscular, he thrived on physical action, and, as a child, had enjoyed nothing as much as copying the death defying acts of Douglas Fairbanks. He believed he had been a stuntman most of his young life; jumping off garages, climbing trees, riding horses, nothing had been too extreme and he had no sense of danger. As a stuntman he could earn plenty of money doing all the things he most enjoyed.

Just as he had become used to looking at a film in terms of its props and its detail, he now came to see them in terms of their stunts and their action and for the next ten years he considered himself to be a stunt man. He had well and truly embarked on the journey of his life. Whilst he carried much of his unhappy past with him into the next phase, he had finally escaped and would never be part of the "ordinary" world again. He could never return to the life of Marion Morrison, and knew everything that preceded that day in the water had been preparation for the rest of the amazing voyage that he was now embarking on.

John Ford on Wayne: "I could always tell the big dumb oaf had something very special, but at the start he was just too skinny and too pretty to do much with. I kept an eye on him, gave him bit parts from time to time and he became the son I would have liked to have. He was my favourite boy."

CHAPTER TWO

Warrior on Horseback

The Making of John Wayne

"My mind as an actor and later as a director, was conditioned by the work I did in my youth. I started out on the Fox lot as a prop boy. I read somewhere that it took genius to be a good prop boy and I felt that made me, in some minor way, a genius too. I learned the movie industry on the Hollywood back lots, from the bottom up. I served my apprenticeship and got a thorough education in the importance of detail."

Steely eyes glanced out over the harbour as they so often did, drawn constantly toward the sea, "I was going to sit outside for a while, look at the boats, the lights. You want to come with me?" The voice was little more than a whisper in her ear, it was another attempt to melt her anger, and she looked up at him, smiling at last. He hated anyone to be angry with him, and he bent his head toward her and brushed his cheek against hers, in a familiar gesture, calmer now. He took the glass that she still held and put it down on his desk, and then taking both her hands in his he pulled her closer toward him. "Well, if you're coming out with me, you better put something warm on, it's getting colder out there."

All week as he prepared himself for Christmas he had been in a terrible, dark mood, barking his orders and giving no one, including himself, any peace. Pat had borne the brunt of his legendary temper, but particularly so when she tried to talk him into going to the hospital for a check up. He knew it was inevitable, but wanted to delay talking to his doctors, despite her nagging, because he wanted to enjoy the holiday, before all the familiar tests started, and before he would be forced to face a truth he already knew. He wasn't ready to take that step yet, but he felt fretful and angry, irritable, on edge. He had cancer again, but he'd beaten that enemy before, he would beat it again, and he told Pat, "I'll be goddamned if I'll spend my holiday in that place, it depresses me. Anyway, what the hell is the hurry? I've put up with the pain for so long, a few more days aren't going to matter — I can put up with it a few more days. Now let's get the place looking like it's Christmas."

To Pat it had an uncanny resemblance to a scene from one of his movies, "Are you hit sheriff?"

"Yeah, but it's just a flesh wound."

He hadn't voiced his suspicions, but she understood him well enough to guess, she also knew him well enough not to argue with him for too long and she had helped him find the decorations, had gone with him to choose the tree, had helped him to do all the things he wanted to do, knowing that nothing would budge him. He would go to the hospital only when he was ready. He'd promised her he would go, and she had to be content with his promise.

"Let's go out then."

By the time they had put their jackets on it was almost dark. There were guests coming for dinner, but he wanted to breathe in some fresh night air before he made the effort of entertaining them. He loved the patio he'd had built when he and Pilar, his third wife, first moved into the house. Pilar was long gone now, but he still enjoyed sitting out there just watching the water, the boats and the sky, feeling the sea breeze on his face. They were the things that were important to him, were what he had always taken pleasure in. The evenings on the patio overlooking the main channel of the bay were the peaceful moments in his life, the rare moments when he sat still, relaxed in pleasure.

He was silent, his mind elsewhere, in a different time, a different place. He had not made a film since *The Shootist,* two years earlier. Even when he had made it the critics had considered the story, about an ageing gunfighter, dying of cancer, to be his epitaph, and they considered it a prophetic slice of history. Tonight he wondered if they had been right. He sighed heavily, "I didn't want to retire you know. I'd like to do another picture. I've seen a story I think I could do. I need to work Pat, I get nervous, don't know what the hell to do with myself, I just keep wondering what the hell to do next. I've made millions and millions of dollars since I began … I haven't got even one million left now … what the hell. I need to make sure there's gonna be enough for everyone when I go. I went without a meal, I've had it all kinds of ways, so I'm not worried about me, but I want to make sure the kids will be alright. The world's a tough place out there Pat."

"Duke, the kids will all be fine whatever happens." She didn't know what to say, he wasn't listening anyway.

"I enjoyed it all so damn much. I had such a good time, and there were such special people in my life, a man just couldn't have known so many dear people in one life time," he wanted to talk about the old days, the studios, the fun, but it was time to get ready for the performance. He stood up sharply, determined it would be a good one, and the two small dogs that had been sleeping in between his feet moaned their discomfort. "Get outta here," he offered, laughing as they played around his ankles. He strode back into the house, tall and upright as ever, leaving Pat to follow sadly behind. She could remember the times when the laughter had never been far from his eyes, when every line of him told of power, ebullience, but it seemed to have drained away so suddenly, so unexpectedly, that she felt unprepared for what she saw now. She hoped she would have as much determination as he had, and after the week she had just spent with him, she knew she was going to need it. He had been irritable about everything and she had stayed out of his way as much as possible. Now she knew he needed her there. When she had gone off shopping alone, just to get away from him for a while, he had been white with anger when she got back. She had taken longer than he had expected and he was livid, but when she tried to explain she had been choosing presents, he growled, "Like hell you were, you were in some bar … Why don't you just get out of here, and leave me alone? I don't need a damned secretary anymore." The barbed words hurt because the accusation was absurd and he was being unfair in the extreme, but he had been in so much pain when she happened to walk in that he had lashed out in uncontrolled fury, attacking one of the few reliable people left in his life. She had walked away from him then leaving him alone, forlorn and helpless. But out on the patio she decided not to leave him on his own again; he hadn't done anything to deserve that. Whatever he did or said, she knew he needed someone. His words might hurt now, but he was also the gentlest man she had ever known, and if he hurt her it was because he was hurting so badly himself. He had been kind, thoughtful, wonderful for six years, and now she would repay him …

John Ford had an enormous impact on the Hollywood version of The American West but his dream didn't include the boy Duke Morrison back at the start; he was far too young and sensitive to put into his romantically violent image. Luckily Ford was not the only director on the Fox lot, and Raoul Walsh was every bit as successful. John Wayne, the movie star, was all his creation.

Many of the directors at the Fox Studio had taken notice of the big prop-man-cum-stunt-man. They acknowledged he was handy to have around, always willing to work hard and so good looking and able they were not afraid to use him in their films as well. But as Duke remembered it now, the start had been a case of him being in the right place at the right time. With the advent of the talkies everyone in Hollywood prophesied the demise of the Western, saying there was no room for the vast sprawling outdoor film, that sound could not be reproduced or recorded outside, and this prevented the very mobility needed to make a good Western. Walsh believed it could be done and he developed special sound units to track outdoor action when he made history, shooting the first western talkie. He hid microphones in bushes and on trucks and although the sound quality was rough it was possible to hear horses clattering, guns shooting and bacon sizzling. He had created a revolution in the film world with the first production made on location, now he wanted to go further and make a spectacle western, an epic, the biggest movie of all time. He planned the film, hired actors from the stage and wanted Gary Cooper for the lead role. Cooper was under contract to Sam Goldwyn and couldn't be released. It was 1929, right in the middle of the country's worst ever recession and Fox, in deep financial difficulty, had already thrown one hundred thousand dollars at the project and they were worried. Walsh refused to give up and continued auditioning every cowboy actor in town. He was getting desperate when, to appease the studio heads, he decided to cast an unknown in the lead role.

There was a shortage of film actors suitable for the talkies and there weren't enough stars to go around anyway, and Walsh was ready to take a gamble. On a hot Californian morning he was on his way to the Fox administration building to talk over his unusual decision. His journey took him past a gang moving furniture. He immediately noticed a tall, bare-chested young man whose rippling muscles were covered in sweat. He watched intently and later recalled, "He was juggling chairs as if they were made of feathers. Someone made him laugh and I was intrigued by his expression. He was so warm and wholesome. I knew who he was. Duke had propped on a number of my pictures, but I'd never watched him before. Now I noticed he had a western droop to his shoulders and a way of moving typical to the westerner. I opened a conversation with him and concentrated on the way he spoke. I liked what I heard. I liked the fine physique of the boy, his casual strength, the grace of his movement and his easy voice." Without ever getting to the casting meeting he asked Duke to grow his hair long for a screen test.

"Mr Walsh I don't want to be an actor."

But Walsh had decided the unknown Duke was going to star in the most expensive epic to hit the screen, *The Big Trail*. He answered, "You never know Duke, you just never know where life's going to take you."

He was staggered when he saw the results of the first tests. Ford would not have been shocked at how good Morrison looked, but Walsh had not suspected that he would be so right, or that he would sound so good for the part he had in mind. He couldn't believe how lucky he had been to walk past him on that particular day, noticing his muscles shining in the hot sun. How much luckier it turned out for Duke that he had laughed at the split second he had been noticed.

The director ran the test for the Fox studio bosses, Wurtzel and Sheehan.

"How do we know he can talk?" asked Sheehan

"You heard him talk. It was a hard scene. He did it well."

"It's too much of a risk," said Wurtzel

"We're not going to get anyone any better" Walsh insisted, "He's the only one I can get for the money you want to pay."

He was sure he'd already found the best, he didn't even want Cooper anymore, knowing Duke would look better in the buckskins designed for the lead character.

"I don't like his name ... it's no name for a leading man" added Sheehan.

Walsh had his man.

Sol Wortzel agreed, "Duke Morrison doesn't sound American enough."

"How about Anthony Wayne?" asked Walsh, an admirer of General "Mad" Anthony Wayne.

"Sounds too Italian."

"Tony Wayne" — too much like a girl — he already had a girl's name, they had to steer well clear of female sounding names.

"Well how about plain John? John Wayne?"

"John Wayne sure sounds American."

Walsh was told to send John Wayne to Sheehan's office the next day so they could decide how much they were going to pay the star of the biggest western ever made. He was earning thirty-five dollars a week as a prop man, standard rate, but Sheehan pondered, "We ought to give him a raise — how about forty five dollars?"

Walsh couldn't believe it, "If it ever got out that we paid our leading man forty five dollars and our other actors five hundred we'd be the laughing stock of the industry." The answer came back, "Well we can't afford to pay him five hundred dollars. We have to hold the budget down, that's the whole point of using him in the first place — if we had $500 we could have got you Cooper."

Finally, to star in his first film, he was offered seventy-five dollars a week and Duke had grinned his delight at the offer of untold wealth, a handsome sum in the wake of the stock market crash. He couldn't believe his luck, a $40 a week pay rise to go and have some fun. He had no idea that all the others would be getting hundreds of dollars. Best of all, he could tell Josephine he was going to be a star, he would be earning a good wage, and his name would be up in lights, he would have status, he would be someone. Although he accepted the money gratefully and was satisfied to be earning what he considered decent money, he bitterly resented the way his new name had been chosen. His oldest friends and his family still called him Marion, newer friends called him Duke, and it was many years before he became accustomed to John Wayne. He never answered to the name John, "No, I've always been either Duke, Marion or John Wayne. The name goes well together and it's like one word, John Wayne. But if people say John — Christ, I don't look round."

The Fox empire was crumbling and the high budget *Big Trail* was intended to save the company. Walsh knew that Duke looked and sounded right for the part he had in mind, but more importantly he was available, he was unbelievably cheap and John Wayne became, instantly, one of the best deals ever generated in Hollywood history. He had wandered blindly into the situation every actor dreams of and once he had signed on the dotted line the studio became a hive of activity, promoting both the film and their newest star. His background was dragged up and put to good use; the studio heads had already spotted that where the creation of John Wayne was concerned, the shaping of the man was paramount, and Duke's personal history perfectly fitted the "John Wayne" image now being put together by the publicists. He appeared instantly the hero, someone who had survived the worst that life could throw at him. Joan Didion later wrote, "Imagine … Marion Morrison in Glendale. A Boy Scout, a student at Glendale High. A tackle at USC. Summer vacations at the Fox lot. A meeting with John Ford, just one of seven directors who sensed that into this perfect mould could be poured the inarticulate longings of a nation wondering where it had all been lost." She continued, "When he spoke there was never any misunderstanding his intentions, he had a sexual authority so strong even a child could perceive it. And in a world we understood early to be characterised by venality and doubt and paralysing ambiguities, he suggested another world … but where did he come from, before he rode through the tall grass?" Where he had come from had been the very place that the mould had been cast and right from the first, the star system intruded into Duke's private persona. He completed studio questionnaires grudgingly, "What's your real name?" … "Marion Michael Morrison."

"What was your first job?" … "Picking apricots."

"Tell us about your ancestors," … "Never looked 'em up."

The answers never changed, they began the legend and created the heroic image, but they were rooted in his own honesty, and had little to do with the publicist's vision. They were instinctive, based on his gut reaction to the situation in front of him, and they served him well for the next fifty years. The studio arranged his interviews, they couldn't control him or the answers he gave.

Still, on the first day he walked up to Sheehan's office his knees trembled as he was ushered in to face the head of Fox Studios, and despite the publicity that followed he felt far from heroic as a five-year contract was pushed across the desk toward him. He had gone to the office alone, read the contract alone, he had no lawyer, no agent and no-one to advise him on the best course to take. He was young, inexperienced and desperate for the chance to develop a career, to earn some money so he could get married. He was clever, he had studied law, he saw no reason why anyone at Fox should want to cheat him, and he signed and felt excited at the blue scribble of his name. It was the first of many one way contracts he signed … always strictly in the studio's favour. He resented for the rest of his life the arrogance with which he was treated; they tried to change his identity, take advantage of his naivete, and they changed his name without any discussion. The studio, he was made very well aware, right from the start, didn't give a damn about how he felt about anything.

For his role in Walsh's epic he had to learn to throw a knife, a lariat, how to handle a gun and to ride like a westerner, because to cut costs further, he was expected to do his own stunts. He was paid nothing extra but he was pleased to be doing work that he felt comfortable with. He was happy to be working at all, able at last to take Josie out in some style and they began socialising with other young Hollywood stars. Duke was surprised to find himself sponsored, as a contract actor, to all kinds of Hollywood clubs and events. One club he particularly enjoyed was the Hollywood Athletic Club, where he often swam, dined and drank. He worked out in the gym there with stars he had idolised since he was a boy and it was heady stuff to be feted along with those who had played such a big part in his life. He was flattered by the attention but also felt unusually at ease in their midst.

And if stardom was within his grasp, then marriage had to be and he grabbed at everything now on offer with both huge fists. Taking what life offered had been his greatest talent and he had never been one to sit waiting for the gifts to arrive. He was happy, content and finally ready to take the plunge with Josie. He filled every day with energy and power, he had uncomplainingly taken what had been dished out, but he put so much effort into living that everything he later achieved reflected an unlimited strength, developed back then. In 1929 every last drop in the tank was put into *The Big Trail*.

Before the company set off on location Duke asked Walsh if he could bring along Ward Bond for company. The two had played football together at USC but weren't particularly friendly until Duke left university and was already working as an extra. When John Ford was having difficulty casting football players for a new film he had asked Duke if any of his college friends might be interested and Bond had turned up along with the rest of the Trojan team. At the time Duke told him he was too ugly to get a part but Ford liked him, ugly or not, and he was taken along with the others. *Salute* was Bond's first venture in the movies and when he was given a bigger part than Duke it led to tension between the pair. Ford's warped sense of humour, his amusement at setting up difficult situations, led him to throw them together as often as possible. Duke was the recognised leader of the student extras but Bond went out of his way to undermine his authority and to give him the hardest time he could. Duke went out of his to prove the folly of bringing the troublemaker along. Both found the location work tough, on call from six every morning and drilling everyday with an army sergeant in hot, wet uncomfortable conditions. But, as Ford had anticipated, they were soon spending long nights carousing together, drinking and singing, and they emerged from the experience the best of friends. Bond had only been given lines in the picture to annoy Duke and he recalled, "I can still see that slow grin spreading over Duke's mug when he realised what Ford was up to. He's always been that way, the first to get a kick out of a joke that turns back on him." Duke never forgot their earliest days together and years later when Bond became disillusioned with Hollywood he reminded him, "I done my damndest to keep you the Hell out of the picture business. But you shoved your fat butt into the bus. You've only got yourself to blame."

Bond and Duke were soon a pair in Ford's mind. Duke remained respectful and preferred to keep a comfortable distance but Bond's outrageous antics often dragged him into controversial pranks, some amusing others uncomfortable, always interesting. In many ways Duke benefited from the association as he was drawn into a closer relationship with the man they both called "Coach."

Bond was given a part in the *Big Trail* and the two set off to start filming in Yuma in April 1930. The production team had got its star on the cheap but they spared no expense ensuring as much historical accuracy as possible. Locations were spread through five states, the cast and crew travelled over two thousand miles making the film, even the wagons were drawn by oxen not horses, and when filming commenced the set looked just like the real thing. The director faced many logistical problems moving the cast, crew, and equipment. He had difficulty with crew members who didn't speak English. He was shooting a German version of the film simultaneously using the same basic cast. He was also filming two separate versions, the 35 mil and the new 70 mil, using different cameras and two crews at the same time. The project was enormous and nothing like it had ever been tackled before. Walsh was under the most terrific pressure organising the group of New York stage actors who hated the heat and discomfort of location work, were having difficulty with repetitive takes and were, for the most part, drunk. Duke recalled, "They and the screenwriter were plastered most of the time. Nights in Yuma were like alcoholic orgies." Duke, hardly a stranger to the bottle himself, gave Walsh, who was impressed by his sobriety, little trouble.

In fact he had been hit by a severe attack of dysentry and was bed ridden for the first weeks of shooting, "I was dizzy, I sweated, I couldn't get up. I was so sick I lost eighteen pounds." He was an unknown prop man, starring in a high budget epic designed to rescue the studio, working alongside major stars. He had little enough confidence, what he did have usually came out of a bottle, and now he felt too sick to go near alcohol. But Duke didn't want to add to Walsh's burden and when the director told him he'd have to be replaced if he couldn't get back to work, he dragged himself out of bed, shaking, pale, and looking very thin and frail. In his first scene he had to carry Tully Marshall, a heavyweight actor, right across the set. In the scene Marshall handed Duke a jug, "They passed the jug to me first and I dug back into it. It was straight rotgut bootleg whiskey. I'd been puking and crapping blood for a week and now I poured that raw stuff down my throat. After the scene I called him every kind of an old bastard."

Walsh said, "He was truly the star on location, following every order he was given, every direction, or suggestion. He was the star pupil, attentive, respectful, willing to be coached. He alone didn't drink, keep late hours or make a pass at the leading lady. His full attention was given to his work and the part he was playing. If Lady Godiva had ridden across the set with her hair cut off it was a safe bet that he wouldn't even have glanced at her."

Much of Duke's work in the film was improvised. Walsh scribbled a few lines down for him and told him to do the best he could. He had already noticed that he reacted to the events in the scene, made up his own dialogue, and was generally convincing in his first acting role,"I stood and watched him shouting orders, and wondered where the youthful linebacker had gone. Instead of a football player, I had a star. His acting was instinctive, he was a natural." Of course Duke knew most people never thought he could act at all, though they were willing to admit he was the greatest star of them all. Walsh saw the emergence of both in 1929, "I take a lot of pride in the knowledge that I discovered a winner."

"No great trail was ever blazed without hardship. And you gotta fight! That's life! And when you stop fightin', that's death! What're you going to do? Lie down and die? Not in a thousand years! You're going on with me!" The line from his first film was pure John Wayne. The cadence, the easy smile and the silent, snake-eyed stare were there, gifts with which he had been blessed, and were already clearly to be seen in *The Big Trail*. Walsh had discovered that one of his greatest strengths was simply the way he looked on film. Back then he was still unlined and beautiful, with the profile of a matinee idol. At the start of it all he possessed a soft, gentle handsomeness, with a face and form better suited to a tuxedo than buckskin. His eyes were tender rather than hard although he could put on the deadly stare when necessary. He did not have a cowboys face, had not acquired the leathery wall of non-communication that spoke of pain, hardship, loneliness, and an inbuilt refusal to give up. He did not possess the ruggedness that showed his determination to tough it out at all costs, or told the audience beyond all shadow of doubt who is boss. That was the character John Ford was waiting for. When he made *The Big Trail* he was wistful, delicate, incredibly sensitive, pure, sweet, shy and demure, the contrast between then and later, huge. But whilst there was not even a hint in *The Big Trail* of what would follow, the image of a man who would die trying to right wrong was there, discovered not by Ford, who chose not to use that impressive image for another ten years.

The film, one of the first to be shot in 70 mm, could only be screened in two theatres in America, and it was more often seen in the conventional 35 mm version. Audiences who saw it in its intended format were overwhelmed by its splendourbut it appeared only average when seen otherwise. The superb sequences of the original cut weren't enough to make money for Fox and the studio was devastated to find it had a failure on its hands. Duke received excellent notices for his performance and although no critic hailed a glorious new star, one remarked, "If I were an artist or sculptor, I would ask John Wayne to sit for me as the personification of the young pioneer. His body is long, rangy, controlled. It is as lazy as a house cat's when relaxed, like the leap of a panther in action." They were not the days of the overnight sensation, reputations were earned through years of hard work, and Duke got precious few chances to build his at Fox.

John Wayne was about to be un-made! In desperation, the studio sent him East, dressed like a refugee from Buffalo Bill's Wild West Show, in a green shirt and yellow boots, his hair shoulder length, as part of a huge publicity package, "Please don't make me do this. I'm going to be an embarrassed man. You don't put a red dress on an elephant. It makes me look like a loudmouth. They're going to laugh me out of New York."

And he was right. He became an instant joke in New York. He was out of place and out of his depth — an embarrassed man.

"Mr Wayne, do you usually wear these clothes?"

"What do you think sister?"

The interviewer, Miriam Hughes, commented on his unaffected manner and his honesty, saying he was not like other young Hollywood stars. Overhearing the remark he answered, "I think I've got sense enough, and that I've seen enough of them to keep myself level-headed."

The Big Trail went out on general release and was a disaster, coming nowhere near recovering its costs, despite the fee paid to its star. Its failure contributed to the already firmly held belief that the western no longer had a part to play in the future of Hollywood. One day Duke had been a film star, the next he was just another seventy-five dollar a week contract player, "I think *The Big Trail* shows I had some potential, but the Depression coming right at the time I made my first picture meant that no one was making big pictures anymore. I thought I was going to set the world on fire ... I realise now that I wasn't ready to handle the consequences of stardom even if the picture had launched me."

Fox executives decided that whilst he was not cut out to be the warrior of the western, they would not give up on him. He fell all the way from cowboy to clean-cut-all-American College Boy in one fell swoop. What followed was like a bad dream. He hated all the films he was next involved with, "I only got into acting at all because they made a big thing about *The Big Trail*, and I was complemented. Then they made me take a dim view of it. The next picture I did was called *Girls Demand Excitement* in which I was a college boy — you know, I had been on a national championship football team, and now I'm playing at girl's basketball to see whether they'll win and get to stay in school. I just can't picture myself not wanting girls in school, and playing them at basketball was just damn ridiculous … I just couldn't believe it."

After six months Fox didn't pick up their option. He was cast adrift, his dreams of stardom shattered, he was out on the street looking for work with so many other Americans. Still, Duke had embarked on his charmed life and he was more fortunate than most of the other out of work actors. Columbia Pictures, under Harry Cohn, was in the process of changing its image and had begun making sophisticated pictures rather than the westerns and comedies they were better known for. Cohn felt Duke was handsome and debonair enough to star in their new product and he was signed immediately. To his great discomfort he was told he had the look of the smooth romantic, he was an excellent dancer and had a great voice. He felt ill at ease but the studio was soon making money out of him and had no plans to change what they were doing with him. Fans had started writing in for his autograph, and even though he was unhappy with the work he was doing, Cohn expressed his love for him and with great foresight told him he was a "money actor."

The conversation with his boss took place on a Friday evening. On the following Monday morning he was shocked when he was refused admittance to the studio. After some days he was told to report to Cohn's office, where he was accused of being drunk on the set and of fooling about with an actresses. Duke was furious and Cohn's vulgarity shocked him, "He thought I'd had something to do with his personal life, which was a goddam lie. But I'd been brought up to respect older people and he talked to me like I was a sewer rat. There was no communication at all. Today when I look back on it, I realise I could have straightened the whole thing out if I would have spoken up, but the fact that he would accuse me of such a thing as he did, I resented, resented to the point of counting to ten rather than throwing him out the goddam window … As you get older you get a sense of humour about these things."

The inexperienced newcomer didn't know Cohn ran his studio as a private hunting preserve where every starlet was considered his own property. Duke, friendly and courteous and not understanding the rules, had blundered into a mistake, flirting with one of Cohn's girls. He was handsome, single, and women found him irresistible. It was not unusual for actors and actresses to have brief affairs while they worked together, it was tolerated and accepted. Many years later when he was asked if he had ever indulged in the general practice Duke explained with a wry grin, "Well, you know, you get a mutual feeling and relationship on occasions with them." At twenty four Duke had been dating Josie for five years and had become quite desperate; she was extremely religious, chaste, and continued to refuse all his advances. He had certainly had many experiences before meeting and falling in love with her. It hardly seems likely that such a virile young man would suffer abstinence for five years given the obvious opportunities that arose for him. Still he never became involved in the general sexual chicanery rife in Hollywood at the time, he always avoided scandal and strenuously denied Cohn's accusations.

The studio head wasn't satisfied with locking his imaginary rival out of the studio and when Duke's contract came to an end, he picked it up and renewed it for a further six months, paying him three hundred fifty dollars a week! He then put him into the lowest-budget films as the juvenile or support! Duke felt naïve and foolish and he never forgave Cohn, or forgot his treatment at his hands. Right then he was sick with anger because he was helpless within the system. From then on he tried to make sure he was never under any studio's control again and he remained wary of men like Harry Cohn for the rest of his life.

Ultimately Cohn came to regret the day he locked John Wayne out of his studio. When Duke was Hollywood's leading man he tried everything he could to woo the star back, tempting him with the best screen plays and top directors. But nothing would shift Duke once his mind was made up, he was extremely obstinate, elephantine in his stubbornness and the length of his memory. Twenty years after the incident Cohn thought he had succeeded in getting him hooked on an original story. Duke, he knew, had tried to buy it himself for fifty thousand dollars. Cohn paid one hundred thousand and was sure the star would make peace, forgive and forget and come back to Columbia. Duke told him with menace that he wouldn't work there if his was the only studio in town, "I would rather leave the industry than make a picture for that son-of-a-bitch," and even the best story he had ever seen wouldn't make him back down. Columbia finally sold it on to Fox and left Cohn saddened that he couldn't get him for the part he believed had been written with him in mind. Fox hired Gregory Peck to play *The Gunfighter*, one of the most successful Westerns ever made. Duke later outlined, scene by scene, how he would have played it, but also explained that his honour had been at stake. Over the following years he made movies at every major Hollywood studio, except one, Columbia Pictures Corporation. He chose when and if he would forgive a slight and Cohn remained unforgiven. Telling Duke to keep his fly zipped turned out to be one of the biggest mistakes he ever made, "I had plenty of opportunities to work with Cohn after that, Harry would come and say, "Duke you'd be just great in this — what do you want?" … I'd say, "gosh, Harry, I just haven't got the time" … that's the only delight I ever had with that guy."

The image of the knight-at-arms, carrying a rifle instead of a sword, the cowboy in the purest terms of chivalry, was created no thanks to Harry Cohn and the incident hurt Duke's career badly. None of the big studios dared touch him, they believed the rumours must have substance, the mud stuck and he was labelled a skirt chaser, a drinker and a trouble-maker. The movie industry was just getting back on its feet but Duke was box-office poison, every gate in town was closed to him, and he spent weeks trudging round casting offices, feet aching and head throbbing. When he had not wanted to be an actor, he was all but dragged off the street and forced into it, groomed for stardom he neither wanted nor cared about. When one studio dropped him, the next was eager to sign him up, but those were the days when everyone was converting to sound, and there was a shortage of good vocal talent. Things had changed and whilst he had starred in four films and been billed in nine others he suddenly found himself an outcast. He was seen as a "leading man type" and the fact that two studios had dropped him after promising starts made him unappealing in an industry bursting at the seams with leading men. If he had been less tall, less good looking, and less athletic he could have been used as a supporting actor, but he was already too large a presence in the film world for that, "Because Cohn had taken me in dislike, for a year I couldn't get any work and I was even thinking of going into the fight racket, which I was too old for. Instead I continued knocking on doors that remained firmly closed."

Eventually he decided to stop begging at the casting offices, not wanting to appear desperate, sure that he was putting executives off. He hired an agent, Al Kingston to do the begging for him. Kingston had been impressed with Duke's performance in *The Big Trail*, but now saw an edgy, shy, and really nervous young man in front of him. Duke confided that he had to find work so he could marry Josie. Fortunately Kingston wasn't put off by the rumours and suspected Duke's good points outweighed the fact that he had failed too often. In an industry full of prima donnas and fakes, he had always worked hard to please, and he promised he would give any job Kingston found him his best shot. He was signed him on the spot and taken straight over to see producer Nat Levine, known as the "king of the serials." He owned Mascot Films, a small company operating on Poverty Row and hired equipment from the larger studios to make the "B" Movies of the era, the cheap Westerns and action adventures.

Duke and Kingston were admitted to the Mascot offices by a short, fat man in thick glasses. He had a huge cigar that stayed in his mouth throughout the interview. Levine was a caricature of the Hollywood tycoon, but Duke was impressed by him, recognising the restless energy that powered him, and he smiled his appreciation, "Nat Levine was an interesting character, a man of tremendous drive. He worked fourteen hour days and expected the same from us. He was also notoriously tight fisted … We had a party one day, lots of guests and everything. Levine had a diamond ring on and, as a gag, they tried to take it off him. Well the son of a bitch put up a hell of a fight and ended the whole party. He wasn't going to give up that ring! And I knew he was close with a buck, if the thieves had come to me first, I coulda told 'em not to bother."

The agent introduced Duke, lying, "He's between jobs while a firm deal is done, so you got a good chance to grab some talent before somebody else does."

Levine glanced knowingly, "He's younger than I expected."

Levine was surprised Duke was up for grabs and unable to find work, "When I met him I was really impressed with his honesty, his character. You could *believe* him. There was nothing phoney about the guy, and that came through on screen … As an actor, he was OK. What helped him more than anything else was his naturalness." He signed Duke immediately asking, "Are you available tomorrow?" Although he was offered considerably less than he had been getting at Columbia, Duke liked the deal because it was non-exclusive. Levine never attempted to shackle people like the big studios did, and Duke saw that as a mark of trust on both sides. He was contracted to Mascot for six months of the year and left free to work anywhere else he wanted the rest of the time.

Levine was lining up a serial about a flyer; the western hero having been consigned to the graveyard by Lindberg's solo flying exploits. Duke was told, "Be ready at four tomorrow morning," and as he walked out of the office Levine was already on the phone arranging photographers, cameramen, a director, extras, stunt men and equipment. The studio boss collected him promptly, saying as he handed him a pastry, "It'll save time if you eat on the way." Levine had also brought make-up and he applied it to Duke himself after he had changed into costume as the car cruised down Ventura

Boulevard. Three hours later they arrived on location to start shooting *Shadow of the Eagle* as the sun rose. Levine was a man after Duke's own heart as far as work and organisation went and the producer couldn't believe his luck in finding a star of Duke's quality for his B-movies. The specially selected crew worked swiftly and well, moving quickly between one set up and the next. There was no effort wasted perfecting scenes, sound or lighting, no wasted motion, no added costs, "We worked so hard on those serials we didn't have time to think. I was paid $500 and we would put 25 reels in the can in sixteen to twenty three days of shooting — and that's nights too. They didn't hire you for acting, they wanted endurance. You had to be able to last through it. They'd change the directors every day, but the leading man had to be there all the time. We never worked less than eighteen hours a day, had to, just to get that much film cranked out. We'd do 101, 102 set-ups a day. Nowadays they get 3 or 4. Back then the most we ever got was 118 in one 26 hour day."

Out on that first location he realised he would have no time for the three hour drive back to Hollywood at the end of the day and decided to stay out on location overnight instead. Some of the crew had bed rolls with them, others had bread and cheese, and as usual there was plenty of whiskey on hand. Duke had nothing with him but everyone was happy to share what they had, and he felt as comfortable with those men that night as he had ever felt before. "This was the way B-movies were made and no-one ever squawked about the treatment." He later looked back on his time at Mascot with fondness, he had always enjoyed the great camaraderie there, "Modern stars complain if there is no cream for their coffee or if the hotel is not up to scratch. Back then we had it good if the producer provided tents and sandwiches were served. It was tough but good training and I loved it. The units were like family. There really was a very strong family atmosphere. We had to learn to work together, we were put into teams and before you knew it you'd made ten pictures together and we had things down to a gnat's tooth. We were always fighting time and sunshine and we had to get on with things. It was pretty much slave labour but I made many wonderful, loyal friends back then." On his first night he didn't bother with bread or cheese, but helped himself to large amounts of the whiskey that was passed round. He was cold and aching, worn out and too tired to eat, but the whiskey warmed him up as he sat by the camp fire, swigging from a bottle with the others. A man sauntered over and crouched down next to the fire. Duke handed him the bottle and the man took a huge gulp. He passed it back saying, "Well Duke, it wont take long to while the night away."

Duke laughed and took the bottle back, "Sure won't."

The man was stunt co-ordinator Yakima Canutt, who had worked on many Hollywood films and was accepted as a star in his own right. Duke had recognised him immediately he arrived on set. Yak had also heard about Duke, having been told, "He's easy to work with. You'll like him. He's great and when it comes to ribbing he'll hold his own even with you!" Yak teased young Duke mercilessly right from that first meeting, "I wanted to get the first strike in fast on the new boy."

He told one of the others to spread the word to Duke that he needed to be careful around him because he reported everything back to Levine, but they weren't to tell him until they had already spent the night talking. Yak later said Duke was friendly and happy to talk. Then, after the others had warned him off, he watched the stuntman in amazement and disbelief as he stood apart writing notes in a book. On the second night when Yak approached he refused to drink with him. Yak offered him a cigarette, "No thanks" he answered and stomped away in disgust. Yak thought it was funny, but was glad Duke obviously believed in loyalty and honour amongst friends. Yak kept the joke going for a week before Duke went for a drink with one of the other actors. As he took a swig he noticed Yak, sitting in a dark corner making more notes in the book. Duke, over-sensitive to rumours and gossip after his brush with Cohn, blew his top, rushed toward the stuntman, and had to be restrained as the others explained it was just a joke. He had been as mad as hell but Yak had now become fair game to Duke and from then on, whenever they got together there was never a dull moment. Whoever came off worst it was always Duke who laughed the loudest. They were kindred spirits and became professional comrades.

Canutt was large and stocky with mean black eyes and a hawk-like nose. He was the most famous rodeo rider on the circuit and had become a stuntman in the days of silent movies. By the time he met Duke he was accepted as the best in the business. Duke was impressed by his physical presence and courage, he was every inch what he thought a real man should be. Yak became involved in most of Duke's films, and even when they weren't working together Duke often sought him out, spending many hours talking about life on the rodeo circuit, and working out stunts in detail. At that time Yak was making more money than the star, and Duke seriously thought about giving up acting altogether to follow in his footsteps. He began studying Canutt in earnest, the way he rode horses, the way he moved, the way he did everything. In fact Duke could already put on the best fight in Hollywood, even without any specialist training from Yak. The two were so competitive that directors let them choreograph their own fights, feeling it was safer than getting mixed up between them. In most of their films there was at least one brawl. Neither was satisfied with the way the fights came out on screen, they were so obviously phoney and they worked tirelessly together to come up with ways to make them more realistic. Occasionally Duke took things too far. Once, when Yak had annoyed him about something, Duke chased after him as the cameras were still rolling, he dived at his legs in a flying tackle and sent the stuntman somersaulting across the street. The action looked great in the rushes but Yak hurt for days and he did his best not to annoy his quick tempered friend for a while.

The no-frills work, where the stunt-man was a bigger star than the leading man, suited Duke. In such a tough, all-male surrounding, it was impossible for anyone to become a prima donna, impossible to take yourself or life too seriously, and Yak recalled, "He was a regular guy. I enjoyed the steady work with him, it became an enjoyable habit for us both." He enjoyed telling the story of an incident he felt captured Duke's spirit perfectly, "Early one morning between takes Duke noticed a hobo cooking stew at the side of the railway tracks. He ambled across to talk. The hobo shared the stew with him and Duke got a big kick out of it; meeting that man was just as important to him as meeting the president."

The friendship with Yak also meant a lot to the film star. By 1932 he was getting increased exposure, but he never forgot his friends, and it was at his insistence that Yak was used in most of his films, "He was never stingy when it came to handing out credit. When Ford interviewed me for *Stagecoach* he called me by my real name, Enos. Duke was one of the few people who knew my name so I knew right away he had referred me to the director. I said to Ford, "I see Wayne has given you all the inside dope on me. Ford laughed, "That's right, in fact he has said so much about you that you are going to find it difficult to live up to it."

Duke often suffered painful falls from fast moving horses, but Yak was always there, encouraging him to get up and carry on as if nothing had happened. It had been his ability to carry on that made so many of his stunts look so realistic in those early films. Most stars wouldn't gamble on loosing money by getting injured performing a stunt, if they even skinned their face valuable days of shooting time was lost while they healed up. Duke insisted on doing them anyway. He wanted his work to look as natural as possible, he enjoyed the stuntwork and was never concerned with looks or torn skin, "I've been hit plenty of times. There was once a big kid, and I told the producer he could fight and that he would save us time in the fight scenes. He hit me so hard he busted my nose and mouth. The producer walked over to where I was lying in a pool of blood and said, "you son of a bitch ... so he'll save us time will he?" Duke never complained about the knocks he took or the tough life on location, "You get used to hardship after a while, and, Christ, you can even look forward to it. I loved making the Mascot serials. We had only one set for interiors, so to show scene changes we had to change our clothes. Some days I had to change clothes twenty times. I began to hate changing clothes. But it was a great experience, and it taught me to realise how wonderful it is to work in an A picture when you get the chance."

The serials didn't have much dialogue and the first take was usually printed. Later, Duke adhered to that principle whenever possible, "I've kinda believed this is what you should do even when you're making a fine movie. If you have a director who knows what he wants, and knows his business, and you have good writers, and professional actors, with a competent guy on camera and good technicians, the first take is the most natural, most spontaneous. For Mascot the idea was just to get the scene on film and move onto the next one. They were rotten pictures. But they taught me how to work, how to take orders, and how to get on with the action. You can waste an awful lot of time when you have someone fussing with lights and shadings of interpretation. That only means they haven't done their homework, have not worked hard enough, that or they are insecure in their work."

Whilst he was making enormous efforts for Levine at Mascot, Al Kingston was busy lining up other work for him, for the six month period he was free. The market for the western had reopened and Warners were planning to remake several of the old Ken Maynard silent films. Maynard himself was now under contract to Universal, and was no longer the slim line star that he had been when he made the original series. Warners were producing four direct remakes, using original footage of the stuntwork, which had been of the highest quality. The high budget films had been shot in beautiful locations with top quality casts and using the original action sequences appealed to the studio because it kept costs down. Duke was introduced to the executives as a prospective replacement for Maynard. Although he looked just right they were worried about the old Cohn rumours and he was questioned at length about his attitude to work. Duke didn't even bother replying, he stood up sharply mid-interview to begin his customary restless pacing, saying quietly, almost to himself, that he was going to shut Cohn's mouth once and for all. Fortunately, he didn't have to, Warners were ready to take a gamble and he was hired. Duke had trouble remembering all the films he made under Kingston's care, he took everything that came his way, including shorts for Universal, films for Levine, films for Warners, films for anyone else who allowed him to remain nonexclusive. He went swiftly from one location to the next, never resting, no sooner catching one bandit than moving on to unmask the next.

Warners were particularly pleased with his dedication and began giving him leeway, allowing him to make some of his own decisions, "I think they helped me a great deal because I was given freedom from the concept of what acting was in that period. In those days the western hero wore the white hat, stood with his fists up ready to fight and never took unfair advantage of the villain. But when a guy threw a vase at me, I picked up a chair and hit him with it. They said, "Jesus, you're the hero" and I said, "You're goddamn right." My dad told me that if I got in a fight I better win. What I did then changed the whole attitude of what a hero should be. They've never made a point of this, but I have tried never to play the pure hero. I have always been a character of some kind, Tom Mix, Buck Jones and Tim McCoy were just clean and pure. I didn't like to wear rodeo clothes, so I started wearing Levis. I'm the first one to wear those brown Levis that they have now. I got Western Costume to make some for me, but these things never came out to the public. But they loved it, loved the fights, and I think they liked the idea of my not being in rodeo clothes. It gave a little more identification let's say. I did most of my things by instinct."

As the result of his heroic efforts he had finally got enough money together to support Josie and after six long years of struggling against the inevitable, Dr. and Mrs Saenz resigned themselves to a wedding. Duke had doggedly continued to court their daughter, obsessed as only he could be, with making her his wife.

His determination won the day, as it so often did, and on June 24th 1933 they exchanged vows in the gardens of the Bel Air estate owned by Loretta Young's mother. Her Father gave Josephine away. And she took Duke's breath away when he saw her standing on the lawn, no man ever felt more proud of his bride than he did as he pulled her toward him and placed her tiny hand in the crook of his enormous arm. They smiled brightly for the traditional wedding photographs, Josie looking coyly up at her hero. There was no sign of the worry she felt about his repeated promise to change his ways, and on Duke's face, the relief was plainly written. He had finally got the prize he had sought for so long. It was a day neither would ever forget as they drank imported champagne, and ate the finest foods in the grounds of the immaculate estate.

He was still under contract at Mascot, he was given no time to take his bride on honeymoon and they settled into their new apartment before he returned to work only days after the wedding. They were special, happy days and they lived long in his mind.

Although Josephine was soon pregnant she wasn't satisfied and she could find no pleasure in Duke's world. He often left for work before five in the morning and didn't return home until late in the evening. She wanted him home more, away on location less. It was the start of a conflict that was to shatter both their lives and eventually their children's too. Duke had more than one contract thanks to the efforts of Kingston and he was working harder than ever at both Monogram and Mascot. She constantly nagged him to stop, to get an ordinary job, be an ordinary man, make their marriage an ordinary marriage, be as she wanted him to be. Duke felt secure at work but the happiness began to fade from his eyes and long-forgotten battles were resurrected once more to haunt him. It seemed that Josie could only be happy at his expense, there was to be no shared joy after all. Instead of making more films, as he would have preferred, he decided to stay home with Josie when he wasn't working for Mascot. He told Al not to bother finding him extra work for his six month break. But time began to drag and he looked forward to getting back into action, his body couldn't be idle, he ached to climb back into the saddle.

He took pleasure in family life, it was what he had always craved and yearned for. He longed to feel relaxed in his own home with the woman he loved and he looked forward with eager anticipation to the day their baby came to complete the picture of domestic bliss. But a main part of Duke's dream included long, tiring hours at work. When he was not working he was a man at sea, lost, with no direction. Days at home were unstructured, he was bored, and as always when he was not working, he had little discipline, he drank more and was more likely to break the promises he had made to Josie. His restless mind soon started to wander, and his itchy feet began pacing the floors of their home. The caged tiger gave him no peace, nor Josie either, though she had no idea why he seemed intent on wearing out their new carpets.

It wasn't that he didn't want to be with her, he had always desired her, but he needed more than just her. He needed his friends, and he needed to find an outlet for the wild side of his nature. Increasingly, even though he was still only working six months of the year, he began spending less time with his bride, and more with his friends. He often spent weeks away aboard John Ford's boat *The Araner* fishing and drinking with the rest of the film fold.

His increased involvement with Ford and Bond inevitably led to a corresponding increase in his desire to get back to work. He knew he couldn't sit around for months at a time, being a husband and an imminent father. His very nature meant that no matter how well paid, six months employment was just not enough. He was never happier than he was working seven days a week, sixteen hours a day, for months at a time. He'd had a nice time with Josie, but the honeymoon was over and he was frustrated by his peaceful existence. He had to fill his time, to find an outlet for the energy that swamped him and his comfortable life, and which eventually engulfed everyone else around him too. His wife could find no place in Duke's world, she simply couldn't keep pace with him. He continued struggling to keep his life in its neat compartments, but he was less successful now than he had been in the past.

Apart from anything else he had changed, he was no longer the sweet young boy Josie had first fallen in love with. He had experienced dizzying success, starring in the first epic western ever made, he had been involved in the scandal created by Cohn, and he had tasted bitter defeat. He had a greatly enriched knowledge of the world, and was used to living in the often rough and ready land of the B-movie. During those years meanwhile, Josephine had remained at home under the watchful eyes of her doting parents. They had moved into different worlds. It didn't mean they didn't still love each other, but Duke came to see the wedding as the start of a bad dream, realising almost immediately that they were no longer well suited. He still wanted her and would have been more than happy to take her along with him on his journey to stardom. He was intensely hurt that she was unwilling to share it with him. Of course on the other hand, he made no effort to fit into the social life she loved. When he came home from a hard day's filming he was exhausted, too tired to want to join her parties, he wanted a bath, food, some pampering care, soft words of comfort and then bed. He passionately longed for a happy and complete marriage, but soon discovered that Josie found no joy in the desire he had loyally maintained for over six years! Many of his films emphasised his sexual frustration and longings he typically had to resist, to save the day. Duke thought it ironic that he was so often called on to portray a man compelled to suppress his desires, how rarely he was allowed to settle down and get the girl. Unlike so many other stars of his day his need and sense of loss was always painfully and realistically obvious.

In one world he was still Marion Morrison, devoted to Josie. In the other he had become John Wayne, film star. In the first he should have found satisfaction after his long wait, but didn't, and in the other he was feted and fawned over, and found his body was in great demand. Marion Morrison, or John Wayne — he was just a man. Still, he had made promises to Josie, and he was a man who honoured his promises, no matter how tough that proved. Duke became the same man he so often portrayed, in his own home, where he had hoped for so much more. Josephine had become a habit in his life long before he married her, and now it became a severe struggle to honour the vows he had made to her. Apart from his obvious difficulties, he had also fallen deeply in love with his life as a film star, and that love affair carried him further and further away from his wife, and on toward temptation.

Whilst both he and Josie had been delighted when she became pregnant the speed with which it happened caught him by surprise and presented him with more problems than he was sure how to handle. He felt the familiar urge to earn more money, if he was going to be supporting an increasing family he had to do it in style and he felt compelled to find extra work. The offers had been drying up since he cut his availability down. His contract had run out at Mascot, and his friend Al Kingston had left the agency that he remained tied to. His contract was not with Kingston, but with the Leo Morrison Agency. Morrison never seemed concerned whether Duke worked or not, he made no effort to find him anything and Duke became increasingly worried; in his eyes, the ability to support his family was the mark of a real man. A man who couldn't feed his wife and children was a failure; how often had his mother said that? Of course he was driven by a need greater than that of merely earning a living and from April to September he "worked like hell" doing any work he could find for himself.

He became just another actor from Poverty Row knocking on the studio doors begging for another chance. He was sometimes lucky, there was some demand for cowboys, he picked up bits here and there and Warners still offered small parts from time to time. But his lack of success didn't improve his frustration or do much for his quick-fire temper either. Josie was getting on frayed nerves and he began making his general discomfort known loudly and regularly. They drifted further apart.

Anger flared to violent temper when he couldn't get Leo Morrison on the phone. He was paying him ten percent of every paycheck he earned, yet the agent was doing nothing. In desperation he sought out Kingston to explain his tough position. Agents at that time signed actors up for seven year stretches and Duke was trapped in the Leo Morrison deal he had signed originally with Kingston. He told Duke he could still get him work, if he could get out of Morrison's clutches. Naturally the agent wouldn't release him, he was too good an earner for that, but he agreed he could work with Kingston and he would still take his hefty cut out of Duke's salary, getting ten percent of everything for doing absolutely nothing. Duke didn't care and Al knew just where to place his old friend.

Trem Carr had set up Monogram Pictures on Poverty Row to make the type of quickie western that Duke knew so well. Carr liked what he had seen of his work and recognised his capacity for earning money. He signed him to make eight pictures a year under the Lone Star banner, at twenty-five hundred a picture. Monogram could wrap a picture in five days! Carr paid a thousand dollars in advance and Duke used it to pay off a mountain of debt.

Trem Carr took a big liking to Duke, he loved him like a son, saying proudly, "He was disciplined and always willing to give a good days work for his money. He had excellent habits, was always at make-up on time, never loafed about on location, and he worked really fast. He rarely needed to be told anything, and usually knew not only his own lines but everyone else's as well. He was an unusual actor; most were slovenly about time keeping and work." Duke worked fast but at Monogram the first real visible signs of improvement could be seen, he was on the way to becoming an accomplished actor and he flourished under Carr's tuition. The head of the studio took the time to get to know him, spending hours talking about old films and the industry. Carr often asked him about his work and where he saw himself going, "The films I made after *The Big Trail*, God I just hang my head in shame, they were mostly low budget musicals about kids in school, and they were goddam ridiculous. And that was embarrassing because the only friends I had then were kids still in school. Goddam! I tell you, when those pictures came out, the razzing I got from college kids. It was murder. Some jerk was coming up with story lines and who did they get? Well, what the hell, let's put Wayne in it! Helen Hayes said, "If you learn to throw away bad lines, that's what will make you a fine actor" … well … I want to tell you … I've had plenty of chances to become a fine actor already Mr Carr. I've been in plenty of pictures that were written in the backroom after the brandy."

Carr told his new star that he didn't see things changing for him at Lone Star Productions, not in the near future anyway.

Herbert Yates, a "testy little Scotsman in a beret," who owned Consolidated Film Laboratories, a processing operation, had noticed how much money both Nat Levine and Trem Carr were making producing B-Movies. He moved in, bought and merged Monogram, Mascot, and some of the other Poverty Row companies, to form Republic Pictures. Trem Carr became vice-president of the new group and insisted on taking Duke to the newly formed studio with him. Everyone associated with Republic, except Carr, was astonished to find that he was already one of the biggest box-office attractions in the South and Southwest. No one was more surprised than he was himself at his rapidly growing fame and fortune.

Meanwhile John Ford had moved to RKO and was directing huge hits like *The Informer*. He and Duke hadn't seen much of each other for some time. Ford appeared to be jealous that it had fallen to Raoul Walsh to give his boy the big break; stardom, he believed, should have been bestowed by him. They had drifted apart as they waited for destiny to take a hand in their affairs, "To this goddam day I don't know why he didn't speak to me then." Duke guessed he was being punished for something he had done to upset the old man, others believed it had more to do with the director's legendary mean streak, but they were not destined to remain distant. Their lives were bound together by some outside force, and eventually Ford was compelled to accept Duke back into the fold. He was never allowed to drift away again, "Whenever I had a vacation or he had a vacation, we usually took them together. Some of these may have been just a day or two on Pappy's boat, others stretched into months."

Their vacations varied from the quiet and relaxing to the hell-raising and dangerous type that often turned into drunken chaos as Ford, Duke, Bond, and Henry Ford sailed off together on *The Araner*, usually heading for Mexico. During the hot days they fished, Duke always smothered from head to toe in thick, white sun lotion in a vain attempt to stop him burning, and at night they drank tequila and told lies. Duke loved it when they docked at Mazatlan where he was able to wander the streets barefoot, staggering drunk, unshaven and still covered in his greasy lotion. Sometimes he sat on his own outside a bar, drinking from a bottle, listening to the bands playing in the saloons and whorehouses with a stupid, fixed smile on his face, alcohol running unchecked down his stubbled chin. The skippers log gave a graphic account of how Ford's boys spent their time on December 31st, 1934:

1:18pm Went ashore — got the owner, Fonda, Wayne and Bond out of jail. Put up a bond for their behaviour.

9:30pm Got the owner, Fonda, Wayne and Bond out of jail again. Invited by Mexican officials to leave town.

The log went on to describe how "Fonda and Wayne" continued, throughout the trip, to slip ashore together to spend their nights in local whorehouses and bars. Though they never hurt anyone else in their escapades, the captain of *The Araner* thought sometimes they were lucky not to have killed each other.

One of the stories that circulated Hollywood involved Henry Fonda who passed out early in a Mexican bar. Duke paid the owner of the bar to place his pet boa constrictor on the dozing Fonda's lap. When he struggled back to consciousness he screamed in horror and threw the snake straight at Duke who was waiting, giggling in anticipation. Considering his loathing of snakes it is obvious he wasn't expecting the thing to come back at him, but nobody ever dared mention his terrified reaction to his face. No one ever knew the truth behind the long catalogue of stories involving Ford's wild stock company; each member was a great raconteur in his own right. It didn't really matter, what was important to them was the enjoyment they found in each other's company. It was during such trips that Duke saw how Ford escaped the pressures of work by drowning himself in alcohol. He learned to do the same. He had always consumed large amounts of alcohol, now Ford gave him licence to carry on ... but only when he wasn't working. In 1934 he and Ford formed the exclusive Emerald Bay Yachting Club "to promulgate the cause of alcoholism." All members were to be "career-orientated" or "gutter-orientated" drunkards. It was a yacht club for people who didn't like yacht clubs, a drinking association that spoofed all the more pretentious Hollywood clubs. It attracted a huge following including James Cagney, James Stewart and Ronald Coleman. Duke's membership was important, it brought him to the attention of many important people in Hollywood and he said at the time, "There is no snobbery in alcohol."

Many people who saw Ford and Wayne together then believed the director was already grooming the actor for the future. Duke had no such belief himself, he still had no intention of going into "serious acting." But Ford was preparing to lift the western to epic proportions, to create a nation's mythology on film, and in John Wayne he had already chosen his mythical western hero, "There's nothing finer to film than a running horse, and no one looks better on that horse than Duke." In Ford's mind he was the man on horseback and no one saw more clearly how John Wayne fitted into the vision, "He was the perfect canvas on which to paint the patterns of the Old West." Instantly recognisable as he rode into the midst of an ordinary town where no one knew or cared where he came from, its citizens had only to glance in his direction to see someone hard, isolate ... a killer, his character capable of facing any challenge on the way to the climax where he inevitably overcame a supreme ordeal before winning his reward.

The movements of Ford's stories almost exactly matched those of his own life and inevitably when he starred in one of his pictures Duke could see, only too clearly, the reflections of the crises of his reality, often with all the same tragi-comedy elements present. It was from his work with Ford that he learned he had to go on, "If you have any kind of strength you can't drop out. If you have any strength left you can't be through with life. It's ridiculous to think that way ... people make mistakes and they come back." For John Wayne there could be no giving up. Ford had seen exactly such quality the first time he laid eyes on the skinny prop man, knowing even then, he possessed the characteristics that would enable him to portray the hero of his mythology. Ford heroes rarely had any involvement with women, and Duke himself freely admitted, "Women scare the hell out of me ... I've always been afraid of them" ... his personal attitude toward women, that of combined idolisation and fear, fitted his Westerner's persona and he hardly had to act at all when Ford did set him against a woman, and his lonely, fearful face told its own story, words were rarely needed. He hated all pretence, frills or anything "too mushy." He conveyed everything visually, often without the use of a line. Claire Trevor said, "There was such power in it. When his face was in close up emotion leapt from his eyes. A close up of Wayne really meant something. Romantic chemistry was built just from the looks he gave. When he made eye contact it was more exciting than anything he could have said."

He hadn't wanted to be a western hero at all, but he always had the appearance of uncertainty in situations where he had to be on the ground, or when confronted by a woman. Those two elements alone so precisely matched Ford's vision of the western hero that Duke really became an obvious choice. How he looked out of the saddle, the way he walked into dangerous situations became part of the mystique that grew up around him, and the walk had of course come in for much scrutiny from the critics and reviewers. William Wellman said of his friend, "He walked like a fairy." Ford however saw the walk of the loner, permanently at risk out of the saddle, as he waited for the next threat from his own kind.

Duke grew tired of people asking him about his walk and his efforts in the early films, "My main duty was to ride, fight, keep my hat on, and at the end of shooting still have enough strength left to kiss the girl and ride off on my horse, or kiss my horse and ride off on the girl — whichever they wanted. The way I walked didn't matter." He never planned to turn the walk, the hesitancy with women, or even his ability to ride into mythological hero status. But Coach, it turned out, always had. All the time he was turning out B-movies at Republic he was being watched, and Ford knew his time was fast approaching. Duke had become bored with Westerns long before Pappy arrived to rescue him. He was desperate for a change and longing for a chance to stretch himself. But he still had to be patient, Ford was not quite ready. He was studying Duke as he continued to learn to use his weapons ambidextrously and precisely, waiting until he was completely at home on horse back twirling his rifle in his huge hand, completely at home in the role he was to make his own.

The waiting didn't come easily and he was unhappy at the way he saw his career going. He tried discussing it with Josephine, but she really didn't understand his frustration. She had little interest in his professional problems. She was looking for a more normal existence with a husband who went out and came home at the same time every day, who didn't smoke, drink or swear. She hadn't chosen well. And Duke knew he didn't fit the bill anymore, he felt guiltily aware he had let her down. In private he swore like a truck-driver, it was a habit picked up in his college days and fine tuned on the film lots. Ella Raines said, "He was prolific in his swearing but he didn't mean anything. I liked the big old lunk of a thing, never mind his four-letter words. They were like black pearls cast on hay … you got over it."

He also drank like a fish. On celluloid he fought like a devil, dressed as a dusty cowboy, never used profanity, but often drank. In his own home he dressed immaculately, was noisy and boisterous, and often consumed so much he dropped unconscious in a heap. Josie wanted someone he couldn't be and there was nothing he could do about it, "Hell, she loved me enough to marry me. The minute we said our "I do's" she started trying to change me into some other kind of fellow." By the time he had become entrenched in the world of the western he wanted a divorce and was looking for an escape from the misery of the marriage he had fought so hard for. He needed a comfortable, gentle kind of love, and longed to feel warmth and security. He never enjoyed the fraught, tense, jealous kind that Josie offered. He worked too hard for that kind of relationship, and his own vision of love was one where he came home after a hard day in the saddle to be met on the doorstep by his Latin lover, who would pull off his shoes, feed him and make love to him, where he didn't have to talk, where she would just know what he wanted. Josie hadn't found her dream, but neither had he. Still, he hated not being able to do enough to make things work out, his conscience troubled him and he tried his best to hang on.

And when he arrived at the studio he got to churn out one more boring western, each one telling the same story as the last. In those early pictures he treated his enemies with absolute brutality, his life was always at risk, but the innocent and the weak were safe in the knowledge that with John Wayne around evil would find no hiding place. All would be well, everything put right by the avenging cowboy in the space of fifty fast-moving minutes. The reputation was building. But it hadn't always been like that. At Lone Star he had hit the screen as Singing Sandy. Although Duke had been the first of the singing cowboys, he thought that was open to debate from anyone who ever heard him sing; he certainly never claimed singing as one of his accomplishments. In fact he was so embarrassed that he fought tooth and nail with his Monogram bosses to drop the idea. He lost the argument but dug his heels in over the clothes he would wear, refusing to budge an inch and Sandy turned up to sing wearing sweat-stained stetson, dirty kerchief, a soiled check shirt, crumpled jeans and old, worn out boots. Duke told interviewers he had to learn to say "ain't" for the part as well, but Sandy's actions were all his own, and the cowboy persona he created then fitted him like a glove for the rest of his career. He became, to all movie-goers everywhere, the cowboy, rough, tough and sweaty, with dust caked deep on his stubbly face. He had won a hard fought battle at Monogram and his victory brought unexpected reward.

At home he was less successful, he lost most of the battles there. He was also less inclined to fight, choosing instead to spend still more time away with his friends. Whenever he had a particularly nasty session with Josephine, Ford was always around to pick up the pieces, and he found himself accepting more invitations to go sailing. They became closer during Duke's troubled times; he was able to pour out his problems to the crusty director who shed many tears over his protégé's ill-fated love life. Still, when he mentioned he wanted a divorce, Ford was privately horrified, after all there were children to consider and Ford, like Josie herself was a strict Catholic. He advised Duke not to rush into anything and was seriously worried about Duke's future. He knew the best thing was to get him away from his troubles and he insisted on taking him away most weekends.

Duke had come to rely on his friends. But he wasn't the only member of the group who needed the free and easy times, Ford enjoyed them just as much as he did. The director had already been around the film industry for many years and was reaching the height of his profession, he found it stressful and taxing. He was also a very complex character, often disliked by those he worked with. Duke and Bond were different and he enjoyed spending time in their company. He drank heavily, but with those two it was never an issue, they could more than keep pace. They never treated him as a famous Hollywood director, they accepted him in a mutually satisfying friendship. Of them all, perhaps Duke stood a little way apart from the rest, wholeheartedly enjoying the camaraderie they shared, but never willing to give himself up fully to them, nor anyone else. There were always other things, other people in his life.

But the years of being able to live successfully in separate, neat, compartments were coming to an end, because in the one place he should have known contentment he could find no peace at all. When he was home he wanted to relax as the man he thought himself to be. It was impossible because Josie wanted him to be someone else entirely. He had grown up hating the sound of raised voices, detesting the angry scenes that filled him with dread, and at home he tried to avoid confrontation, and rather than argue he apologised, "In those days I was always apologising for something." He was weary of apologies, and of trying to be someone he knew he wasn't. He had already left his wife and family behind and they saw only the worst of him. He saved the best for his work, his friends and for John Ford. Duke's third wife, Pilar, wrote many years later, "So much of my husband's character and lifestyle, the good and the bad, seems a product of those days on the *Araner* and his association with Pappy Ford. Pappy had always wanted a hell-raising, hard-working son of a bitch like Duke for a son. If Duke hadn't existed, Ford would have had to invent him. Perhaps in a way he did."

He buried himself in his work. Many of the films he starred in for Carr and new boss Herb Yates were made on location in the deserts he knew so well and few Hollywood actors understood better how a man should look when he was living and working in those parts. Into each of his undistinguished B-movies he carried an aura of knowledge that won him a legion of fans, all eager to see John Wayne ride onto the next adventure. The reputation grew in direct correlation to the huge effort he was putting in and it was all about to pay off.

Duke understood Yates, recognising him as a man who cared nothing about movies, only about money, "He never involved himself directly in production and only came on set once in a while, but he had a sharp pencil on budget. He just wanted to show profit. He was a business man and I got on with him fine. My movies had always been money makers and whilst they continued to triple his investment Yates was a happy man." He never took the time or trouble to look at film scripts and had no guilty conscience about the quality of the pictures his company turned out. That attitude gave Duke his big chance, allowing him to take on more responsibility himself. He found he had increasing power at Republic because he did care, and knew what was required to get a film out. He was becoming a big fish in a small pond. The merger of the Poverty Row studios under Yates meant the pond was suddenly much bigger, his own influence grew accordingly. Yates didn't care enough to stand in his way whilst the results were making so much money. He trusted his star to get the work done, and he could just sit back and reap the rewards. If Yates was a happy man, Duke was less so. He enjoyed the sensation of getting his own way but was more aware than anyone else that the films he was turning out were disregarded, "Some were better than others, some were high-quality-B-movies." He continued to do his best but said, "The aura at Republic wasn't so much Poverty Row. That wasn't really the problem. Let's put it this way ... it was a Western action studio, and the Western was largely ignored. It was the bread and butter of the industry but all the bigger studios looked down at what we were doing there."

As his popularity grew he ached for another chance to work on an A-movie and to get away from the Western studio. He longed for success, perhaps seeing it as deserved compensation for the misery of life with Josie. The more unhappy he was at home the greater was his drive to succeed away from it. When his aching head hit the pillow and his eyes closed on another back breaking day, it was to dreams of stardom, of fans clamouring for his attention, and of walking around the big studios and talking to the biggest moguls. He could feel success deep inside. Then he woke to another day of grind on Poverty Row, another day of struggling in the dust churning out one more fifty minute oater.

At any time Ford could have offered a helping hand, but explained, "Duke wasn't ready, he had to develop his skills as an actor … I wanted some pain written on his face to offset the innocence … but I knew he had what it took to make it in the movie business. He was hungry." He chose not help. He waited instead for the instant he saw hunger. But as he struggled Duke was also watching; the relationship worked both ways and he began copying Ford's ideas in his own pictures. He developed his own trademarks and worked as hard as he could on every aspect of the business, studying everything and everybody, determined that superior knowledge would lead the way to better things He already knew much of what went on in the backroom, knew what the lighting technicians and soundmen did, the cameramen, the prop men, and technically he never wasted a moment of his time on a film set. As an actor, however, he admitted he still had a long way to go, and he hated seeing himself on screen, "I felt so damned clumsy all the time." But he forced himself to watch and learn from his mistakes. In those films he was always kissing the girl, and though he felt uncomfortable, he concentrated on what he had to do, and eventually began playing his love scenes more smoothly, performing with more conviction. He learned well, if not easily. Other cowboy heroes of the time such as Autry and Roy Rogers fraternised with their horses, but even though he denied it, and was obviously uncomfortable around women, Duke was, right from his very earliest movies, a ladies man. That alone set him aside from all the other cowboys of the day. It also increased his box-office appeal by fifty percent. A female fan once whispered longingly in his ear that it was his wonderful thighs that she went to see! He laughed at the idea that any woman would pay money to see his thighs. She had not been interested in him because he tried harder than anyone else, or knew more than anyone else, but because he had nice thighs, if only he had known that was all he needed!

Despite the fact that he was primarily a western star, it seemed the strong sexual undertone of his work appealed to women, and they enjoyed the hard-action, often violent B-movies. The natural and obvious discomfort and vulnerability were all too evident and a few understated, graceful actions made his longing almost tangible, the eyes communicating an urgent desire to the audience. He believed characters only came to life when they expressed desire and love for women and no one knew better than Duke that real men needed women. His longing for love set his pictures well apart from all the rest.

The women liked his body, his looks, would pay to see his thighs, and his leading ladies liked being kissed by him too. Louise Brooks, who had been a star during the silent era, made *Overland Stage Raiders* with him. She first bumped into him on set and was completely bowled over, "He was a giant of a man, so big he overshadowed everyone around him. His height alone gave him the most amazing sexual authority. Looking up at him, I thought ... this is no actor but the hero of all mythology miraculously brought to life. His physical presence was his greatest asset then, central to the image he created, both in real and symbolic ways." In that first instant she had seen exactly what Ford and Walsh already knew. Brooks enthused, "He did everything with full gusto, everything was full force, when he laughed everyone heard it, when he put his arm round my shoulders it felt as though a tree had crashed down on me; but I felt protected and safe within that arm. There was so much more ... He was innocent and awkward, naïve, a chivalrous romantic, at the same time he remained stubbornly independent. He rarely lost his head over a woman."

Though he worked so hard at developing a character that related naturally to women on screen, his intention was to define "the real man." His every action was designed to reflect the parameters of ultimately masculine behaviour and it was the way he behaved toward women that made him the "ultimate male" for generations of American men. He was consistently tender, gentle, low-key, and soft in his courtships, his passion restrained rather than carnal, both on and off screen. Maureen O'Hara said of him, "He is the softest, kindest, warmest, most loyal human being I've ever known."

If his dealings with women came across in his films well it was because he studied all the early mistakes so carefully. He puzzled constantly about how he might have done something better ... if only ... Each film was scrutinized in the minutest detail as he searched for ways to improve. He hated almost everything he saw, and could often be seen squirming in embarrassment as he watched. His obsession with doing everything more realistically inevitably meant a total break with Hollywood traditions as he began insisting on innovative changes. He saw no reason why a low budget should imply a split from the real world and by introducing that he was sure

B-movies could be improved. He actively sought ways to develop the cheaply made films and soon spotted where improvements could be made. Whenever he was attacked in a film he began retaliating with anything that came to hand; that was how he believed a real man would respond. His instincts and reactions rarely let him down and his fight scenes immediately improved. He and Yak started choreographing the action scenes themselves and what they achieved was revolutionary. Duke explained, "I'd made up my mind that I was going to play a real man to the best of my ability. I felt many of the early western stars were too goddam perfect. They never drank or smoked or wanted to take a girl to bed. They never had a fight. When a chair was thrown at them they just stood looking surprised, and they didn't fight in that spirit. They were too sweet and pure to be dirty fighters. Well, I wanted to be a dirty fighter if that was the only way to fight back. Hell, if someone throws a chair at me I pick it up and throw it right back. I wanted to be a man who got dirty, who sweats and who really enjoys kissing a gal he likes, who gets angry, who fights clean when possible but will fight dirty if he has to. You could say I made the western hero into a rough neck. That was why the singing cowboy idea was wrong, it was phoney. My fighting had to be realistic; I tried to copy the style of Jack Dempsey who was a tough street fighter. I was being Dempsey when I traded punches with Yak or any other heavy. I loved playing the fight scenes. I bought some newsreel of Dempsey's fights and tried to duplicate some of his moves; and how he moved his arms and fists. At that time actors were punching each other in the shoulders and faking it, but I put all my strength into my punch, and the stunt men taking those punches had black and blue shoulders. They didn't like it, but no one said anything except ole Yak, who complained there must be a better way of doin' it. I couldn't hold back when I felt myself gettin' worked up with hatred for the villain — I wanted to kill the son-of-a-bitch. Matter of fact I liked those old fight scenes better than any other stunts I ever did. In a fight in the movies there are no rules and you purposely have to exaggerate every punch you throw. And both men have to stay in balance. In a real fight of course the idea is to knock the other guy off balance. Well one day I was sick of Yak bellyaching about his bruised shoulders so together we tried to come up with a better way. The cameraman said if he put the camera at a certain angle it would look like my fist made contact with Yak's face, even though it actually passed right by. When we tried it and checked the rushes it looked real good. "The Pass System" became the accepted way of doing a fight. The best thing about it was I could now punch as hard as I liked, put all my power into it and not hold back. I've been told I've had more fights in pictures than any other star — I've also had a few fights off screen."

He remained keen to do his own stunts and fights, no matter what objections his producers or directors raised. It was his favourite part of film-making, though he made plenty of mistakes, and was always getting hurt. In A-pictures the mistakes could be edited out, but in the world of the B-movie they usually remained for all the world to see. The custom of one take was almost law and some fine examples of his early mistakes were caught in his B-movies. In *The Trail Beyond* he was supposed to leap off his horse onto a wagon, a stunt he had performed many times before, but he couldn't get his horse close enough to the wagon and he ended up falling, hitting the ground hard, rolling over three times before coming to a stop. His reaction to the fall was unusual. As the cameras kept rolling he stood up, climbed back into the saddle and carried on to finish the job he had started, racing after the wagon and completing the transfer at the second attempt. What the person in the cinema saw was a man doing his job, a man willing to get injured and determined to give his best, and his first failure wasn't such a bad error. Eventually, with Yak's help, he mastered the art of leaping onto, and off, a moving horse!

Duke recalled the days at Republic, after he began to establish himself, through rose-tinted glasses, "The atmosphere on the lot was down-home Texas ... lots of cowboys. We put the Western and Republic on the map. The studio might have been small and unsophisticated but we had adequate equipment ... not color at first, and of course we shot fast, but we had some of the best technicians and some of the very best action directors ... no peers on that. Thinking back I had one hell of a time. I was out there doing things that keep a man fit. I was always in prime condition, even with my drinking, because I was out there in the open. Yeah, it sure was a hell of a good life then."

He hardly gave a thought anymore to Josephine and his marital problems, things were less difficult when he ignored them. He stayed away, casting off his worries off like an old shoe. Later he couldn't think back to that time with anything less than the most excruciating feelings of guilt about what he had done. He had been allowed to make choices, but had been tortured for the rest of his life for making them. Over the years he had never stopped trying to make it up to Josie and their four children. He became a man of great power but was never, despite the years of effort, able to do what he knew he should have done, had he been a "real man." Back then learning his trade had seemed more important, and he had willingly sacrificed everything to his craft. The more he learned, the more he enjoyed working, and the more he drifted away. He couldn't remember the day he decided to leave home, his departure just crept up on them all.

He spent his days perfecting a variety of difficult skills, the hardest of which was, he said, was the art of delivering long and boring speeches, "All actors should try to deliver the boring speeches I had to make. Anyone can act hysterical, or angry, but it was really difficult being boring!" He developed his unusual patterns of speech then to accommodate those speeches, "Nobody can be natural. You have to find your own way. I have found that if you put your ah, ah, ah's in the middle of a sentence, if you say, "I think I'll … ah …" the audience is with you, now they're looking at you, and you can stand there for twenty minutes before you say, "go to town." If you say, "I think I'll go to town, ah … pause" they've left you. The other way they're waiting for you. That's where these bastards try to imitate me … they don't know what I've actually done, where I can take all the time I want. I know what I'm doing. I was in so many pictures that weren't exactly things of joy, but I watched them, to see if I got away with certain things. I got away with talking like that, so I used it. People listened to me when I paused mid-sentence."

Later he dealt with the problem of long speeches by an even simpler measure — whenever he could get away with it he cut his dialogue out altogether. As his power in the industry increased he began choosing his own scripts and had others altered to suit. He deliberately slowed his speech down which, together with the breaks and pauses, gave it an unusual melodic quality. Everything he did was meticulously worked out as he searched for a style of acting that suited his strengths, and the developments he made eventually powered him out of the B-movie and on to superstardom. He worked tirelessly to create a character that could be transferred from one role to the next and then for the next fifty years laboured just as hard to protect the image so lovingly constructed.

For millions of Americans in the South, Southwest and the West his was becoming a powerful message, increasingly well delivered. Every Saturday night large numbers gathered at the cinema to watch, cheering as he restored order to a disordered world. They watched through the lens of the Depression, where there was no order at all, only immense hardship. The John Wayne they identified with was always the outsider, riding alone into trouble, to put things right. He created dozens of brilliant images in a thousand unsentimental, throw-away comments, to illustrate the qualities they so admired. There are many memories of the lone warrior riding through a stark, desolate, dangerous landscape … isolation a thing he embraced, it was not a trial for their bold, confident hero. He attacked all comers and all problems head on, his gun and his power resolutely pitted against evil and guile. He didn't always work within the law, but he was always on the side of justice and there was always a clear difference between right and wrong. The sparing use of words reflected his hardness and his stoicism was to be seen in the codes he lived by. "And a killer ..." He was, of course, but as he continued to develop the characterisation, he inflicted surprisingly few fatal wounds on his enemies. His purpose was only to right wrong, not kill those who stood in his way. His stubborn pursuit of justice was much more likely to see him wounded or killed, and he tended to outlast his opponents rather than outshoot them, his power of endurance always greater than theirs. Still his adversaries knew, without any doubt that he was *prepared*, and above all, *able* to kill without a flicker of the steel blue, snake-like eyes.

There was something soft and sweet about his performances too. That, ultimately, left him vulnerable. He might stubbornly refuse to show his tender side but no one could ever doubt it was there. From his earliest films a delicate gesture, a shrug of the shoulders, a turning away of the head, a body movement peculiar to him reflected it. His understated gestures added a power to his work not shared by any other Hollywood star. He had no slickness about him and his feelings and thoughts were obvious without words ever having to pass through his tightly clasped lips. His were the gestures that reflected loneliness and frailty. It was acting of a most subtle kind, learned first on Poverty Row, but which, over the years had an immense cumulative power. Peter Bogdanovitch commented, "He brings to each new movie he makes a resonance of the past, his and ours, he fills them with reverberations above and beyond his own quality, he is a measure of the movie star. Today's audience is denied the kind of contact he made ..." The sheer number of films he cranked out ensured his audience felt they knew him, he was like an old friend, always there when they needed him most. A warm familiarity grew between them. They trusted implicitly, that he would not fail them. When they paid their money to see a Wayne movie, they sat back, confident their expectations would be met.

But so convincing was he as the man separated from all others, defined as he was by a strict personal moral code, that his own identity began to be inevitably bound up in it. It became harder to separate the real Duke from the characters he played. He tried his best to produce the required goods on screen, but he also tried to be the man his fans wanted him to be, sacrificing himself at his own altar. He was once asked if he had always just been playing John Wayne, he felt irritated by the implication that he couldn't act, "I am happy when people say that. I like the idea of being popular with a great number of people and having identification with them. Now if they identify me as a rich, conceited actor over in some corner place, and they're saying, "Hell, Jesus, he's good in his racket but he's a mean son of a bitch" that would start to limit their attitude toward me. They would start looking at me instead of being with me, in order to identify with the cowboy, the Western man, I always try to be something they can easily identify with, therefore I have tried never to let my ego enter into my performance to the point where it makes a many coloured male bird that may attract attention for a while. I like a steady character, and the more they say, "now Jesus, that's just the way he is" why the better it is for me in the business."

The interviewer persisted, "But that isn't the way you are, doesn't that bother you?"

"No, it doesn't bother me. The intellectual, left-wing types belittle me, scoff at me. I don't care, I really don't care." Of course he had not always been John Wayne — and he had to learn to forgive himself for his weaknesses and his mistakes, he had to understand he was John Wayne, flaws and all. Living up to the reputation hadn't been easy but he never stopped trying, "I may fail. But I can't quit."

He made the most enormous effort to appear natural before the cameras. He still hated much of what he saw in his own performance, and particularly disliked his walk. He attempted to modify it but it was a walk, all his own, that became as famous as the drawled speech. People said he copied it from one person or another but school friends argued he always walked the same way, stood the same way, and Duke himself once told writer George Plimpton, as if imparting a secret from the depths of his soul, with a straight face, but tongue firmly in cheek, the story of how the walk had been developed, "It was my Dad who worked it out. He held my hand and told me to put one foot in front of the other, and that was walking. Do 'er the other way round, and that's walking backwards!" He hadn't copied it perhaps, but he did later deliberately develop it to suit himself. Katharine Hepburn said, "Nobody walks like John Wayne ... he is a man with great legs and tight buttocks, and small sensitive feet, he carries his frame lightly and his walk is fine and light." Whenever anyone mentioned that his walk was sexy he simmered with anger, "God, I get hot when they say I wiggled my rear and all that stuff." But he also confessed, "Well, at one time I guess sexuality was part of my appeal ... I don't know whether I still convey that ... all that crap came from the way I walked ... there's evidently a virility in it, otherwise why keep mentioning it?" He had always been quick to say he wasn't conscious of his walk, but smiled when he agreed, "I must walk different from other people, but I never went to school to learn how."

He developed the walk and accentuated elements of it in exactly the same way he perfected the other mannerisms, which were more studied than anyone could ever have guessed. The slightly raised eyebrow, the sudden stillness that came over him when he was threatened, the shrug of shoulders, were inimitable because he had spent long hours studying and perfecting each movement. Critics assumed he was John Wayne playing himself, that he was not acting at all. In fact, he was simply very good at acting naturally. Duke often said the only difference between him and all the other struggling actors in Hollywood was John Ford, but his stock mannerisms were all in place long before Ford came along with *Stagecoach*. Appearing to be natural was an act of artifice on his part, and he knew, even early in his career, that he could act very well, "There's no way of being natural on screen, you loose your tempo. You just have to keep going and hope your personality gets you through."

He had spent many hours working with Yak and noticed that he was a terrible actor, making grimacing faces and shouting when called on to speak, "But I noticed that when he was confronted with real danger he behaved exactly the opposite, when Yak was in real trouble he would get a humorous glint in his eye and talk very straight and direct to his opponent — gave the impression of a steel spring waiting to be released … I tried to explain that his real attitude looked better than his acting did. He never reacted to this, but I did." He added his own glint to the straight and direct look and way of talking. The character he was developing came straight from the western novels he had loved to read as a lonely boy, where the cowboy was lean, tough, a loner who disliked small-talk, a man who was willing to impart rough justice and protect the weak. And then he added the physical characteristics that he either copied, developed, or were natural gifts.

And cinema goers everywhere liked what they saw as he grew from boy to man, almost imperceptibly, before their eyes, creeping steadily into their imagination. People had started asking him for his autograph when he was spotted out drinking, and he loved to talk to them about films. Just a few years before he had done everything he could to hide his skinny, six foot four frame, now he took pleasure in the fact that his fans couldn't miss him. He grew to be comfortable talking with ordinary people and came to love the fans who made it so obvious they enjoyed his films. Recognition became his life blood, a transfusion, replacing the love he had needed earlier in his life. He couldn't get enough of it; not because he had the ego of a star, but because he appreciated the sensation of being cared about. Apart from anything else the fans proved to him that his work was acceptable, they made him want to continue doing more and better films. He always remained conscious of their demands and expectations, and chose his films with care, not wanting to disappoint them.

Whilst the public appreciated his effort, Josie made it clear she didn't. His sense of guilt and his inability to find any peace at home led him to suffer continued bouts of deep depression. He worried constantly about his value as a man, and Josie always managed to make him feel like a failure. In private he had to agree and although he was doing well financially, he believed he was a useless husband and father. He had everything he had ever wanted, regular, steady work, his beautiful wife, and a family of his own to love and cherish as he hadn't been, yet he remained unfulfilled.

Both he and Josie had put their hearts into making the marriage work, but it just didn't. They wanted different things and lived different lives. He found it unbearable that he couldn't make his marriage work. He was tormented by thoughts of his parent's failure and by the unhappiness they had caused him. He dreaded putting his own children through that experience. In every film he worked on then he played a man of honour, and in his own life he had a deep sense of what was right, what was wrong, and yet here he was, doing what he knew to be wrong; it wasn't honourable to walk away from his wife and children. But he had changed, he thought the years of courting before they married had been too long for them both, and he at least, had come to want very different things during that period. She had turned to religion and become heavily involved in the social and charitable scenes, she was a leading personality in the local Catholic enclave. He never had the slightest interest in religion. Josephine had moved in aristocratic society all her life. He, of course had not, but now found that on several evenings a week he was expected to attend the formal dinner parties and soirees that he hated. Josie expected him to curb his drinking at such functions, as if dressing up wasn't bad enough, and he was only allowed one cocktail, a few glasses of wine with his meal and a brandy later in the evening! He felt like a fish out of water thrashing around gasping for air, he considered himself a second rate actor from Poverty Row and to get through such evenings at all he needed a few drinks inside him. Josie, disliking his slurred, sloppy speech, and his blurred eyes when he had been drinking, forbade him the concession. He dreaded arriving home. He was scared he would be hustled straight into a suit, refused his glass, and worse, be expected to smile and make small talk with a nun! He just could not function at that level. If anyone loved the sound of laughter ringing in his ears it was Duke, he appreciated a joke more than most and found humour and laughter everywhere he went — except in his own home where it mattered most, and where a sense of pervading misery seeped through everything he touched and did. Josie couldn't give him what he needed and he was hurt by her coldness. She made him feel inadequate; if anything was designed to destroy him it was exactly that. During their divorce hearing when her frosty attitude was brought up, she pointed out that they had four children. He commented, "Yeah, yeah — four times in ten years." He knew he was not being fair, after all he still loved her, and he regretted saying it as soon as he opened his mouth. He felt ashamed he had been overheard and reported, knowing how badly he had hurt her. But if she was hurting, so was he.

He didn't understand what had gone wrong, what he had done wrong. He knew it must have been his fault, because everything was always his fault, what upset him was that he could do nothing to make it right. His intentions had been good, still the marriage had turned into a nightmare for both them and their children.

Perhaps after all it had been the long, long delay between his falling in love and finally marrying her that led to such frustration in him, for he already resented her by the time they married. He had never stopped wanting her, but his urgent need had made him angry. He had fallen in love too soon in their relationship and she had made him wait too long. Her constant postponement of their marriage led to a mistrust deep inside him, he had always been afraid that he was about to loose her, so that by the time she did give him her love it was already too late for him, he no longer trusted it, didn't believe in it and was always fearful she was about to snatch it back, just as his Mother had always done. Marriage was not what he had expected at all but for many years he had been unable to do anything about it. He accepted things, was miserable, but was too afraid of failure to move out. Much later, once he accepted the idea that it was OK to fail, to accept defeat with grace, he became adept at turning failure into ultimate success, "I may fail, but I can't quit!"

He became less considerate of Josie's feelings and more concerned with his own. He couldn't remember if he withdrew because he found her frigid and boring, or if she had become cold toward him because he gave everything he had to his work. Whatever the reasons, it was the westerns of Poverty Row that won his heart and soul as Josephine never could. He had seldom indulged in affairs, as was the accepted solution to such difficulties in Hollywood at the time. Always a "one woman at a time man," he was not a chaser. But he did need a woman to complete his life, and he felt empty, lost and alone without one at his side. He didn't want any woman. It had to be someone special, someone he could love. John Wayne was a very unusual movie star for the generation he belonged to! He was surrounded on all sides by beautiful women eager for his attention, desperate for him, but he could show no interest in them just because they were available. A press agent once said he had never seen Duke make a pass at anyone! So he remained lost, frustrated and bored.

Duke had reached a point where he could not get through another day at home and he was forced to concede defeat. He made the decision that if any of them were to survive in tact, he had to get out. He had done the best he could and it hadn't been enough — he wanted a divorce and yet the thought of it made him sweat. Eventually, and after much drinking, he brought himself to mention it to Josie. His heart was racing as he waited for the inevitable explosion. They had been arguing violently yet again when she had said they should part and he replied, "Let's get it over with." But Josie didn't shout back at him and he was unprepared for the tears which always reduced him to a quivering wreck. He had expected opposition but instead she clung and pleaded with him to think it over. They were both desperately unhappy and he believed divorce was the only way either of them could ever find happiness again. His mind was made up and he set about making sure that neither reputation was tarnished and that no one else knew he was leaving. There were no rumours, no gossip, but he slowly began to cut down the number of functions he attended with her. He still made every effort to appear the good husband, not wanting the gossip columns printing anything about either of them, especially that he could no longer cope with his life or that he needed several glasses of whiskey before he could attend a dinner with her.

He continued to allow her to be boss at home and he didn't drink in the house, though he more than made up for her rules as soon as he escaped. He'd had a bully of a Mother, and had accepted Josephine as the dominant force in his home. He allowed her to do as she wanted, allowed her to bully him. She was far less tolerant than he was. He never asked her to give up her parties or her religion, but he consistently put his work, his greatest need, before her. He and Josie were forced, by his demons, to travel different paths, but they never stopped loving each other and both always knew where the other was at any given time along that path. They could always find each other in time of need, and both knew the other would always come running to help out when necessary. On a personal level he felt sad that people assumed there had been no good times when that had been far from the case, "I can't deny I'm not an easy guy to get along with, because I do have a short fuse. I have a temper. I guess I hurt Josie many times. I never meant to. Maybe we should have separated sooner, but I loved her and when the kids came along we both wanted to make it work out. I felt strongly about the children. I didn't want to break up. I grew up in a home of bickering and I knew how children suffer when their parents fight. I also know how hard it is for them to take their parents divorce too. So we stayed together and our children came out just fine. I give all the credit to Josie."

He wondered if things might have worked out if he had drunk less. He was a rare drinker, always able to consume the most enormous amounts of alcohol without it seeming to affect his mind or his body. And he did drink enormous quantities. He loved alcohol and his consumption was averaged out at a quart a day for over forty years! He never measured a drink and took absolutely no notice of the amount he drank. He enjoyed it so much that he even liked talking about it, and about his favourite drink, tequila and glacial ice. Sometimes he took no liquor at all, at others he drank until he dropped where he stood. He rarely indulged himself when he was working, and never allowed it to affect his day on set. However, one friend recalled watching him make himself a jug of Martini at a party. He downed the whole lot, swigging back the equivalent of eighteen shorts in a couple of hours. Duke was still, reportedly, standing up when everyone else left, "This was a scientific impossibility. I collapse myself after four of Duke's Martinis. Duke can hold his liquor." Although he was not alcoholic most of his friends were, including Ward Bond, his favourite writer, Jimmy Grant, and even John Ford himself. Perhaps they all spent too much time around a man who could sink eighteen martinis at a sitting. His self control was the envy of all them all. No hangover ever prevented him working, or doing whatever task he had set for himself. Sick or healthy, sober or hung-over, he was always first on set ready to get on with the day's work. Even just before he was struck down by his final illness, whilst he was making The Train Robbers he went out to dinner with the rest of the cast. One by one they fell by the wayside until Duke was left drinking alone late into the night. But the next morning he was up, breakfasted, in full costume and driving himself off to location before any of the others had emerged from their rooms. He sat patiently waiting for his eight o'clock start. The others arrived two hours later, exhausted and bleary eyed, and unfit for work. He was twenty years older than most of them, yet there he was, laughing at their discomfort, offering no sympathetic words. He sometimes thought about the amount of time he had spent, sitting around waiting for other people to catch up with him.

He saved his serious drinking for the wild sessions that he inevitably shared with Bond, Ford and Fonda. When they got drunk together, wherever they were, all hell was let loose. They started fights with anyone who happened to be around, though more usually it was with each other, and one or other of them was generally suspended from the bars and clubs in Hollywood until they paid for smashing them up and scaring away more dignified customers. Their fun together, as their fishing trips amply demonstrated, was far from sophisticated "man about town" stuff, but was rather more slapstick, and could have had tragic consequences, if they had been less lucky. Once when Bond and Duke went hunting they became hopelessly drunk before they had even spotted anything to shoot. They started laughing hysterically at nothing in particular and fighting each other boisterously, as they often did. Duke took a strong liking to Bond's new gun and asked to have a look at it. When Bond refused he begun pushing and pulling at the gun and, in the midst of the drunken brawl, he managed to shoot Bond in the back. Terror sobered him up and he carried the prostrate actor, who weighed more than he did, on his back until he reached help. Once he realised his friend was in no danger he found the whole escapade highly amusing, and continued to demand to see the gun, telling him he would buy it from him, "Just name the price." Bond replied, "You can have it over my dead body." Duke continued to laugh, but years later was deeply traumatised to find the gun had been left to him in his friend's will.

Despite the fun he continued to find in the company of his friends, he still struggled to come to terms with the split from Josie, and he was about to be hit another devastating blow. His father had been ill for some time, his heart trouble worsening along with Duke's domestic problems. He and Duke often went to football matches on Sundays with Florence and Nancy, Duke's stepmother and sister. In 1936 Duke noticed his dad had difficulty climbing the stadium steps and Nancy told him his dad was always tired now and had trouble breathing. Just days later he died in his sleep. Florence called him at work to break the news and he dropped everything to race to his step-mother's home and the two of them then went to collect Nancy from school. Duke was heartbroken. He cried all day, felt crushed by life, and sobbed uncontrollably in the car as they drove home together.

Salvation lay in work. It no longer satisfied him, but it exhausted him and drove other thoughts from his mind; not even alcohol did that for him. He flung himself at it, drowning his sorrows in effort. It saved him at what was a dreadful time but it may also have been his downfall, for it took him further away from any hope of reconciliation with Josie. He worked all the hours he could, starting at dawn and continuing late into the night. He had long since become fed up with Westerns, but after his dad died, he found even less pleasure in them. He told close friends that he sometimes felt ashamed of his efforts, trapped in the horse opera, when he didn't even like horses.

When his Monogram contract expired he decided to escape the western for good and he talked Trem Carr into letting him make some other pictures. They were all disasters, "I made a big mistake, not because they weren't westerns but because they were cheap pictures." His fans wanted to see straight-shooting Wayne. They weren't interested in seeing him as anything else, and only his fans seemed to be interested at all, "I lost my status as a western star. I got nothing in return. Finally I had to go crawling back to Old Man Yates and beg for mercy. Yates put the screws in me. Sure he would sign a new contract. But there was no more talk of twenty-four thousand. I had to settle for sixteen. And I still had to do those terrible stories they had. He wanted a five year deal. Mr Ford had told me not to sign any long term contracts. I held out for a two year deal. Yates promised me a shot at a high budget picture they were planning about Sam Houston if I'd sign the five year deal. He knew if I could choose one character to play it was Houston. He had a philosophy of life that I have done my best to live by. The ring he wore was inscribed with the word "Honour." It was buried with him. I signed the deal. When they started shooting I was not given the part."

Instead he was given the most boring roles ever, in movies that looked as if they were strung together in a morning. If he had been ashamed of his work before he now felt complete humiliation. Still, his fans were glad to see him back in the saddle, they hadn't deserted him whilst he had been away. Duke didn't understand why they loved his good-guy western hero, especially as he saw most of the films as nothing more than junk. He did not understand them perhaps, but knew Old Man Yates was telling him clearly just were he stood in the industry. He had sunk even lower than the B-movie and been left to pick up juvenile trade. He was at his lowest ebb. Mary St John had just started working in the typing pool at Republic and she long remembered his haunted look, his sadness at the loss of his father, the obvious fear that his career was bottoming out, and the sense of defeat in his personal life, "He was absolutely a wounded puppy."

Many film-goers noticed that after the trauma of his father's death and his divorce his face often carried a wistful smile, he appeared more remote, and was never again possessed of the child-like, carefree air that had so marked his earlier performances. Directors used the pathos of his own life in all his next films, and Ford at last began to see what he had been looking for.

Duke continued to survey his life with dark despondency. In 1937 he felt he had achieved nothing and contemplated only the same pattern for his future. Whilst he still often spent his social hours aboard John Ford's boat laughing, drinking, playing cards, and generally avoiding the torment of home, Ford had never shown any inclination to find that better movie for him that he'd always promised. Sometimes he made a point of letting Duke know he was no good. His constant and unjust criticism saddled Duke with self-doubt for much of the rest of his career and he certainly never anticipated getting any work from him.

His moods swung from sullen acceptance of what was on offer at Republic and the feeling that he'd reached the end of the road. Still, whilst he hated everything he was turning out, he continued to plod on. And he discovered his strength lay in his ability to plod, to outlast everyone around him with an endurance greater than everyone else's and in his inability to quit. Right then he wasn't striving toward success, rather, he was running as hard as he could away from failure. He wasn't shooting for the stars but fleeing the nightmare of darkness. He made so many cheap films for Republic that his audience considered him part of the family and, as he raced onward, he now carried with him a whole generation of fans. When he finally graduated to the A-movie they simply moved on with him. Wherever he went the increasing army of fans travelled. They had grown up together, learning together just how hard life could be. To them he had become the ultimate symbol of how a simple man could control his own destiny. It was an attractive message to Americans and he provided the handsome embodiment of the American ideal. The very fact that he had to fight so hard for his prize, that success wasn't handed to him, that he was just like one of them, made the image so much brighter and more attractive. He felt at the time that he had reached a dead end. In fact he was standing on the springboard that would thrust him into superstardom in the decades that followed ...

Ford invited him on a fishing trip in November 1937 and Duke expected a drinking session and possibly a game of cards. They both liked to play cards and Coach was good at poker, though he was better, he was usually the only one who could beat the old man. They always played for high stakes (fortunate then that he usually won). Ford later said he only continued playing against Duke to beat him out of a few dollars, in fact he rarely managed to, unless Duke took pity on him, or was too drunk to concentrate. On that occasion he was the only person Pappy had invited along and there would be no cards. Instead Ford placed a short story in his hands, "The Stage to Lordsburg" written by Dudley Nichols. Since the advent of sound Ford had not made a western, but he loved this story as soon as he saw it. He paid four thousand dollars for the movie rights and, together with Nichols, created the screenplay himself. He said nothing as he handed the script over. Duke had looked at hundreds of western scripts and knew instantly he was holding something very special. He studied what later became the screenplay for *Stagecoach*, about a hazardous journey made by assorted characters through Indian territory. One of the passengers was the lonely gun fighter, Ringo Kid, who had escaped from prison, seeking revenge for the murder of his father and brother. Duke knew he was a natural for the part but considered himself a second rater, a no-hoper, because that was what Ford kept telling him.

"I need some help from you Duke."

"Sure Coach."

They had dinner. They did some serious drinking and talked of other things.

Duke had a headache, which was unusual, but he was tough enough not to let Ford know how much the game of cat and mouse bothered him. Ford, as usual, enjoyed the sport of tormenting his favourite son, "You must know plenty of young actors. Do you think any of them would be right for Ringo?"

Duke was tired, mad, and knew Ford was toying with him. Sometimes he almost hated him. However he didn't expect any favours and eventually he gave up hope and began to consider some of the young actors he knew, "How about Lloyd Nolan?"

"Jesus Christ, I just wish to hell I could find some young actor who could ride a horse, but act a little too. Goddamit Duke, you must be able to do better than Nolan. But then you've been out at Republic. I guess you don't get to see much talent out there." The verbal swipe stung, he was used to Ford's cruel jibes and though he tried not to take them too much to heart, on that occasion he felt hurt. It was standard fare for Ford to attack him in front of their drinking friends, but Duke never commented, he didn't enjoy it, but he always let it go, and it was rare for Coach to bother when they were alone. He was confused to suddenly find himself under fire again.

Ford, ever eccentric, said nothing further, got up and went to bed, leaving his baffled friend alone to think about it. Duke had another drink, and then another and finally gave up and carried the bottle off to bed with him where he continued to drink until he passed out, fully clothed. He spent the night fitful and restless, tossing and turning, dreaming and seeing his situation clearly, knowing that every major studio had a sign up under his photograph, "John Wayne. Over 30. Blue Eyes. Six foot Four. Brown hair. B-westerns."

When the blue eyes finally struggled open next morning it was to look, yet again, at the ten years he had spent in the business, in which he had achieved precisely nothing. He had been going to tell Ford what he could do with the story, but instead he collapsed back onto the bed, out cold. When he did finally get up it was very late, the headache was worse, he was hung over and dry-mouthed, and the last thing he wanted to do was play games. What he wanted didn't matter, and for the rest of the trip Ford tormented him with references to his work at Republic, and the problem he was having casting Ringo — Duke said, "I felt like a spider having its legs ripped off, one by one."

At last as they docked, after Coach had had his fun, he snarled, "Duke, I've made up my mind. — I want you for Ringo."

"Sure Coach, I know." He smiled, but later admitted, "I felt like he'd hit me with a baseball bat!"

Obviously that had always been Ford's intention from first inviting him aboard. He had always intended to offer him the part, but why did he always have to torment him? Many have commented that though he was a brilliant director he was a rotten human being, sadistic even. He had spent ten years watching his "friend" sink, and had presumably enjoyed seeing it before finally offering any help. The deeper Duke sank after *The Big Trail* the more plaudit Ford expected for pulling him up and establishing him, once and for all as a star. He had to "de-create" him after *The Big Trail* so that he could establish his own role in the rise and rise of John Wayne. Duke had to be a no-body before he could "discover" him. Of course, on the other hand, it could just have been that he didn't realise until then that Duke was good enough to play such a role; that he hadn't then acquired the haunted look he was after. Duke later heard that Ford originally wanted Gary Cooper for Ringo. He was still second rate after all.

Ford was petty and Duke was certainly intimidated by him, he believed the director when he told him he was no good, and believed that he would never amount to anything unless he was being directed by him. It was not until he made *Red River* with Howard Hawks, ten years after *Stagecoach*, that he realised he had any talent at all. He often wondered whether Coach had kept him squirming just for the fun he had watching him? He had never really known but he refused to hear a word against Pappy Ford. He had been the catalyst, and he owed him everything. He was Pappy's creation, and without him in his life he would have been nothing. Duke believed Ford provided the trip out of the degrading world he had sunk into. When he'd been at his very lowest along came Coach to offer him the ride on the *Stagecoach* that led him on to the next glorious part of the adventure. He felt he owed a huge debt.

Duke had been the last cast member hired, but Ford had known since first buying the story exactly who he wanted for Ringo, and he never seriously considered anyone else, not even Cooper, for the part. He carried with him the vivid images of Duke in his earliest roles, and he believed (though never told him) that once he had shed his youthfulness, put on some weight and a little character that he could be a fine actor, if only in his hands. He later told anyone who would listen that, "Wayne always moved like a dancer." He sensed in him the charm, charisma and vulnerability, which he knew audiences would identify with, but beside those things, which were increasingly obvious to all, Ford also saw Duke's phenomenal, pathological drive. He knew that he had what it took to survive in Hollywood. He knew he was now hungry in every sense, and that he had a huge appetite for life.

Though Ford may have always intended to provide the dinner in the end, the budgeting for *Stagecoach* also meant it was essential for him to find a cheap star; which was exactly the same reason that Walsh had used him ten years earlier. Just as Ford was what Duke needed right then so he was exactly what Ford needed, if *Stagecoach* was to be made at all. All the director needed was a western actor, tall, handsome, able to ride a horse and carry a gun. He didn't need to be too fussy in his choice. Duke would be ideal.

When he arrived on location in Spring 1938 to work for Ford in what was only his second big film Duke was incredibly nervous but later told friends, "Monument Valley in 1938 was heaven. I was impressed by the scenery and felt at home there straight away." He had arrived at the very spot he was meant to be. And then Ford turned up. It was immediately evident that Duke was going to be the whipping boy on the picture and right from the first day Ford bullied and berated him in front of the cast and crew, never letting up on him or giving him any peace. Duke had entered the Valley feeling insecure and worried about working with a collection of well established stars. Another director may have handled him gently, seen his nervousness, but instead he was criticised from sun up to sun down. His speech was made fun of, "Chrissakes — stop slurring your lines, you dumb bastard — I can't hear you."

"Faster-faster." His movement was pulled to pieces, "Can't you even walk — don't skip, you're not a fairy. Put your feet down like you were a man." Ford was hardest on him in the scenes he shared with leading lady Claire Trevor, "Can't you even get mad? You look like a baked potato."

Miss Trevor, who had a soft spot for Duke, said, "Ford was so tough with him. You never knew what he would do to poor Duke next. I felt so sorry for him. He wanted to succeed so badly and here was his big chance. He and Ford had been friends but Pappy'd grab Duke by the chin and shake his head about until he got the look he was after. He did it right in front of everyone and Duke took it all like a soldier. He continuously called Duke a dumb bastard in front of us all. John Ford, though a genius, was so hard. Once he started he went right on after him. One time he was yelling, "Can't you even wash your fucking face? Don't you ever wash at home? You're dabbing at your face, you're just splashing water on it." He made Duke do the scene over and over until his poor face was raw from rubbing it. When Duke was having difficulty with a love scene, he frowned. He was really confused. It was exactly the expression Ford was looking for, but poor old Duke was a wreck at the end of filming that day.

He was a much more complex person than he seemed and if you were his partner in anything, my God you had to be on the ball, really fast. I was always surprised, given his quick-fire nature, that he responded so well to Ford. I think perhaps he enjoyed the fact that you simply couldn't predict Jack's next move. That kept him alert. He might also have appreciated that no one got preferential treatment on a Ford set; Duke had no time for any of that nonsense and always liked to be one of the boys."

He could do nothing right. Here was his last chance to get out of Poverty Row. He was working even harder than usual, doing everything he could to please. Yakima Canutt was also working on the film and he hated watching him, head down, slouching around the room they shared at night. He hated what Ford was doing to his friend. Every night Yak rehearsed Duke's lines and movements with him ready for the next day so he knew every part off by heart. It made no difference; the director was never satisfied.

All the cast and crew felt deep sympathy and embarrassment for the young star and they often recoiled in horror as Ford started attacking him, sometimes physically, sometimes bringing tears to his eyes. At other times Coach changed his angle, and three weeks into shooting he mentioned casually that Duke looked good in the rushes. Rich praise indeed and Duke was amply rewarded. He believed Ford knew just when to turn the heat on him and how to get a performance out of him. He very rarely got mad with Coach whatever he did, but there were some memorable occasions in Monument Valley when he was heard muttering under his breath that he was, "Going to have to take the old bird down." Sometimes only Yak could calm him down, taking him aside and reminding him that if he showed any sign of rebellion now, he would be finished in the industry. Yak was, of course, right and Duke rarely made any disparaging remark about the director in public. It was a mark of how much power Ford had in Hollywood that Duke always played safe after Yak's warning. And for him the humiliation was worth what he saw in the rushes, "Sure he got me angry. He would turn me inside out. I would want to murder him. But he knew what he was doing. First — he made me feel emotion. He knew he wouldn't get a job out of me unless he shook me up so damn hard I'd forget to worry about whether I fitted in. He knew how hard it was for me to be playing with the likes of Claire. I was ashamed of all those B-westerns in the company of those stars. He also had to be sure I turned in a performance. That wasn't all there was to his tricks either. He also knew that when an unknown is put into a key role in a movie, well there's resentment on the part of the veterans toward him. Now Mr Ford wanted those veterans rootin' for me, rootin' for the picture, not resenting me. By kicking me around he got the other actors on my side and hating him. Hell, they did everything they could to help me out after a few weeks of taking his abuse. Mr Ford only wanted to do one thing and that was to make good pictures, and to do this he would do anything, anything."

In private he was more hurt than he chose to admit, but he was never going to say anything that might harm his career. It was well known in Hollywood that Ford required complete control of the people working for him, and the Ford stock company, the actors Pappy retained around him and used in film after film, knew better than to question him, or even make suggestions. Actors working for him kept quiet, or they got out and never worked for him again. *Stagecoach* launched Duke to stardom but it was a reward earned the hard way. Relationships between the old friends were strained during working hours, with Duke was not so much the favourite son he had been. Stresses appeared between them that hadn't been there before, driving a wedge between them, creating tension that lingered many years. Although he always paid fulsome homage to Ford, Duke had ambivalent feelings toward him from then on. He tolerated the abuse, was ever grateful for *Stagecoach* but he was also a proud and self-made man. He admired Ford and recognised, "probably the finest artist I'd ever known," but privately acknowledged he wasn't completely beholden to him! When he walked into the Valley in 1938 he'd already had ten years experience in the business. Certainly he was nervous, but he was also experienced, and probably knew more about Westerns then than Ford did. That didn't stop Ford treating him like a novice, sometimes shouting at him with his face pressed up against his own, to act only with his eyes, that he didn't want to see his mouth moving. Ford later said he had always known that Duke's personality would come shining through his eyes on screen, that he was confident they could reveal everything he wanted to show about the Ringo Kid. He had absolute knowledge of Duke's vulnerability and his strength and that was exactly what he wanted to see there. Years later in a draft of an autobiography, *My Kingdom*, Duke wrote, "When you look at an actor's eyes you've got to feel the cock-a-doodle strength coming at you." He had learned his lesson the hard way at the hands of the master. He hadn't enjoyed the process perhaps, but that was too bad.

Things on location might have been tough but he was grateful to be allowed to do most of his own stunt work. Ford was sure it would help him attain a better sense of reality as he worked because that was the way he made his B-movies. But if star and director were happy about the possible danger, visiting producer Walter Wanger was horrified when he dropped by the set to see Duke climbing out of the moving stage and up onto its roof. Wanger blasted Ford, "Wayne isn't being paid as a stuntman. Tell him he's got to stop."

"Tell him yourself," Ford snapped back.

But when Wanger did tell Duke, he got a slow, considered drawl of a reply, "Now Mr.Wanger — there's no need for you to worry. I can handle myself. I've been doin' my own stunts for years. I'm not an actor, I'm just a stuntman who reacts." He repeated, "I don't act, I react" — a throwaway line heard over and over throughout the rest of his career. If anyone ever got him talking about his acting, his films, his relationship with the great directors, it was sure to come into the conversation. "If you have a script where you're the bystander, the reactor, you have a class A script. Because if you have all the dialogue, you're telling the whole damn story. The best script to have is where you're reacting to what other people are saying, doing. I was in so many quickie pictures that it had become obvious to me when I could use my own true reactions."

Ford more than any one else was responsible for Wayne's belief that he was not an actor. It wasn't a fair summary of a man who could certainly act, as his best films amply demonstrated. It was said John Ford understood the souls of his actors, maybe he didn't treat them well, but he understood them, and his direction often took on the quality of a movie itself. The rituals of his work were carefully designed to make each set significant, to make each day's work meaningful to cast and crew. It was his way of establishing a total involvement in the film they were doing together. He knew the terrible boredom that most actors suffered from, the debilitating effects of sitting around for hours between takes, so he shouted, got each of them boiling mad, and no-one was ever bored on a Ford set. And for Duke, every time he finished work on a Ford film he was already looking forward to the next, no matter what he thought about him as a human being. Each film he made with him was a significant moment in his life, "There has never been enough credit given to Mr. Ford as to how far he goes to make an actor feel comfortable — oh, sometimes he will get you so mad. He has gotten me so goddam mad so many times — but I love him. He knows what he is doing. He always knew who to pick on, and when." During the filming of *Stagecoach* he took it in turns to humiliate each of the actors. As he began to wind things up he realised he had not been tough enough on Andy Devine, and also it was Duke's turn again! He asked Duke to watch the rushes with him and asked him what he thought about Devine's performance.

"Fine ... but he holds the reins too loosely."

"Hold it Duke. I want everyone to hear this."

He called the cast together, "I want you all to know that our new star here thinks the picture's great, that we're all doing one hell of a job — but Devine stinks."

Duke stood rooted to the spot in embarrassment, unable to say a word in his defence, knowing to speak out would make things worse. Fortunately Devine had been around Ford long enough to know the game and he winked at the mortified "new star." Duke breathed a sigh of relief. It was O.K. and they both meekly accepted it was probably better to be Ford's victim than to be ignored by him. Ford had accomplished what he had set out to do, the rest of the cast couldn't help but want to help the dumb bastard who had previously failed in everything he had done. They had no choice but to root for him to be a success this time around. Ford may have wanted the cast on Duke's side, but on the whole there may have been easier ways to accomplish it, and Duke certainly thought Coach could have been a little easier on him.

Under the great man's direction Duke became Ringo with his first appearance, late in the film, in what is acknowledged as one of the most stunning entrances in cinema history. It had a mythical quality about it. One out of focus shot of Duke's face, slowly sharpened, a longer shot revealing Ringo carrying a bedroll and twirling his rifle in an action already recognisably his alone. The scene established in seconds the role he would play ever after.

His opening speech was long and delivered with all the mastery picked up during his apprenticeship in the B-movies. The spectacular entrance, and the power of that first speech, instantly, and as if by magic, took him into the hearts and minds of movie-goers everywhere. He had spent ten years wading through quickie Westerns, building up a base of loyal and faithful fans, now, in an instant of motion picture history, he entered the imagination of the general public. He was to remain firmly fixed there for the next forty years. Suddenly he was a celebrity, his life changed forever, nothing would ever be the same again for him or his family. Ford had shown him the stars.

Everything about the symbolic love story emphasised his own natural ease of movement and shy vulnerability that suggested the Western outsider, it also reflected Duke as he was at that time. Both he and Ringo were naturally withdrawn and shy, perhaps only really comfortable in the company of men, or when involved in manly activity. Ringo is portrayed as better than the system and better than those who misjudged him. And John Wayne often felt the same way, believing he was misrepresented, misquoted and ultimately misjudged. He gave to Ringo the violent changes of pace that characterised his own life, the slow burn of trapped energy that he understood so well. Both Duke himself and Ringo were full of conflicting extremes, brutality and gentleness, hate and love, protectiveness and vengefulness, care for the community and individualism, they were one and the same person.

Stagecoach was full of standard B-Western characters, lifted by Ford's direction and the brilliance of the actors into a masterpiece, but for all the fabulous performances Duke knew that he stood out head and shoulders above the rest. Ford's vision of the American West had miraculously become his movie. He knew it, understanding the effort it had taken to produce what he had always known was there, inside him. Unfortunately he also believed it was only the skill of Ford that released it. And that was exactly what Coach wanted him to think. Ringo was the most fully developed of the characters travelling on the stage. His philosophy "There's some things a man just can't run away from" was central to Duke's performance, and was what made a man, as far as Ringo, Duke and John Ford were all concerned. When Duke was shown some of the early rushes, Ford asked him what he thought of Ringo, "Well — hell — I'm playing you, so you know what that is." No one, least of all Duke, had expected Ringo to be Ford's alter ego; the rugged loner, the warrior on horseback, the individualist always set outside society, but that was exactly what he was. Ringo was also the same character Duke had created ten years earlier, Ford had simply refined it, "Anytime there was a chance for a reaction he took the reaction from me, so I'd be part of every scene … I knew he liked Ringo and liked me. I think Ringo was what he thought a young man should be." Ford hadn't needed anyone special to play Ringo, he didn't even give him many lines, all he needed was presence. What Duke unexpectedly gave him was presence so powerful it seemed to explode from the screen and was bigger than the Valley in which it was made. Neither foresaw it happening, it occurred as if decreed by a preordained force greater than either of them. Ringo, Ford and Wayne were part of a fascinating, complex tapestry; Ford, the delicate artist, who was at the same time intrigued with machismo, wanted to be like Duke was on screen, a two-fisted, brawling, heavy-drinker. He had always admired and envied Duke his physique, and he used it for Ringo, creating on screen the man he wanted to be himself. Physically Duke was completely overpowering, now Ford unexpectedly discovered that no one else came close to reproducing his screen power. He found himself unexpectedly tied to him and he used the image over and over again through the coming years to create a vivid self-portrait. Whenever Duke was asked what made him different from other stars, he smiled knowingly, before saying two words, "John Ford." And he was tied to Ford. The tapestry was complex indeed.

Stagecoach was previewed in the grand manner at Fox Westwood Theater, Los Angeles, on 2nd February, 1939. On the morning of the screening Duke called into his office at Republic, as he always did. He was too nervous to sit around at home. He walked into the typing pool and paced around. Mary was well used to his restlessness and she handed him a coffee. She tried to calm him down, but he was edgy and she noticed that his huge hand shook as he took the mug. He had invited some of his Republic bosses to the preview, and he asked if she was going along with them. When she assured him that nothing could keep her away, he smiled his relief. He had never understood why he found her such a comfort, but now he tried to explain the tension he felt welling up inside, "Once this movie comes out ... well, everything's going to change ... nothing's ever going to be the same for me again ... it's kinda scary ..." he hesitated, as he often did, and she waited, but actually she did know; he had not wanted to be an actor maybe, but once he had made his first film he was completely hooked. He had striven every day for ten years to make it. Most people would have accepted defeat long before. He had been unable to accept it, and now he was either on the edge of stardom, the reward for his work over those years, or on the precipice of failure — he was about to reach the heady heights of celebrity or he was finally finished — either way, his life was certainly going to change for ever.

Mary knew he hadn't slept for sometime, he looked exhausted, and so tense that the muscles along his jaw stood out sharply. As usual she wished she could do something for him, but he never let anyone in, and didn't like talking about the things that troubled him most. She began chatting about nothing in particular, the kind of things that she might talk about to her girl friends; and he soon got the message, as ever quick on the uptake, and he rewarded her with the crooked grin. "What you wearing tonight?" he asked, always interested in her appearance.

"Oh, Mr Wayne, you'll have to wait and see — but it's not pink ..."

When Mary got to the theatre that night it was to find a hall full of college kids, it was a tough place to preview a western. The film started, and as each character was introduced the kids settled back, seeming to enjoy what they saw. But at Ringo's astounding entrance they actually cheered. Duke told her later that he felt like a college kid himself, "They stomped, they screamed, they ... goddamn, nobody ever enjoyed a film like they did tonight. They were quiet in the right places. Jesus, it was like watching and knowing that this guy had them by the ... Well, they were just mesmerized by the picture weren't they?" He was overjoyed at the reaction, he hadn't expected it, hadn't known what to expect, but now he was carried away on the tide of their enthusiasm, and Mary was delighted for him, delighted at last to see a smile on the haggard face. His bosses were less than mesmerized however, and they appeared to be completely unimpressed by the whole thing. They crept out at the end of the performance and none of them even bothered to speak to him the next day at the studio. He waited a few days and, finally, when he couldn't stand the silence any longer, he plucked up the courage to ask what they thought of the film.

"You better leave it to us to make your westerns Duke" was their only comment, and they continued to ignore him. He had never understood their attitude, "I just could not believe what I heard … I mean it was the classic western of all time, and these Guys say, "better let Republic make it."

From then on he and Mary came into contact with each other more. She had noticed him originally because he was good looking, all the girls in the typing pool watched him when he walked in, but he also attracted her attention because he was so noisy, loud and full of fun. She recognised instantly that he covered up his overly sensitive soul under the bravado. She saw the gentle, soft and sometimes lost boy, who was struggling to make it in a tough, tough world. Whenever she saw the "wounded puppy" look she worried that he was too soft to survive in cruel Hollywood. After the preview she watched him mooching round the lot looking desperately unhappy, hurt by his bosses' indifference to his stunning work. She worried about him but never doubted him.

She and the other typists obviously took a keen interest in him, they wouldn't have been human if they hadn't, but Duke had also noticed her. He liked the way she smoothed his path, he liked her soft voice and efficient manner. Instinctively, he trusted Mary St John. He loved her sense of humour, and the knack she had of making him laugh uncontrollably, of course that didn't take much, but she could always manage to make him see the funny side of things at Republic. They were often seen standing around together, he with head bent down toward her and she looking up at him as they both giggled helplessly in a shared moment of joy. Sometimes he thought she was the only one who showed him any kindness at all at the studio.

He was developing a plan in his mind. He'd wanted to start his own production company for some time, and since Republic had caused him such hurt he decided the time to break away from the Poverty Row set up was fast approaching. He knew he couldn't drag them into the world of the A-movie, but now he was determined to get there himself. If they didn't want him, had no interest in developing him, he would make his own films. For the time being it remained a dream, but Mary was already an important part of it. She would be the perfect secretary and assistant.

He hadn't known her long perhaps, but he knew he trusted her, and he was fairly sure that when the time came to jump, she would be willing to jump with him.

After *Stagecoach* had been fine-tuned it was put on general release on March 2, 1939, and overnight the western was back in vogue. Ford's film worked because of the collection of characters and the stunning scenery, and also because of Duke's stunning power. But his performance won him no great accolades, and no reviewers recognised what he had put into it; he had already made the difficult look easy, too easy for his future good. The critics of the period seemed uncomfortable praising a western which was perceived as being firmly part of the B-movie genre, nor could they congratulate John Wayne who was recognised as part of the Poverty Row set. Many reviews even criticised the film. The American notices had a devastating effect on Duke, he saw the chasm opening up once more, and he read them all with increasing horror. It marked his earliest realisation that the Eastern critics couldn't understand or recognise his acting or his films, it was a conviction that never left him. He felt he had been unfairly criticised, and that he was finally finished. History was repeating itself, he had starred in an A-movie ten years ago, and had slid all the way back to the rubbish generated on Poverty Row immediately after its release. Now he was terrified of the looming failure he could almost smell. He didn't think he could go back and decided he would have to find some other employment.

The release of *Stagecoach* in 1939 coincided with the expiry of his contract with the Leo Morrison Agency. Considering the lack of effort that Morrison had made to get his client work, Duke's achievements of the period were even more remarkable than they at first appear. All the biggest stars of the day relied on their studios to keep them in the public eye, they were an integral part of the machinery, valuable properties and they could rely on the studios to fight for the best material and the best directors. Meanwhile Duke had Republic, who made not the slightest effort to fight his corner, and he had Morrison, his agent for seven years who had given no support at all. Now he had achieved some success, Duke thought Yates was crazy not to ride on the back of it. He was getting close to the top of his profession and yet was still struggling along almost single-handedly. On reflection, he guessed, it had been that struggle that made him tougher than the rest of the pampered stars, and gave him greater independence than any of them knew.

In spite of his concern for the future he signed up with Charles Feldman, an attorney who had become a top Hollywood agent. Feldman became instrumental in all Duke's future success. He no longer felt so alone during negotiations with the big studios. Feldman insisted his clients didn't sign long-term studio contracts, but rather made one picture deals. He got them two or three times the money to make one film that the studios normally paid for a year's work. His client list at the time included Marlene Dietrich, Tyrone Power and George Raft. Feldman was one of the first to arrange package deals for the Hollywood stars, buying the rights to books or plays, commissioning screen writers, and then selling the whole deal to the major studios, always with the provision that his director and stars went with it. He won great contracts for everyone who signed with him, and when he went to work for Duke after *Stagecoach* both were destined to make a lot of money. There would be no more failure.

Duke's contract with Republic still had four years to run, and Ford had been forced to bargain hard with Yates to get him freed to work for United Artists to make Stagecoach. Now he was in a stronger position to negotiate, and although he agreed to stay with the studio, and accepted the same measly amount he was already getting, he insisted on having the freedom to make pictures for other studios as well. Yates had finally recognised Duke's worth to his company and accepted that it was better holding onto him than letting him get away to a bigger rival. Duke had become, almost unnoticed, a very valuable asset in Hollywood, and Yates wasn't in any position to resist his demands. Duke had at last acquired real bargaining power and he knew exactly what he was looking for.

As he had known it would, *Stagecoach* changed his life forever, he had finally made his name in the western, won his spurs as a western star, but in the next three years, of the eleven films he made, only four more would be westerns.

I'm not an easy guy to get along with. I do have a short fuse.

CHAPTER THREE

Warrior of the "Just" War

Tests, Allies and enemies

"*Never think anyone is better than you, but never assume you're superior to anyone else. Try to be decent to everyone, until they give you reason not to.*"

"Well you see, you have to look at my career as a long fight to get to the top — almost by my bootstraps. I never had a studio behind me, fighting my corner. I don't call Republic a studio, and Herbert Yates, though a nice guy, didn't know shit about good or bad pictures. I never had a studio executive who would build me up. Look for good stories for me. Find directors. Develop me. Publicise me. I had one good break, John Ford loved me. Best director in pictures was on my side and he was loyal to me. He put me in a beautiful part in Stagecoach and later gave me other good parts. He showed other producers and studios my potential, see, and I got other jobs. I've been thinking about Coach a lot ..."

Pat had followed him back into the house, it was too cold to remain outside however pretty the boats looked across the harbour. She noticed his eyes had gone a dull, misty blue, clouded over as he turned back to gaze out of the window. His words shook her. As long as she had known him Duke had insisted on looking forward, thankful for each day he was given. He rarely dwelt on what had gone, the disappointment or the joy, he preferred to anticipate happiness to come, and he hardly ever spoke about the old days. Tonight he seemed locked into them, unable to shake sombre thoughts. She sat down and watched him closely, if he wanted to talk she was happy to listen. He didn't look in her direction, his vision was focused on another time, another place. He hardly seemed to notice she was there at all. He was mumbling and she had trouble picking his words out, but he really wasn't talking to her, the words were to himself, for himself.

"1939 ... it was the turning point ... but it was only the start ..."

After completing *Stagecoach* he went straight back to work for Republic. He'd hoped to be liberated from the world of poor quality, but that wasn't the way things turned out. Despite being miraculously transformed into the embodiment of the western hero the studio now insisted that he return to complete his quota of B-movies for them. He had to spend another year fulfilling his contract, producing a string of poor quality films, playing typical leading men roles and he had to wait for another Ford movie, *The Long Voyage Home*, for his next good picture, "I was under contract to these guys who hadn't said "hello, or kiss my backside, or what have you" after *Stagecoach*. In order to do that picture I had to make three or four films for them, one backed right up to the other, six-day pictures. This was just before I made *Long Voyage Home*. For the whole month before I made it I couldn't go over to rehearse or have anything to do with the part. Christ, I just had to walk in. I stopped work at twelve one night on a quickie western and the next morning I'm on Ford's *Long Voyage*. And they're right up to where I have to work too.

I started the very last minute that they could wait for me. I guess those are the things that other people aren't interested in, but it was tough. Sounds like I'm making excuses ... but I'm not ... Had to have a Swedish accent for the part, and I'd not rehearsed at all. There was this one line, "Ja, jag ga hem" or something that Ford gave me. So I said OK Coach. Christ this is my mentor, so I said OK. My own ear told me I said it wrong, but Ford was happy with it. But I got to thinking about a long scene I had to play with a woman later, I just had to sit and say these lines, I begged Coach for some help. So he said, "Well, Jesus, all right if you want to be a goddam actor. You don't need it." They got this girl to coach me. Had a beautiful accent ... after we worked my accent out together, Jack just left me alone when we got to the difficult stuff ... I never had a chance ... it was a tough spot to be in."

The way his career now developed led him to believe that if Ford didn't take an interest in him he would never be offered any more good parts. However talented he appeared to be in the skilled hands of the master he was certain he was destined to continue making B-movies at Republic with an occasional chance to stretch himself, "Because of the work I was doing at Republic, and then with Ford they started the thing around the business that the only time I was any good was when I was with John Ford ... you know for Christ sakes, I'm making a six-day picture one night, then playing a Swedish sailor with an accent ... I wanna tell you, that's quite a switch ... From knocking people around. But what the Hell ... I hero-worshipped Jack ... I loved him ..." His career was adversely affected, the big studios wouldn't risk touching him on his own, "*Stagecoach* established me as a star, it took another director to establish me as an actor. It couldn't be Jack who did that, because all the critics were on my back saying Wayne's no good without Ford. So it had to be someone else who did that, it fell to Howard Hawks and *Red River*, ten years later. But *The Long Voyage Home* was still just a beautiful picture." The film marked the first time that he played outside his normal range of character; his earlier films developed the heroic image, *Voyage* showed his sensitive side. The familiar Wayne was there, but there was something deeper, fuller ... a rounder image was emerging at last. It was to Ford's credit that he recognised Duke possessed the qualities that would enable him to play Ole Olsen, to his credit that he drew out the innocence, gentleness, and as ever, the soft vulnerability on screen. Both Duke and Ford were proud of the performance.

John Wayne always gave the impression that reviews were unimportant to him. It was never true and he was particularly worried about what the critics would make of *The Long Voyage Home*. He scanned everything that came out of the East, checking everything written about the movie and was gratified to find it unanimously considered a work of art. The unstinting praise it received embraced everyone connected with it, even him, not one report ridiculed the accent he had worked so hard on; in fact they hardly seemed to notice it. The reviewers loved the film and called it "arty" and complex. One critic said, "It will take all the top honours, except those at the box-office," and he had been proved right. Hollywood was in the business of creating heroes and there were non in the film, it was also laden with political overtones. It lost money, but hurt no-one, least of all Duke, who was able to move on, more confident as a result of his success in it.

And the next project that arrived finally gave him his chance to escape Ford's cloying influence. Cecil B. DeMille was casting his new film, *Reap the Wild Wind*. He had been enthralled by Duke's performance in *The Long Voyage Home* and was a big enough personality in the business to take a gamble on him. He rang Duke with an offer. Many years before, De Mille had given him the brush off when, in his quest for work, he had approached all the studios, pleading to be given a chance. He never forgot those who helped him during that time, neither did he forget those who had scorned him. "Just tell DeMille I said a lot of water has run under the bridge since I seen him last."

"For the first time in his life he could say "Fuck You" explained ever faithful Mary St John, "He never did it much, but now he felt he could." He was not impressed by DeMille's offer, but he didn't just say "No …" He sent a seventeen page document suggesting changes to the script, telling Mary he guessed that would "wash the idea up" once and for all. "Well, I was sure surprised when he phoned me. He was damn polite and flattering and said he wanted to see me. He said he needed me. Well, I have to admit it kind of won me over. But I was still against working for him. When I went over to see him he came out from behind his desk to meet me half way. He had an office, well it was big, seemed like you had to walk and walk from the door to his desk."

DeMille told him, "I read your letter sir. It had much worth in it. But if we are to work together you must trust me." Duke replied softly, he did respect him but had no desire to work for him.

"Under no circumstances?"

"Well I might consider it. But I'd have to be protected. I know Paramount will protect Ray Milland, and I don't want to wind up with a supporting role."

DeMille said as he put out his hand toward Duke, "I give you my word of honour that I will do you justice." And he always trusted a man who gave his word of honour; it was how he liked to work himself. He was softened up by the offered hand and the sincere words. He was willing to take a chance and firmly shook DeMille's hand. Still he found himself unable to resist a final swipe, "I've heard you bawl people out. I don't want to get a bawling out from you."

DeMille replied seriously, "John, I never bawl anybody out who does not deserve to be bawled out. I am fair. If you want the job, you got it."

He took it, and remained forever grateful.

Duke had no trouble with De Mille, he got no bawling out and came to remember the film as one of the most pleasant experiences in his career. The director treated him with respect and it was an unusual experience for him. He was fully aware it was his effort to make up for his previously harshness, "Because he put me in his picture I never again had trouble holding up my head in Hollywood, even though Republic were still trying to mess me up with their rotten pictures. Republic just couldn't make good pictures, except once in a while by sheer accident." After *Reap the Wild Wind* all the studios wanted him and he was finally able to settle down into a rhythm of work that matched his energy, drive and emotional needs. Offers rolled in, he was in demand, able to name his price. He no longer had to search for the next project, they were stacking up awaiting his decision.

In private he also began to move on, resigning himself at last to the tragedy of his broken marriage. He rarely slept at home anymore, preferring to stay at clubs or the homes of friends or, better still, away on location. He had learned to build protective walls out there to hide his vulnerability, he allowed nothing to touch him behind the façade. All the time he was working, acting out the roles he knew so well, he was safe and the world he increasingly came to inhabit, deliberately constructed, became a comfortable one. It wasn't that he hid there, but he chose to wrap his soft human soul in the tough public image he invented and perfected as his career finally took off. As soon as one picture finished he was busy preparing for the next and from 1939 onwards he became increasingly reluctant to leave the security of a film set for the real world.

Other changes had taken place. Having finally given up on Josie, he was suddenly released from his need of her and for the first time he began enjoying the attention he received from his leading ladies. He was, of course, still married, but he rarely saw his wife now, and although he felt himself to be basically honourable he no longer felt tied to her as he had in the past. He was flattered, though amazed, that so many women wanted him. The female leads in most of his films tended to be strong characters, happy to take the romantic lead, both on and off screen after the cameras stopped rolling, which was fortunate as he remained the tongue-tied, blushing man at thirty three that he had been as an adolescent in Glendale. He never had the inclination, nature, or personality to be a good womaniser. He had little experience, remained naïve, made plenty of basic errors of judgement, but he did experience some free and easy times at last. Few rumours attached themselves to his new-found lifestyle and that was not typical Hollywood fair, but just because he didn't hit the headlines as so many of the other leading stars of the day did, it no longer meant he was resisting the delights on offer.

He starred with Sigrid Gurie in *Three Faces West* for Republic, and she was only one of many to fall hopelessly in love with him. Gurie was his first experience with a European woman and more specifically with a liberated Scandinavian. After her he was introduced to Osa Massen, the coach called in to help him with his accent for *The Long Voyage Home*. He had been nervous about the role and taken the part seriously, but he obviously enjoyed all the lessons he received from the experienced Miss Massen. Duke appeared to be inhibited with American women, and was always more at ease in the company of foreign ones, he felt safer, more confident, away from the strident tones of his own countrywomen. He was happier talking to small, delicate Latin Americans or Europeans, and particularly the Scandinavians that seemed to cross his path at every turn. Though he eventually married three Latin women he said that was because he preferred to take his holidays in South America, and they were simply the women that he happened to meet when he was under no pressure.

As his confidence grew, as he began to believe in himself and to trust his own instincts, he no longer shuffled around the Republic offices looking lost and unhappy. He was increasingly seen standing around, more relaxed, laughing with film crews or other actors, or more likely now, actresses. He moved on a pace in his private life too. His brief encounters with Miss Masson and Sigrid Gurie paved the way for his next adventure with another strong European who was overtly sexy. Marlene Dietrich was an unexpected event in his life, but was definitely the next adventure!

Their first meeting was pure Hollywood, directed and orchestrated by the colony itself. The German star was the sex symbol of the forties, a powerful and magnetic personality, noted for her intelligence and ability to get what she wanted. She had been hired by Joe Pasternak for the Universal Pictures' movie *Seven Sinners*, and he and director, Tay Garnett, were looking for a big, rugged he-man to play opposite her. Garnett had Duke in mind but was overheard commenting to Pasternak, "T'aint goin' to be easy." Dietrich herself had overall casting approval, she would not be dictated to and she was known to be choosy. Pasternak and

Garnett cleverly arranged for Duke to be around the studio on a day they knew she would also be there; they hoped she would notice him and select him herself. But when the paths of the two stars crossed the executives were bitterly disappointed and she walked straight past Duke as if he didn't exist. The director shook is head in dismay, he would have to think of someone else. Then Dietrich paused, turned slowly, looked Duke over from top to toe, taking in every detail, and whispered, "Daddy, buy me that." Duke was bought and paid for and his immediate fate was sealed by the purchase.

He was ordered to report to Miss Dietrich's dressing room straight away. She was, at that time, very much the superstar. He never considered himself in such terms and he did as he was told, going to the meeting in some trepidation. He knocked on her door and was told to enter by a deep sultry voice. He ambled in, a picture of innocence, and was shocked when she locked the door behind him. She turned to face him and whispered seductively, "I wonder what the time is." Before he had time to answer she lifted her skirt up to the thigh and he had his first glimpse of the watch she wore there on a black garter. He was rooted to the spot, and felt every bit the big dumb oaf that Ford called him, blushing and saying nothing. She added, like a line from a film, "Oh, it's early, we have plenty of time."

"I just did what any other red-blooded male would have done in the circumstances!" Duke confessed. He said later that the Hollywood of the thirties and forties was a combination of Peyton Place and Sodom and Gomorrah, and added that its stars, despite being forced by their contracts to lead exemplary public lives, behaved like stallions let loose in a mare's barn in private. Duke's own background and personality made such behaviour difficult and his mother's attitude toward his father continued to affect his own actions, as did his run in with Harry Cohn. For many years he had resolutely avoided temptation despite his unhappy marriage, and his overly romantic nature, but Dietrich knew what she wanted, he was powerless and didn't resist her allure. She liberated him from his past in every sense, making an affair inevitable from the moment he first laid eyes on her and she made her momentous choice.

He had first fallen into tender, romantic love at the age of nineteen but had found his wife cold toward him, at the very least, she was not as passionate by nature as he was himself. In Dietrich he found the exact opposite and a bed mate ideally suited to his needs. But she became much more to him than that and he was soon hopelessly and deeply in love with her. She made a habit of telling him she believed in him and in his work, she was interested in him, and nobody, least of all Josie, had ever encouraged him like that before. It was a new experience and the care she showered on him had immediately positive results. Before she entered his life, he felt mistreated and misused by a string of women, but she made big John Wayne feel all man, a real man, in his own terms. Marlene even enjoyed cooking for him, they liked similar foods and whilst she had never been a big drinker she never minded that he drank a lot. She accepted him as he was and he appreciated every aspect of the life they shared, most importantly, their singular interest in, and dedication to, making films. For them both their work was their life and though they shared many interests; they loved to go to football matches and fights together, they went fishing and hunting and for long drives, neither had any hobby that distracted them from the movies. Outsiders believed that when Wayne and Dietrich were together they were locked in passionate embraces, in fact they were just as likely to be running current movies and analyzing them critically. They worked together on three movies, *Seven Sinners*, *The Spoilers*, and *Pittsburgh* and his work benefited enormously from his association with her. As a man he benefited more, and he was grateful for the happiness she brought into his life. The two of them were so alike that their relationship was one of great friendship and more, it was a meeting of mind and body. He believed with all his heart that she was his perfect woman, and she meant the world to him. In every area of his life that mattered he had found a perfect mate and friend. She brought him the intellectual, emotional and physical stimulation he had yearned for. He allowed her to take control and she wielded huge influence in both his bed and his business matters. He rarely discussed the relationship other than to mention softly that she was the most intriguing woman he had ever known, but friends believed he wanted to marry his best friend, his equal partner.

Strangely, given his track record, and despite rarely talking about her, he made no attempt to hide the affair, it would have been both dishonest and impossible for him, he was deeply in love. They regularly went out together in public, a generally acceptable custom in Hollywood, and, although he didn't flaunt the relationship, they were often seen in restaurants together. When he took her out for dinner he generally made sure they were surrounded by other people, and the relationship never became public property in the same way her affair with Gary Cooper had, but he wanted to be with her, and he didn't want to hide his feelings for her. Whilst they worked together on the set of *The Spoilers* he and Marlene had a minor argument. He knocked into her as he turned to walk away from the quarrel and she fell awkwardly. He was really sorry, and begged her forgiveness as he reached down to pull her back up onto her feet, but Marlene didn't mind. She made a fist and pretended to hit him, and he hugged her, pulling her tightly against his chest, refusing to let her go until she laughed, and kissed him. This was a rare reported occasion of anyone seeing him "getting personal" in public.

In fact he got personal all his life; he loved nothing more than to be hugged and kissed whether in private or public, especially by his children and grandchildren, or really by anyone else who wanted a hug or a kiss. His tree trunk arms were often thrown round the shoulders of a by-stander, he was often seen bending to plant a huge kiss on the cheek of a fan. The small bodies of his children were always seen crawling all over him, on set, or as he played cards, fiddling with his ears, mouth, nose and hair. There were a million treasured pictures of John Wayne getting personal. But whilst he got personal with Marlene, his public relations people were hard at work, still busy portraying him as Duke the family man, "If he suspects one of the kids has one degree fever, he goes wild." And that was true, but the creation of the legend had begun. He was no longer the family man he was painted for the public. Whilst he was obsessively building his career, his home and his family life crumbled into the abyss. "I don't know when, or even if, I stopped loving Josie." But he knew the pain started the instant he ceased to be the centre of her universe. He had needed her to share his interests, his world and his friends. Instead she filled her own life with religion, "I felt like I had to get permission from the Priest when I wanted to kiss her." Marlene walked in, picked up the pieces and put him back together, filling all the voids in his life. He had embarked on several affairs before meeting her, but his behaviour had left him feeling cheap and dirty. He also valued the idea of family life, he wanted things to work, but eventually he had to look elsewhere for love. Many years later although he confessed to the cook on his boat, "When I was young I was screwin' everything I could get hold of," his affairs never became the stuff of legend. Mary said, "Duke was deeply romantic. He never really understood women. He put them on a pedestal but he was generally uncomfortable with them, they scared him. And he became madder than hell when a leading lady took liberties with him during a love scene. He complained bitterly when they did. And many of them tried. The more famous he became, the more it happened to him, but their obvious desire gave him no pleasure." There had been the famous incident when he had been making *The Conqueror* with Susan Hayward who groped him in front of the crew. He hated to feel used by anyone, hated to feel as though he was out of control, and he was storming angry to have been taken advantage of when he couldn't do anything about it. The scene, just as shot, including the look of shock on his face, remained in the film! He never became accustomed to such advances and, although he by no means rejected all his opportunities, it said a lot about his extramarital activity, which was in fact, almost non-existent by the standards of the day and of the world he happened to inhabit.

Still Josephine worried about the scandal she now saw brewing. Up to now if he'd had any affairs he'd been discreet, but now she saw articles in the Press about Marlene and her husband at every turn. As Dietrich was often described as a woman who devoured men with an insatiable appetite, usually spitting them back out again in rapid succession, Josie was naturally disturbed. Mary St John said Dietrich was as romantic as a cash register, that she moved rapidly on from one man to the next and she always felt the romance between Dietrich and her boss meant nothing to her, but that he was obviously crazy about her. In 1979 an interviewer asked him if he had ever fallen in love with any of his leading ladies, "Well, yeah, Marlene Dietrich" came back the speedy reply, without thought or hesitation. To his closest male friend, Ward Bond he was more explicit, "She was the best lay I ever had." He continued, all his life to think of her in those terms. Marlene would have been more than happy with the memories she left behind.

Despite Mary saying she moved from one man to the next quickly, their affair lasted over three years. Other stars thought it was cute when she brought him picnic lunches out to location. Those occasions were some of the only times he had ever been distracted from his work. Once when he had been racing back to the set from her hotel he even crashed his car. He was unhurt and returned in the same haste after shooting finished that night.

The affair finished as suddenly as it started, ending on a bitter note. He refused to tell any one what happened between them, but she wrote about him in her autobiography that she simply got bored with him, that it was time to move on to the next man; she called him "nice, but dull." Many believed he ended the affair, shattered when he discovered she was bi-sexual. Once it was over they went to great lengths to avoid each other for many years ...

When the Duke invited guests to dinner they arrived at 2686 Bayshore Drive promptly. Everyone knew he was not a man to be kept waiting, and not even his greatest friends, nor the closest members of his family would run the risk of wilfully earning his displeasure. They would all be hurrying toward his home, and he didn't have long to get showered, changed, and to prepare himself for the evening and the ordeal that was to come later. He had continued talking to Pat for some time, dwelling on wonderful, warm memories, but if they didn't both get moving soon people would arrive before things were just as he wanted them. He directed Pat to further efforts in the kitchen even though he could already detect delicious smells coming from that direction. He left her to fret over things there and rushed away to get changed himself. Together they had created the exact look he wanted in the house. The tree stood full and tall in the corner, bedecked, dressed by his own hand as usual, and all the decorations and trimmings were tasteful and after his own style. He felt the most enormous satisfaction in everything that now met his eyes as he looked slowly and appreciatively around him. Once again he checked all the minutest of details, nothing was to be out of place … everything about his home had to FEEL just right on this most memorable of Christmas Nights.

For some reason beyond his understanding, or even thought, he wandered back into his den, the 60' study that said everything about him, rather than to his shower. He had always been happy that visitors to his home were suitably impressed by the aura of that room when he showed them around, in fact, by his aura that filled it. As soon as he entered he felt himself relax, comforted by its warm familiarity. That room was, and always had been, the only place where he truly felt at home, for he had built it himself and filled it with his own life force. It was light, airy, spacious, just the right size for him, and it was full to bursting with special moments from his life, awards, decorations, even a phial of sand taken from the beaches of Iwo Jima and sent to him by the Marines, and of course, there, mounted on a specially made plinth, his one Acadamy Award — the most treasured possession, swamped amongst so many treasured possessions earned during a lifetime of endeavour.

There was the "Fifty Years of Hardwork Wall" which was covered with faded, slightly blurred old photographs, old memories, a wall worth a fortune to him for he had earned his fortune creating it. There were framed poems hanging there, written by his children and given pride of place, and which undoubtedly meant more to him than anything else because they represented his most valued prize, love. He never took the wall for granted, and now once more he found himself stopping before it, looking at it carefully, with both his hands pushed into his waistband for comfort as he felt another wave of pain begin. He leant slightly forward to ease it, and the action took his face close to an old colour photograph —

"Jesus! There's a picture!"

He spoke with all the wonder of someone who hadn't seen the four young men captured in a frozen moment of laughter on a fishing boat before. He found himself looking at his own handsome face, at Ward Bond, Henry Fonda and John Ford, who were all staring straight back at him, laughing. "It was taken by Gregg Toland down at Baja, Gulf of Cortez ... each of us was a professional, every damn one of us had hundreds of dollars worth of camera and film with us ... and that's the only photograph left ... Jesus ..."

It was said with infinite sadness to himself and the ghosts who shared the room with him, it was said with pain, and he breathed, "It's getting to the point where I know more dead people than alive ..."

"Duke, are you going to get changed or not?" Pat was standing quietly in the doorway watching, she felt a need to rouse him from his memories. He took no notice as he sat back down at his desk and began to doodle endless straight lines on a pad, ripping off each sheet as he filled it, to start a fresh page. He said nothing more for a long time. It was rare for him to loose sight of what was expected of him and he recognised suddenly that he had to fulfil his promises, it was of the utmost importance to him not to fail those expectations tonight. Tonight he wanted, above all else, to provide everything that the people coming to his home anticipated. It would be the very last time they would come, the last time he would do this. He shook his head slowly as if to clear his thoughts, and he looked straight at her, "It has such a sadness in memory ... but I've always tried to look straight ahead Pat ... I guess you're right ... Better go get ready ... avoid the reminiscing huh? ... Just keep looking ahead?" And of course that was exactly where he would rather not look, what he longed to avoid ... if only time could have stood still as it had in Gregg Toland's photograph.

As he rose to his feet he could feel the mood of despair lifting from his shoulders, felt the dark despondency ease from around his heart, felt himself coming back to life, suddenly, once more seeing clearly what was expected, and he began to feel the familiar tick, the buzz that never failed him, as he began to get himself into character, as he began to prepare for the role he would play tonight for his chosen audience. Tonight he would be the endearing, charming, courteous and affable Duke, the man who ensured the comfort of all who ever stepped over his threshold.

He took the loose polo shirt off in the warmth of his own room, and discarded it thoughtlessly, screwing it up into a ball before throwing it on the floor, someone else could pick it up later. He walked across the room and suddenly caught sight of his image in the huge mirror and was shocked by what he saw and he quickly averted his eyes, getting on hurriedly with the business at hand. The pants were unzipped and pulled off and left in another heap at his feet. Soft white towels were piled on a chair in the corner and he took one as he stripped off, then he wrapped another around his neck for he couldn't bear to see himself again, even by chance, as he crossed the room. He had been a mountain of sun-bronzed flesh not many months before as he sailed down into the warm Mexican waters on his boat, lying contentedly snoring on its decks. He had been a giant of a man who unconsciously seemed to overshadow everything and everybody around him, even as he dozed, curled up for comfort, on a couch at the back of his boat.

Since his last brush with cancer he had struggled constantly against the massive weight gains that he seemed powerless to prevent. He couldn't take the same amount of exercise he had before losing his left lung, and he'd always loved his food, any food, especially that prepared by his favourite cook aboard his boat. He devoured massive heaps of anything that came his way. He had always been so skinny that it never mattered what he ate until 1964 when the pounds piled remorselessly on, and one studio after another had demanded diets of one type or another, so he would look fit for their films. And he followed each one of them religiously, because that was what was required of him. How he hated all of them, sometimes complaining that he only existed at all on watermelon and gristle. He felt deprived and unhappy when he couldn't have his candy, his donuts, his steaks, his ice cream, when he had been limited instead to salad and fruit, and worse still to milk drinks.

Groups of dieticians ventured into his home, sat in his living room and planned their campaigns of torture for him. They huddled in groups as he paced to and fro, keeping his distance, until he heard things like, "He'll be allowed a quarter teaspoon of salt a day for three weeks."

He had bellowed his despair, "Hell … I put more salt than that on my ice cream." They all ignored him.

"Will he drink milk?"

"Not unless one of you wants to try holding me down, while another holds my nose and another does his best to force it in my mouth, he won't gentlemen." And still he was ignored as he performed before them like a sulky child.

Unexpectedly now he caught another glimpse of his body as he emerged from the shower, he removed the towels slowly, unwrapping the horrific sight and he forced himself to take a long look at what life had made of him, what the ravages of time, and the unhealthiest of habits had done to his once heroic body. He had abused it beyond imagination, always taking his health for granted, and it had not let him down until the "Big C" first hit him. And now he had come to this, and he could hardly believe it. It seemed strange to him for it only seemed like yesterday that he had been so lithe, so strong, so indestructible, and he was still able to see on TV as they regularly screened his films, what a handsome man he had been. It seemed unfair that he kept being shown what he had once been. Time was condensed for him; hadn't it only been yesterday that he swept Maureen O'Hara up into the strongest of embraces in *The Quiet Man*, hadn't it only been yesterday that he'd been in peak condition? And now, where had that body gone? Where had his life gone? Once before he had been forced to survey his own mortality and now it seemed so unfair that he should be forced to go down that road again, and as he lifted his head to the mirror once more he saw clearly the scars from his last run in with the mighty cancer.

But what he also saw, that frightened him so much more than the horrific scarring all over his body, was the drastic weight loss. He was no longer the mountain of soft flesh he had been, he was no longer tanned brown and healthy, he was a pale shadow of the man he had been. He would have been pleased to have been able to loose weight so quickly not so long back, now as his fat fell away he was just scared. No one else seemed to have noticed, thankfully, not even Pat. He'd taken to wearing loose fitting clothes. If anything, outsiders were saying how well he was looking, better than he had for some time. Of course they didn't see him as he got out of the shower, they couldn't see the body as it was being eaten away, they didn't have to look in the same mirror he did, nor feel the same fear he felt.

Now though, he knew he smelled good, fresh, smelled of soap and toothpaste. His skin tingled and was still slightly damp as he rubbed on his oil, a ritual that had kept his skin in the finest condition despite the roughest of treatment in the deserts and heat of the film studios. He put on the clean, crisp white shirt that had been hung up for his use, and his dark suit, and the finest soft kid shoes. The hairpiece was smoothed down, and he felt a little better as he tilted his head back again to look into that harsh mirror that he had come to hate because of the story it told him, and he felt immediately relieved. He suddenly looked like the John Wayne of the big screen, not the weak old man he knew himself to be. The physical transformation complete, all he had to do was play at being John Wayne once more, a role he understood so well. He stood up, watched himself intently, just as he had done at his earliest films, looked for flaws and areas he could improve on, but tonight he was happy with what he saw once he had covered up the skin and bone. He looked closely and what he saw there was immaculate, tall and proud. John Wayne flashed a grin back at him...

Back in the 1940's the power of the affair with Marlene shook him to his foundations, it had also helped him to forget there was a growing and all-pervading sense of conflict in the world at large. She took his mind off everything but the tiny space they shared. But at the same time, John

Ford was busy doing everything he could to force him into realising what was going on in the world outside Hollywood.

In 1939 Ford, Wayne and the rest of the gang went sailing on *The Araner*. Ford kept talking about the war in Europe, already sure that trouble was coming and that America would soon be pulled into the fight. He was especially concerned about the threat from Japan. Ford was a lieutenant commander in the naval reserves, and as they fished the Mexican waters he insisted on keeping watch for any unusual activity along the coast. On one trip they came across many Japanese sailors when they went ashore and he was convinced they were on reconnaissance missions. At the time Duke discounted Ford's observations as fantasy. He agreed with him that America should be prepared to enter the war in support of Britain and the Allies, but saw no risk from a few Japanese tourists to Mexico. He had no interest in military issues although Ford talked to him at length about establishing a naval reserve unit made up entirely of Hollywood professionals. He had just completed *Stagecoach*, only his second A-film in ten long years of struggle, and he was far more concerned with the state of his career and with Marlene than with world affairs. He had, as he patiently explained to Ford, clawed his way up from Poverty Row, and after a back-breaking time spent in the wilderness he had just seen the glimmer of a chance of entering a world he had believed lost to him. In 1939 as Europe trembled to the first sounds of war he had almost reached the summit of his own personal mountain, and in that one vital year he was aware only of a deep need to keep climbing. He was American, remote from happenings in Europe, protected, as were most Americans by the vast oceans surrounding their boundaries, safe from events that were tearing apart much of the rest of humanity. World politics were inevitably less important to him then than those even of Hollywood.

He had just become contracted to do several films at various studios. He was afraid to risk breaking any of them by joining Ford's unit, especially when he had no reason to think then that Ford might be right about the threat from Japan. Such action could cost him the ultimate prize, bringing to a halt the career that had only just begun to take off. He was the complete professional, totally dedicated to his craft, wanting only to create beautiful images, obsessed with, and consumed by, his work. Mary St John said he was terrified everything would be snatched away from under him, "He wasn't very good at hiding his feelings, and you could tell he wasn't happy. He felt Republic were exploiting the work he did in *Stagecoach*, exploited him and cheapened him, and actually he was quite right — he had become a hot property and Republic held the rights to him. What was going on at the studio troubled him then more than what was happening in Japan." His own situation, the internal politics of Hollywood and at Republic, were his main concerns until, on December 7 1941, the Japanese bombed Pearl Harbor and America was suddenly dragged into the war.

Duke, like all Americans, like the rest of the world, was shocked at the turn of events. He'd had no political involvement or interest up to that point as he busied himself instead with his career. At college he had considered himself a socialist and throughout the thirties his own unformed leanings had tended toward liberalism, he was staunchly anti-fascist. Most of his Hollywood friends, including John Ford were on the left of the political spectrum. But if he had friends that were left wing he also rubbed shoulders with outspoken conservatives and Ward Bond was as far to the right as Ford was to the left. Duke had rarely become involved in the heated debates that often raged between them. He might venture an opinion if anyone bothered to ask him, but he never willingly volunteered his position. That wasn't unusual, for of that group of friends he was always the one who sat on the sidelines, refusing to get drawn in, even when they were only discussing the price of a packet of cigarettes. Given the white-hot political atmosphere flaming through Hollywood, he surprisingly and steadfastly remained outside the in-fighting. He was a fairly simple, hard-working man, so tied up in making movies that politics at that time were little more than a minor abstraction, almost an irritation. The public rarely heard tales of John Wayne's affairs of the heart, because he kept his own counsel, the same was true at that time about his political views. He kept his mouth shut, believing his politics were his own business.

Still, by the end of the decade, after listening carefully to what everyone had to say, he began to drift away from the left and toward the right. He remained reticent and was careful to avoid becoming involved in the issues that were beginning to tear America apart. The only organisation he took any real interest in was the Screen Actors Guild and it was here that his mid-west political instincts began to evolve into his own philosophy. Of course he cast his lot with the actor's union, which was made up of people who had so often originated from working class backgrounds; few of them held any recognised political ideology, Duke was no different to the rest. As a group they wielded great power and had long resented The Screen Writers Guild, which was, they believed, made up of a group of smug and arrogant writers who were considerably influenced by the Communist Party and held enormous power over their own careers. From the deep resentments that existed between the two groups a split developed which eventually cut Hollywood into two factions and finally tore it apart.

Everyone, including an unwilling Duke, would necessarily become involved. At the time he was driven by his need to satisfy the movie-going public, he had little time to give to emerging political thoughts, no time to worry about the state of the country, nor the world at large, despite the efforts of mentor, John Ford, to awaken the sleeping dragon.

The world was at war. There was deep political unrest in Hollywood, and throughout America. Many of Hollywood's leading men were already serving their country, but Duke was concerned with life immediately around him. Stories about his political inactivity, and his not going to war like so many others, surfaced later to his discredit, but at the time were not remarked on. Because of his age and the fact he had four children he was exempt from the call-up. Americans who didn't go to war were hardly a rare breed.

He was working hard, happy that the public continued to pay to see his films, yet despairing of the films that Republic were using him in. He was hit hard by the reviewers attitude but admitted himself, "I hated the films I was forced to make, how could I expect the critics to like them?" He had decided he had to get away from Republic. Whilst he continued to work slavishly for them, to do what was asked of him in front of their cameras, he gave nothing extra to his performances for them. They made no demand on his talent, no one at the studio had any expectation of him, no vision of the lengths to which he could stretch himself when called upon, had no idea of the quality lying just beneath the surface. They could have found gold, instead they saw nothing special in him, only recognising that his films always earned them a good return on investment. That was all that mattered to them, they had no desire to spend money on a better vehicle for him.

Hollywood had started making its first war films, not just as entertainment, but as propaganda, and there was no stronger propaganda machine in the world. All the major studios were putting out films warning the American public about the dangers of Fascism. In the aftermath of Pearl Harbour the Hollywood moguls were able to point out to those who questioned such films, that they were right to prepare America for the crisis they anticipated. Most of them were Jewish, and of European origin themselves, and were more aware than most, of the horrors unfolding across the Atlantic. They became more willing spend money to produce the films they wanted the world to see.

What none of them foresaw was that the crisis they were busy highlighting would also make John Wayne into the greatest star Hollywood ever produced. Even he didn't anticipate that his moment was finally about to arrive. At the outbreak of war he accepted he was still a long way behind the likes of Clark Gable, Robert Taylor, Cary Grant, and countless other leading men on the Hollywood treadmill. The lifespan of a leading man was limited, he believed his time would run out before he ever got where he was going. Already over thirty, he was still not at the top of his profession, and although he was full of ambition he wasn't sure he had enough time left to make it to the very top. Now a war had come along to interrupt his dreams, to erode more of his precious time away, to snatch away the fruits of his effort. As fast as his moment approached he felt it being eaten away from under him. Like the rest of humanity, he had no idea what the war would bring, he had no way of knowing that the onset of the war would coincide with his career finally taking off, with him finally becoming established as the biggest star the world had ever seen. He became a megastar because of the war, but it also changed him as a man forever, giving him some of the worst moments of his life, and just as it destroyed millions of ordinary people's hopes and dreams throughout the world, changing all their lives for ever, so he could not be left unchanged or unmarked by it either.

His personal life became even more of a disaster than it had been before. He and Josie had made many futile attempts to stay together, now they made the final split. Duke's friends had always seen the cold and frigid Josephine as a strange choice for the lusty Wayne. They were glad for him when Marlene entered his life. The home that he and Josie kept seemed like a fortress to them, yet they had not known her at the start of the adventure. They didn't realise he had chosen much of the decor, antiques and art that hung in the fortress himself. They were also unaware that when he first met her, all he thought about was finding any career that would enable him to marry her and have children. They had no idea of the depth of his love for her in the beginning, only meeting him after he had stumbled, unwillingly into the career that tore them apart, changing him, making him obsessive about success, and making any kind of a stable marriage an impossibility. He was rarely home as he jumped from one film to the next, eager to further that career, always away on locations unsuitable for his socialite wife, especially after the birth of their children. And when he went home it was to comparisons between his wife and his lover, who were as opposite to each other as it was possible to be, in one he found joy, in the other only coldness. But he also suffered the most enormous guilt and was fully aware how badly he hurt Josie. He paid a heavy price for his joy, unable to forgive himself and remaining unforgiven also by the children he continued to love and miss.

From his earliest childhood memory he had been emotionally extreme, obsessive about work, love, or anything else that came along and took hold of him. But once he became bored with the obsession he could lay it aside and move remorselessly on, apparently unencumbered. He didn't pass from adoration to indifference either quickly or easily, but once he tired of something it was final. Once he tired of Josie she was put aside as he moved on to Marlene, though he never gave up his attempts to appease their children. "I've tried to make it up to them," were words often heard on his lips following the most minor disagreement which he always saw as signs of their unwillingness to forgive him. His interpretation was a reflection of self-guilt; if his children never forgave him, neither did he forgiven himself. He hadn't set out to hurt Josie, but he had been deeply scarred by her coldness toward him as he had been by his Mother's indifference.

Duke wasted many hours pondering the mess that was his life until he began looking to the future once more, concentrating on the only thing that really mattered to him, making films. He began looking forward again at exactly the time others were putting their futures on hold to go to fight a war. Many of his best friends had joined up and by 1942 some 12 per cent of the men and women of the film industry had entered the American armed forces. Duke remained safely in Hollywood making films about the war, and instead of leaving the mess far behind, he waded deeper and deeper into a mire of his own making, no longer in the professional wilderness, but in a chaotic personal life where he carried the guilt that seemed attached to every move he made.

Men of his age, with children to support, were exempt and not expected to enlist. Instead they were encouraged to do something useful at home. What could he have done more useful for his country than turn out propaganda films and face up to the fact that he didn't go to fight alongside his closest friends? However nothing altered the fact that he stayed home and he had the greatest difficulty in justifying his non-involvement, even to himself. He remained tight-lipped about his embarrassment and never made any attempt to defend himself or his actions even though he was later heavily criticised for remaining in Hollywood. He tried to enlist in the navy as soon as war was declared, writing to mentor Admiral Ford, "Have you any suggestions on how I should get in? Can I get assigned to your outfit, and if I could, would you want me?" There is no reply on record from Ford. The Navy again turned him down. He never mentioned his rejection and instead he went on to serve as an air raid warden in Los Angeles.

As usual he tore himself apart with guilt, but as the first rumblings of criticism started he refused to discuss it with the press. Many columnists alluded to old football and surfing injuries, and also to his severe ear disorder, picked up making *Reap The Wild Wind*, assuming they ruled him out of the war. He never attempted to excuse his absence. He wrote to the navy on at least three separate occasions after the outbreak of war but was rejected each time. They didn't want him and he considered himself a failure, he was as bitterly disappointed as when he wasn't accepted into Annapolis. Perhaps he could have made more of a push to go to war, but he had just signed a new contract with Republic, and Yates, having heard of his attempts to enlist, threatened him with a law suite if he didn't honour his contract. The studio head had no sympathy for Duke's plight, "You should have thought about that before you signed a new contract. If you don't live up to it, I'll sue you for every penny you've got. Hell, I'll sue you for every penny you hope to make in the future. God Damn it, nobody walks out on me."

He was trapped. Because he was exempt he thought Yates might win a court battle and take him for everything he had achieved over the last thirteen gruelling years. Legally Yates was in the right; Duke could have walked out on his contract and marched straight to the nearest recruiting station, but he had worked harder than anyone in the business to get where he was now; on the threshold of success; not quite there … but only a breath away. Deep down, he knew he ought to tell Yates to go to Hell, go to war, and take his chance against any case the old man might raise. Because he had known what he should have done, and didn't, he went on torturing himself with ever-unforgiven guilt. It was true he avoided making a concerted push to join up, but did what he could to get into the Navy. The guilt of not going to war tormented him all the rest of his life. It was brought up and thrown in his face regularly later, but at the time it meant he was one of the few marketable leading men left in Hollywood. His way was clear to finally and fully establish his place in the consciousness of the movie-going public when there was no opposition in sight, when there was no competition left. The Hollywood leading man had become a rare breed, in need of protection, and Yates looked after his most valuable asset in every way he could, using any dirty trick to keep John Wayne out of harm's way, determined to keep his only star out of uniform and in front of the camera where he could continue to make money for them. Duke was afraid of losing his new status, still too unsure of his own worth to risk doing battle with the boss. He wasn't afraid to go to war, rather, he was afraid of Yates finishing him off. As the image shone and grew through the war years, the man shrank a little inside. He had never spoken to anyone about this period of his life, but his third wife, who he met ten years after the war ended, said the guilt he felt over his rejection by the navy and his own failure to push for enlistment in another of the armed forces, never left him, "He would become a "superpatriot" for the rest of his life trying to atone for staying at home." He had slaved for over ten years to reach the summit of his profession. Having finally got there he found the prize to be worthless and the taste of success tainted.

He may have stayed home, but many at Republic knew it was not through any choice of his own. Many were aware of his continued efforts to get the navy to accept him, he was constantly writing to military officials, desperately trying to get a posting. He had a fairly fragile ego that was easily bruised and the navy's continued rejection of his efforts dented it badly. He chose to hide that rejection from the public, fearing it would damage the image he had been carefully building. He had always played the hero. It was what he believed he should be in reality. The navy never gave him his chance.

He suffered terrible embarrassment over his war record, but did everything he could to contribute to the effort, frequently visiting the war zones and making several USO appearances. Nothing made any difference and the war led to a crippling fracture between his screen roles and his reality that never healed, and shaped all the rest of his life. A devastating blow had been struck against his image and he found it so hard to bear. At the very time he could have become a real hero, he was the one that the forces didn't want, it was hardly surprising that he never spoke to anyone of the searing disappointment he felt then. When he was criticised for avoiding the war he never defended himself, believing his attackers had right on their side. He could not defend the indefensible and it wasn't in his nature to explain, believing it belittled him further to try.

When he visited a military hospital and some youngster asked what unit he had fought in, he had no answer, either for them or himself. To the man who believed life was about testing oneself to the extreme, his ultimate test remained forever un-taken. Even his little brother, Robert, served in the navy, exacerbating his raw nerves and leaving him wide open when his Mother sarcastically commented, with perfect truth, that her Robert was the one, not the big tough guy, who served his country. Mary vividly recalled the look of thunder on the sensitive face as he told her how sick he felt when Bobby was drafted.

He couldn't sit back and take everything thrown at him, for that wasn't in his nature either. He began working harder than ever in an effort to serve his country, turning out films that paid his own heartfelt tribute to those who were fighting in his place, "Mine became the task of holding high and ever visible the values that everyone was fighting for." He decided to keep his head down and get on with his job as best he could, becoming a one-man propaganda machine, making the films he hoped would keep Americans at home happy about what was going on overseas. They were more than propaganda, he believed there was a continued need to provide entertainment and light relief during those darkest of days. He exchanged his saddle for cockpits and ships decks, his carbine for cannon and machine gun.

He was an honest man and the issue of the war came to be the most painful episode of his life. It forced him to live a lie and for the first time he couldn't relate to the image or to any of the films he was making. Playing the role of the war hero who never went to war changed him forever. It was a debilitating blow to someone who hated to make a mistake. From then on he carried an obvious flaw, a weakness he couldn't hide. He made the most of a difficult situation by reinventing the image to reflect what he now felt himself to be. He put the flaw to use and his war hero adopted what became a characteristic self-derogatory pose which remained part of all his future performances, he never allowed himself to be seen as a flawless hero again. He was shocked to discover that the uncovering of weakness had the unexpected effect of strengthening the image. His willingness to admit imperfection and weakness became central to the public's perception of his character and was undoubtedly the reason he was accepted as a hero at all, despite his obvious vulnerability. Just as he had epitomised the rugged, lonely westerner, he now became the ultimate warrior involved in the "Just" war, the defender of his nation and the whole of the free world.

As one of the only stars left in Hollywood he found himself in a good bargaining position and he negotiated ten per cent of the gross of each picture he made during the war. His share of the profits alone on *The Sands of Iwo Jima* was three hundred and eighty thousand dollars; wealth unimagined by him just a few years previously. He had never been in greater demand, an ideal situation for the man who used work to escape from the reality he hated. He was unable to make peace with inactivity and the war meant he could work as often and as hard as he liked. Mary said he never learned to do anything but work, that he was a slave to his energy. He had no hobbies and never found anything to replace work; it was his escape, his relief, his pleasure and his passion. Whilst he was on set he lost all sense of reality, able to immerse himself completely in the part he was playing. He deliberately exhausted himself before the cameras so he had no energy left to give to his physical restlessness or to the thoughts that tortured him. He couldn't stop and he didn't want to.

On location his pattern of work shattered everyone else; it merely kept him ticking over. He was always up by 4.30 am, and Mary explained, "He just never, ever slept in late. Once awake, he had to get up, his body simply refused to lie still. He drank his coffee and was then raring to get on with the day, determined to make the most of every hour he had." It was too bad for those around who didn't wake at dawn. He might let his family sleep until 6.30 but after that he began to get irritable. He had been up with energy pumping for two hours by then, and if the day's action hadn't already started he would be badly in need of company and diversion by that time. If he wasn't on location, where the working day traditionally began at 6.30, he endured long, long hours of boredom and loneliness in the early hours of the morning until he could persuade someone to get up and take breakfast with him. His family resented being dragged out of bed in what they considered the early hours, but he needed them. He hated the loneliness of first light when he had no day's work to anticipate and he dreaded periods of inactivity, as did all his friends and family.

In the early days of the war such times were mercifully few. His home life was empty, as was his social life, his marriage was over and his friends were mostly overseas, there was no structure to his day when he was not on location. But all through 1942 he was able to work at a frantic pace, driving the demons away and never allowing himself the slightest rest. All the studios wanted him and in that year he made five A-films, and two others were premiered. Each one consistently portrayed the philosophy of the "right of might in the just war." He hoped they gave encouragement and hope, and in fact the power of the message he generated in his work then was awe-inspiring to a public craving comfort during dark, terrible times.

The characters he played added to his personal image of dignity and strength. The fact that the reality was different seemed not to detract from that in the least and from a crisis that almost destroyed him as a man, the biggest star the world had ever seen was born. He found more than emotional relief in the enormous power and wealth that came his way as a result of his frantic pace of work. The world had suffered agonies and so had he, but just as it now began to emerge into a period of reconstruction, so too did John Wayne.

Still he worried that the time was fast approaching when he would no longer be in demand. Once the war ended, and the big stars returned to their deserved heroe's welcomes he fully expected to be thrown back onto Poverty Row and he planned for that time, earning as much as he could for as long as he could. But however hard he worked, however much he earned, it never seemed to make any difference, he still never had any cash, and despite earning millions of dollars during the war he remained insecure. Marlene Dietrich was horrified by his inability to handle his capital. He lived a simple life, was never flashy, but equally he took no care with money, spending it on anything or anybody that he felt was a worthy cause. He supported not only his estranged wife and four children but his brother, his mother and her new husband, his father and his new wife and her daughter. After his father's death he continued to look after Florence and Nancy, who were accepted members of his family by then. He liked buying people presents and though he rarely went shopping he loved browsing through catalogues, choosing gifts for family and friends. He always picked up the tab whenever he was out drinking, often leaving a blank cheque behind the bar when he left so everyone else could continue drinking at his expense. He had perhaps been too generous a human being to ever have saved money. It had no meaning for him as a symbol of power, it was only for spending, and he enjoyed every penny he earned. He fell for every hard luck story and those who had ever helped him along the way when things had been tough were more than repaid now. Marlene estimated he spent millions on handouts to down and outs over the years. He lost further millions on the dubious investments and enterprises of friends. He was unable to say "no" to anyone. He never told anyone that he was giving his money away, and to a large extent he never knew himself where it disappeared to; all he knew was that he never seemed to have much in the bank.

Marlene told him he needed a business manager and suggested Bo Roos, who handled many Hollywood star's finances. Duke admitted, "I had tax problems like any other business. I had to bring my expenses into line with how much I was making. Roos wanted to put me on a budget, but I wouldn't go for that. However he made a lot of sense and I trusted him." He signed no contract, he rarely bothered to put pen to paper, a handshake was usually enough for him, and on the basis of that particular handshake, he handed over every penny he had made, and would make in the future, to a man he didn't know. His money was invested in projects that interested Roos — Duke had little or no interest at all in what he did with his cash.

The only investments he ever did find any interest in all happened to be in Mexico. Together they started going South on long business trips, Roos always at Duke's expense. He spent much of his hard earned money in Mexico, but was also introduced to the country he fell in love with. He was so impressed with the interior landscape that when he started producing his own pictures he shot many of them there, rather than in America. He had been to the west coast many times with Coach of course and had always enjoyed it, but what he discovered across the border with Roos exactly suited his tastes. He began to holiday there regularly, particularly enjoying the relaxed atmosphere and the peaceful lifestyle he found. It was one of the only places he ever found real happiness, it was the one place he could sit back and relax, even rest a little. For two years he had worked with complete indifference to his health. He had pushed himself too hard, hustling all the time, glad to be in such demand, and afraid to slow down. 1942 had seen the release of seven of his films, and by January 1943 he had not only exhausted everyone around him, he had wiped himself out too, which became evident when he collapsed on a film set and was rushed to hospital. Doctors told him he needed rest.

Roos introduced him to many Mexican attractions, and primarily one Esperanza Baur Diaz Ceballos, known to everyone as Chata. Roos cost Duke millions of dollars over the years, but Chata cost him a whole lot more than that. John Wayne was no longer the inexperienced boy he had been when he fell in love with Josie, still it was a shame he had forgotten the words he had uttered so long before, "Why does no one ever tell you how much it hurts?" when he was first introduced to her. And as for Roos, most people went to great lengths to avoid his company, why had none of them warned him how much he could hurt either? His clients rarely liked him but unfortunately Duke did, and he had a disastrous tendency to trust anyone he liked.

He had known of Roos from a time long before he had any money to manage. The accountant was a fringe member of The Yachting Association and he accepted him now as a kindred spirit, another heavy drinking, powerful man with several top Hollywood stars for clients. Duke dreaded a return to poverty and knew he had to start making some return on the capital he was now making. He trusted Roos, a man he could share a drink with, and unfortunately, as always with Duke, the first order of business was to have a little fun. Like all big stars he enjoyed and valued his time away from the public who craved his attention. Roos led him to Mexico where he could do just that, where he could relax before getting down to business. Roos liked to go there with his clients, have fun and put the trip onto their accounts. In August 1941 Duke, Roos, Ray Milland, Fred MacMurray and Ward Bond went together to Mexico City on a business trip. Duke had been working hard and was completely exhausted. He had been advised by his doctors to rest and he went along with the others only with the idea of relaxing. He felt too ill to join their partying.

He hadn't been home for some time, partly because he couldn't bear his children to witness the coldness that now existed between himself and their mother. He stayed away but felt sick whenever he thought about what he was doing to them. He could never decide whether what he had suffered at his parents hands was any worse than what he did to his own children in an effort to protect them. He was finally free of

Josephine but he was never free of the guilt he felt over his children. His third wife said "He was too good a man to have failed in marriage and too subject to human frailties to have made it work." Since realising he couldn't make it work he had deliberately worked until his body could no longer cope with the demands he placed on it and he was exhausted by his effort to forget.

He planned to sit in the sun in Mexico, drink tequila and not even bother talking to anyone. He was worn out, and, for the time being at least, he intended to avoid women at all costs. When his friends tried to persuade him to go out with them they found him in anti-social mood, and he was furious with Roos when he was told he had to attend a function with them. He never stopped moaning that he would rather be anywhere than at a business lunch as he changed into a white suit. He felt obliged to go but when they entered the reception he hung back, dragging his heels, still complaining loudly, saying he wanted to go back to get some much-needed beauty sleep. Then he was introduced to Esperanza by Ray Milland. She was known locally as Chata, Spanish for "pugnose" but translated as "cutie." Duke didn't take any obvious notice of the dark, sultry woman gazing so intently at him. She was exotically beautiful, but that had more to do with her personality than physical perfection. She had bad skin which was covered with thick make-up. She had long black hair, and white teeth. When she laughed anything that wasn't perfect seemed to vanish and as soon as she flashed the brilliant smile at Duke, he forgot his aching tiredness. She whispered to him in broken English that she was an actress. In fact she was a high class call-girl, born in the slums of Mexico City, and everything about her was blatantly sexual. She had noticed John Wayne the instant he walked in although she had been waiting at the bar for Milland who had already paid for her services for the evening. Chata lost interest in the man who had bought her, and she made sure she was seated next to Duke at lunch. Milland was furious with her and his long friendship with Duke was about to end abruptly. When they got back to Hollywood they never worked or socialised together again and they didn't contact each other again until 1969, when Milland wrote to Duke to congratulate him on winning his Oscar for *True Grit*.

Esperanza was instantly drawn to the tall American. He fascinated her when he made no apparent move toward her. In fact of course he had taken note; as he had already pointed out on more than one occasion, he was just a normal red-blooded male. As they ate lunch he spoke to her in halting Spanish, and she was charmed by him. She knew all about John Wayne and had recently read an article about him saying how devoted he was to his wife and children! She had no reason to doubt the things she had read about him, particularly as he seemed polite but distant, even shy. In fact he and Josie had already been living separate lives for two years when he met Chata.

Mary commented later, with a hint of bitterness, "In every man's life there is a woman who other women do not understand. Chata was that woman in Duke's life" — Almost immediately after their first meeting rumours began flying round Hollywood. Duke had heard the rumours about her past but, always the romantic at heart, he ignored them, fictionalized and romanticised it, and even admired her for surviving. She told him about her childhood and he believed her when she told him with great sincerity that she wanted to put everything behind her. He didn't care what had happened before he met her, and that a man in his position had no right to pass judgement on another human being.

If he had been exhausted and irritable before meeting her he soon found his energy levels miraculously restored and his temper steadily improving as the trip took on a life of its own. Needless to say he didn't follow doctors orders, and he didn't get his much needed rest in Mexico. Like Marlene before, Chata satisfied his needs, and he felt blessed. He had fallen in love again and ten years later, when they were going through a messy public divorce, he still thought of her as the love of his life. She was mesmerized by him; while Milland had treated her as a possession, Duke was consistently courteous, kind and gentle. He never mentioned the past and treated her like he treated all women. No one had ever put her on a pedestal before, she liked the way he made her feel. Everyone who saw them together, with the exception of the furious Milland, found the situation sweetly reminiscent of the scenes in *Stagecoach* where Ringo softly courted prostitute Dallas. Like Ringo, Duke only saw in Chata what he wanted to see. He needed her, and was overwhelmed by her. How easy she had been to love and he had been swept away on a tide of uncontrolled emotion. He couldn't put her out of his mind, and Duke always had his obsession with Latin women, "I'm a guy who likes girls, all kinds of girls. No nation has a monopoly on beauty. But I consider the women of South and Central America to be unusually warm and lovely. They have a good feeling for family life — and so have I. I've always liked taking vacations in Mexico. I work so hard when I work. But down there they loose track of time. They know how to relax. Hell — when a guy is on vacation there he meets Mexican girls. I happen to like brunettes."

That may have been true but he was still legally tied to his original Latin beauty who hadn't made him happy and who was still stubbornly refusing to grant him a divorce. And whilst Chata rarely left his thoughts he recognised a great contradiction in his needs. One minute he still longed for his faithful, submissive wife, at others he wanted the wild animal who laughed and drank as much as he did. He had known very little warmth or physical comfort from his faithful wife during the years of their marriage. He was romantic and amorous and needed a woman in his life. He would have preferred that woman to be his wife, but when Chata wandered along offering blatantly sexual charms, he found himself drowning in his needs and turned to her for satisfaction. Too honourable to enjoy the concept of an affair, he was still far too human to deny those needs. He craved romance and was searching for a deep, meaningful and abiding love. At the same time he yearned for a Latin American sex object. Almost the instant he laid eyes on her he believed Chata could give him all of the things he was looking for. Even then he knew he was being unfair in his expectations. He built her up into his idea of the perfect woman, the answer to all his prayers. But he had no firm plans for their future and decided to take his opportunities without getting too involved too soon. Duke's best laid plans.

On that trip, he spent most of his time lying on the beach, sleeping, getting a tan, drinking, playing cards and going sightseeing with the others during the day. He didn't seek her out but noticed she always seemed to turn up at night. He felt drawn to her, as though they were thrown together by some strange fate. He saw her at another function and she looked sensational in a white silk evening gown, she was a vision of freedom and pleasure. The attraction was immediate and obvious; she was the very opposite to Josie. Where she had no interest in his work, Chata hung on his every word and he liked the attention she gave him. Josie was solid and dependable, her life rooted in Church and society, Chata offered untold pleasure. He hated going to the society parties that filled Josie's life, and he had gained a reputation for sulking, "he would wander around her parties looking tired, unhappy and oh, so bored." He was heard moaning, "I was up to my ass in Catholics!" He was not the most important thing in Josie's life, as he needed to be. He had to be the centre of his woman's life, and Josie made it so painfully obvious that his concerns were not hers. Duke's women had to worship him, which was unfortunate because the very quality that always drew him to a woman in the first place was the sense that they were their own person. And then Chata arrived, willing to share his interests, his loves, and she was all fun and hot passion.

And her joy in him was uncomplicated, she looked at him as a child might, full of wonder at the big movie star, she loved listening to him talk about films, she loved it when he tried to speak to her in Spanish. She was attracted by his air of innocence. The night she wore the white dress all he wanted was to be alone with her. He knew it was wrong, but, hell — he was in Mexico on holiday and he couldn't help it. They danced and talked, and strolled out in the soft, warm Mexican air. He kissed her gently. It was pure romance, the way he saw it in the movies … the way he wanted it, and just as it had all started with Josie too. But Chata wasn't like Josie, nor any other woman he had known. She told him she didn't want to go back into the reception, it was an invitation. He refused it, telling her that he was honour bound to return for the speeches! But at sunrise the next morning they rode together on the beach. Chata liked to ride, swim, fish, hunt, and generally enjoyed the same outdoor life that he did, just as Marlene had, but somehow, because of her Mexican origin, she seemed more interesting to him. He was fascinated by her sultry looks, by the hidden promise. She introduced him to her mother and his fate was sealed. The rich, famous, handsome, film star, who reportedly only cared about his wife and children had fallen in love with a Mexican prostitute, almost at first sight, and despite his not making any attempt to search her out he also made no attempt to cover up the fact that he spent every night of his vacation in her arms.

When he returned to Hollywood it was to find that Josie was already fully informed of all the sordid details. This was the first time he had flaunted a girl in public. With Marlene it had been different because she was a film star, and leading men and women often dined together. He had also acted with restraint, doing his best to protect Josie from the gossip. Scandal rarely attached itself to him, but this time Josie knew she had a problem when she heard the words, "I won't try to hide it — because I'm serious about Chata."

For the children's sake Josie was still willing to close her eyes to the affair. But Duke had changed and he tried to make her understand that he would no longer remain in an empty marriage, and that separated to him meant single and free to be with whoever he wanted to be with. He pleaded with her to divorce him. He wanted to start a new life and he moved out of the family home permanently, renting his own apartment rather than staying at friends or at clubs as he had been doing. And still she refused him his divorce as she searched for a solution.

The Catholic wives of Hollywood were willing to put up with minor indiscretions, they refused to permit them to destroy their marriages. Josie believed he would come back to her, certain he still loved her. But after Mexico he was, for the first time, cold toward her, he no longer pleaded, nor shouted his rage and frustration either. Whatever had happened between them in the past, he had never been cold or distant, he had always burned for her, and been reduced to begging. But now his eyes were steely and she saw only resentment there. It was too late to give him what he needed and in 1943 they were legally separated. They had been married nine years, and together for seven years before that. She was angry with him and refused to speak to him for the next two years and would not allow him into their house during that time. Mutual friends collected the children when he wanted to see them. She still refused to divorce him, hoping he'd change his mind, love her again, and return home, the boy he had been. Of course he could never be the person she wanted; he didn't want to be anymore, he knew too much, had done too much to ever want to go back. But meanwhile he suffered as he waited for his divorce.

If he was worried about Josephine and the kids, he was even more worried about the studio's reaction to what he was doing. All stars had to sign a morality clause with their contracts, *"The artist agrees to conduct himself with due regard to public convention and morals and agrees that he will not do or commit any act or thing that will tend to degrade him in public ..."* Many of the morality clauses were instigated by Mary Ford, wife of Duke's mentor, and a woman who held huge power in Hollywood and over certain stars at the time. She tried to persuade her husband to force Duke into giving Chata up. "Force" in this case meant threatening him with no more work, but whilst he didn't threaten him as demanded Ford did give him a stern lecture. And Duke was worried about his contact at Republic. He'd obviously broken it on more than one occasion, though this was the first time he had openly flaunted an indiscretion or committed an act likely to degrade him in public.

The clause was judged on a sliding scale, with some stars able to get away with more than others, but breaking it had led to the swift end of a number of glittering careers. Europeans were generally able to get away with more than the "Wholesome Americans" and Duke felt particularly open to attack and he was extremely sensitive to the problem. He hated to be seen doing anything wrong. He presented himself as the classic American hero, tough and uncompromising on the outside, decent and honest on the inside. The image created was of a man who did not avoid the "just" war, who certainly did not leave his wife and four children to have a wild affair with a Mexican prostitute! And he was uncomfortable with the reality. For more than a year after their first meeting he dithered. At times he longed for her and took himself down to Mexico just to be with her, he kept her photograph openly on his desk, and she was often in his thoughts. At other times he was determined to hold onto his new found freedom, urged on by the promiscuous Ward Bond to forget all about her.

But he was slowly being sucked in. He began writing to her; the number of letters and visits steadily increasing. Chata had told him she was an actress, and he toyed with the idea of obtaining a contract for her at Republic, of bringing her to California where she could share his life. They could spend all day together on location; Chata and work, his two favourite things rolled into one package. At other times he shuddered at the idea of being married to an actress, a self made prima donna, the sort of woman he hated. The fearful thought didn't prevent him sealing his fate when, in a moment of weak loneliness, he offered her a stunning proposal, telling her if she came to stay with him he would get her a screen test.

He sat back and waited for her to fly into his outstretched arms. She had told him she wanted a Hollywood career, but her letter back was brief, curt and impersonal. He wrote again. This time her reply took a long time to arrive. He was worried, and had no idea what he had done wrong this time. The Duke had called, Chata hadn't jumped. Finally her Mother wrote explaining she was unwell. As always, mention of the word "illness" frightened him, and he was filled with terrifying visions of his love, lying at death's door.

He was friendly with Howard Hughes, and one night as the two were out drinking together he told the pilot about Chata and his dilemma. He moaned about her being ill in Mexico and his inability to get to her, and about his own loneliness. In his drunkenness all he could think of was getting to her. Hughes simply replied, "Why don't we go down there then Duke, now?"

He promised to get him back to the studio by Monday morning as he was in the middle of filming *The Flying Tigers*, "What the hell are we waiting for then?"

Needless to say Chata wasn't dying, she was toying with him, tightening the line and reeling him in. In his relief, he forgot to question her about her apparent good health and before he left he persuaded her to go to Hollywood for the screen test. He was now well and truly caught and Chata soon arrived on his doorstep, suitcase in hand.

The frustration he felt and his fear for the future led to him becoming increasingly angry with Josie. He was now living openly with Chata. In the Hollywood of the forties his behaviour was considered outrageous. By actively and openly pursuing his happiness he was risking an awful lot more than his marriage and his children's regard, he was jeopardising everything he had slaved for.

But the studio in Duke's case was Republic. It had more to loose than he if they went ahead and enforced the morality clause. Yates had already proved by not allowing his hero to go off to war how unwilling he was to let Duke escape his clutches, and now he decided to stand by him, reluctant to loose his only asset. He decided on a course of damage control. It was vital for Republic that Duke remained popular and that the public was firmly on his side, so Yates protected the image and continued presenting him to the world as a decent family man. He fought desperately to keep Duke's messy private life out of the papers. He gave Chata a contract with the studio and sent Duke back out to work, whipping him out of Hollywood and away to a distant location, far from the prying eyes of gossip columnists.

Duke was a lucky man. As he left town to cover his tracks, the rest of Hollywood sank into a summer of the wildest scandal imaginable; and none of it had anything to do with him. Errol Flynn was about to stand trial for rape! It was open season on sexual scandal, and somehow Duke missed all the mud flying round. He was up to his neck in the mire but nothing stuck. He wasn't even in town when Hollywood blew up and his name wasn't mentioned in the columns so full of condemnation for his fellows! His indiscretions were minor compared to what the others were up to in Babylon!

Still he knew he'd had a near miss and when he returned to town from location late in the autumn he came back determined to put his life into some kind of order and to try to be the decent, honest character he portrayed on screen. He would take no more risks with his career or his image as he started living his life according to public perception. It wasn't only his fear about the possible public reaction to his exploits that caused him to suffer, he also hated what he had done in private. Guilt made him feel bad. He planned to do things right in future. In fact guilt brought its own rewards as he seemed to mature on screen through his suffering. He knew he looked and sounded better than he had ever done before. He was no longer the young innocent hero and he had managed to change the persona to suit. Life's experiences were helping him out on screen and he used them to full effect.

Republic meanwhile were turning out war stories in the same way they had the western, they were cheaply made, and not very good. Duke only had to turn up on time, go through the motions and then, as soon as he finished, rush straight on to the next. When he got back into town in the autumn of 1943 he was hustled away to make *The Fighting Seabees*, one of the few Republic scripts he ever liked himself. It was a nice, safe piece of cinema. All the studios were cautious about the films they were making then because the Government was acting as a board of censors, vetoing anything that didn't serve the public good. *The Fighting Seabees*, a story about teamwork and co-operation, was a peace offering from Republic to the Government. It became a solid hit for Republic and both the studio and Yates made vast sums of money at box-office on its back.

But Duke, more than anyone else, benefited from it and the rest of the formula pictures he was turning out with such monotonous regularity. In each new story he embodied the spirit of the American fighting man. No other star, not Cooper, Tracey or Bogart could play the hero like he could, despite the fact that they were the real heroes. He was constantly put into Republic's cheap war films, and all he had to do was slightly develop his screen persona from American western hero to American war hero. His war pictures were effectively no different from his westerns. He remained the tough, difficult, uncompromising, but always truthful, loyal and ultimately likeable guy he had always been. The public had loved his cowboy and now they loved what they saw as a new role, accepted him and were happy he was still around to deliver the message of hope. They needed a hero to celebrate and Duke was there, steady and sure as ever, fulfilling their every dream.

On screen, the hero, in private, a complete mess. He hated it when people said he was the same off screen as he was on it. He was all too aware that he wasn't, at least not during the war years. Later he might try to be the man he knew people wanted him to be — but right then, as he worked flat-out on his war films, his own life was heaped full of moral dilemma — as he said, tongue in cheek, "I was REAL brave."

He had spent seven years trying to win Josie and now he began to wonder if it was going to take that long to get free from her. Though he longed for his divorce so he could marry Chata, all was not well on that front either. His wife had always hated him going out with Ward Bond and now he was living with Chata she too disliked him drinking with his friends, and she too disliked the loud, bullying man who occupied so much of her lovers time. Bond was generally unpopular, but his flaws endeared him to Duke, who merely laughed at his constant complaining and belief that he always knew best. He deliberately baited him and laughed all the louder as he watched Bond grow red with rage. Bond's temper subsided as fast as it arose, no insult was carried around by him for long, and Duke was secure in his loyalty. He knew that no matter what he did it would be Bond who forgave him first, he was the one person who never made him feel guilty and he needed him in his life to ease his burdens. As he walked around in despair waiting for a commission to materialise, hearing people openly criticise him for not pushing harder, it was Bond who stood by him. Both men had just left their wives and though Duke moved straight into another relationship he continued to spend as much time as he could with his friend, giving and taking support. Outsiders condemned them both, but Duke always had a happy knack of bringing people around, and making them like him, no one could stay mad at him for long. Bond, on the other hand, remained heartily disliked and his association with him probably did him no good in the eyes of the world. Still, he needed him; he helped him retain his perspective in the insanity of Hollywood.

During his life Duke left two women behind, and his third marriage also failed, but he never deserted a friend! He needed and loved his women, but needed and loved his friends more and no friend was more important to him than Ward Bond. He was conceited, self-centred, hard-drinking, difficult and prickly, but he served as Duke's safety valve in every crisis. He remained ever-present in Duke's life, helping to relieve his boredom and the pressures that he always felt when he wasn't working, he shared his sorrows and guilt, but ultimately he was there to share his fun. Throughout the war they continued to act as if they were still back in college, still playing the old pranks and childish tricks of those carefree days. When they were drunk, as was so often the case, they did anything that seemed like a good idea at the time. One night Duke wanted Bond, who was in a deep sleep, to go out drinking with him. He repeatedly called him and tried various attempts to rouse him, when everything failed he poured vodka on his chest and set light to it. Another time when they were both staggering drunk, Bond bet Duke that he could stand on a newspaper and that he wouln't be able to knock him off it. When Duke accepted the bet, Bond placed the paper down in a doorway and closed the door with Duke on the other side. "O.K. you dumb son of a bitch, now hit me" … and Duke duly obliged, smashing his fist through the door to knock Bond clean off the paper and win the bet. How they survived those years was a mystery to all who knew them and the things they got up to.

But even Bond couldn't rid him of all his demons and Duke often got involved in fist fights and brawls. Whilst filming *The Fighting Seabees* the director banned him from going into local bars. He was loosing as many fights as he won and Ludwig said he was worried he wouldn't get him through the picture in one piece. As it was, the make-up man had a hard time disguising the lumps and bruises he was covered in throughout filming.

As soon as he realised his commission wouldn't materialise he felt the need to do more for the war effort and he worked tirelessly, giving his time in The Hollywood Canteen serving meals to the needy. He carved the meat there on Thanksgiving, and gave generous donations at Christmas. He made his propaganda films and visited hospitals. He stopped writing letters asking for a posting and instead increased his USO Camp Show tours to the South Pacific and Australia. His attempt to make a personal contribution alleviated some of his guilt and suffering of the troops at the same time. He was asked to gather some information whilst he was overseas by William Donovan, Ford's commanding officer. He filed his first report with Donovan on his return from one tour, and in return a plaque was issued saying that he had served in the OSS. Duke believed Ford set the whole thing up to make him feel better and he never collected the plaque, feeling it really meant nothing. As an entertainer helping the troops he was more successful. He spent three months touring the Pacific bases and battle lines, performing two shows a day, and visiting as many hospitals as he could. He talked constantly to the injured and visited areas subjected to nightly bombing raids where there was likely to be enemy infiltration. Each performance carried its own danger. He sat up all night talking with troops. Day time temperatures often hit 130 degrees and the stage was made up out of crates. Duke was deeply moved by the endurance of the soldiers as they sat, indifferent to the climate, waiting for his appearance. Only as he shared their discomfort did he feel any better about himself.

In 1944 he returned from one tour to a mass of unexpected publicity. Newspaper pictures showed him being welcomed home by his four children. Nowhere was it mentioned that he no longer lived with them or that his private life was in turmoil. He had felt better when he was away, but as soon as he got back to Hollywood he was forced to look at what he had done to the people he really cared about, and when he saw the picture of his children clinging to his legs he cried with shame. Nothing ever drove him like guilt. He had done his bit, now it was time to find relief in front of the cameras.

He had seen a story called "Tall in the Saddle" in a magazine in 1943 and persuaded RKO studios to buy it for him. They gave him a free hand in script development and were keen to involve him in production. It was the first time he had been given any responsibility and after the experience he started seriously developing the plan that had been brewing in his mind for so long. His intention remained to take more control of his career but he knew there was still so much to learn. *Tall in The Saddle* was produced by Robert Fellows from a screenplay written by old friend Paul Fix. Working closely with the two of them convinced him that he had to become more involved in the business he loved if he was to survive in it after the war. Once all the big stars came home he knew he would be displaced and whether he knew enough about the business or not was no longer the issue, he had to take a gamble, "There were so many reasons for getting into production; a bigger slice of the pie, more control of my own destiny, a chance to stay in the business I loved. It was also a chance to get away from a studio for which I had no respect. I hated the films Republic made, they offered me no scope to develop a future career. I could walked through their pictures with my eyes closed." He had worked with the best and naturally he wanted to be with them, constantly pushing and extending himself. He dreamed of a future where he was producer, the boss, in control of his own destiny, but both Republic and Josephine continued to stand firmly rooted in his path.

Josie was a Hollywood wife, a woman without a man living in a town run by an industry which consumed the time and energy of its men, demanding everything of them. From the moguls, to the producers, directors, writers, and stars, they were all slaves to the industry that fed the town. The star and his wife suffered the most; the star because he projected and carried the consciousness of a nation, the wife simply because she was a "Hollywood wife." John Wayne carried his position with tremendous responsibility, and Josie suffered all the more because of it. Whatever went on in his private life he always knew what was expected of him as a star, and however he chose to behave in private he rarely let his public down. He understood, with sharp clarity, that he represented a nation's hopes and dreams, he was much more important than real life to the cinema-going public. And as far as he was concerned, no matter what happened to him, no matter his own tragedy and sorrow, however often he got knocked down, he knew he had to get up to make his next picture. That was what was expected of him and his every anxiety in life surrounded the next film, the next script, and the public concept of him. He knew his responsibility, it weighed heavy, and he needed an understanding wife to help him shoulder it.

Suddenly, in 1944 Josie finally filed for divorce, charging him with extreme cruelty, and causing her mental suffering. In court she stood up to recount the nights he had not come home, his refusal to explain his actions, of finding a lady's coat in his car, of his comment when she had threatened him with divorce, "Hurry up and let's get it over with." He contested nothing, offered no defence, and the divorce was granted on November 29, 1944. A generous settlement had been agreed before they went to court, "She damn well deserves it. She's done a wonderful job with the kids." Josephine made only one public statement, "In my eyes the divorce is a purely civil action and does not affect the moral status of the marriage." She remained Mrs Marion Morrison, and continued to regard herself as his real wife. She brought up their four children to hold the same view.

Almost immediately Duke realised he had made a drastic mistake and from that point on his life lurched from bad to worse, "It was the stupidest damn thing I ever did in my life. Not only did I desert the first woman I had loved, but I also left my four young children whom I also loved. Many of our friends naturally deserted me, and I don't believe my eldest child will ever forgive me for deserting his mother. It breaks my heart." It became another situation over which he tormented himself. Sometimes he felt he was harshly judged, but no one was ever as hard as he was on himself. He felt he should be better than he knew he was, and he never saw that his attempts to be a good man were enough. He hated the weakness he saw in himself.

He grew to be more understanding after his divorce, more mature, and a little more tolerant of others if not himself. Whilst he began to reflect increased internal maturity on screen, there was no corresponding change in his physical appearance. He retained the juvenile looks of the dashing hero that he had already played for so long. He worried that as he aged there would be no place for him in the movies, but his looks remained unaltered until he was well into his forties, enabling him to continue playing the male lead and delaying the time he knew must come, when he would have to branch into other areas of the industry. The preservation of his rugged good looks also delayed the need to establish his own production company, and although he had finally cut his ties with Josie he continued churning out films for Republic, and any other studio that needed a box-office boost. At the time no one, least of all himself, had the slightest idea that his genius would lie in portraying older men. Not even Ford suspected this element in his protégé. Some film stars were born to play young heroes and it looked as if Duke were one of those; he had always been the raw, romantic, innocent young man. A part made in heaven for him, but as it turned out as he aged and showed a deeper emotional strength he lost non of the raw innocence. His most successful performances all corresponded with his physical ageing. He had expected the end of the war to coincide with the end of his career, as it was, he had only just embarked on the journey into legend.

The war and his divorce coincided and almost destroyed John Wayne the man, neither had any effect whatsoever on John Wayne the film star. Had he been the weak man he thought himself he would have been finished, but he proved to be made of much sterner stuff than he imagined. He survived the tough years and that survival led to the most miraculous results on screen. Suddenly, he could play characters that showed the most extreme rage, bitterness and even violence, at the same instant as great tenderness, heroism and love. It was an impossible combination of emotions. No director could have evoked it or even dreamed it possible, it was something that emanated from the depths of his soul.

He was both simple and complex, a man full of contradiction, both more and less than he appeared. Here was the ultimate soldier, who never served, the cowboy who loved the sea, a sailor at heart, a man whose image was violent but who always longed for peace, and a man acknowledged by all who came into direct contact with him as the most gentle, kind and courteous of people. He abhorred his own cruelty but saw his softness as weakness. He saw little of value in himself, but he never gave up trying to be better, neither did he fail in his attempt to become the hero others believed him to be. To those who knew him, and to his movie going fans, the contradictions were the very root of his charm, were what made him one of their own, were exactly what made him a man. If he used what life taught him up on the screen, he also learned many lessons from his films, he used them over and over again in every role he played from then on. And the performances got better and better.

The end of the war brought new hope to the world. Everything had changed, there was a brighter future on the horizon. And from somewhere he found the courage to go on with his life, to emerge from the shadows of playing the warrior who never went to war.

All I do is sell sincerity.

CHAPTER FOUR

The Professional Warrior

The hero's transformation

"I saw no reason why low budget should imply a split from reality and I decided to play a real man to the best of my ability. I wanted to be a man who got dirty, sweated and really enjoyed kissing a girl."

Duke had been around the movie industry for fifteen years and had become the complete professional; the image he had promoted from the start became the man, and the man, the image. In the years following the war it was an uncomfortable fit, but the public either didn't notice, or they didn't care. John Wayne, with his increasingly complex range of characterisations, needed to work harder and admitted, "I figured I needed a gimmick, so I went to work on this Wayne character." He continued to credit his enormous success in reinventing his screen role to his directors, saying, "I was just the paint for the palettes of Ford and Hawks." In fact he was turning out performances rooted deep in his own rapidly developing personality and that was precisely what the audience wanted to see.

The most enduring image he created then was that of the displaced loner, always uncomfortable in the civilised world, always carrying a sense of some wound, loss or grievance from the past, and that of a man who learned to feel a deep and abiding love despite the violence lying just under the surface. The gimmicks he dreamed up, developed and used to suit himself, were based on the most painful realities of his own life and on his understanding of what a real man should be. The roles he played at any given moment became almost unimportant because each had a common thread running through it that was John Wayne, the man Duke longed to be, a man consistently honest despite a now obvious multitude of flaws. The professional film star carefully considered the characterisation, it was all important, he understood its value and recognised the need to protect it at all costs, "I'm an investment. I got to protect that investment."

As his power in Hollywood grew he chose to work only on projects that coincided with his personal vision, accepting only those roles that fell within his strictly defined set of guidelines, "In my movies I try always to remember that people are dropping bills at the box-office so they can relax and enjoy. That's why I like to keep it decent." Sometimes he demanded the authority to change scripts before he signed a contract. Studios, moguls, producers, directors and even, sometimes his own family, were irritated and annoyed by the ferociousness with which he protected his image, by his extreme sensitivity toward how the public perceived him as a man, "You tend to manage your life and your thinking in a manner that is expected. I would not want mine to be different." He knew beyond doubt what his fans required and he made superhuman efforts to let neither them nor himself down. The characters he chose to play were simple and direct, they could be hard and cruel, but never mean or petty. If he was offered a part that didn't fit the guidelines he turned it down flat, saying, "Nuance is out of my line. I'm not that good an actor." His determination to stick to the roles he knew his fans wanted generated the mythological figure and turned the man into an icon. It never made the slightest difference to anyone when he protested that he was just an actor, that he wasn't the same in private as he appeared on screen, for his own personality was intricately woven into the fabric of the John Wayne story, filmgoers the world over knew it and he felt the responsibility keenly.

Whenever he wanted to wander off the path he had to think long and hard before taking the risk. Sometimes when he took a gamble the public ignored the film altogether, refusing to accept it as part of the legend. Late in his career he made *The Cowboys*, a film in which he met a violent and gory end, brutally murdered in front of a group of young boys. He was profoundly troubled about filming the death scene and had to get drunk before he was able to go through with it. He was worried about what the fans would make of it, and his worst fears were confirmed when, despite rave reviews, they stayed away in droves. He had his answer, and a deafening silence greeted a great performance. They didn't want to see the legend murdered, they wanted to see the hero overcome all odds. "You say all my pictures are the same, but that's what I want you to think, I want people to say, "Hey, lets go and see Duke at the pictures"… I try to do things that people identify with." Every so often he experimented, but in general he gave people what he knew they wanted. He also tried his very best to become the man off screen that they thought he was. That proved to be far less easy.

He took his car and some clothes when he left Josie. He gave her every cent he owned and left all his personal possessions behind when he walked out. He was supporting an ever-increasing number of hangers on. More and more people were making financial demands on him, but there was plenty of work lined up and he believed his future was secure now Bo Roos was taking care of his money. He and Chata were living together and all was well in his world. Nothing outside mattered because he had the enchanting Chata inside and for the first few idyllic months her idiosyncrasies went unnoticed. Her melting smile turned the tough man to jelly. He had been warned about her past but he made light of it; she was irresistible, intelligent, fun to be with, and she was happy to join him in everything he wanted to do, either roughing it with his drinking friends, or equally, at the more formal dinner parties he was obliged to attend. Best of all she was happy to go away on location with him, wherever he was she wanted to be, and he adored her. Their life together was perfect and when his divorce came through in January 1946 he married her immediately at a small gathering in Long Beach. Nowhere was it reported that they had already been living together for several years. Coverage of the event was kept as antiseptic as possible.

The celebrations had scarcely ended before Chatas' mother moved into their modest rented love nest! She moved in at Duke's suggestion and he had no one else to blame for one of the biggest mistakes he would ever make. At the wedding Senora Ceballos, was so drunk she cried throughout the ceremony and reception. Later, when it was time to return home to Mexico, she cried even more. Mother and daughter embraced and sobbed uncontrollably, devastated at the thought of separation. Duke, that soft touch who could not bear tears, in a fit of typical insanity, insisted that Senora Ceballos stay with them a while. Following his divorce from Josie, Duke had very little money and the apartment he was renting was tiny but he willingly offered to have his den converted into a room for his mother-in-law! She was overwhelmed by his generosity and, even before he and his bride left for their honeymoon, she was making herself at home, becoming another heavy drain on his already stretched finances.

Still he went off to Hawaii a happy man to share a time of romantic wedded bliss with his bride. It rained every day they were there. They didn't notice and it didn't matter. For three weeks they were soaked to the skin, walking, swimming, and sightseeing in the rain, holding wet hands, kissing and pressing soaked faces together. At night they visited night clubs in the rain, and when they made love it was with the sound of driving rain pounding against the window. Duke loved every minute of it, he loved being in love and he loved being with Chata, he loved the rain, and nothing else mattered for those three short weeks.

They were over before he knew they had even begun. As soon as they got home he went straight back to work, making two films back to back, *They Were Expendable* for John Ford, and a light comedy, *Without Reservations*. Republic had finally given way to his demands and agreed to let him produce his own films. Yates had seen all the other studios gathering for a piece of the Wayne action like vultures and recognised that he had to make some concessions or loose him. Everything was falling into place for the deeply troubled star, the war was over, he had divorced Josie, he had films lined up as far into the future as he cared to look, a new bride and now, at last, Republic acknowledged his potential. He was already working on *Angel and the Badman*, and now had an agreement that he could produce all his own films for them. He negotiated a new, non-exclusive deal with Yates, agreeing to make one picture a year for him for $150,000 plus ten percent of gross receipts. He was looking at over a quarter of a million dollars for each Republic film and he was still free to work for any other studio that wanted his services. For years he had been turning out four or five films a year, sometimes more, and he expected to make vast amounts of money now. The new deal was the start of his rise to prominence in Hollywood. The agreement allowed him to hire and fire his own staff and he began to gather around him a close group of intimates, people he knew he could work comfortably with, and who wanted to work for him. One of these was James Edward Grant, who wrote the screenplay for *Angel and The Badman*, and who was to become a big influence in Duke's life.

The honeymoon over, Duke's perfect lover seemed to change before his eyes. At first, whilst she got what she wanted from the deal, Chata went along with him and gave him what he needed, maybe even, she really loved him. But as time went on she, like Josie before her, found herself unable to abide by his rules. He had discouraged her acting career, finding any number of weak excuses to deter her. He longed for a wife who was always available for him, he was prepared to give in anything in return, but he wanted to be pampered, babied, made a fuss of. The deep rooted desire was etched into his very being and stretched far back to his earliest memories. Chata couldn't be the woman he wanted, and she began to rebel. She had always been a heavy drinker but now, together with her alcoholic mother, she seemed to be permanently drunk. And like her mother, when she was drunk she became violent, suddenly turning on him like a wildcat. He was unprepared for physical abuse, he personally was a gentle lover, always very much the romantic, passionate perhaps but never violent, and he had no idea how to cope with her when she had been drinking heavily. She shouted, argued and attacked him with anything that came to hand, just as often as she made love to him.

Within months he was regretting rushing into marriage as both Chata and her mother became a severe drain on his emotions, filling his days with pain and anxiety. He was the big, tough hero of the silver screen, six foot four of pure muscle and being beaten up by his own wife! It was a living nightmare in which he loved, shouted, and had to defend himself against two female bullies.

His friends avoided him, embarrassed to witness Chata's tantrums and the way she treated him when she was drunk. John Ford screamed at him on location, "Did you have to marry that whore?" angered by the effect she was having on his best boy. Duke replied with dead calm, "You're talking about the woman I love," before walking away from his long time mentor, head hanging in shame. She put an enormous stress on the long friendship and worse, damaged their working relationship. Ford was under pressure from his own wife who hated Chata and all she stood for in Duke's life, and she constantly nagged him to put him straight and tell him to get back to Josie and the kids where he belonged. He had fallen for the oldest trick in the book and Duke felt humiliated. He had never thought of himself as a fool, but that was exactly what Chata had made of him. She had been happy to make both promises and love, and now he had to pay for her favours. The payment wasn't only financial but in the prestige she found attached to being Mrs John Wayne. He felt completely degraded by her, by the fact that he had fallen in love so easily, and because, lost in love as he had been, he had allowed her to tarnish the image he had worked so tirelessly to polish, he had allowed her to destroy his vision of what a real man should be. "Chata" … he whispered her name with the deepest longing.

Although he still loved her dearly she caused problems in every area of his life. He wanted to see his children but Josephine was reluctant to hand them over knowing his new wife would be around, probably drunk and possibly violent. He was forced into a compromise, if he wanted to see the children it had to be when he was away on location and Chata wasn't there with him. His working hours became the only time Josephine allowed him access to the children, and so he began leaving his wife at home more often. Whenever the kids were on vacation they were ferried to some out of the way film set and though the compromise suited both parents, it didn't necessarily suit either the kids or Chata, and the pressure inevitably built up for all concerned. Duke was doing everything he could to keep everyone happy; he accepted Josephine's compromise, made every effort to see his children, he did what Chata wanted, even allowing her mother to live in his home, and the patterns of discontent, formed early in his life, developed as he moved in his ever decreasing circles.

Strangely, given their history, Duke and Josie returned to their old and long gone, relationship of relaxed, deep and mutual friendship. She finally permitted him to return to the family home whenever he wanted to see the kids, and he found a haven of peace there, "I believe I got along better with Josie and the kids after we were divorced. I had the feeling that we actually spent more time with them, even though I was working as hard as before. I think what it was was that the fights stopped. I only saw how much hard feeling had built up after we split, and realised this had made the children nervous. Josie was a wonderful mother to them. I know that at first there were recriminations on her part, which I don't blame her for, but she forgave me as time went by, and one thing I am grateful for — she never made the kids hate me. I'll always be grateful for that. If I was intending to take the kids out I would ask Josie if she had anything planned first — I never wanted to force them into being with me if they didn't want to be, or out of a sense of duty. We had bad quarrels, but when it came to the kids, those quarrels stopped right there. No matter what, we always remained partners for the kids. I was always allowed to be part of their lives as they were growing. I was always there and Josie always knew she could call me. Josie and I were blessed with four great children." At least he hadn't repeated the pattern laid down by his own parents, and he and Josie remained the best of friends, sharing a great and permanent tenderness toward each other and their children.

His growing power in the industry coincided with ever growing problems at home, and Duke already foresaw the shadows of tragedy approaching. In that first year he made only two films, he had been contractually obliged to go through with those, but he spent the rest of his time in long production meetings with Jimmy Grant, planning *Angel*. He had discovered a new and exciting aspect of the film world, he was fascinated by it and he relished the new challenge that production offered. Chata found Duke's film world and in particular, Jimmy Grant, boring. The two men spent endless hours together on pre-production, engrossed in the task of developing scripts and hiring cast and crew. Frequently they worked from early morning to late night and Duke joked that they might as well move in together. His interest in the project bordered on obsession and Chata complained that he talked about the film constantly, that he talked about it all through breakfast, lunch and dinner, and the rest of the time he spent working on it. He became temperamental, both at home and at work where he had frequent outbursts of wild temper; he had learned more than his craft from John Ford. He found it difficult to give any direction without resorting to bad or insulting language. Unlike his mentor however, he was always quick to apologise. "I'm always apologizing to someone" was Duke's constant lament.

One person he never had to apologise to was Gail Russell, the stunningly beautiful female lead of *Angel and the Badman*. Her career had started in Hollywood long before she graduated from school. She explained to Duke that everything had happened too fast for her, one minute she was still an innocent, naïve schoolgirl and the next she was being groomed for stardom. He understood the enormous pressure the industry put on her, knew that before he hired her, other producers, directors and stars, all eager for her sexual favours, had taken advantage of her youth and innocence. She was beautiful but extremely fragile, sensitive and afraid to say "no" to anyone, she was unsuited to the cut throat world of Hollywood. John Wayne appeared to her like a knight in shining armour. He treated her with a natural gentleness and politeness that she was unused to, and it was inevitable that she would form a strong emotional and physical attachment toward a man she saw as her protector. She was obsessed by him and followed him around, hanging on his every word, longing for his soft kindness. Soon Hollywood was alight with gossip. Duke swore he never took advantage of the frail star who said of him, "The one word that defines Duke is "honest" he's an honest man, and he can't be otherwise."

He was willing to act the father figure, and he listened intently as she poured her heart and her problems out. He felt his customary need to protect the weak, and he continually advised, "Gail, you have just got to learn to say "no" to some of this shit." She was his employee, he had hired her, and he wanted her at her best for his first production. He also well remembered how it felt starting out in a rough world; at the start he had been little better equipped than her to cope, but he had survived. Now he felt the responsibility for helping another person overcome the difficulties. He had been helped along the way by Harry and Olive Carey, John Ford, and many others, now it fell to him to do his bit.

In the film she played a Quaker who converts Wayne, the violent gunman, into a peaceful man. It was widely rumoured that she led him into other activities off set as well. He had always been adept at covering his tracks, at avoiding scandal, but he never wavered in his denial of an affair with Gail Russell, even though the honeymoon period with Chata was fast receding into a dim and murky past! He was back in the old routine of arriving home at night exhausted and things were even worse now than when he had been with Josie. It was often as much as he could do to manage a bourbon and ice. If he bothered to eat anything he didn't bother to speak before collapsing into bed, and then he was too tired to satisfy the passionate Chata. He never wanted to go out, had no interest in parties and he became to her exactly what he had been to Josie before. Where Josie had wanted dinner parties and guests over all the time, Chata wanted to go night-clubbing. All he wanted was sleep; when a reporter asked the newly married couple what they did in their spare time Duke replied, "Chata reads. I sleep." She attempted to teach him better Spanish, he was too tired. She tried talking to him, he was too tired to listen. She tried babying him, offering massages and showers, he was just too tired. He might show Gail gentle consideration during working hours but he had nothing left for his bride when he got home. His industry, his profession, his life called and he went running, just as he always had, and always would. He thought Chata should adapt herself to his needs, and he argued that she had known what he was when she married him. He was unreasonable, for she could have had no way of understanding the depth of his passion, nor that his profession would always come first. She was not even sure that it was his career that was taking him away from her then, and she was much more jealous of Gail Russell's influence over her husband, than she was of his work.

When Chata moaned about Gail, he had no idea what the problem was. He hoped she would eventually get used to his co-stars because there was nothing he could do about the fact that he made films with beautiful women. Chata had instantly picked up on the rumours flying around Hollywood about him showering Miss Russell with attention, about him going to her dressing room alone, about how she frequently went to his. She was uneasy; possibly with some cause, about Miss Russell's intentions toward her husband. She resented the fact that he was willing to spend time with his co-star when all he did was fall asleep when he got home to her. She drank heavily every night while she waited for him and by the time he fell through the door exhausted she was already in a drunken rage, screaming at him, and demanding to know where he had been. Mary said, "Chata was so jealous that any time Gail even came toward his office, Duke headed out of the back door." He even asked Mary to make sure Gail understood that he felt protective toward her but nothing else, "but do it gently" he added.

The day filming finished Duke took the crew to a wrap party. Chata hadn't been part of the film and wasn't invited, but she wasn't used to the workings of the film community and she sat waiting for him to come home. At two in the morning she began ringing round desperately trying to find him. Finally she reached one of the crew who told her the party had ended some time before, and that Duke had taken Gail home. She rang Miss Russell's house and was told that the two of them had gone off to a motel! She was devastated and bolted the front door before going to bed. When he eventually arrived home she refused to let him in, "Chata, come on let me in. It's Duke." She didn't answer so he kicked a glass panel out of the door and let himself in, as he did in so many of his films. Chata raced to meet him brandishing a loaded automatic. She waved it in his face and told him she was going to kill him. Duke, falling-down drunk, was unconcerned and muttered under his breath that she was mad, that he hadn't betrayed her, that he didn't know what she was talking about. He collapsed on the couch but later said he was conscious of Chata and her mother "yabba-yabba-yabbing in the background." In fact only Chata's mother prevented murder that night when she pulled the weapon from her daughter's hand before any harm was done. Chata desperately shook him as she tried to rouse him from his stupor to demand why he had bought Miss Russell a car and why he had spent the night with her. "Oh, don't worry," he mumbled, "it's nothin' to get upset about." And that was all he ever said on the subject. He never mentioned Gail Russell either to his wife or the press until some years later when he commented that he believed it was unfair to drag Gail's name into his messy divorce, "If she'd testified against me, fine, but dragging my friends into it, and making white look black … poor Gail."

He felt truly sorry for her. He had paid a lot of money to buy her contract, but Republic were only paying her a small wage and she was working for very little on his film. He remembered how it felt when studios took you for granted, and he gave her money out of his own pocket, calling it a down payment on a car. "It was open and above board," he said later. "And sure — I did take Gail home after the party, but her mother and brother were there. I offered to drive her home in her car. We left the studio and were following some friends in another car….we lost them in traffic…We went to a café in Santa Monica and had something to eat and I ran into some old friends from Glendale and we were there a while … then I took her home …"

He was asked, "Were there any improprieties between you and Miss Russell?" … "Absolutely not." "Were you at a motel at any time that night?" … "Absolutely not."

"What happened when you arrived home?" … "I got home about one-thirty a.m. My wife refused to let me in. I could hear her and her Mother talking about me loudly. I rang the bell but they wouldn't open the door. Then I broke the glass panel and opened it myself. Later Chata and her mother, they came charging out. Chata had a .45 in her hand. She and her mother were fighting over it. Then it quietened down."

That was his version, given under oath at the divorce trial. At the time of the incident he hadn't even been married a year and he couldn't understand why his wife was so jealous. She must have known how much he loved her, surely, she must have known. He knew now that she hadn't and that he should have told her instead of falling asleep.

There was a long way to go and much heartache before reaching that divorce. He and Chata were always fighting and then making up again. She was drinking almost as much as he did himself, and if she hadn't been an alcoholic when they first met, she was now, and evil with it. She had been raised in a family where it was the custom to resort to violence as a speedy solution to life's problems. He often appeared at work covered in scratches and bruises. Gentle, motherly Mary, once joked, "Looks like someone got even with you," when he arrived at Republic with a deep gash across his face. He answered, "Yeah, my wife," as he walked past, eyes fixed straight ahead. He called her into his office to explain that Chata had been drunk at a party and had insulted other guests, "I felt embarrassed and suggested we leave. She screamed that she was having a great time and wanted to stay. When she refused to go quietly I picked her up and carried her out to the car." The argument became more heated and she reached across to scratch him across the cheek. When they got home, he locked her in her room, "Next morning she couldn't even remember having been at a party. I'm really worried about her."

Mary felt guilty about her earlier comment, "But, Duke, I thought this was a love match."

He cried sadly, "So did I."

Despite the coldness of his own childhood he had never known physical abuse and now he didn't know what to do when his wife lashed out wildly at him. He didn't even know what he did to enrage her but he hoped the tension would pass once she came to accept his world and his devotion to his craft, once she got used to him and his working patterns. When he wasn't working he intended to devote every second of his day to her and he wasn't unduly worried at first. She might hit out at him when she was drunk or upset but she could also make him feel better than anyone else ever had. He loved making everything right again, wherever they happened to be; putting the world to rights was the best part of being with his fiery wife.

But things didn't go well and he didn't make things right often enough. Instead he got tied up in post-production problems on *Angel* and abandoned Chata to her own temper for long stretches. Meanwhile he bitterly resented his ever present mother-in-law who had become a source of constant irritation to him. When he complained to Chata, asking her to send her mother home so they might have a chance at building a proper marriage she just shrugged.

Another major problem turned out to be his fastidious cleanliness. He liked the feel of his skin after showering, he liked to dress in fresh, clean smelling clothes. People always noticed and commented that he smelt so good. Chata, on the other hand, was less than fussy, either about showering or the washing of her clothes. She cut her own hair and applied her make-up without caring how she actually looked. At first he didn't comment about that or about the fact that she didn't shave her legs, but Mary recalled, "It drove him nuts but he was afraid to say anything to her, he didn't want to hurt her feelings!" Eventually Mary was called in to intervene on his behalf and he soon noticed Chata was washing and shaving a little more regularly. It had been fairly painless to overcome. Getting rid of her mother was another matter entirely, she was a problem no one else could help him with.

It was often Senora Ceballos who triggered Chata's jealous rages when they had been drinking. She convinced her daughter that a man like

Duke, working with so many beautiful women, could not possibly remain faithful. Once her suspicions were aroused Chata turned into a woman possessed as she attacked her unsuspecting husband. She was furious with her mother for bringing the subject up, but mad at him in case she was right. Living at home was reminiscent of his childhood and his days with Josie, where he was constantly dragged into battles against his will. He became morose, depressed and difficult to handle as a result. He was angry, restless and unhappy, "I turned into a grouchy old bear." Everyone close to him agreed and did their best to stay out of his way.

Worse followed as Chata's jealous nature turned every leading lady became a threat. She really didn't know her husband very well. He still clung to all the old-fashioned values that his parents had taught him, Mid-western virtues, deeply held. He longed for nothing more than the chance to work hard and come home to a peaceful, loving wife. If she had only understood who he really was their marriage might have survived. She saw the handsome film star surrounded by beautiful women, and she knew and understood all about men ... she had been bought by such men. But she didn't know him at all. And he began doing what he had always done when he could find no peace, he stayed away, longer and more often, following patterns established when he was a child. The longer he stayed away the greater was Chata's fury when he got back. After each uncontrolled outburst she cried and begged his forgiveness. He was helpless in the face of her tears and gave in, promising to change his ways, to spend more time at home, with her. They both kept their promises as long as they could before it started over again, and their marriage had a fascinating pattern that neither was able to break. Chata got drunk, they fought, she cried, they made up and then, to celebrate, she started drinking again.

He hired Gail Russell again to work with him in *Wake of the Red Witch*. In the light of Chata's suspicious nature and their failing marriage, it was a really foolhardy thing to do, and it triggered many violent outbursts. Chata had made him promises that she couldn't keep, and he had made promises she believed he broke. Either his work or Miss Russell was getting his best, Chata neither knew nor cared which it was, he wasn't there for her when she needed him. She began taking lovers and drinking more, sparking terrible times between them. Right from the start everyone knew about their fiery relationship, all his friends warned him to steer clear and no one expected the marriage to last. He never listened to a word against her and couldn't even consider this marriage failing. He was irresistibly drawn back to her every time they parted, loving her intensely when she rushed headlong into his outstretched arms, loving her wildly as they forgave each other once more. And yet he hated the explosion of anger and violence that inevitably followed. She had been swept up into his way of life. Whatever she had been before he knew her, she had never been exposed to alcohol, as she now was. Her attorney later said, "She became enmeshed in a whiskey-soaked atmosphere."

Duke might worry about her drink-sodden days and nights but he still left her alone to go off on location, where he concentrated on making films. All through those exciting, passionate but violent days with her, he was busy establishing himself as a leading man, pulling himself up by sheer effort until he was at the very top of his profession. He was successful at last and, despite their heated arguments, he could never see this time as being all bad. He had always been dedicated to his career but he would never again permit anything to distract him from it and Hollywood took everything he had to give for the next thirty years.

Descriptions such as "Tall in the saddle," "man of action," "American institution," were increasingly applied to him. He acted the Greek hero of tragic legend, acted in comedies, in action films, in seafaring adventures, westerns, war films, and he developed his own technique through them all. His roles came alive, often with a minimum use of words and a personal style he had long been developing and learning from the master, John Ford. He had been defined as the western star but the films he made during the years he was with Chata tended to be erotic, realistic and in them he demonstrated a greater flexibility as an actor. His range and professionalism were given full stretch during this period when he turned out film after film, very few of which were westerns. He worked constantly, with hardly any rest. It was a period of wild, wild times with Chata and of sheer exhaustion.

Film makers, critics and audiences alike, referred constantly to his moral and physical stature, and he was often portrayed as the huge, hard, unyielding figure of authority. But both Duke himself and the characters he played often spoke with irony about his height and toughness. He knew he couldn't play the bluff, romantic leading man for much longer, and he began working out a different characterisation, one which could survive long after he was finished as a romantic lead. There was a more fatherly side to his best performances of the period, he was often a man who taught his wisdom to the next generation, even if that only meant teaching them to avoid the mistakes he had made. He began rounding and filling out the heroic image. He promoted his softness and introduced an almost maternal element to the films in which he had no female lead. He started contrasting his obviously physical hardness with a less obvious, soft vulnerability and a willingness to nurture, he became less the protector, hunter and killer, and more the comforter. It was a strangely unique combination. Possibly, because he pandered to Chata's insecurities, having surprisingly few sexual encounters in the films made during the years he was with her, he was left free to develop what became his defining role.

Despite the fact that Chata hated him, it was Jimmy Grant who helped Duke attain the characterisation he had been searching for, and it was he who wrote the flexibility and tenderness into the tough, uncompromising facade. These were personality traits very close to Duke's own, and Grant successfully picked out the essence of the man in his scripts where his toughness was never shown as just a matter of hard masculinity, but rather, of an ability to endure punishment and carry on to do what has to be done. The character devised in Grant's screenplays could be reinvented over and over again; neither age, nor later, illness, made any difference. The strength of the character was tied not to toughness, size or handsomeness, but simply to an ability to endure pain and survive. It suited the Wayne persona to perfection. His physical presence might be his biggest asset but Duke was a man who could play the father figure from an early age, who easily assumed the responsibility of teaching children and soldiers under his command, who might be tough, but could also be tender, humorous, sad and miserable, moody and difficult, a lover or a loner, a simple fighter or complex man of deep obsessions. Unfailingly, the persona had to be heroic, a professional who got the job done. He appeared the professional on screen and he emerged as a fine actor in a variety of roles, moving easily from the light-hearted, simple man, to the darker more mature one. Through them all, where Grant wrote the lines, he was understated. Ford had told him, "Less is more," it was how Grant wrote and the way Duke was. He knew he appeared to best advantage when he had few words to say and he developed his acting skills based on that principle. His critics accused him of being unable to act at all, and he was self-deprecating about his talent, laughing loudly when he said, "Many fine actors get lost in their parts ...," long pause, hard John Wayne stare ... "you seldom see that happen to me ... The man I play can be cruel, tough or tender, but never petty or small. Everyone in my audience wants to identify with that kind of character. He may be bad, but if he's bad he's bad. He's no mean little winner."

A reporter asked him why his character was so popular, had it anything to do with his acting style? Duke offered a simple answer, "Number one, I like people. I think that shows, and I think it has a lot to do with it. And number two, I've been very lucky with the people I've worked with. Jack Ford, Howard Hawks, Henry Hathaway, and Raoul Walsh, were just great for me. They developed an aura in their pictures ... well ... the younger ones just don't get that anymore … they were just great for me … and it mattered to them, what a man was. That man dealt with basic emotions, he hated, loved, got angry, felt kind. It was what people wanted to do. They come and do it right along with me, or through watching me on screen." He rarely mentioned his own effort when trying to explain his success to reporters, but that didn't mean he didn't understand the power of his understated performance. He created the legend via his own personality, his own instinct, as much as through Grant's words and the greatest directors of his day. It was created through his personal devotion to a career that destroyed everything else around him, and by hard, hard effort. The persona remained immensely popular with audiences. They experienced it instinctively rather than through the superfluous use of words; they knew who he was, could feel his pain, recognise his ability to endure, knew they were safe in his hands. Words were unnecessary, less was more. And just as it mattered to him what a man was, so it mattered to the people sitting dreaming in the darkness of the theatres. *He* mattered to them.

Duke was busy planning his future and all his next moves, devising his persona when he was called once more by John Ford who told him he needed to see him urgently. When Ford called he went running. As the war was still raging at the time he was surprised to hear the directors voice and asked him when he'd been discharged, Ford told him he hadn't been but he was making a film for the navy about a squadron of PT boats in the Pacific, a patriotic story of duty and sacrifice. Ford enthused it would not be just another war movie, but one that reflected America's heroic tradition, one that recorded history as it happened, and was to be made alongside the men living through it. He was offering Duke another chance to do his bit for the war effort and told him, "This won't be your typical gung-ho Wayne-hero movie. I'm using navy personnel wherever I can. There will be no exaggeration of the story." Still, the first thing he did was call the gung-ho hero to offer him a part. Whatever story he wanted to tell he recognised it would work best, and do better box-office with Duke in it. He needed a volatile, impulsive boy who was more than ready to do his duty, a character undisturbed by the idea of sacrifice, who was ready to die performing any heroic deed. Who could play that boy better than John Wayne? So he made the urgent call and Duke put himself at Ford's immediate disposal, dropping every other commitment.

When he called at Ford's office Frank Wead, who had written the screenplay, was already there. He was known to everybody as "Spig." He had served in the navy during World War One, been a career officer and a pioneer of naval aviation. He had fought for the development of the aircraft carrier in America. He was a real hero. In 1927 he had fallen down the stairs and been left paralyzed. (Later Duke played the part of Spig in the film *Wings of Eagles*). Wead was a natural story teller who Ford had known for many years. He began writing after his accident in an attempt to keep his mind busy, but by 1930 he had become a successful writer of screenplays and was a well known Hollywood fixture. Like all Ford's friends, Spig was a big drinker, heavy gambler, was reckless and wild, and attracted everyone who came near him. When Duke walked into the meeting he was awed to find himself in the presence of a real navy hero.

Robert Montgomery, who was to be the star of the film and was a serving naval officer, was also there. All three men were on leave from their war time duties to make the film *They Were Expendable*, and were dressed in naval uniform. Duke arrived in casual clothes. He had just finished work on one film and was about to embark on his production career, and he was immediately struck by feelings of inadequacy. As Ford began outlining his plans for the film with great enthusiasm he noticed how subdued his star was. Duke appeared to be sulking, as only he could. The others sat talking and drinking heavily as Wead took notes. Duke added nothing to the conversation and volunteered none of his usual banter, but he wasn't sulking, he was suffering the deepest feelings of embarrassment and guilt as he sat amongst naval officers talking about making a film about real war heroes. He was living his recurring nightmare, and had suddenly, and without any warning, come face to face with his own reality. Ford, that cruellest of tormentors, knew exactly what the problem was. But for once he hadn't intended to hurt, and when Duke excused himself to go to the bathroom he dismissed Wead and Montgomery. When he came back into the room he found himself alone with the director, Ford knew big tough Duke Wayne had been crying and he took pity on him. He pushed him toward a chair saying, "You big dumb bastard, we've got a film to make. In three weeks we are on location and you better be there. You can bring the fat Mexican with you if you want, but be there. I'm going to work your ass off on this one Marion, and you're not going to let me down … and another thing when I ask you to come to a meeting I expect you to talk up, I need to know how you feel about it too." He continued attacking him in his brusque manner and Duke knew instant relief. He relaxed as they discussed the film. He was shocked the old man was allowing him to take Chata along, wives were normally forbidden on Ford sets, and instinctively knew things were going to get rough.

Ford was both producer and director on *They Were Expendable* and Duke studied him at work, as he always had, standing at his shoulder, watching the master, taking note, learning how to do two or three things at once, learning to juggle all the different elements involved in putting a film together. He saw stories in literary terms, he didn't experience reality through sight but through emotion and he had to learn about picture composition and pictorial values by studying those directors who were gifted. It didn't matter to him that he wasn't a natural like his mentor, that it didn't come easy to him, he believed he could learn enough by watching closely. For him the essential prerequisite to success was hard work and he slugged away, determined and never wavering in his effort.

Determined and never wavering ... As he stood at the side of the master of composition, the first seeds of John Wayne's obsession took root. Whilst he studied Ford producing and directing *They Were Expendable*, a film about sacrifice and duty, he suddenly had his own blinding vision and the dream of making a film about the battle of the Alamo began. He too could see the bigger picture of honour, bravery, heroism, duty and above everything else, sacrifice. And from the mid 1940's onward he carried the vision with him everywhere he went. He had already been planning his future before Ford called him up for this film, he was over forty and knew he had to get into production. He didn't want to struggle into old age, gradually disintegrating before the camera, "I have much work to do and a lot of life to live. I intend to be around motion pictures for a while yet and when I begin to creak at the hinges and take on the appearance of a water buffalo, I'll play character parts. Because I know my trade as well as the next man in Hollywood, I'll direct and produce. But no matter what, I'll always be part of the picture industry. It has been my life, and I love it."

He was in the process of setting up his own production company just so he could keep his place in the world he loved. But now there was more to it than that, he desperately wanted to make his own tribute to brave men. In the meantime there was much to learn. He studied every move Ford made, how he planned everything on paper, how explosions were mapped out, how each scene was shot to fit with the others, how he continually improvised, continually made Wead rewrite scenes, using each situation as it developed.

Both Duke and Ford were pleased to be back working with old friend Ward Bond who had a supporting role in the film. Pre-production was a light hearted time with Duke generally at the centre of the fun. Then suddenly the mood changed when Ford became restless, apparently unable to forget his men, away fighting the real battles. As usual Duke found himself the target of his spleen, but the treatment dished out this time was much harsher than normal as the director at last released the resentment he felt toward him for not going to war. He had never said much about it before, now he let him know how angry he was about his failure.

The other actors watched in horror as Duke was reduced to a quivering pulp as he was bullied without pity, "He shredded my flesh. But he knew what he was doing." Ford certainly knew where to hit him to get the truest performance out of him, and he gauged his ultra sensitive spot with precision. He was completely vulnerable to the war issue, Ford knew it, drew a bead and shot directly at it. He moaned at him all day and long into every night, constantly referring to him as a dumb oaf, and telling him he had no idea how to move like a real sailor. If anything was designed to touch the rawest of nerves that was it. He could never be a real sailor now of course, and there was the nub of the matter. Ford had finally come out and said it, drawing everyone's attention to it, reducing hero to coward in one well-chosen sentence. But if there was one ounce of pride in Duke, it was in his ability to move well. He had no confidence about anything else, but he had worked so hard at developing unique movements, and he had already starred in a number of successful war films, as marines, sailors, soldiers, and flyers. He knew that if he could do nothing else, he could move well, at least he looked like a hero. He took the bullying in his stride, refusing to show the slightest resentment or reaction, and even when Ford commented loudly before the assembled cast that Duke couldn't salute properly, he merely bit his lip and held himself in. Although the director constantly stepped over the line of common decency it was Montgomery, not Duke, who finally reacted. He walked toward Ford, placed his hands on either side of his chair and leaned forward to whisper, "Don't ever talk to Duke like that again in front of me. You should be ashamed of yourself." The set came to an abrupt and stunned standstill. Cast and crew held their breath, but the expected explosion never came, instead Ford seemed to calm down for a while. The attacks were resumed later with increased brutality, but only when Montgomery wasn't around.

When the scene in which Duke's boat is strafed by machine gun fire was filmed, the windshield shattered, spraying glass up into his face, cutting it deeply. Duke, never one to suffer fools gladly, chased the technician who had fitted a real glass windshield round the set with a hammer. Eventually Ford called a halt, sternly ordering Duke to leave his crew alone. He refused to take the star's part or defend his interest. Duke felt humiliated and, for perhaps the first time, he rounded on Coach to argue heatedly as he tried to make his point. To spectators it was painfully obvious that he idolized the director, that he was hurt, and needed and expected some words of comfort. Ford couldn't give it; it would have been unmanly and weak. Duke had been angry because his face hurt, Ford really didn't care. Pain seemed to go a long way to ensuring he got a good performance out of Duke and that was all that mattered to him. Duke suspected his deep affection was returned in some measure, that his talent was valued, but he always needed more tangible demonstrations of concern that were so rarely forthcoming from the Master.

The war ended just before the film premiered. The critics were sure that no matter how artistic or well made it was, people wouldn't be willing to pay to see another war picture, they were sure it had come a few months too late. Fortunately for the success of the film Duke had demanded his part was expanded, giving it more emotion so it became more of a personal story and less of a documentary. Ford trusted Duke's judgement on what the public wanted and had accepted a lesson from the pupil. When it was finally released, the Wayne formula worked in the film's favour. He had assessed the country's mood better than Ford or the critics and the public took no notice of anything other than that fact that here was another John Wayne adventure. It was business as usual at box-office.

Ford had been immensely important to his early development but Duke was now establishing his own identity as he steadily came out of the director's shadow. He needed him less, and even though he believed he owed everything to him and remained tied to him in his own consciousness, from that point on the relationship between them underwent subtle shifts. In 1945 Duke was still the best son and Ford the stern father, but as his stature grew in the industry it became less easy for the director to intimidate him. On the set of *They Were Expendable* Duke had discovered he could give voice to his own opinions, could make demands, could even argue, and his view would get some respect. The end of filming exactly coincided with his emerging position in Hollywood. He now held his future securely in his own hands. Ford's influence declined and even Republic lost control as Duke saw for the first time that his popularity was not dependant on anyone else. The knowledge released him and allowed him to begin pouring his time and energy into his new obsession, making his own films.

Yates, who trusted Duke's judgement and was now scared of losing him, signed another agreement, giving him control of the films he made at Republic. He now worked as an independent within the security of the studio set up. One of his first actions under his new contract was to hire Mary as his personal assistant. She had been born in Missouri and had dreamed of a career in law but dropped out of school when she realised that America wasn't ready for female lawyers, and in 1936 took a job in Republic's typing pool instead. During the intervening years she and Duke built up a strong working relationship and when he told her in 1939 that he would one day ask her to be his PA she had known he would keep his word. Finally, in 1946 he offered the promised job and she went to work for him, remaining loyal to him from then on, standing by him through thick and thin, ever faithful, always there when he needed someone to talk to, always firmly on his side. She picked up the pieces after each of his romantic disasters, saw him through economic failure, was with him through every triumph and every disappointment, through political controversy and ill health. She worked for him as a paid member of his staff, she was also one of the best friends he ever had, bestowing an unwavering loyalty on him. She never faltered and Duke trusted her, "My father told me when I was a boy, not to expect gratitude or loyalty, and I'd never be disappointed. I knew he had been hurt many times. But I took his advice, and he was right." In Mary's case he was never let down. She never betrayed his trust, and she never hurt him. When she talked about him her eyes shone, and the reason for her devotion was simple, "You just couldn't possibly encounter in one lifetime more than one human being like this. No matter how famous he became, he never thought he was anything special. Nothing ever altered our relationship. He is considerate of all his staff, of all his crew on every film. He knows everyone by name, who their families are, what their jobs are, what ailments each might have, he talks to each and every one of them every day. He has gathered around him a fairly regular staff and crew, and if any of them are ever in trouble he is always the first there offering his help, either financial, or whatever they might need. On *McQ* a stuntman turned a car over, it was Duke who ran the fastest to get him out. He completely spoils me, I have never had any desire to work anywhere else, no matter how much money I might be offered."

Mary watched him develop as a professional, "There's a regular lifestyle he has worked out on location. Many of the crew have worked with him for years, they all make it easy for you when you're a newcomer. It's sort of like his family. Usually Mr Wayne has dinner with Luster Bayless, his wardrobe man, Dave Grayson, his make-up man, and Jack Casey who handles publicity. It's usually early because he likes to get up so early the next morning." She knew how he liked his day organised when he was on location and she made sure nothing got in his way. He loved her simply because she was as professional as he was himself, "When people you work with do their job and still have time to smile and get along with others ... well, they're the people I want around."

As he worked non-stop through the war planning his next moves and gathering around him the staff he wanted he was busy generating a safe position for himself within the industry. The result of his effort during those years produced dividends so much greater than any of them ever dreamed possible. By 1946 he was grossing over one million dollars a year, paid $175,000 per picture. He was full of plans for his blossoming career.

Then Ford came home from the war offering him the chance to star in his next series of pictures which would reflect his mythical vision of the strange beauty of war and the way men bonded and interacted during conflict. Naturally Duke was the biggest part of his plan, for with him came receipts. He wanted to paint the picture but needed Duke to ensure people came to see it; he too had learned a valuable lesson from *They Were Expendable*, it seemed the public could never get enough of John Wayne. He wanted to use him now in a series of films, not based on The Second World War, but on tales of the United States Cavalry, in stories set back in time and employing the western imagery that he so loved. He believed that the impending death of any soldier must arouse great emotion in the characters involved and also in the watching public. He knew his old pupil was adept at evoking such emotion but had been surprised to discover he had also somehow become the embodiment of the American fighting man. And Duke found he had to put his own plans on the back burner. He was still tied to Ford's vision. Throughout the war he had unfailingly portrayed men true to a code, men of honour and courage. His performance had forged an unbreakable bond with his audience. When he starred in a film they knew what to expect. It was those expectations that Ford now wanted to tap into.

As a man Duke had been shy and lonely most of his life, a man of simple pleasures, easily moved to either tears or laughter, happiness or anger, and though he tried to live according to his own strict moral code, he was really nothing like the hero of his films and he found the expectations of Ford and his public weighed heavily as he strove to meet their demands. Increasingly, living the dream involved adapting his personality, toughening up to become the man everyone wanted him to be. Many Hollywood stars become legends, but few of those legends ever reflect the real person the way his came to. He was by no means perfect. He had legendary weaknesses and it took the most tremendous willpower to live his life according to the expectations of others, took heroic effort even when he was not always a real hero.

And he was far from the hero at home where his life had come to resemble a chaotic soap-opera. He and Chata were either loving and tremendously tender toward each other, or they were screaming and fighting, both hot tempered and stubborn. When they divorced Chata sited one incident when she had been inside the house. She heard a loud noise coming from the back and went to investigate. She found Duke repeatedly throwing a patio table against the door because she hadn't gone out to him when he called her. He never denied his violent streak, but it was rare for him to direct it at anyone but himself. Chata found to her cost that ignoring him unfailingly ignited the short fuse.

The one thing she did that always drove him crazy was run back to Mexico just when he wanted to talk things over with her. Everyone who knew him, knew his fiery, wild temper and became accustomed to the sudden flare up, followed by the almost instant apology, and his burning desire to put things right. He couldn't follow his normal course of action with his wife, because she never waited for the charming apology. Once he raised his voice, Chata flew, "Mrs Wayne made it a practice to find every excuse to stay away from me. I loved her deeply, but we were like a pair of volatile chemicals continually thrown together to create a series of almighty explosions, each one destroyed us a little bit more."

They were both consuming vast amounts of alcohol. When they drank together she stirred him to the greatest anger, and despite his own natural softness, he exploded violently also. Luckily, neither usually had much recollection of such incidents, though she once accused him of dragging her off the bed by her hair. When Chata got drunk she enraged him. When she was drunk she told him about her other men and played on his weaknesses, pushing him, stinging his ego and hurting him until he could take no more. Then he lashed out, usually verbally, sometimes physically, in self defence. Her actions were all designed to arouse his jealousy and stimulate him into showing how much he cared. All she did was arouse his blind rage and she said, "He often bashed me." In fact the evidence all pointed the other way and he later implied that her mother was the one in the household who generally did the beating. He insisted he couldn't remember ever hitting Chata but he was never quite sure what depths he sank to when he was drunk. The thought that he might have struck her haunted many of his darkest dreams. The reality was that they carried the equal bruises of a fragile marriage.

Love was always the prime mover in Duke's life. When he went home after exerting enormous amounts of self-discipline on location, he wanted nothing more than to relax, make love all night and have some quiet fun playing cards or chess during the day. Chata, who had been waiting longingly for his return, burned to go out and party as soon as he walked through the door. It became a constant problem for him because he hated the Hollywood gatherings that she favoured. When he gave in and took her out, he drank heavily to alleviate the boredom, usually remaining just sober enough to be embarrassed by her outrageous behaviour. At the first hint of trouble he started shouting at her to stop showing him up. He anticipated a scene and almost triggered it himself in his desperate attempts to keep her quiet and all their wildest fights inevitably began at parties in front of his friends. He felt deep shame as he warded her blows off, forced to defend himself without honour as she kicked and scratched like a wildcat. Other guests supported his claim that the only time he was ever rough was in his own defence. However he knew he wasn't always the innocent party, or the injured one either. And whenever he contemplated his life with Chata it was with regret.

1947 became a year of emotional turmoil at home. He was forty and deeply unhappy in his marriage. Both his age and his unhappiness led to a great outpouring of physical and emotional activity as he once more turned to work for release. The result was three of the best films he ever made, *Fort Apache*, *Three Godfathers*, and *Red River*. He had assumed he was in the twilight of his career; as it turned out he was at the blaze of his noon. In this single year he became an actor, acknowledged finally even by his fiercest critics, after almost twenty years in the business. The average studio life of film stars was short, perhaps five years, some superstars like Gable, managed to last fifteen, and then there was Duke, already twenty years down the line and only just about to become the biggest box-office sensation of all time. Everything that took place before was only a prelude to what followed now, and which amazingly continued to the time he could no longer work due to ill-health, some fifty years after first meeting John Ford on the set of *Mother MacRee*. 1947 was the miracle year that changed his life forever. He had never been able to find any explanation for what happened. His energy had been drained by his domestic situation and his continuous arguments at Republic, he was depressed by the reception of his first production, *Angel and the Badman*, yet somehow what he turned out against all the odds then took him to the top of his profession and gave him a position of huge power in Hollywood. Each picture was far from the routine western he had previously been associated with, each was highly wrought and complex, and in them he was directed by two very demanding men who required huge amounts of physical and emotional effort. With utter indifference to his mental fatigue and physical exhaustion he threw himself at their demands to create not one but three great films. From somewhere he had acquired a self discipline that enabled him to perform the miracle, but neither he nor the directors ever knew how he managed it.

Fort Apache, a Ford movie, was shot entirely on location in Monument Valley, and starred Duke, Henry Fonda and Shirley Temple. The location was rugged, and even the two biggest stars of the day shared a shower block with forty other men. Duke continued to enjoy the camaraderie and Michael said of his dad, "He knew what space he occupied. He told me, "When you start believing your own bullshit, that's when you're in big trouble." Duke enjoyed the silent, peaceful nights, where the only sound came from the film crew and raucous stars, and said, "Very occasionally, out in the distance, you could hear Indians singing their traditional songs … I just loved it out there after the pressure I was under at home. Took me some weeks before I could start to relax in that wonderful atmosphere and I guess Jack found me a little more difficult than normal …"

Duke played Captain York, a charismatic leader of men. Fonda represented the politics of the army. Together they provided the imagery of personal appeal versus a system of explicit law. A passionate, warm, friendly man, York was flexible toward his men. He didn't live by regulation, nor did he expect the soldiers to. Fonda, as Colonel Thursday, was strict, disciplined, and constantly criticises York and the men, although he was ignorant of the West and its ways. With no knowledge of the Indian, he believed humiliation and conquest were necessary to deal with them. York got along with them through respect and understanding. Thursday wanted to wipe the Apache out for good, and planned to use York as a decoy, forcing him to break his word to Cochise to trap him. When he refuses his orders, Thursday tells him there is no such thing as honour when dealing with Indians, York replies, "There is to me."

A student later asked him what he had been thinking about when he did the scene where he threw down his gauntlet at Thursday's feet, "I meant it. My honour was being forsaken, I had made certain suggestions that the Indians had agreed to, and this bastard was double-crossing them. It's a funny thing, the Indians now are against me, but I believe I always gave the Indian his human dignity in my films. I never allowed myself at any time to do anything that would take their dignity away from them, and that to me, is the most important thing in a man."

Shirley Temple and her new husband John Agar also starred in the film and Ford was his usual aggressive self to the newcomers. Agar hated the experience and was on the point of quitting after a particularly harrowing day. He was already packing his things when Duke raced to the rescue. He had been watching Agar for days and recognised the signs of trouble.

"Mr Wayne I just can't take any more. I can't stand him another day."

"Now just hold on a minute there. Mr Ford insulting you don't mean he don't like you or admire you. It's when he doesn't insult you you need to worry. Let me tell you about what he did to me on *Stagecoach*, and on plenty other occasions too." He explained Ford's technique to get the performance he wanted, telling Agar that it didn't matter to him whether he was dealing with a newcomer or a veteran. He told him it would soon be his turn to meet Ford's displeasure and that he should just get on with his job. He ran over Agar's lines with him, as Yak had done with him so long ago, went out riding with him and gave him some of the other lessons he had received from the stuntman. In fact, although Ford didn't turn on him, Duke believed the only reason he was left alone was because Coach knew how depressed he was about Chata.

When Ward Bond arrived on location he paid the pilot of the light aircraft to buzz the set before landing. Duke glanced up, knowing who it was, and commented knowingly to Agar, "Well, I guess you can relax now, he's found another whipping boy!" Duke treated most young stars with warm, good natured generosity. Agar went on to star in many of his next films and remained completely loyal, willing to do anything for Duke, "I'd go to hell and back for him. No one ever worked harder than him. I'm not sure who I admire most, John Wayne the person, or John Wayne the dedicated actor. Let's just say he is about the best human being I have ever known."

Fort Apache, a film about combat, military tradition and belief in absolute order, was largely based on Ford's own World War 2 experiences. Some years after making it he was asked, "'When the legend becomes fact print the legend' is a line from *The Man Who Shot Liberty Valance* — it could equally apply to *Fort Apache* — Do you agree with the sentiment?"

He replied, "Yes, because I think it's good for the country. We have a lot of people who were supposed to be great heroes, and you know damn well they weren't. But it's good for the country to have heroes to look up to." Whilst he was talking about *Fort Apache* he could equally have been speaking about how the public perceived his protégé. He believed that in Duke he had created a hero for the country to look up to, it did not matter to him that it wasn't a realistic vision, "Print the legend," and relentlessly forge the ultimate figure of all Western mythology. Duke also naturally believed in the legend, "Hell! I think it's kind of silly to put the cowboy on the psychiatrists couch. What's the point in ruining people's folklore? The cowboys laughed lustily, and they hated heartily. That's the truth, and that is what I hope I showed. Remember, the man on horseback conquered the world. In those days life was a matter of survival, and sometimes you had to be a bit of a bastard to make it. I hope I showed that too."

Captain York wasn't Duke's idea of a good part. He watched old friend Fonda strutting around and shouting a lot, Agar getting the girl, Victor McLaglen and Bond getting the humour, "All I had to do was quietly, and with whatever dignity I could, display a sense of honour, duty and service." They were the crumbs Ford threw and he accepted them gratefully, knowing he would never be a star in the eyes of the genius. Still the film was praised by all as a classic western, and the critics loved his performance, describing him as powerful, forthright and exquisitely brave. There was no other recognition of his effort, he received no Oscar nomination.

After completing *Fort Apache*, Ford, Wayne and Fonda went off sailing together along the Mexican coast to relax. Duke hadn't enjoyed working on the film, partly because he didn't like his part, partly because of the trouble he was having with his wife, but also because he hadn't got on with Ford's brother, Eddie O'Fearna, who had been on location with them, and who made things more uncomfortable than usual. There had been an unusual amount of tension between cast and crew and little of the normal fun, and even Ford and Bond had argued a lot, with Ford calling Bond "big and double ugly" all the time. It had been hot and unbearably uncomfortable, with frequent high winds and desert storms. Ford had been in a particularly difficult mood and Duke believed the physical conditions they encountered had a lot to do with his temper. As soon as they left Monument Valley Ford started drinking heavily and by the time they arrived in Mexican waters he was too drunk to leave the boat. Duke couldn't relax, neither did he want to go home. He wasn't sure what he wanted to do. It was time for another period of thorough self-examination and another change of direction.

Before embarking on *Fort Apache* he had started work with Howard Hawks on *Red River*, the film that finally established him as an actor, (when Ford saw the result of their collaboration he commented wryly, "I never knew the big son of a bitch could act!") Duke was looking forward to getting back to the set where he felt appreciated. Hawks had been saying publicly that he couldn't make this film without him and when he heard that he felt a little less sorry for himself and more confident about his long-term position in the industry.

At home things had deteriorated with Chata going out of her way to cause him as much pain and public humiliation as possible. Like Ford, she knew exactly where to hit him, seeing quite clearly that his pride in his rugged masculinity was his Achilles heel. She played on his anxieties and aroused his jealousy at every turn, taking delight in storming out of the house mid argument to race off to a Hollywood bar where she knew she would be seen picking up strangers. Frequently she turned up in Las Vegas with a new lover in tow. It was important that he knew about her exploits, and she did her best to embarrass him, "I did love him, but he left me alone too often and I was lonely."

And he still loved her. In the interludes between their fights he still knew moments of intense passion and tenderness toward her, but he was not so much in love that he would consent to making just one movie a year as she demanded. He wanted her, but on his own terms. Shades of his relationship with Josie, but in many ways it was worse for Chata. He wanted more children but their dream of starting a new family remained unfulfilled. She later used that as a slur on his manhood, telling anyone who would listen that age was the problem and that he was impotent. He continued to tell her that he would make just one more movie and then settle down with her to make babies. But films, and not Chata, were his destiny and he always had "just one more picture" to do. Nothing could stop him and he could never foresee the day when there would be no more films to make.

Offers flooded in, all the studios wanted him. He had proved his worth as a money earner and by the second year of his marriage to Chata he was finally enjoying his position in the industry. His head told him it wasn't going to be snatched away, but still, in his heart, he was never quite certain. He refused to take anything for granted and accepted most of the offers that came his way. As long as he was working he felt secure. The 1940's was the decade of the Western in Hollywood, *Stagecoach* had reopened that territory, and Duke's position within the genre was at an all time high. He was recognised as the cowboy, and if a studio was going to spend millions making a Western, the first name that sprang to the producer's mind was "John Wayne." Having his name on the credits would guarantee the success of the movie, he would earn millions for them and he was always available. He grabbed every chance they offered with both hands. The work piled up as he took on more and more.

Although Chata was left further behind, his children became an increasingly important part of his life and, picture or no picture, he always made time for them. They were far more flexible than Chata, they made fewer demands and were more prepared to go on location with him. He enjoyed their company and liked having them around his film sets. Josie was happy to let them go with him too, she knew how lonely he had become and how much the kids lifted him. One or other of them generally accompanied him wherever he happened to be in the world, and as they went away with him more often, eventually, almost inevitably, the lives of his boys became enmeshed in his as they developed their own careers in the movie industry. Duke couldn't have been happier or prouder as he began to share his greatest passion with them. Chata often objected about the time he spent with them, about the fun he shared with each, but even though she was jealous of their place in his heart, she was also fully aware that the movie industry was her biggest rival. He was fanatical about working, as he always had been, but now he began trying to justify his efforts by saying he had two families to support, debts and taxes to pay, a lifestyle to support. He never admitted, even to himself, that he slaved because he had to, because work was the love of his life. He couldn't do anything about it, not even though it meant loosing everything else that he cared about.

Before he had even seen the edited version of *Fort Apache* he was putting the finishing touches to *Red River*. Originally the film was to star Gary Cooper, but he had turned down the part of Tom Dunson at the last minute, believing the obsessed and cruel character wasn't right for him. He had also probably noticed that Dunson was missing from the action for long periods. Cooper hadn't been interested that Hawks planned turning the story into a classically complex saga about man's relationships, territorial expansion, economic survival, about matters closely tied to the heart of capitalist America, nor that it would be an epic tale with all the panoramic scenery and beauty of the West. Hawks wanted to tell a story about the workings of the human heart, a tender love story and Duke thanked his lucky stars that Cooper didn't like Dunson. As soon as he saw the script he recognised the power of the character, and jumped at the chance. He loved the part and didn't want Dunson softened up, he believed a westerner should be hard. He was, however, worried about Hawks, "You don't make westerns sitting around a pool. I could see that what he knew about making a western didn't amount to a pitcher of warm spit. He had a budget of a million and a half. I told him if he couldn't get United Artists to spend at least two million five, he would never make this picture — Hell they were thinking in terms of a blockbuster. Actually it cost three million, and grossed ten. Hawks wanted Cooper, and Grant to play Cherry. I was younger than the two of them, but he figured I could play the old man! Now his idea was the old man was senile and afraid, honestly that was his thinking. Hawks was an easy man to talk to, but as I sat listening to him in that first meeting, I thought "Christ, what have I got myself into?" I let it go that day, I didn't want to say anything in front of everybody, so I waited till the following day then went in to see him and I asked if he'd been down Texas lately? Had he noticed how the older, stronger, top ranchers have more power and a dynamic personality as they reach maturity? They're not puppy dogs. He wanted me to play an old man with grey hair, wrinkles and a shuffle. I was supposed to be tough and hard and walk like that? Hell, I was thinking about those old cattle guys that I knew, and there wasn't one of them who didn't stand tall. Mr Hawks said, "I get it Duke." And I played Dunson my way. I wanted to show a man with some human weaknesses, but not a weak man. We did have a few fights about the scene where two fellas are supposed to stand up against me. Hawks said, "Now here's your chance to go for the Oscar Duke." I said, "I think its Acadamy Award stuff to play it that sure, I'm afraid of the two men, but for Chrissakes, I've been tested many times before this. You've had me play a strong man up to this point. I wouldn't all of a sudden become a goddam coward. We also had a slight argument about the scene where the herd is taken from me. He wanted me to cringe … just slightly. Well, there was just no way John Wayne would ever cringe … even slightly. I told him, "Howard a man can kill, be mean and viscous, and still hold his audience, but let him show any sign of cowardice and he'll be lost … I'm not about to cringe … ever. He accepted I knew what I was talking about. Didn't have much trouble and I was always happy to work with him."

Hawks listened and learned fast, at every step of production he was happy to take advice and instruction from the undisputed champion of the Western. On one occasion the director even continued shooting on the actor's advice. A storm had blown up and it rained in the area for the first time in one hundred years, it was devastating weather, but Duke had learned his craft at Ford's elbow, and he told Hawks the lightening would look good on film, and that the whole scene could be re-written to suit the shots they got. It produced some of the best work in the film, and despite the whole cast and crew suffering as a result, no production time was lost. After that Hawks allowed Duke to remain at his side where he worked as assistant director, writer, suggesting action sequences and stunts.

His most important contribution was teaching Montgomery Clift how to stage a fist fight so the climax would seem more realistic. Harry Carey Jr, who had a small part in the film, said, "Duke coached him a lot … I'm not sure how much notice Monty took, but Duke never gave up on him. Hawks handled us with kid gloves, he was nice and gave Duke a free hand. If Ford had seen Duke telling someone what to do he would have jumped all over him. But Duke didn't want to out — John-Wayne Monty, he wanted that last scene to be honest. He knew he shouldn't be able to intimidate him. I don't think Duke was always right when he told other actors how to play things; he wanted everyone to be ballsy, like him. I'm sure he didn't think Monty was tough enough, and he was right. He didn't show much tact when he tried to improve things but between them they worked out a terrific scene."

The film didn't show Duke in a good light; Dunson is cold hearted and driven by ambition. He is filled with greed for land, is anxious to carry out his plans regardless of the cost, he can never admit he is wrong. He is a man scarred by the loss of the only woman he loved. She is killed in an Indian raid after he rides away from the wagon train, and he is forced to accept he had been wrong to leave her behind. After the success of *Red River* he often played characters scarred by loss or deception, a man who covers pain in obsessional behaviour and by denial of his human needs. He played the role increasingly well for in reality he was also personally scarred by his own losses and he too hid in his obsessive need to work.

No one had to tell him about Tom Dunson, he understood him with the sharp clarity of self-awareness. Duke's existence depended on his glittering career, a career based entirely on individual power and an ability to work harder and more single-mindedly than anyone else. Just like the tyrannical Dunson he could allow no human interference to stand in his way, he could wait for no one, could not slow down or stop. He knew everything there was to know about the complex Thomas Dunson who was full of contradiction, cruel, hard and mean. Duke knew he trod a fine line when he accepted the unusual part and he was not sure his traditional audience would accept him in it. He had to create a character that they could emphasise with; they had to care whether he lived or died in the final scene, if they had come to dislike him the climax would have been pointless. He somehow pulled off a seemingly impossible task, eventually restoring the character of Dunson. His fans loved the performance, his risk paid off and the movie became a smash hit. When the reviews first came out Clift and Hawks were singled out for much praise, the film was considered great, but Duke's part in it was completely overlooked. Once more the critics of the day missed what he brought to it, he was taken for granted and hardly rated a mention. That was how it had always been for him, and although he was getting used to it, he didn't much appreciate it.

Many years later, critics admitted that only John Wayne could have played the role, "At all times he commands the viewer's attention, even, as in the scene where Garth takes the cattle drive away from him, when he does nothing. His presence dominates the film, even in scenes from which he is absent. He is rock solid, slightly over the hill, unbending in his stated commitments and intentions, using that inflexibility to mask his insecurity and vulnerability." Thomas Dunson or John Wayne? It didn't matter, the two were one.

Although he had played the type before he had never breathed so much of himself into a part, never given so much of himself, never been such a fine actor. It was well worth the effort, despite the fact that the critics of the day ignored him, because he knew he had been accepted as an old man. Now he would be able to play the same role over and over again, and for the first time he knew his position as an actor was safe. Hawks used make-up to age him, but he knew that when he got to sixty he would still be able to play characters like Dunson. From *Red River* onward he knew he would be able to continue working in the movies.

Ford had created a star. Hawks established Duke as an actor and he came to play an increasingly important role in his future, "Hawks told me he couldn't have made the film without me. Told the Press the same thing, and the only power I ever got was after Hawks made that film. Then people started saying, "Well maybe it isn't just John Ford. Maybe Duke really can act." The way I was really helpful was in getting the Russell and Remington pictures to him, and talking to him about different levels of movement, the cattle and the background action. But Hawks didn't need *Red River*, he was already pretty established by then, I needed him though. After that I went from chasing girls to chasing cows. After that directors knew I could carry a film. I no longer had to be just part of a group. I started to make money because producers no longer wanted to spend money on other stars."

Box-office was all that mattered in Hollywood, it represented power, fortune and a future if you made money for the studio. When one of the short sighted critics of the day wrote, "What gives?" as he wondered why, after twenty years, John Wayne's career had suddenly taken off, John Ford offered the simplest of explanations, "Duke is the best actor in Hollywood, that's all." Gladwyn Hill, the feature writer, believed it was just that Duke was "Hollywood's hardest working and least ostentatious star." What actually gave was the simple fact that John Wayne was box-office gold. Throughout his twenty years in the business his movies had consistently made money. Unfortunately, the prevailing attitude of the day was that cowboy actors just weren't actors at all, and no matter how much money people paid to see THE cowboy, when the 1948 Academy Award nominations were announced, the name of John Wayne was nowhere to be seen, "Montgomery Clift was in *Red River* too, and they wanted to give that kid an Acadamy Award so bad they simply forgot about me. Clift was acting they said. Duke's only playing himself. But Hell, I played an *old man* in that. And I was only forty."

Hawks continued singing his praises, "The key to his acting style lies in his size and strength. He has so much physical power that his presence dominates the action of a scene, even when he is silent or static. He dominates the other actors and his least action can bowl over anyone else in the frame. I found out very early that you need a strong man up against him … and only the fact that Clift was so good kept Wayne from completely dominating the film. What makes Duke so good is his ability to control his strength. He is always physically aware of every body else and everything else in the frame. He constantly measures himself against his environment. At the end of the film he had to walk through a herd of cattle, he looks directly ahead, not at the cattle, the movement of his body seems to control that of the herd. Nothing can stop him. The power of his walk comes from his uncontrollable obsession. It reflects the insanity of his stubborn determination to control the world about him. What made

Red River so important for Duke was that it allowed him to unleash some of his natural power for the first time, it was power that had gone unnoticed before. I saw in him a latent capacity for brutality that Ford had not used, and did not until much later. He acts with the same brutality in some of his later films but never with the sustained intensity that he shows in my film. *Red River* gave him the confidence to use his own strength. He was a helluva lot better actor than he was ever given credit for, and it was hard for him to ever play a bad scene. He once asked me my theory on good acting and I told him, "Duke you do three or four good scenes and don't offend the audience the rest of the time and people will say you're a good actor." Today when he says, "What's comin' up?" I say, "This is one of the ones where you'll offend them … get it over as soon as you can … don't do anything … And I guess that's the secret of his talent … apparently not doing anything when he is actually dominating everything around him."

Duke was hurt by the lack of recognition, but while members of the Acadamy sat around voting he was already hard at work on his third film of the year, *Three Godfathers*, another Ford film. By the end of the same year he was busy on another two of the best films ever to come out of Hollywood, *Wake of the Red Witch*, and *She Wore a Yellow Ribbon*. Most of Hollywood's other leading men would have considered any two of the films he made in that year a stunning basis for a whole career, to John Wayne they represented seven months of work and a truly heroic effort.

Harry Carey, friend of John Ford, and father-figure to Duke, died in 1947 leaving both men devastated. *Three Godfathers* was Ford's tribute to the great star of the silent era and Duke's memorial to a man who had been such an influence on his life. Ford decided to make a new version of the film he first shot in the silent days with Harry Carey himself in the lead role. Now, following his death, he decided to use his son in the remake that carried the opening title, "To the memory of Harry Carey, bright star of the early western sky."

Duke played the leader of three bank robbers, Dobe Carey and Pedro Armendariz the other two. Armendariz had made other films with Ford and Wayne, but on this one he made the mistake of arguing with the director about his costume. In the end he wore what Ford wanted but he was never asked to work for him again! The heated argument set the tone for the rest of the time they spent together in Death Valley, the most horrific location, and none of them much enjoyed being there.

Duke shared a tiny room in a cabin with Armendariz, and Ward Bond and Carey another. If Ford was tough on Armendariz, he was even worse toward young Dobie Carey. It was his first big role and he was nervous and had little confidence in his own ability. The film was also being made to the memory of his father, he wanted it to be good. Though he was polite and followed every order Ford gave, he rarely satisfied the director. He, like many before him, was terrified of Ford, although he had known him most of his life and called him "Uncle Jack." Occasionally Ford even kicked him to stir him up. He once ordered Duke to do it for him and although he felt embarrassed, he did as he was told. When Ford became too tough on the boy though it was always Duke who smoothed things over, and he knew Ford was using him for that very role. He was often heard telling Dobe, "Don't take it seriously, he's just kidding." At the best of times Ford mumbled, at more stressful times he chewed on a handkerchief and his speech became incomprehensible. Carey said he was "bearable or unbearable, but never nice." Again Duke had to resort, as he had with young Agar, to telling stories about the vicious treatment he had suffered at the hands of the master, reminding him that he was only really nasty with those he liked. This time even Duke's generous spirit didn't help much although Carey later admitted, "When he stood up for me I could have kissed him for his brave intervention. Duke was something special."

Dobe's earliest memories of his hero dated back to 1939 when Duke often stayed at his parents home. Just after finishing *Stagecoach* he had arrived in town to open a rodeo, "He was slumped against Josie on the back seat of a chauffeur-driven car. She had to help him out of the car he was so smashed. He had bleary eyes and couldn't even stand unaided. Together, Josie, the chauffeur and myself manoeuvred his weight to a couch in our house. He tried to explain that he was just exhausted, he'd had no sleep. He and his wife had been out celebrating. He said they had danced and got drunk, and then they had gone straight on to the rodeo. They had both obviously had fun and enjoyed being together. Dad said they looked like they had in the old days. He lay on our sofa for some time and then sat up, rubbed his eyes and said he thought a drink would straighten him out. My mother brought him a bottle of whiskey. He drank a large tumbler, shook himself like a big dog and then straightened out with a huge grin on his face. His eyes had cleared. Then he ate a huge breakfast. Within a couple of hours he was completely normal again, making jokes, telling stories, and smoking cigarettes by the dozen." Dobe had grown up with Duke always around, he thought of him as a big brother, and he remained ever grateful for the way he protected him against Ford.

Working on *Three Godfathers* was a terrible experience for everyone involved, with central scenes of the three stars struggling through a desert storm. Sand became lodged in their eyes, mouths, inside their clothes and boots, and became unbearable for all of them. They worked for three days without shade from 8am to 6pm. Duke and Dobe both had fair skin and they got badly burnt by the relentless sun and raw from the sand blasting them. Although Duke drank gallons of water his mouth became burnt and painful.

Life only improved a little in the evening when it was cooler and they sat around talking, playing cards or dominoes. Duke asked with a wry grin at the start of each game, "What's worse than going to Hell?" The others answered in harmony, "Playing dominoes with Pedro Armendariz as your partner!" Duke, who teamed up with Bond against Ford and Armendariz, was kept in a permanent state of amusement by the other three. He laughed at Ford's attempts at cheating, at Armandariz who lost his temper with Bond, and at Bond who was useless at all the games they played. Every time he and Bond lost a game Duke laughed, "Thank God fellas ... the heat's off! Ward's done it again." He knew problems only started when Ford lost. Winning at night meant punishment the following day and Duke often tried to get the others to throw the games as he did, always to no avail ... Of course he had plenty of unintentional help from Bond.

Repartee between them was brutal. Bond greeted every day with the words, "This would be a helluva picture except Wayne's got my part again!" Duke fell about as Ford quipped, "Oh hell. There goes my day ... I thought the shit had a day off." Ford allowed no alcohol at all on the desert, not even at the weekends. Duke, Bond and Armendariz broke the rule only once and Ford's revenge on Duke was swift and cruel. In the scene where he is awaiting trial after being captured he is seen eating a piece of chicken. Ford forced him to do eighteen takes before he would print it, and Duke repeatedly had to excuse himself to go and throw up before continuing. Carey said that although Duke did have fun, he could also appear distant and withdrawn, "I loved "Himself" but no matter how many times I worked with him, unless I was totally alone with him and had his full attention, I was never quite sure he had heard a word I said. This trait of his, this, "I don't really know you're there," expression drove everyone bonkers. It made people butter up to him ... and he couldn't bear that. If someone on set told him off he would most likely say, "Jesus, I'm glad you showed some guts." His far away look probably had more to do with his personal problems than anything else at that time, and whilst he might have been less alert than normal he was certainly well aware of everything going on around him.

By the time he started work on his third film of 1947 Ford was helping Hawks edit *Red River*. The footage he saw shocked him as he realised for the first time that Duke was a good enough actor to carry a film on his own. As soon as he saw what he had done with Hawks he decided to use him for *She Wore a Yellow Ribbon*, a narrative about the last week in the military career of Captain Nathan Brittles, a man who at 64, and after forty-three years of service, is about to retire. Ford wouldn't even have considered Duke for the role of the dignified officer who was weary of Indian fighting, was warm and kind hearted, powerful and sensitive. But after seeing him act his way through *Red River* he knew he had the required finesse to do a good job.

Bond and Armendariz were both missing this time when Duke and Ford returned to the splendour of Monument Valley. Dobe commented, "It must have been pretty hard on Duke, here's a man who is carrying the whole picture, trying to learn his lines, has to make sure he never misses his mark, and he has to play cards every night on his own with Ford, and make sure he looses!" Carey even thought the film was finished ahead of schedule because there was less card playing than usual. But Duke didn't mind being alone with Ford, he appreciated working with him and late nights never bothered him, he enjoyed the old man's sense of humour and they shared much laughter. As they filmed a scene were Quincannon, played by Victor McLaglen, makes a special announcement to the assembled troops, a stray dog wandered onto the set and fell asleep in front of the line of mounted soldiers. Typically Ford decided to write the dog into the scene so that when McLaglen began to speak he had to notice the dog and pause before asking who it belonged to. In the re-written version the Irishman was supposed to say, "Nice dog, Irish Setter." Unfortunately McLaglen didn't get the joke and said, "Nice dog, Cocker Spaniel." Duke began laughing and Carey later said he thought he was going to have a stroke. Filming was delayed for hours because each time the shot was set up again Duke began giggling helplessly.

In a very un-John Wayne-like movie, Duke had little action, was not his normal aggressive self, he counselled peace and sorted arguments out amongst his men. He had more strength of character than physical strength. He was fearless, gruff, warm, sensitive and understanding, with more than a touch of sadness about him.

Ford had allowed the co-star, Joanne Dru to bring along his own daughter, Barbara, for company on location. Together they stood mesmerized as they watched Duke film a scene, "Why are we standing out here watching him film this?" Barbara asked her friend. Dru replied, "Because he turns us on." Barbara agreed, "When he was on horse back he was the sexiest man alive, but once he got down he returned to being Uncle Duke." He was Uncle Duke to her and big brother to Dobe. They trusted him and often turned to him for help and advice, which was always freely given, though he didn't always give the answers they hoped for. After his father died Dobie asked Duke what name he thought he should use in the movies. He was shocked when Duke advised him not to go into the film industry at all, "Find yourself another line of work. You're gonna have a rough time in pictures, you just aren't a handsome looking fella. You can't be a leading man. There aren't many parts for young character actors. What did your Father-in-law tell you?"

"He said to ask you!"

"Well my advice is, get a sideline because you aren't going to get steady work in movies."

The advice was offered before they made *Three Godfathers*. After they finished it Dobe again approached Duke to ask how he should be billed, his reply was very different, "Don't make any difference now what you use, Dobie, Harry Carey Jnr, Joe Blow. Fortunately, you have a little talent!" He added, after a long pause, "but I'd still get a little sideline, were I you."

By the end of the decade he felt better about his career and knew he had never looked better on screen, "I was at my best age physically and mentally, and in my attitude to life in general." All the other stars of his generation were ageing, but somehow, his face had only just begun to weather. The early callowness had been replaced by experience, loneliness and pain. And he had never been in greater demand. Over the next three years he starred in a further eight films. By 1950 he was firmly established as Hollywood's leading box-office attraction. His image was securely linked in the public imagination with American's past, present and future. He had become "an American hero." Finally some of his detractors were beginning to notice, "He's a champion who belongs to everyone, and thus we can kick him around. Wayne himself doesn't give much of a damn what anyone says of him. He was middle-aged before he reached the top, and he'd already been twenty-five years in the business. After all that time, he knows he's good. To some, he may be just a big man. But to those who understand, he's a giant."

Whilst all the films he worked on in 1947 and 1948 were hits, and some were beginning to be aware of the John Wayne phenomenon, each performance was conspicuously ignored by the voters of the Acadamy. He thought they were afflicted with a curious blindness. He understood they never found a way to cope with his creative force because he didn't fit into any of their theories, "The critics ride me, but there's too much emphasis on it and I really don't care. I try not to fight them, they've never been able to overcome me. I don't accept anything they write … I don't accept anything, and what they write is their own palaver. Lately however they have started to observe me, rather than subject me to their writing. Sometimes I see they have taken some notice of my work. I think I did quite a good job in *She Wore a Yellow Ribbon*, and a helluva good job in

Red River. But I really didn't get any recognition. Maybe I deserved a kudo here and there." He went on, resigned to the fact that the critics would never recognise his technique, "I don't think it matters. Motion pictures are like sitting in a room with someone and talking across the table. If you overact, they're quite aware of it. If it's your ego they can have fun with it, but you can't get away with it unless it's that. If they start looking at you, trying to work it out, you've lost them. You can't stop what the Press chooses to say, the average critic comes along and says, "You've had lots of fights in bars," and I say, "Well actually I haven't." Then in two minutes he's saying, "I'll bet guys have said to you after a few drinks ...," and I say, "Well, actually, no." But they keep the same question coming at you until you give some kind of answer to shut them up. That puts you right in the framework they have already decided to put you in. They get irritated when you won't fall in line. So as a rule I just go along with whatever they want. After about the third question I usually know what they're after, and I say, "OK what do you want?" Gets me in plenty of trouble of course, but it saves me time and them irritation. Meant I stayed in the saddle even when I was overlooked, sometimes broke, and incidentally, blackballed over the years. They damned near shoved me out of the business. I'm not kidding. But I learned how to deal with them."

After finishing three films in seven months he told Hedda Hopper, "I guess I'm pitching for the record." Some of his critics were asking if it was possible to star in too many films, how much exposure could he take before his public tired of him? John Wayne, they thought smugly, would surely soon find out. He was unconcerned about over-exposure, "Who can complain if a man sees a chance to make a buck? That's business. And I jump at the chance to keep on working." What the critics wrote stung although he continued to deny that he cared. Their words never affected how the public saw him or his films, but the fact was he cared very much that his talent was consistently overlooked. Luckily his fans understood him instinctively and he felt they were much more aware of his talent than the critical intellectuals. And from 1948 business couldn't have been better, there was no sign of flagging interest. The critics might try, but there was no way big John Wayne would be shoved out of the business. At the start of the year he lay thirty third in the Motion Picture Herald poll of exhibitors, by 1950 he was number one. In the same year Photoplay readers voted him Favourite Male Actor, that was repeated in all the movie journals. In 1951, 1952 and 1953 he was voted number one film star in all the polls, and for the next twenty years he remained in the top five, setting records unlikely ever to be equalled, "I'm a box-office champion with a record they're going to have to run to catch."

In 1949 he received his first Oscar nomination for his portrayal of Sergeant Stryker in *The Sands of Iwo Jima*. He didn't win, and he later commented dryly, "I don't need an Oscar." Ford consoled him, "You'll never win anything. You'll always be taken for granted. It's just a cross you'll have to bear." Though he was now at the top of his profession, was always in great demand, and not a day went by without he received an offer or a script to look at, he still analyzed himself and his performances to try to explain his treatment at the hands of his peers, "I guess that I am never chosen because the kind of acting I do is not considered acting by anybody. I know the hardest thing to do in a scene is to do nothing, or seem to do nothing, because doing nothing requires extreme work and discipline. I just stand there — or so it looks to the critics. They say "Well it's only John Wayne being John Wayne. He is not acting." They have an idea that acting is putting on a disguise and being somebody you are not in a kind of blatant way. But, look, when I played Tom Dunson — was I a cattle rancher, a Texan? Or was I a marine sergeant? Or was it me being the captain in *She Wore a Yellow Ribbon*? I was disappointed at not even being nominated for that, because I played a man sixty years old."

Those critics mystified by his sudden upsurgance equated acting with distortion of what was assumed to be the actor's real self and they always assumed John Wayne played himself, without ever bothering to find out who he really was. But to the directors and producers who chose him to star in their films, above every other star, his acting was recognised as something very special indeed. He was a mountainous presence on screen, a gift to them, the movie industry, and the audience.

Two generations had watched him foil corrupt business men and criminals and win the war almost single-handedly in a collection of work almost painful in its sincerity. His position at the top rested on a bedrock of honesty that was never simply part of the act. He had cemented his success in his country's need for a hero. Conflict had arisen in his own life because he had only been able to fulfil his country's needs by not going to war, by not being a hero. By not going he had claimed his predestined place in the imagination of the world and remained secure there in the face of the critics. As a result he became his own sternest critic. He was a man to whom integrity was everything and yet here he was, the most successful star of them all, a hero in everyone's eyes, who never could be in his own. He never forgave himself for missing his opportunity, for living a lie. The foundation was false, he had played the hero people wanted him to be, giving form to the values the free world cherished, showing the rock-like image of America that defeated all evil. At no other time had so many Americans gone to the cinema and at no other time had John Wayne made so many films. Richard Schickel wrote, "For some of us who have grown up in his shadow, measuring our changing personalities against his towering constancy, Wayne has become one of life's bedrock necessities. He reminds us of a time when right was right, wrong was wrong, and the differences between them could be set right by the simplest of means."

And Andrew Sarris years later, "Wayne confronted evil directly with ruthless, unblinking violence. Civilization must eventually sweep before it a class of men, its own precursors and pioneers, so remarkable both in their virtues and their faults, that few see their extinction without regret. He is the very last cowboy saint. Year after year nothing changes, Duke, like the Christmas tree, always comes out looking the same."

His private turmoil, his inner self-knowledge was unimportant, his draft status immaterial, affairs and divorces meant nothing to any one but himself. Because his intentions were honourable it tore him apart every time he heard himself described as a hero, but it was only what he appeared to be that mattered to everyone else, it was only his image that America was interested in. By the fifties he had become more comfortable with his place in the industry, he was more mature and better able to make choices he had shied away from before. He finally saw that as an honourable man he had a duty to speak up about the things he held dear. After the war he allowed everything he had come to represent spill over into his own life and as the Communist threat developed he saw an opportunity to stand up and be counted at last. He willingly threw himself into that arena of conflict. He had missed one opportunity to be a hero, he could not afford to miss another, and through the fifties he began attempting to live his life according to the screen image, becoming deeply involved in the political minefield of The Cold War. After the war others were longing for peace and wanted only to get on with their lives, but Duke saw communism as a threat to all their hopes of a secure future. America had won its battle with its external foe, he was haunted now by a vision of an attack from within. He sat firmly at the top of his profession and now he began to live his life according to the image. He would let no subversive element spoil everything he had worked so hard for.

At the same time, the Second World War was again becoming big business in Hollywood. In 1948 Edmund Grainger saw a newspaper article about the battle for the sands of Iwo Jima accompanied by the famous photograph of a group of marines raising the American flag at the summit of Mount Suribachi. He asked Jimmy Grant prepare a treatment. The story line was basic, about a tough sergeant who has to turn a group of diverse individual soldiers into a crack Marine unit. Grainger didn't have far to look for his harsh, abrasive leader; Duke had also seen Grant's script and said, "It was a beautiful personal story. I wanted the part so badly I could taste it. I would have begged on my knees for a chance at it." Grainger never had any doubt about who he wanted to play Sergeant John Stryker, even though he also wanted to make a realistic movie with no one being called upon to perform acts of great courage, or self sacrifice as in most of Duke's other war films.

It was an important role and Duke grilled technical advisors for hours about the movement and attitude of warrant officers. Mary St John said that for a while he became Stryker, and John Agar who played his convert in the film said the part was right up his street, showing all his toughness and his softer side, "Stryker was very much how he was in real life. His eyes conveyed such conviction, that when I was talking it was as if I was talking to sergeant Stryker, and as usual he was completely encouraging."

When the film was premiered at Grauman's Chinese Theatre, Duke was to put his foot print in the cement of the famous pavement outside. Despite his size, he had a pair of small dainty feet, and the bootprint looked like that of a dancer. To lay such a notion to rest he firmly jammed his massive fist into the wet cement next to it.

His performance in the film was so powerful that he received his first Academy Award nomination. He didn't win but felt some gratitude and said, "I don't care about the critics or their acclaim, what I really care about is the money!" *Sands of Iwo Jima* earned $3,900,000 and was a huge success for both him and Republic, and on its back he was officially listed as Hollywood's most polar star. Timing had been everything! Wayne and America emerged from the war years together to reach the height of their power, and throughout America and the rest of the world, the two were seen as synonymous, with Duke the handsome symbol of American power. His personal strength in films of the west and the war assumed iconographic proportions, "Not until John Wayne created the role of Sergeant Stryker in Sands of Iwo Jima and then merged his own personality with the character did Americans find a man who personified the ideal soldier, sailor or Marine." Other actors portrayed military characters but it was John Wayne who symbolized all the American ideals of duty and service to country. He was still living in the shadow of his own creations. From the billowing flags of *Fort Apache* to the flag raising ceremony at the end of *Sands of Iwo Jima,* John Wayne was tied to America's destiny. He had created the image and now could do no better than live his destiny out.

Although he had offers stacked up he still jumped eagerly when John Ford offered him the chance to work on his next film, *Rio Grande,* the last of the cavalry trilogy. The picture paired Duke and Maureen O'Hara for the first time. She was just the kind of woman he would have chosen for himself; tall, beautiful, strong and opinionated, she was his perfect screen match and the film became a huge romantic success. He had also found another true and loyal friend who would be there for him all the rest of his life, "She is a terrific girl, warm, nice, talkative. One of the guys. Oh, how she loves to tell stories."

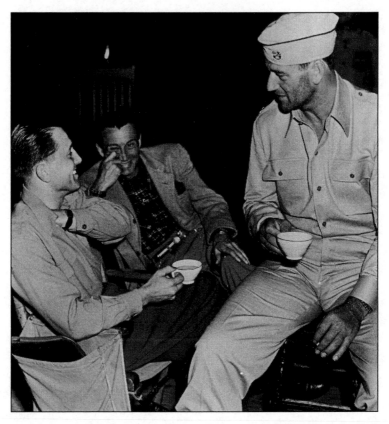

You may disagree completely with what I say, but I will defend to the death my right to say it.

CHAPTER FIVE

The Political Warrior

The approach of crisis

"We built a nation on the past ... it can't have been that bad. Our yesterdays tell us that we have to win not only at war, but at peace. I hope that in our anxiety to have peace, we remember our clear and present dangers and beware the futility of compromise."

John Wayne rushed headlong, like a child, to answer the door, excited, his face wreathed in smiles as he pushed Pat playfully out of his way.

"Duke, I was trying to tell you … it's only a delivery of extra champagne … it's no one …"

"Well, it's sure *someone*, see, it's a kid with a crate of champagne … Hi kid!" he bellowed at the top of his voice before relieving the boy of the crate, turning and putting it carefully down behind him. He pulled a roll of notes from his pocket, peeled one off and handed it to the delivery boy who was still standing hopefully in the doorway. He was impressed, not so much by the size of the bill he had been given as by the enormous man who had placed it in his hand.

"Thank you, Mr Wayne … I …" and he lapsed into the speechless state that Duke recognised as a mark of respect, almost of reverence. He looked down at his feet, laughing softly, feeling as usual, embarrassed by such scenes, and wondering as always why he had that effect on people, wondering why he had never got used to it. Still the boy stood there, not moving, seeming as though he were suspended, frozen, his eyes staring up in wonder.

"Well kid … Happy Christmas …"

"Mr Wayne?" there was a note of desperation in the voice,

"Yes?"

"My Dad, he loved all your films — loved you — he was a real fan, he used to tell me that if I wanted to be a man, just be like John Wayne, and I couldn't go far wrong … he used to follow you to appearances, get your picture and then you'd always sign them for him next time he got to see you. His name was Bob …"

"Yeah … I remember … I haven't got around so much lately, haven't seen him …"

"He died last year. He would have been so thrilled to know I delivered to your home, anyway, I just wanted to tell you … I'm sorry to have bothered you."

"No bother. Hey, did you want to come in, sit and jaw for a while?"

"Duke … the kids'll be over …" Pat began but already knew that nothing would shift him, for he was about to engage in what he loved doing best.

"Got half an hour to talk about your old man, son?" he asked as he threw a massive paw out toward the boy to drag him in over the threshold of his home, "Let's go get comfortable in the den." He poured two glasses of lemonade and handed one to the shocked delivery boy.

"No alcohol son, not when you're driving, always remember that."

"Yes sir. Mr Wayne I didn't want to disturb your evening … I just wanted you to know …"

"Yeah, I do know … What's your name?"

"I'm little Robert sir."

"OK, tell me about your dad, little Robert."

"Well, the first time he took me along to catch a glimpse of you was around Christmas time, 1973. You were being presented with some Pro Football Hall of Fame Award at the Waldorf Astoria. He wanted me to see you so much that he had already planned how he would crash the security surrounding President Ford who was supposed to be there that night. We hung around your hotel, The Pierre, I think, all afternoon, but you didn't come out until it was time for the dinner. We followed your car to the Waldorf. There were thousands of fans when we got there, and I still didn't get to see you. Dad started to talk with some other guys, they were plotting their strategy for the evening. We stood around for maybe four hours or so, talking about your films, that kind of stuff. Then, on some kind of signal, we rushed toward the elevators, and I got carried right along. We were past security, no one there was interested in the President anyway, and you had no security. You just stood there, smiling and waving, not troubled at all. You couldn't get an elevator because they were all full of fans trying to get to you, so one lung and all, you took to the stair well …"

Duke was laughing at the vivid memory so suddenly and unexpectedly recalled, and brought back to life. He had been with his sons Michael and Patrick, and the three of them had trotted down the stairs followed by a few of his more determined fans. He recalled that the chase came to an abrupt end around the fifteenth floor when he had come across some guys shooting dice in the hallway, and he had joined the game. Eventually an elevator had stopped at the floor, and when the door slid open to let a hotel guest out, he had rushed straight into it, followed by the boys, and a couple of others, Bob, and little Robert here.

"Yeah … I remember."

"Dad asked you to sign some of his collection of photographs, you laughed and asked him where he'd got them. You posed for a couple of shots with your sons. Then when we arrived in the lobby, you shook hands and went off to some club."

"It was the 21 Club, and you guys all beat me there I think. Every time I turned around you were right there."

"That's right. That was where we wanted to be. Near you. You were my dad's hero and that night you became mine too. After that, whenever one of your films was on TV, I watched. I started reading everything about you … Mr Wayne you were, and are, my hero, even more since my dad died. I can't explain how I mean … I don't mean in any weird way or nothin'."

The boy was emotional. Duke wanted to divert him, "I bumped into you

193

both on more than that occasion you know. I guess you guys think we don't notice, but I sure always did. Mostly I enjoyed all that stuff, course sometimes it got a little out of hand, but mostly it was fun. I probably needed you more than you needed me you know. Can you remember the next time?"

"You went to Philadelphia to promote *The Shootist*. We lived in New York then, but travelled across with a couple of other fans. None of us knew the town so we couldn't follow you around so much, and we just hung outside the hotel. You were really friendly this time, it was better than before, you let us take lots of photographs, signed autographs every time you went in or out of the hotel. You went to some art gallery and me and dad followed. You suddenly turned round and asked us how we always knew where you were going to be, you walked over to talk some, until we were shown out the door."

"And you were still there waiting when I got out!"

"There were lots of us by then but you chatted to everyone, signed all the books, had pictures taken with anyone who asked. You were a king that day Mr Wayne," little Robert had warmed to his subject and was less in awe of his hero, "The very next time you were in New York, for a TV Special I think, I camped outside The Pierre in pouring rain waiting to see you in person again. People don't ever get tired of seeing you, they need to be near you once they have met you once. That evening there were hundreds of us, all soaking wet. When you came over I asked if you would sign the pictures we had taken in Philadelphia. You were on your way out to dinner I guess, and it was wet,"

"Was I a miserable son of a bitch that night?"

"No ... not exactly ..."

"It's OK, I was a son of a bitch ... I'd had some kinda argument, nothing much. I didn't sign them did I?"

"Not then you didn't, but we followed you to the Paramount Building to see if we could get near you, it was hopeless so we went back to The Pierre, just to wait ... you looked real tired when you got back, and we didn't want to bother you ... but you noticed us. We'd been standing around in the rain all night and you didn't go into the hotel, you came over to us. There were newspaper photographers pushing you around, and us too, and you were getting soaked through now as well, but you still tried to oblige everyone there."

"Was I still a miserable son of a bitch?" he laughed, trying to remember.

"No you were a hero. The hotel staff kept trying to push us away, and drag you inside, but you wouldn't have it, and you signed every autograph book put under your nose. You laughed and waved as you left. That was the last time I saw you until tonight."

"What happened?"

"Once my dad was too ill to trail you I kinda lost interest. Then he died, and I left New York, to move out here, I thought about trying to get a job in Hollywood, but it's so tough, I'm doing deliveries down here until something turns up. I can't tell you how good it feels to be able to talk to you, I could never have imagined this would happen to me tonight, I thought I might get a glimpse of you if I was real lucky, but I never dreamed … I still watch any movies they show Mr Wayne, some send a shiver down my spine, they remind me of my dad …"

"I'm sorry about your dad Robert, but I'm glad my films make you think about him. Keep watching them won't you?"

Pat stuck her head round the door and coughed.

"Well, that's my call, I'll see you out. You're right about it being tough out there Robert, but never give up, if I made it anyone can, just you keep working at it."

As Robert walked away through the elegant Japanese front garden, both he and Duke were full of memories of the good old days. He was reassured that as long as prints of his films existed he would live on in peoples hearts. No matter what happened in the future his place in the world was assured, his screen image, if nothing else, was indestructible.

In recent years he had stood firm against a flood of ridicule, as a film star, an unfashionable patriot, a political dinosaur; he had been under constant attack. He withstood all of it simply because that was his way, and because of the fans like little Robert and his dad who had given him the confidence to speak openly about his own private beliefs. It was an unwritten rule in Hollywood that its stars didn't stick their necks out. Such foolish action was to run the risk of alienating half a potential audience. In his early days he would have hesitated to do it but once his career was well and truly established he felt more able to express himself. He had the power to ignore the unwritten rules …

The Motion Picture Alliance for The Preservation of American Ideals was founded on 7th February 1944 at a mass meeting held in the grand ballroom of the Beverly-Wilshire Hotel. Fifteen hundred people from all walks of the motion picture industry and representing every union were there. The director, Sam Wood, was elected president. The group came to be known simply as the Alliance, and members included Walt Disney, Gary Cooper, Ginger Rogers, John Ford, and Cecil B. De Mille. Duke was relieved to find others had finally recognised the danger that communism presented to the American way of life, but he was still too busy, and perhaps he was not really interested enough either, to attend Alliance meetings. Despite the fact that many of his friends joined he still held out against signing up and called it, "My period of listening." He sensed rather than understood the political undercurrents swirling around Hollywood after the war, was vaguely uncomfortable about the Left, but still considered himself a liberal and voted for the Democratic party. He was far from being the right wing extremist that he was later painted. His politics were unformed and remained that way until he started work on the film *Back to Bataan* when he had his first close up encounter with communism. It was a confrontation that changed his life, ended the "period of listening," and led him into the political arena for the first time.

The film told the story of General MacArthur's return to the Philippines to recapture the land lost to Japan in 1942. Robert Fellows, RKO producer and friend of Duke's, intended making an authentic tribute to the American and Phillipino fighting forces. Fellows had an agreement with the army to provide the best technical advisors available. He had already signed Duke as his star, and wanted the director, Edward Dmytryk, to work with him. When it was being planned, the war was still raging and Fellows intended to have a film ready for a release that coincided with the actual re-taking of the Philippines. There could be no delays, it had to be shot and ready in ten weeks. Production speed never bothered Duke and, compared to his schedule at Republic, ten weeks seemed like a leisurely pace.

He was, however, edgy, short-tempered, a "grouchy old bear," as filming started. He had only agreed to do the film on the spur of the moment as a favour to his friend. But he had not worked with Dmytryk before and the two didn't hit it off, their working relationship couldn't have been worse and the whole thing quickly degenerated into a personal, professional and political battleground.

He had been listening to political conversations in Hollywood for some time and had increasingly drifted to the right. He was unable to support Roosevelt or The New Deal, the proponents of high taxation, but his own politics remained unformed, and were not much more than a fairly random collection of ideas, values, theories and principles. He was not prepared to say one way was right and another wrong, his beliefs were his own, not those laid down by any organisation. The only thing he was sure about was that Communism was a threat to Capitalism, to his world, and he was, therefore, quite naturally opposed to it.

Whilst making *Back to Bataan* he also found himself opposed to Dmytryk, and also to screen writer, Ben Barzman, both active members of the Communist Party in America. He made an early, half hearted, effort to get on with them in a fragile and uneasy truce. Duke was well aware of the powerful position that every screenwriter held in Hollywood; films started and ended with them, and he was generally wary around most of them. Barzman was more powerful than most and he felt very uncomfortable in his presence. Whilst allowing both Dmytryk and Barzman to call him "Duke" he also let them know, in no uncertain terms, that in itself, didn't confer friendship. As filming got under way a private war was declared; director and writer ganging up against star, hitting him with frequent script alterations, continually writing changes the night before they were due to be shot, giving Duke no time to learn his lines, and Duke hurling insults as only he could. He would tolerate many things, but unprofessional conduct drove him crazy. He was particularly quick to pick up Barzman's mistakes and vindictively reluctant to let them go unnoticed. It was not like him to be ungenerous on a film set, but he couldn't abide lack of discipline. Each morning as he scanned the hurriedly written changes, Duke commented in a voice loud enough for everyone else to hear, "Now let's see what kind of golden hero our boy genius has made me today." He left himself wide open to attack from Barzman and Dmytryk and the writer found it easy to retaliate through his script. He knew Duke enjoyed doing his own stunts, preferring to do the dangerous work himself. That knowledge gave him a decided edge, "Eddie and I started to invent stunts that we were sure would make Wayne cry for a double." He never did, despite the writer's desire for revenge being magnified by the director, who was known throughout the industry, as a man fascinated with sadism and pain. They considered no stunt too extreme and one cold night stood smugly watching as a scene was shot with Duke lying under freezing water sucking in air through a straw. Dmytryk waited in vain for him to ask for a double, though at one point, blue-lipped and dripping icy water, he emerged to take a shot of whiskey. He commented menacingly, "You better be goddamn sure we don't find out this is something you dreamed up out of your little heads as a parting gift."

It wasn't his relationship with them that was the real problem however, and he could handle them both easily enough. He could have gone through the motions with his eyes closed. The real trouble started when he noticed the way they were treating army adviser, Col. George Clarke, a professional soldier, who had been one of the last men to leave the islands when the Japanese snatched them. He was a tough military man with very little sense of humour. Whenever Duke was not around the crew unmercifully made fun of his religion, his patriotism, sung the "Internationale" in front of him. Duke recalled, "This colonel came up to me and asked what was happening. They were driving him up the wall."

Once he knew how a real hero was being treated he confronted Dmytryk, asking him outright if he was a communist. He told Duke he wasn't, but added that he didn't believe communism would harm American people. From that point on Duke avoided all contact with his director, the truce was over and it was a miracle the film was ever completed at all, let alone that it became hailed as a piece of classic propaganda.

Barzman and Dmytryk reinforced Duke's developing political beliefs, and seemed almost to trigger the patriotism that distinguished all his following years. Many commentators believed it had been his failure to serve his country that later made him so fiercely outspoken, but it had just as much to do with his distaste for Dmytryk's blasphemous jokes and the torment he and the colonel went through during the filming of *Back to Bataan*. He emerged from his experiences supersensitive to sneering cracks against the president, the flag, God, patriotism and American values in general, and hypersensitive to the threat of communism, "I am not a political figure. I hate politics and most politicians. But when things get rough and people are saying things that aren't true, I sometimes open my mouth and eventually get in trouble." It took *Back to Bataan* to trigger his political awakening, and he said that looking back, his politicization took him out of the narrow world where the sun rose and set only on pictures. The War, Communism, the Alliance, and the actions of two people on a film set jolted him out of his customary habit of standing on the side line until, by 1950, he found himself firmly in the middle of the fight. In 1948 he had been one of the least politically active stars in Hollywood, doggedly steering a path away from all the heated arguments that were tearing Hollywood apart, and he would much rather have preferred to continue standing on the outside, remaining distant and personally intact, but once he was directly targeted and he understood the threat to the industry that he held so dear, he had no option but to plunge headlong in, finally prepared to roughhouse with the Left and any other enemy of the movie industry, his town and his country.

He never thought that made him a monster but once he took the step he found himself fodder for the right wing, regarded by them as a supremely attractive and powerful figurehead, already huge box-office, and worth his weight in gold, a powerful ally. And just as he became the darling of one side, those of the other were more than happy to use him as their prime target, finding him easy prey to bait and attack. Neither group judged his position accurately and he said, "Now I always thought I was a liberal. I came up very surprised one time when I found that I was a right wing, conservative extremist, when I have listened to everybody's point of view that I ever met and then decided how I should feel. But people never really listen to me. They make an early decision as to what I think. These people are articulate enough to influence the Press, and they force out that image to the average person. If someone wants to make a cheap shot about my films they call them "John Waynes" meaning rigid and on the right, and yet the first person I ever proselyted for was a Democrat. And I don't think that as time goes by people will care about my politics anyway. I hope what they will look at will be my performances."

He had spent so long listening to everyone, that his politics, once he chose to involve himself, were really neither of the right nor the left, they were simply his own. He naively expressed a loose collection of thoughts and believed that, in the land of free speech, he had the same right as the next man to speak his mind. He never understood why he was so vehemently attacked for holding Republican principles and he never assaulted anyone the way he was rounded on by those who didn't share his opinions. The way the Press reacted to his increasing political voice could have seriously harmed his position in Hollywood, but Duke had finally seen a way he could be of value as an American citizen. No one knew better than he did what he owed his country, and now he saw participation in the political arena as a down payment on the debt.

In 1948 his agent, Charlie Feldman, sent him a script for *All the King's Men*. Duke read it carefully and by the time he had reached the end he was throwing ashtrays around the room in temper. When he replied to Feldman he asked why he thought he would have any interest in starring in a film that "smears the machinery of government for no purpose of humour or of enlightenment" and "degrades all relationships." Everything about the story struck an exposed nerve, he could not understand why anyone would want to make a film that "threw acid on the American way of life." He advised Feldman that if he had any such clients to send the script to them. Feldman was eventually proven right about the film's potential when it won rave reviews and an Oscar for its eventual star. Duke had turned down a great role but never regretted his decision. He knew Rossen, the scriptwriter, and his reputation. He had been a target of the House Un-American Activities Committee (HUAC) in 1947 because of his ties to the Communist Party. After his dealings with Barzman, Duke, who had often willingly worked with known communists before, was worried not just about the script, but also about Rossen. The screen writers who embraced the communist ideology were no longer a small group with little influence, they held huge political sway. When Feldman sent him Rossen's script Duke finally decided it was time to make a stand. There were some things he just would not do any longer; lending his voice to the Communist party was one of them. The passionate letter he wrote explaining his position became his political manifesto, stating all the things he believed were right or wrong with America. He wrote it just as the political battle lines were being drawn in Hollywood, and it was his line in the sand. Elsewhere in the world the Cold War was reaching its height and there was an all-pervading atmosphere of danger and implied threat. One war had ended, but the Communist block countries posed a huge and realistic menace to America and the rest of the western world. Within America, Hollywood became the front line of the domestic Cold War. Here was a war being fought in Duke's own backyard, one that threatened his very existence. His time to fight had finally arrived.

Tensions that had long existed between the Hollywood liberals and Communists on one side and the right wing on the other, increased after the war, with the left revering the politics of Franklin D. Roosevelt and the New Deal, and the Republicans who were ready to stage a fight back, targeting the high taxes and deficit spending of the Democrats. American Communists, who were preaching the idea of "world revolution" targeted Hollywood, that huge image-making machine, as their way of reaching and influencing vast world audiences. They established the Hollywood Popular Front to promote the cause. The conservatives, wary of the power the controllers of Hollywood had, resented the Communist screenwriters and producers advancing their political agenda in this way.

A letter was sent to Democratic senator Robert Reynolds, stating, "We believe in, and like, the American way of life," and confirmed a "belief in freedom, and the right to succeed or fail as free men according to the measure of our ability and our strength." It called his attention to the films *Mission To Moscow*, and *The North Star*, saying both were, "eulogies to Communism and The Red Army." It warned of a developing crisis in the motion picture industry and called for an investigation. It was signed, "A Group of Your Friends in Hollywood." As a direct result, the Joint Fact-Finding Committee on Un-American Activity was established by the Government and what liberals later called the "witch hunts" began.

The Alliance, under its president Sam Wood, believed many of the Hollywood guilds and craft unions were controlled by the Communists, and Walt Disney was convinced that Communist agitation had caused a strike at his plant as far back as 1941. The Communists and liberals branded Alliance members Anti-Roosevelt, anti-Semitic and even fascist; charges powerful and emotive enough to ruin Hollywood careers. Wood, Disney, and other political leaders felt the time had come to keep a check on developments. The FBI had already identified John Lawson and Robert Rossen, the screen writer that Duke had been so worried about, as being behind much of the campaign against the Alliance as the battle lines hardened.

Naturally organizations of both the left and right were busy recruiting stars according to their box-office value, and though at first he had refused to be drawn into the fight, once he did enter the fray, there was no one to compete with Duke at that level. Although he had now been firmly attached to the anti-Communist cause he remained a free-thinker, still floating around the political pond and he considered himself independent of all party politics. He often alienated both Republicans and Alliance members with his expressive gut reactions. elf time to think about how his words might be interpreted by the media. He believed that the best government was the one that governed least. He distrusted all politicians who supported programmes where "everyone is cared for from the cradle to the grave. In my life I've gone without a meal or two, and I never expected the Government to give me anything. Hard times aren't something I can blame my fellow citizens for. Years ago I didn't have all the opportunities either, but you can't whine and bellyache 'cause somebody else got a good break and you didn't. When I was at USC I was a socialist myself, but as a fellow gets older and gives more thought to his and his fellow man's responsibilities, he finds that it can't work out that way — some people just won't carry their load. I believe in welfare — a welfare working programme. I don't believe a fella should be able to sit on his backside and receive welfare. I'd like to know why well-educated idiots keep apologizing for lazy and complaining people who think the world owes them a living. I'd like to know why they make excuses for cowards who spit in the faces of the police and then run behind the judicial sob sisters. I can't understand people who carry placards to save the life of some criminal, yet have no thought for the innocent victim. I just can't understand why our national leadership isn't willing to take the responsibility of leadership ... when you allow unlawful acts to go unpunished, you're moving toward a government of men rather than a government of law, you're moving toward anarchy. I've done a lot of things wrong in my life, I'm as imperfect as everyone else. Christ, I don't claim to have the answers, but I feel compelled to bring up the fact that under the guise of doing good, these kids are causing a lot of irreparable damage, and they're starting something they're not going to be able to finish. I can't understand politicians. They're either yellowing out from taking a stand or using outside pressure to improve their own position."

Whilst he stood up for the Alliance, hitting out against Communism, he also lashed the conservatives when he felt they were in the wrong, and in particular over censorship in the industry. Later he even financed his own spots on radio and TV to talk about the danger he saw in that, "I'm glad I won't be around much longer to see what they do with the motion picture industry. The men who control the big studios today are stock manipulators and bankers. They know nothing about our business. They're in it for the buck. Some of these guys remind me of high-class whores. As much as I couldn't stand some of the old-time moguls — especially Harry Cohn — these men took an interest in the future of the business. They had integrity. They took it upon themselves to stop making gangster movies, they were doing a discredit to the country. No censorship from the outside. They were responsible to the public. Today's executives don't give a damn. In their efforts to grab the box-office that these sex pictures are attracting, they're producing garbage. But they're going to reach a point where the American people will say, "The hell with this." And once we do, we'll have censorship in every state and there'll be no way you can even make a worthwhile picture then. But ratings are worthless, every time they rate a picture they let a little more go. Movies used to be made for the whole family, now the average family stays at home and watches television instead." He hated what he called perverted films, but he hated the idea of censorship even more, and fought against it tooth and nail. However bad he felt the films were, and however much harm he considered they did he could not support the Republican attempt to introduce national censorship. He believed in self-censorship from within the industry, a censorship that was dependent on the bankers seeing the error of their ways and suddenly becoming filled with vision, "Don't get me wrong, I'm awfully happy there's a thing called sex. I see no reason why it shouldn't be in pictures. Healthy, lusty sex is wonderful, but when you get hairy sweaty bodies in the foreground, it becomes distasteful. I can remember seeing pictures in the thirties that were wonderfully risqué. They were done with intimation. When you think of the wonderful picture fare we've had through the years and then realise we've come to this shit, it's disgusting. If they want to continue making these films, fine, but my career will have ended. I feel the business is going to fade out from its own vulgarity. When the curious go to see gore and violence they make the bankers think that is what the public want. They seem to forget the one basic principle of our business — illusion. We're in the business of magic. Perhaps we have run out of imagination."

Although he spoke against both that never prevented the Left using his naturally conservative nature to foster an image of extremism. Duke had all the mid-westerner's suspicion of the true believer, whichever side of the fence they sat on, but when he rounded on the Communists he was making up for previously missed chances. He would miss no more and at last he became his own man, the real man he wanted to be. Cooper and Gable were happy reading prepared speeches on behalf of the Alliance, he insisted on writing his own. If he was to speak at all it would be an expression of his own ideas, in his own words. He refused to read from a script. Nothing ever made him shift from that position. He spoke from the heart when he said, "I am not in the Alliance as an actor but as an American."

His intentions were honest but his forthright approach from the late forties onward did much harm to his reputation in the film world throughout the next years. If he had wanted acclaim for his acting talent, rather than for being an American, he knew he should have been less sincere, less naïve, and perhaps should have read the same prepared speeches that Coop and Gable read.

Alliance members co-operated fully with the HUAC, providing detailed lists of known Communists working within the industry, and when subpoenas were issued, the leaders of the Communist Party were correctly targeted. Authorities said there were 50-60 high profile activists at the core of the Hollywood radical movement in the forties, and the HUAC took 19 known left-wingers to court. Although Duke undoubtedly welcomed Government intervention to rid Hollywood of the threat of Communism he always carefully avoided the "naming names" issue so that when the FBI carefully scrutinised Alliance activity there is no mention of John Wayne in any of their detailed reports. When the hearings began in 1947 Alliance members like Cooper, Ronald Reagan, and Robert Taylor, testified against those on the list, but Duke refused to give evidence before the House Committee. He was even prepared to stand in their defence when he thought someone was being unfairly treated.

At each of the hearings the Communists pleaded the Fifth Amendment, standing on their right as American citizens to refuse to discuss their political beliefs, and Duke also believed that an American had as much right to be a Communist as he had to be a Republican or Democrat. On the other hand he knew only to well that the power of the movie was too strong to leave in the hands of Communists who intended to use it to indoctrinate ordinary Americans. His own experiences making films like Back To Bataan had shown how easy the Communists were finding it to force everyone else out of the business. He could not sit back and allow it to happen because they weren't fighting fair.

Whilst few confessed to being members of the communist party, refusal to answer questions meant the end of careers. For most that was preferable to jail, and of those subpoenaed only "The Unfriendly Ten" were sentenced, the rest faced the blacklist. Alliance members claimed that they had been blacklisted for years and Duke agreed, saying members of the MPA were constantly faced with ugly smear campaigns over the years. He opposed any form of blacklist and his own production company never blacklisted anybody, and he remained willing to work with any fellow professional. Non of that made any difference, once he joined The Alliance in 1948 and was elected to its Executive Board, he found himself described as a right-wing extremist. The label stuck and nothing he ever said or did changed the way he was portrayed. He tried to ignore the growing press frenzy against him, but in 1949 when he replaced Robert Taylor as president of The Alliance, he found even some sections of the public turned against him.

He had originally turned the post down but pressure was exerted until he finally gave in. He made a very short acceptance speech, saying he believed both Hollywood and the nation faced a crisis, and that he saw no reason why America should tolerate a political party within, that was controlled by the country's Cold War rival, and that was opposed to the nation's existing political and economic system. He later explained his position more fully, saying he believed the Communists to be both rotten and corrupt, "actually we were the real liberals. We believed in freedom. We believed in the individual and his rights. We hated Soviet Communism because it was against all religion, and because it trampled on the individual, because it was a slave society."

It had been a complex mix of personal worries and international events that led to Duke's political awakening but he found a strange contentment in fighting a cause, in pulling his weight at last. Politics became a distraction from the other problems in his life and he immersed himself in his new crusade, warming to his subject, studying economic policy and political science, determined to be enlightened on every aspect. His prolific reading led him from a vague mistrust of Communism to a hearty dislike and whilst he continued to regard himself as liberal in his outlook, he came to understand why others might see him as conservative.

Because his politics were a mixture of many ideologies, because he walked the way he wanted to go, he left himself wide open to attack from all sides. His opponents were often confused by his stance, and believed him to be ignorant. The Press found he could be provoked into making outrageous comments, which he later tried to explain — the explanations of course were never included in the reports. He made it easy for them to show him as extreme and even stupid. Those who happened to disagree with his views would not be interested in finding out why he held them views. Despite the way the Press represented him, he personally was tolerant of different opinion, even attending President Carter's inaugural celebrations, and calling himself a member of the "loyal opposition."

He liked to talk about the thing he enjoyed most, work, and it depressed him that the only things most people ever wanted to discuss with him were his politics or cancer, and he hated the fact that people either loved or despised him simply because of what they read about his politics. He had never understood why that had been the case, "They say I'm a right wing extremist, a monster, yet I hate politics, I've stood up for one or two people of both sides of the political fence, and for that I'm branded." He had become embroiled in politics but the integrity of the movie industry was really all he cared about. If Hollywood had not been targeted by the Communists in the forties he would have remained forever aloof from a world fraught with personal danger, a world he didn't particularly enjoy inhabiting, a world he didn't really understand. But as with all things "John Wayne" once he got involved he was deeply involved, branded simply because he did everything with such enthusiasm and force. When he made a political statement it was done with absolutely no regard for the rules of the game or the fashions of the day — he said exactly what he thought in a huge voice and in uncompromising language — he did it even though what he thought was completely out of vogue. He could do nothing half-heartedly; full steam ahead was the order of the day and the force of his presence was enormous. He took huge risks and left himself easy prey; he could hardly complain when the Press baited him, setting traps that he fell into time and again. Interviewers generally started talking to him about films, one political question might be tossed in, he would give the rash answers that so delighted them, or even better, a pithy comment that could be printed out of context. It bothered him greatly that his sincerity allowed them to paint him an extremist, "In my own mind I'm liberal to the point where I listen to every point of view, which I believe takes me out of the extremist class on both sides. And I have much love for my fellow man, and I enjoy them as much as anyone. I wish I could show you the mail I get everyday … I've got two secretaries, one just to separate the fan mail from the other kind."

He believed he was deliberately misrepresented, particularly in the infamous *Playboy* interview that he gave in 1971, where he made some flippant and extreme remarks and emerged looking racist, authoritarian, a superpatriot and a reactionary. Lewis, the editor of Playboy, took on the role of Prosecutor, and sharply cross-examined him about his attitude to Indians, Communists and politics in general. Throughout the interview he was questioned and then not permitted to clarify his answers. Naively, Duke allowed him to get away with it, "My remarks were taken out of context, blown up out of all proportion. They would not take a premise. I thought that was obvious in the *Playboy* interview. Now I've done as much as any man to give human dignity to the Indian. I assume the Indians know that I have a great deal of respect for them. Well this guy (Lewis) and I were talking about funny things and he says, "Well, what do you think about the Indians taking over Alcatraz?"

Well, it's such a ridiculous thing. What did he want, a serious comment about it? So I said, "Let them have it. Nobody that ever lived there wants to go back and none of the guards wants it. I think they ought to pay for it, like we paid for Manhattan." Now when it comes out in the magazine it came right after something serious, so all of a sudden I start getting letters from Indians. It looked like I was belittling them, and I wasn't. I was talking about a bunch of jerks, not the entire race. Good God, they're American citizens, they have every right we have and some we don't. I always tried, in my pictures to show the Indian as noble. I, probably more than any one else in the industry, gave them an image of a strong moral-coded people."

Lewis had been searching for the headlines he wanted, he wasn't interested in printing the truth, he was printing the legend. He gave thousands of dollars away to anyone in trouble, even buying clothes for complete strangers, people only had to put pen to paper to ask for his help and he gave whatever they wanted. He just didn't like being told by government what to spend his money on. Despite the fact that everyone knew he was a soft touch his acts of generosity were rarely reported.

From the mid forties onward Duke's political convictions were also shaped by his worries about his personal financial situation. For the first time in his life he was earning large amounts of money, and seeing his tax bill rocket accordingly. In 1944 he owed the Government 68% of his earnings if he took more than $100,000 a year, 88.6% when his income was in excess of $500,000. Mary St John said, "He worried about taxes all the time I worked for him. Sometimes he felt there was no point in working so hard when so much of what he earned went straight to the government. Especially as he hated politicians and big government." He always voted for the government that promised to reduce tax burdens and to cut spending on programmes he didn't support. For a man raised in the Midwestern conservatism of Iowa, it was as natural as day to support the Republican party, and by the late 1940's he began his rebellion against the New Deal taxation and spending policies of the Democrats, saying, "Human behaviour won't change much. We're being conned into Keynesianism and socialism right now, but it isn't going to stop the selfishness of human behaviour. It isn't going to stop the greed. If you take twenty dollars and give a dollar to every son of a bitch in a room and come back a year later, one of the bastards will have all the money. It's just human nature, you're not going to whip it with laws. I think as communication gets better and you make people conscious of somebody in trouble, the average person will help. I'm optimistic about that."

Although he naturally sided with the actors guild, the fact that the philosophy of the Alliance coincided more or less with his own had been good luck rather than judgement on his part. Still, the instant he saw America heading into The Cold War and understood the outcome might be disastrous, the painfully exposed nerve had been touched, "It was a confused time, dissension because one clique wouldn't go along with another. Hysteria on the Right, the liberal writers trying to run people out of the business. High taxation, high government spending, blacklisting, the threat of Communism. "He could not ignore what was happening any longer and the position he took could never have been in any doubt. Still he found it all an irritant, something demanding time he could ill afford. He would have preferred to keep making films, non-stop, for that was the only time he was really happy, the only time he was focussed. External circumstances had eventually forced him into action, but he was a man with little patience or time for the external aspects of life, or even the lives of others. It was his total dedication that had made him a star in the first place, effort that set him apart, and above all the other stars of his era. Now he was being pulled and pushed in directions he didn't want to go.

Whenever he spoke about accepting the presidency of The Alliance he talked about the atmosphere of the time, the influence of his friends, about his tax problems, and the danger to the industry and the country he loved; he never mentioned the guilt he felt about the war. Mary believed he definitely regretted not having served, and that guilt was the prime mover in his decision, "He was not the kind of man to dwell on it or talk about it, but you always knew he did. You could see it in his face when anyone mentioned his war record. He would just tell them that he had not served, and it made him feel like a hypocrite."

If he had managed to avoid trouble before, his acceptance of the presidency at exactly the time the Cold War was entering its toughest phase put him in harm's way more than he could ever have anticipated. To him and to people around the world it appeared that the Communists were willing to go to war to achieve their objectives-it was not an idle threat and the dangers were real. The intention of Russia and the Communist Block was the destruction of the Capitalist system. He stood as president for four years from 1949 to 1953 — the most crucial years of the Cold War, years that saw Communist victory in China, that saw the Soviet Union successfully detonate the atomic bomb, the emergence of Joseph McCarthy, and the outbreak of the Korean War. It was a period that shaped the political futures of many and turned Duke into an outspoken advocate of the right. He was dragged unwillingly into the fray but once there he stood his ground and shouted his beliefs for all to hear, including those who mocked him, at the top of his voice, and by some miracle whilst he became the butt of the progressive elements he also made the politics of the right popular and acceptable to many who might otherwise have found Conservatism staid, abhorrent or even just boring. His politics were those of the establishment, but he had never been seen as part of the system, his image had always been that of the loner, the individual, "I've always rebelled against something in society. I was never much of a joiner. Kids join things, but they like to consider themselves individuals capable of thinking for themselves. So do I. Mine is a personal rebellion against the monotony of life, against status quo. The rebellion of today's kids seems to be a kind of dissension by rote." When John Wayne said something, even though the Press and the Left attacked him for saying it, people listened. Because he said it, it became possible for other people to stand up and admit they too supported the right. He might be ridiculed mercilessly for his patriotism, but it also won him the adoration of millions of like-minded souls, "John Wayne is a champion, but out on the streets no one claims him." His intentions were honest, he didn't fool around, he said what he meant, there was no coyness about his words. He was an easy and obvious target because he didn't hide in an era of security leaks, loyalty oaths, the enemy within, political paranoia, an era when whole nations rose and fell and of wholesale change to the values and systems of world governments, when nations were seen as "absolutely good or absolutely evil."

Duke navigated the raging domestic political waters with some success, at least he didn't go under like so many others. People instinctively felt that when he said something he was telling the truth. In every Press release he gave out the same message he exuded from the screen, and his private life became further entangled with public perception. Increasingly the images became blurred in his own mind as well as in those of his audience. As the classic nineteenth century hero of the screen he had always been identified with the American ideal of self sufficiency and individualism, he had lovingly created the image over many years. And John Wayne, the man, was a survivor, was himself a typical product of 19th century America. He was becoming one with the screen persona, turning into the living incarnation of the Western hero he so often played, racing to the defence of society, the 19th century hero defending 20th century culture. He was undoubtedly displaced in time, but still, in an age of hype and hysteria his words held the constant steadfast ring of truth, people trusted what he said because he was "John Wayne," a personality generated in the public mind through a film image of quality, strength and honesty, repeated time after time, repetition solidifying his stature as an honest man. John Wayne did not lie. He was a man of his word, and even the unforgiving media gave out the message, it was safe to trust what John Wayne said. When he said that Hollywood housed a high proportion of communists who were tearing the industry and the town apart, were forcing decent people out of work, everyone knew it must be the truth.

Duke's highly emotional and all-out attack on the Communists made him unpopular in some quarters but it also touched the hearts of the millions of Americans that Duke called "The silent minority." His importance to the Right lay in the warm affection in which he was held by those people and in the immense attraction of his screen image. They used him mercilessly in an age of political hysteria, making him the voice of the right.

During the forties many producers promised the actors of the Alliance that they wouldn't employ communist writers, or anyone who they suspected of advocating the overthrow of the American government by force or illegal means. Duke knew the producers never kept their word and that if they had done the situation might have eased quickly and without any of the ensuing difficulties. A handful of the three hundred Hollywood Communists might have been blacklisted, but members of The Alliance said it was their members who continued to suffer at the hands of the producers who felt Alliance members made it difficult to get on with the job of making films. They preferred not to employ its members, and during the late forties and early fifties many right-wing actors also found themselves unemployable. When Duke joined the Alliance he faced enormous danger from within the industry. He stood at the watershed of his life, following the release and successes of *Fort Apache*, *Red River* and *Three Godfathers*. Herbert Yates advised him once again to stay out of trouble as he still desperately tried to protect his interest, his star was worth more to him now than he had been at any other time. Yates had successfully kept him out of the war, now he warned, "This'll put you on the skids in Hollywood Duke." All his financial advisors agreed and advised him, "Just keep your head down and keep working." This time he would listen to no one. He hoped, but was far from certain, that his position in the industry was strong enough now to enable him to say what he wanted, but later admitted, "I was a victim of a mud-slinging campaign like you wouldn't believe — I was called a drunk, a pervert, a woman-chaser, a lousy B picture western bit player, an unfaithful husband, an uneducated jerk, a tool of the studio heads."

By his second term as President the Executive Committee of the Alliance had stated that Communists constituted a clear and present danger to society and demanded that all members of the party should be registered by Los Angeles City Council. Registration was seen as a step toward "delousing Hollywood." By 1951 The Screen Actors Guild, The Screen Directors Guild and even the Screen Writers Guild openly supported the HUAC, and had all offered their complete co-operation and support.

When the HUAC first targeted the communists in Hollywood they offered them the choice of confessing, renouncing their beliefs and getting on with their lives, or face going to jail or being blacklisted. Those who confessed were expected to name other communists. Americans were worried about the inroad Communism was making into the American way of life through the back door, through the movie industry, but The Red Scare was not just an issue in Hollywood and the film world, and anti-communist activity extended well beyond the brief of the HUAC. The country's two leading unions purged its membership of Communists, and opposed US recognition of the Soviet Union. The Executive Council of the Congress of Industrial Organisations said in the early fifties, "If Communism is an issue in any of your unions throw it the hell out ... and throw its advocates out along with it. When a man accepts office ... paid office in a union ... to render service to workers, and then delivers service to outside interests, that man is nothing but a damned traitor." The Purges were even common in left wing organisations, to the extent that the only organization open to American Communists at the time was the Communist Party of the United States of America itself. Duke was hardly out of step in his beliefs and what he said was more than acceptable in mainstream America. He tended to be a little softer in his personal attitude toward the communists than most, and he was always willing to forgive. Hollywood, under his leadership, was happy to welcome back former Communists who confessed to the HUAC. He stood open armed accepting them back into the fold, despite the clamour for their heads throughout the rest of the country and even his own industry. When Larry Parks (Al Jolson in *The Al Jolson Story*) was told he would not be used again in Hollywood if he did not name names, the question of his blacklisting was put to Duke. He agreed to speak up on Parks behalf, "I wanted to say something good about him. This was a crucial issue. Parks was breaking not just with the Party but with all his friends. He needed our moral support so other witnesses would be encouraged to break." Duke felt sorry for Parks, who had begged for forgiveness from the industry. He believed it should be freely given and he certainly felt the deepest unease over the naming names issue himself.

After speaking up for Parks he attended a meeting of The Alliance. He stood on stage before an audience of over a thousand motion picture workers to announce Hedda Hopper, the powerful right wing columnist. She rounded on him, attacking him without warning or mercy, "I was shocked as I read the statement of our president John Wayne ... I'm wondering if the mothers and families of those who have died and the wounded who are still living will be happy to know their money at the box-office has supported and may continue to support those who have been so late in the defence of their country?" Duke made no reply. Her unprovoked and unprecedented attack caused uproar at the meeting, some defending the furiously blushing Duke, others supporting Hopper. As a body, The Alliance decided not to support him over the Parks issue, saying they didn't feel it was safe to trust any person who had been a communist. Duke was devastated, both by the unexpected ferocity and personal nature of the attack, and by the failure of the Alliance to support him. He trusted everybody, opposed the blacklist, and was uncomfortable about Hopper and Bond who clearly felt all communists should be run out of town. Now he also stood alone against his so-called friends, too tolerant for them, when he told the highly charged meeting that any person who co-operated with the HUAC should be free to continue working within the industry. The difference between him and Bond, and one member of The Alliance and another, seemed thin to the Hollywood Left, but over these issues the division was vast. Duke stood resolutely on one side, and Bond and most of the rest of The Alliance members on the other side of a line that separated the conservative from the reactionary, "You'd not believe this but at that meeting one member even suggested The Alliance recommend a "preventative war" against the Soviet Union! That was how strongly people felt about things back then. Back then, you'd have called me Radical, 'cause I talked them out of that one!" Duke later recounted with a mighty roar of laughter.

When Geraldine Page worked on *Hondo* with Duke and Bond in 1953 she said she was horrified by Bond's attitude, "John Wayne would talk so sensibly and Ward Bond was just an oversimplifying bully-when I listened it seemed that John would wander out towards something that made sense to me and then director John Farrow would take what he had said and twist it into something else, Duke was a reactionary for all sorts of non-reactionary reasons ... I swear that if John Wayne ever got transplanted out of this circle of people that are around him all the time, he would be the most un-reactionary force for good." She had hit on the truth. Decency and human dignity ranked high on the code that Duke lived by. His politics were pure and simple-he felt an urgent, gut instinct to protect his country during the Cold War, it was under attack from the inside, he had not gone to its defence before, but he would not fail again, he had to protect the American way of life whatever the personal cost.

On a personal and professional level things could not have been more different. He was tolerant of the mistakes individuals might make, he had made so many himself after all, but he was much less tolerant of an industry that was busy producing films like *All The Kings's Men*, that famous Oscar-winning film originally offered to him. He spoke openly and at great length about the movies that he found distasteful in the extreme. He could not forgive film-makers who criticised American tradition and institutions and he hated the idea of using movies to get over a political message, hated it because he understood the power of the message. Still, by the early 1950's he changed his mind, deciding that if it was OK for the radicals to do it then maybe he should try it himself. He began making his own statements through the films that his company produced.

He hated making speeches and found getting up on stage difficult, particularly after Hopper's attack. He was uncomfortable in meetings and committee sessions, too restless an animal to sit quietly, waiting for his moment to come. He knew that saying what he wanted to in a film, his natural medium, was a much easier way to reach people and it became an obvious alternative. He was far happier saying the things that really mattered to him when he was removed from his audience, when he was up on screen, safe from sudden hostility.

He still had to make personal appearances of course, when he was expected to make statements, and difficult though he found it, as he got older, he became more adept. In 1972 he agreed to accompany Bob Hope to talk on the USC campus. Hope told Duke he would get a monologue scripted for his use. Duke replied, "Hell, no. I write my own speeches," but when Hope saw what he planned to say he told him, "Duke, you just can't say those kind of things to students anymore." He suggested changes, and tried again to get him to accept a script, but Duke stubbornly stood his ground and would not consider alterations. He strode out to centre stage and Hope took himself off to the safety of the wings where he hoped to avoid the textbooks and other missiles that he anticipated flying in Duke's direction. Duke, ex-USC student, took a mouthful of tequila before starting to talk about the resentment he personally felt about the trouble being stirred up by radical students. He told them that a university should be a place of learning, a place to share intellectual maturing, and to enjoy socialising, a place to acquire a feeling of responsibility. He told them they should consider being respectful toward their teachers and the buildings and facilities they shared. He told them about his love for his own fraternity, Sigma Chi, and about how much USC had done for him. He explained that Californian taxpayers were tired of the damage that the students were doing at the university, and he reminded them that it belonged to those taxpayers, not to the students. At first he was met by loud booing, but gradually the students fell under his charm as they listened to what he had to say, and finally, mesmerized by his presence, they gave him a standing ovation. The youthful rebellion was touched by his honesty and that something that was special about him, touched by that the same something that made his conservatism attractive to so many. There was something naturally pleasing about his individualism and strength and the students warmed to him as they listened and appreciated what he told them that day. Bob Hope couldn't believe that Duke emerged with his scalp in tact, much less that the kids actually cheered when he finished.

Though he continued to make public appearances he now much preferred putting his message across on film. Through the fifties in particular he made a string of uninspiring movies, all carrying his personal message of duty and loyalty, and a warning to guard against internal subversion. He might do his career untold damage by running from the political platform into the film world, that warm, safe place, and yet strangely, despite the poor quality of the films he turned out, he continued to be America's leading box-office attraction. Nothing, not poor films, nor lousy scripts written for him by his friend Jimmy Grant, not his presidency of The Alliance touched his popularity at box-office, and he remained on top of his world. He understood the power of the business and because his fans continued to flock to see anything he made, he was increasingly convinced it was time to put his own dreams on film.

All the people in his life had their own unfulfilled dreams. John Ford's wanted to return home to make a film about the mythical land he imagined was Ireland. Yates wanted to create a new profile for Republic. And Duke dreamed of making a film that talked to Americans of their past, present and future, talked about patriotism and about what was right with America. The three men, whose lives had been interwoven for so long walked separate paths, but they all arrived at the crossroads at the same time. The very dreams that had brought them together now became the ones that drove them apart.

John Ford had first seen the short story, "The Quiet Man" in 1933. In 1935 it was expanded to become the best seller — "Green Rushes." It occupied his mind for well over a decade, and as early as 1944 he spoke to Maureen O'Hara about making a film based on the story. She had agreed to make herself available whenever he was ready. He had handshake agreements with Duke, Victor McLaglen and Barry Fitzgerald, but financing his dream proved far from easy. He pleaded and badgered RKO, Warners and Fox with determination but none of them had any interest in a light story set in Ireland that couldn't make money, no matter who he had lined up to star in it. Seventeen years flew by and Duke said, "Each year Maureen and I held our summer open and each year there was no money to make the film." But Ford refused to abandon the vision and between 1947 and 1950 he made five Westerns under his company banner always with the stars he wanted to use in *The Quiet Man*.

Finally Duke gave him the chance to make his dream, putting together Yates the cash register and Ford the creative genius, "As long as I was stuck at Republic, I thought I might as well try to get Jack to come out there too. I knew Yates wanted to start making A-pictures. I told him he should get Ford to come and make pictures at Republic. If he got him, then other big directors would come too." Yates asked what he would have to do to get Ford to agree, Duke replied, "Let him make a property he owns called *The Quiet Man*. Give him fifteen percent of the gross and tell him no one checks his budgets." Ford would be given his chance to make his dream, and Yates also saw his opportunity. He nodded his head, wrote a contract out there and then in pencil, signed it and handed it to Duke to give to Ford next time he saw him.

Duke rushed straight around to see Pappy that night. Ford read the contact carefully, screwed it into a ball and threw it into the fireplace. He didn't say a word to Duke, who recalled, "He never said, Duke that's a hell of a deal, but I don't trust Yates — he never said another word about it! I thought he was mad at me for buttin' into his private affairs where I had no business." Once more he was mystified by his mentor; he had given him his chance to make his picture, he had given Yates his chance, had agreed to work on the film cheap, and it had all been thrown back at him. In fact the mentor probably resented the power his star pupil had acquired and didn't like being handed out favours by him.

But no one else came forward, no other opportunity arose and eventually he signed his own deal with Yates who insisted, "I'll finance *The Quiet Man* on one condition. I want you to make a western with the same cast, same director, same everybody, to make up some of the money I'm going to lose on the Irish story." And the Ford Stock company went to work on *Rio Grande*, the masterpiece made very much on the cheap in Utah in 1950. It was a huge box-office hit, and on the back of it, Ford was given permission to go ahead with *The Quiet Man* that summer.

Rio Grande teamed Duke and Maureen O'Hara for the first time. There was an immediate and obvious chemistry between them. She was not only his perfect physical match, he also liked her very much, "Maureen O'Hara is one of the most delightful, charming women that I have ever had the pleasure of meeting. I enjoy every minute of working with her. She is a professional and she comes ready to work." He could treat her as an equal, she presented no threat, he could talk to her easily because she spoke her mind in the honest and forthright manner that he respected. Whenever he lost his temper on set she was one of the few who could ever control him as she pointed an accusing finger in his direction, and shouted, "Go and sit down for a while until you cool off."

Many looked at him and considered him a simple cowboy, a man who personified the rough, macho male-bonding professional. He was consistently shown as clumsy around women, treating them all with a wide-eyed innocence, even fear, but he was steadfastly uncomplicated and honest in his intentions toward them.

Whilst he was regarded as an inept lover, directors always set him opposite women of charm and spirit, and over the years he became expert at portraying passion, loneliness, and world-weariness as his own romances faltered. Ford in particular loved the way he unfailingly underplayed his feelings, preferring Duke's sad expression of loss to the false tears shed by so many other actors. *Rio Grande* gave him ample scope to express loneliness in a story of lost love. He and O'Hara leaped off the screen and into the hearts of the audience, and it was then that they practised moments of tenderness and bitterness, losing and later rediscovering love and happiness, in preparation for *The Quiet Man*.

Altogether, the stars, director, and even Yates were pleased with the outcome, it was the perfect film to precede *The Quiet Man*, which was the first Republic picture shot outside the United States. Because Ford insisted on using Technicolor, it also had the highest budget of any Republic film to date, and Yates was still far from enthusiastic about the anticipated outcome, calling it a film that no one would pay to see. Late in the day he called Duke into his office to spell out the on-going dangers he saw for the studio, insisting that the part of Sean Thornton was wrong for him and that it would harm his career. His constant complaints and obvious lack of faith rattled both him and Ford. Between them they agreed to cut some of the production costs and Maureen and Duke starred in the film for well below their standard rates. Whilst Duke was holidaying in South America Ford cabled him "After much fuss and feathers, much wrangling, fist fights and harsh words the budget is set excepting, of course, for your salary."

When they all eventually got to Ireland everything should have been perfect for Ford, but although many of his family and friends went on location with him, he was far from happy. He worried about the politics of the story and suddenly jettisoned much of the script, deciding that the atmosphere of heavy IRA politics didn't mix well with the comic love story that he was personally more concerned with. The politics went, and then he was left concerned that perhaps Yates had been right, perhaps a simple love story wouldn't stand up on its own, with or without Duke and Maureen. Then, a third of the way through filming, he became ill, or rather, too drunk to continue directing. He and Duke had made a pact not to drink whilst they were working in Ireland, both broke it from time to time; Duke discovering a lasting passion for Irish beer and the social life of the village pubs, but Ford was in bad humour and he took to his bed to drink alone. He was used to working where everything was geared to getting the best product, now he was with Republic, where the only thing that mattered was getting the cheapest. Duke said, "In all the years I knew and loved Jack Ford, I never saw him so down and so willing to admit his fears." He was deeply worried about the director and told him to get some rest and that he would oversee everything himself.

Their relationship was severely tested and they had several huge blow-ups on location. One was caused when Ford, in an attempt to cut costs, refused to allow Duke's personal make-up man to travel to Ireland with them. But his skin was sensitive to make-up and his face was soon swollen and sore after a bad reaction. So much for saving money — production was delayed as they waited for Web Overlander to arrive in Ireland. Again, Ford's economies led to Web doubling up as an extra when he wasn't attending to the star. Other arguments arose daily because Duke had become such a perfectionist that if he thought he could do a scene better he demanded a reshoot, much to Ford's annoyance, who still preferred using the first take. Duke described one major confrontation, "It was a scene where Maureen goes and slams the door and locks me out. The way they had written it, I go over, pick up my boxing gloves and throw them into the fire. Well, shit! They had me kow-towing and saying "Yes Ma'am" and "No Ma'am" all the damn time. I was beginning to wonder if they were ever going to let me show some balls! I brought this up with Pappy and he just gave me a dirty look. But he did later change the scene, "Duke I'm going to let you do what you always do when a broad locks you out. I'm going to let you kick the fucking door down." It was a goddamn hard script for me. For nine reels, I was just playing a straight man to those wonderful characters, and that was really hard. I had to fight for my place in it." Fighting for his place was just business as usual for Duke, and confrontation no longer bothered him as it had once done, perhaps that was one reason Ford drank alone in Ireland.

Duke had taken Chata along on the trip even though they were in desperate trouble. He enjoyed the time he spent with her there. He was in expansive mood, happy and relaxed. He fell in love with Ireland and when shooting finished ahead of schedule he stayed behind long after the others had all returned home. He and Chata went on a protracted pub crawl, drinking heavily in celebration. He, in particular, was in no hurry to go home, he was enjoying the time with his wife, far from the pressures of Hollywood. She rarely went on location with him, they had spent so little time together, but in Ireland they enjoyed each other's company again — for perhaps the last time.

Ford's casting of Duke and O'Hara for *The Quiet Man* was a stroke of genius. One critic commented, "*The Quiet Man* pairing of Wayne-O'Hara becomes one of the highest evocations of passion — suppressed on film. Wayne is seen as unmanly by O'Hara because he won't fight for her dowry, no one but Wayne, the epitome of masculinity, could have played the role with such conviction. Because O'Hara plays the Irish prude it falls to Wayne to play the erotic role, though he has no dominance over her." In fact he found the suppressed love scenes very difficult, "It was tough … Really uncomfortable filming the scene in the churchyard where we are both soaking wet. Jack wanted me to hold her so close! It was what he wanted to do himself of course." His expression of lonely frustration was put to full effect.

The finishing touches were added as soon as he arrived back in Hollywood and it was screened for the heads at Republic. Yates hated it, he even hated the title, considering it too weak for a John Wayne film. Yates wasn't the only one who worried. Even Duke had serious reservations, considering himself little more than the straight man, only there to set up lines for everyone else, he had enjoyed working in Ireland but it hadn't been easy and he had found the role professionally taxing. But he trusted Ford and was confident about his own persona; he hoped it would be enough to carry the day. And Ford was exactly spot on with the film, right to assume that the audience would understand that whilst it was John Wayne playing Sean Thornton, Sean Thornton was John Wayne, and soon enough the quiet man would roar! It was the very fact that the audience did know John Wayne that carried the whole premise of the film.

It may have been OK for Wayne to trust Ford's instincts, but Yates didn't. When he first saw it he feared he had a disaster on his hands. He demanded cuts were made in what he considered an overlong film that looked "too green." But long before the film had even been fully edited, and despite Yates' worries, everyone else around the studio was talking about it. Mary recalled people walking round after seeing it shaking their heads in awe, and when it was finally released the critics raved about it. Suddenly Yates was a believer, saying, "I never doubted its success for a minute."

On Oscar night Wayne collected Ford's award for best director for *The Quiet Man*. He also collected the award for best actor on behalf of Gary Cooper for "High Noon" — the fact that he won nothing himself wasn't lost on Hollywood insiders, who knew how unfairly he was always treated come Oscar time. The awards that year followed the HUAC hearings and people in the business were playing for keeps. The industry recognised that Duke didn't even get a nomination that year because of his presidency of the Motion Picture Alliance. Mary said "Duke's politics definitely hurt him. *The Quiet Man* was his best performance to date. In a film nominated for a half dozen awards he was simply ignored."

The film grossed well but Ford believed Republic was cheating him by not paying his promised percentage. Ford turned his venom not on Yates but on Duke, blaming him for getting him involved with the head of a B-studio in the first place, conveniently forgetting it had been he and Yates who enabled him to make his picture. In the end Yates coughed up and Ford patched up his differences with Duke. The star himself was less forgiving of Yates. He had always been uncomfortable about Republic's business practices, and as far as he was concerned there could be no excuse for trying to cheat Ford. At the same time old man Yates had been trying to cheat Ford he had also tried to back out of a promise that he had made to him personally. To Duke that was unforgivable.

The Quiet Man had been Ford's dream. Making A-movies had been Yates', but Duke had a dream of his own. For seven years he had been waiting to make a film about the men who had been willing to stand and fight for their beliefs at the Alamo, "Yates had promised me I could do this picture, I had found a location … a really perfect setting." Now, with *The Quiet Man* finished he turned his full attention to his own dream. He had budgeted his film at $3 million, but suddenly Yates told him there would be no location shooting, it would be made on the Republic lot, he wanted to cut down on extras, wanted to shoot the film in black and white, and everything he suggested cheapened the vision. They had many violent shouting matches over it, with one or other of them usually storming away in temper. Once, Duke marched out of his office without telling Mary where he was going. He called her half an hour later and told her to pack all their things up, "We're moving." He was furious and no quiet words from her placated him, "I've sent a truck round to pick up my personal things." She hurried to do as she was told, ignoring the Republic staff who got in her way. At the same time the van arrived a bemused Yates appeared. Mary told him curtly, "He's gone." He ordered her to stop packing, "Who are you working for, him or me?" — She answered his screams with quiet determination, "Duke." She picked up her own belongings and also walked out of Republic. Neither ever returned. Herbert Yates had lost his biggest asset, he had also lost America's most popular movie star. Within ten years of Duke leaving, Republic had completely fallen out of the movie business.

He could have walked out for either one of Yate's big mistakes that year; cheating Ford or trying to frustrate his own plans. He had stayed at Republic for six years longer than he needed to. At any time he could have used his popularity to negotiate a better deal elsewhere but loyalty had been important to him, and he had stuck with his original contract. Of course Republic had also been like family, he had worked there amongst friends, felt safe and unthreatened, he had been happy. But Yates had pushed him too far and now he dug spurred heels in, stubbornly refusing to listen to anything else the old man offered.

At the time, although the studios still controlled the industry, their grip was weaker than it had been after a 1950 court decision gave independent producers the right to arrange distribution of their own films. Duke decided to take a chance at last, "Sink or swim, working independently had to be better than working for men like Yates and Cohn." He became one of the first stars to form his own production company, Wayne-Fellows. When other's saw how well he and Robert Fellows were doing they rushed to establish their own companies. Duke said he wanted a bigger slice of the pie, but what he really wanted was more control. He hated the power that producers had over creativity and once told his son, "You're not supposed to point, but it's permissible to point to select a French pastry or to point at producers." The producers job was to make sure no money was wasted but to Duke it was criminal to save money by taking short cuts. He accepted there was never enough money to go round but thought what there was should be spent creatively, up on the screen. He hated the role of the producer and thought by going into that line of business himself he could cut the problem out of his life, "Producing my own films was worth all the added stress and effort. Gave me increased artistic freedom and better economic reward, my earning potential rocketed without my having to do anything. I could decide what I made, who I worked with, I had control over script selection and development." Stars with high salaries paid up to ninety percent in tax, but if that star formed his own company to make a picture and didn't pay himself a salary then sold his interest in that film as a capital asset he only paid twenty five percent tax on its earnings. Even if he chose to pay himself a salary, the tax paid as a company director was just sixty percent.

As corporate tax rates were less than those of an individual a company was a sensible place to shelter capital! Duke had never been a wealthy man despite all his years in the industry, "Last year I made over $500,000. Though I live conservatively in a three bedroom house and I don't throw parties, I'm all but broke — still, I don't owe a dime in taxes!"

He wasn't broke but he had a point. He had never lived like a Hollywood star was expected to live, and he hoped his new company would enable him to close the gap between the illusions of his fans and the realities of his life. Wayne-Fellows allowed him to make creative decisions whilst Bob Fellows controlled finances. Fellows had been around the business as long as Duke and they had known each other since 1940. They shared a deep love of the film industry. Neither feared the spread of television as most of the rest of Hollywood did, neither was worried about the future of the industry, both were confident they could carry on making films that people would pay to see.

Shortly after going into partnership Fellows signed a deal with Warner Bros. On behalf of the new company. Duke already had a multi picture deal with the studio and he liked Jack Warner personally, but the contract Fellows signed worried him. It was exclusive and would have prevented him working for another studio and that defeated the object of setting up as an independent. He pushed for a non-exclusive deal and eventually, despite his friend's arguments, he signed a non-exclusive deal with Warners who agreed to finance and distribute Wayne-Fellows productions and to pay Duke at least $150,000 per film and ten percent of gross receipts.

As he became increasingly involved in national politics he used his new position as an independent producer to serve his own ends. The Hollywood Left always thought he was suspiciously well informed and believed he received inside information, in truth he was only just starting to move away from his interest in local problems, and telling anyone who would listen that world issues had become too serious to ignore. The country was involved in Korea, President Truman's popularity was on the wane and the Republican party sensed that at last Democratic control was coming to an end. The Republicans promised to cut taxes, reduce Government spending and Duke gave his wholehearted support to Sen Robert Taft. Moderate Republicans thought Taft was too far to the Right to win much support, but as usual Duke had no interest in compromise candidates. He liked what Taft had to say but admitted his delivery was stiff and that he needed to work on his image; if anyone knew about image it was Duke. He wanted to help, but before the Republican convention Duke was already back at work for Warner Bros. He decided that if Taft's image was all wrong, if he couldn't be relied on to deliver the

Republican message, then he could. He began making films that he personally hated, like *Big Jim McLain*, a frank and preachy propaganda film, warning decent Americans about the dangers of Communism. There were many anti-communist films coming out, all generally failures. Duke wanted to make a controversial picture that would generate profit. He was so successful with it that even the FBI took an interest in the project and J. Edgar Hoover started investigating him. FBI interest combined with viscous attacks by the liberals led Duke to predict a box-office bonanza. As usual, he had his finger on the pulse, the public loved it. Audience reaction to this picture proved that if his politics were out of step with the Eastern critics, they were mainstream everywhere else. The success of the film was remarkable and a clear sign that he had been right in believing himself exempt from the general decline in the film industry, also that he was right in step as far as his political beliefs went. The major film reviewers disliked him, his films and his politics, it hardly mattered anymore, he had risen above all that. The pattern laid down then was perpetuated for the rest of his career, poor east coast reviews, Republican politics, very successful movies.

Whilst he worked on *Big Jim McLean* his marriage to Chata took a sudden turn for the worse, and their final fight occurred in Hawaii as it was being filmed. In a last ditch attempt to patch things up he had taken her with him on a boat trip to the islands, inviting her to share a second honeymoon. He still loved her, still wanted her, but he found out on that trip that he actually didn't like her very much. Almost as soon as they set sail she began drinking, and as usual, as soon as she had a drink she started looking for a fight. They argued bitterly throughout the voyage and even when they disembarked in Honolulu they continued shouting. Duke had allowed himself a week's holiday before shooting started, it was a week filled with furious conflict. She cried, she spat, she threw things at him and she cursed. That same John Wayne who refused to cringe for Howard Hawks certainly did so when Chata started swearing.

In 1947 he had attended all the award ceremonies alone following a blazing argument with her. She had wanted to go on location with him when he made *Fort Apache*. Violence erupted when he explained that Ford wouldn't let her. She fled to Mexico, setting a pattern for all their future arguments. She stayed away for months, giving rise to gossip and much speculation, but he always denied they had separated. Once he had cooled off he followed her and pleaded with her to return. That had been the start, but the same thing happened over and over after that, and his life consisted of arguments, fights, running after Chata and making up. He had developed an ulcer and John Ford worried about the health and emotional state of his favourite son. He wrote to him begging him not to ruin his life over her. To his cost, Duke paid no attention.

The day before filming began on *Big Jim McLean* Duke wanted to get to bed early, but Chata insisted that they attend a party being given in their honour by the Vanderbilts. Duke went along reluctantly, and warned his hosts that he couldn't stay long as he had an early morning shoot. At nine o'clock he tried to get Chata to leave the party. She was already very drunk and refused to go. For another two hours he tried to persuade her to leave. Finally at eleven he left for the hotel alone and asked the Vanderbilts to put her in a taxi when she was ready. At four o'clock in the morning he received a phone call from the hosts saying Chata would not leave and he had to come and get her. He sent a driver to collect her, but she would not move for him either. An hour later Duke received another frantic call, "Please come and get this Mexican bitch out of my house!" Just before seven the next morning Chata wandered into the hotel just as he sat down to breakfast. She had hitch-hiked back from the party, she had no shoes on and her dress was torn. He asked her if she wanted to talk about what had happened but she refused, "Nothing happened, I had a great time at the party after you left. That's all." She staggered to the lift and he went to work.

Only a few days later they attended another party and exactly the same situation arose; Chata got drunk and he wanted to go back to the hotel. This time he was really angry and tired after a hard days filming. He threw her shawl to the ground in temper and physically dragged her away, not wanting any more early hour calls. Back at the hotel he got no rest, all hell let loose as he pounded the walls with his fists in frustration, calling her vile names, and throwing pillows at her. The next day she booked a flight home when he told her he had finally had enough, that the arguments were too painful for him to bear. He had taken her to Hawaii to try to rekindle their marriage, it ended with her leaving him.

He had put up with his mother in law living with them for over two years before he finally told Chata to choose either him or her mother. Duke knew she needed her mother but felt she was a bad influence. Chata was an alcoholic who drank even more when she was with her mother, and he bore the scars to prove she was more violent when she was with her too. He had always believed that if he could cut the emotional cord between them he could have had the wife he wanted, so he bought a new house for her in Mexico. Chata found it very difficult living without her and she fled back there so often that he found it impossible to even begin to sort their problems out. At first she ran back for a week, then a month and then several months at a time, and by 1948 and 1949 she was spending more time in Mexico than with him. Strangely, he never considered such times as separations, they were just both sulking, long distance. As far as he was concerned he still loved her, and he was often away from home for months at a time himself, he couldn't complain if Chata went home to her mother now and again. His work put a tremendous strain on them both, and he understood her loneliness. He didn't mind her going to Mexico while he was on location, but he needed her home when he got back. On the occasions when she wasn't he usually went down after her to beg her to come home. He spent hours crying and pleading, telling her how much he needed her. She said, "He called himself a big jerk, and told me he knew how horrible he was to me, and that he would try to do better, that he just needed one more chance."

In 1949 she returned to Los Angeles for a while but at Christmas 1950 she told him she was going back to Mexico. It was summer 1951 before she returned, just before they all went to Ireland to film *The Quiet Man*, where she had been relaxed, even getting on with his children and drinking less. Stupidly he believed they still had a chance, if he could only get her to stop running away. As soon as they got back to Hollywood she demanded that her mother come back to live with them.

They needed to talk openly about their marriage, Chata didn't want to and he was usually too busy to make the effort. She did though confess to being jealous of his work, his friends, and she told him she resented the time he spent away from her, that she was lonely and depressed. Duke was so terrified of failing in another marriage that, after listening to her, he decided to do his best to please her in every way he could think of. Much of his effort consisted of giving her material things. He showered her with presents, flowers and any surprise he could think of that might make her happy. But he never gave the only thing she really wanted, he could not give her any more of his time. He refused to change his life for her or for anybody else. Work came first. He wanted and needed her to complete his life, but she could never be everything to him.

His search for a new home for her illustrated the lengths he went to in his attempt to please her. She had always, from first getting married, complained that their home was too small. She believed they should live somewhere big and grand, in a house that reflected his position in Hollywood, and that was also large enough to accommodate her mother. Duke had never seen anything he liked and really made very little effort to look, he was satisfied with what he had. Then just before they left for Ireland Chata told him she had seen the perfect house, it had everything a Hollywood star's home should have. When he went with her to see it, he said he thought it was too big, and that he wasn't really interested, but agreed to think about it while they were away on location. When Chata went to look at it again after they got back, she was furious to find the house had been sold. She ranted at a subdued Duke, telling him he should have thought about it sooner, and that he should have bought it before they went. He shook his head, defeated, accepting the criticism, then smiled brightly and told her, "I did."

His generous act put the marriage back on track for a while. And then mother-in-law moved back in and the fighting started all over again. Duke complained that she was a drunk and an embarrassment to him. He didn't want her in his home, and he told Chata he badly needed some privacy and peace. Chata screamed that he had no sensitivity. Every day was an intolerable struggle for them all. He resorted to old habits, rising long before anyone else in the household, eating alone and then escaping to work, doing anything to avoid the conflict.

Duke and Chata had planned to have children. She never became pregnant and blamed him, saying publicly that he was infertile. He felt so ashamed he agreed to undergo tests but later told Pilar, his third wife, that he thought, "Chata was too evil to conceive." She wanted them to adopt children but he showed no interest and a close friend said he knew by that time the marriage was doomed. He was deeply concerned about her drinking problem. Most of his friends were alcoholics and he was hardly likely to miss the signs. She and her mother were usually so drunk during the later years of their marriage that he spent much of his spare time nursing the sorry pair.

In December 1951 they had an argument. Neither could later remember what it was about, but he ended up throwing a glass of water at her in temper. She retaliated with an ice bucket before starting a more sustained attack. He had rarely fought back before, he generally held her off at arm's length, but this time he threw his drink at her. She consulted a divorce attorney soon after the incident. Duke murmured when the story hit the Press, "I blame myself for our troubles. I devoted too much time to business and not enough to her." But he had lost interest in reunions and when Chata later sent a forty fifth birthday present to his office, he told Mary to return it. He made no effort to contact her or to chase her to Mexico, "I'll be damned if I'm going to go get her — if she thinks that she's crazy."

Eventually he wrote to advise her that if she didn't come straight back he was renting the house out. He was angry that he had spent a fortune on an estate he'd never wanted and now found himself alone in. She didn't reply and he leased it out and rented a small apartment for himself. Chata, commenced immediate legal action against him, petitioning for maintenance. She demanded he throw the new tenants out and she moved back into the estate herself. She didn't want divorce, but equally she didn't want a reconciliation either, she only wanted to keep him dangling, uncomfortably. Duke, although sickened by the thought of a second failure, unhappy because he hadn't been able to make it work with Chata, filed for divorce himself in a rare move for the time. He agreed to every demand she made but left his lawyers to sort everything out, "Oh hell, give her everything she asks for, I'm not going to haggle — I'll do four pictures a year instead of three." He didn't even want to go to court and took himself off on location instead to try to forget the soap opera that was his life.

When he arrived back his butler informed him that another man had been staying in the house with Chata. J. Hampton Scott asked for a private interview and Duke emerged from it pale and shaking. Scott handed him an envelope containing a scrap of paper from a note pad. Chata had doodled the name Nicky Hilton on the pad. She had also written Chata Hilton a number of times, and "Chata and Nick." Duke later said he had to go to the bathroom to throw up after seeing it. There had long been speculation about the state of the marriage in the Press, but now things became very difficult. Ernie Saftig, a close friend, advised him to get away from Hollywood for a while to do some location scouting for his Alamo project in Peru. He left almost immediately. Chata rang Mary to find out where he was and screamed, "The bastard, he knew I always wanted to go there." Chata hadn't realised this fight was any different from the other times she had fled from him. Duke had always come running and been consistently tender, passionate and full of remorse. Now she waited in vain as Duke took off for Peru. Both their lives were about to change dramatically when Duke was introduced there to Richard Weldy, a tour guide who led safaris up the Amazon. Duke liked him immediately and they shared many drinks before Weldy recommended they set off to look for exotic locations. Duke wanted to see a remote area called Tingo Maria, a small village surrounded by dense jungle where local films were often shot.

At that time it took ten years before American movies hit Peru, and whilst many locals had heard of John Wayne, he was by no means a star there. That had always been the attraction of South America for him, and when he first arrived in Tingo Maria he strolled unnoticed into the local hotel. He was immediately struck by the sight of a Peruvian actress dancing barefoot in front of an open fire. He was introduced to the girl, Pilar, who turned out to be the estranged wife of his tour guide. A photograph taken on the instant captured pre-ordained destiny, she gazing longingly at the man towering above her, his shirt hanging out, a huge hand tightly clutching his drink. He is beaming down, eyes fixed intently on hers.

When he set out to charm someone, Duke didn't fail. He was tall, handsome, rich, famous, had that walk and that talk, and within minutes of meeting him Pilar was lost, "All I could do was stare. He was the handsomest man I'd ever seen. I couldn't believe anyone's eyes could be so turquoise, so piercing. He looked at me with lively curiosity. Standing barefoot, my head didn't even reach his shoulder."

He spoke to her but she felt awkward, especially as her estranged husband was with him, but later said that when he spoke he had an interest so intense and powerful that it left her feeling breathless, "He possessed much more than sex appeal, good looks, had more than his success, more than fame, there was something very special about him, a sense of great strength, something millions of filmgoers already knew, something real, something essential about him as a man. It had nothing to do with his status as a film star."

Pilar continued to sing and dance until he beckoned her to join his party. He stood up and waited politely until she sat down. She said, "He did everything with such natural grace." She had dinner at his table that night. She told him she thought he had been good in *For Whom The Bell Tolls*. He smiled and answered, "Do you like Westerns?" She shook her head, "Not really." He laughed and never told her he wasn't in *For Whom the Bell Tolls*. She may not have known who he was, but she loved his deep drawl and the way he spoke almost exclusively to her that night, she loved his sincere charm, his graciousness. All through the dinner she felt too embarrassed to speak, but found herself unable to prevent herself staring into his blue, blue eyes as he made small talk. Whenever he stopped they gazed at each other. That night she told Weldy, her estranged husband, she was filing for divorce.

Pilar was very like Josie to look at, small, thin and frail, with huge dark eyes and a warm, open, innocent smile. She was quiet and sweet. Chata had offered exotic pleasure but made his life hell, Pilar appeared tranquil by comparison, and that was exactly what he needed then. Although he didn't stay in Peru long, Pilar soon turned up in Hollywood. She was there to dub the dialogue for *Green Hell*, the film she had been working on when he met her. Their paths crossed on the Warner Bros. lot, by accident, according to Pilar, by design according to many others. When she was leaving the set she pushed open a heavy stage door to find him waiting to come in on the other side. He looked every bit the big movie star as he stared down at her in an apparent effort to recall her face, before breaking into a broad, lopsided grin of recognition and inviting her to dinner that night. It was suggested that he arranged for her to be brought to Hollywood. He always smilingly denied the charge, tongue very much in cheek.

He was late for their first date and Mary St John eventually rang Pilar to explain that his house had been mobbed by the press and he couldn't get out. He had just been voted top box-office star for the second year in a row. Mary continued that he was very anxious for her to go to his place instead. When Pilar arrived she was surprised to find his modest rented apartment surrounded by a pack of reporters all pushing and fighting amongst themselves. She rang the bell a number of times before anyone came to let her in. The rooms were crowded with more members of the Press. She couldn't see Duke and felt very nervous until he finally strolled into the room, he towered above everyone else and smiled straight over at her. He beat a determined path toward her, gently elbowing other guests out of his way. He took both her hands in his huge ones, "I'm so glad you are here to share this with me." She noticed immediately how much he enjoyed being feted by the Press, how he responded generously to all their questions with good humour and charm. Although he held onto her hand tightly all night he let her know, right from their first public meeting together, that his heart belonged to his fans, to the Press and to the movie world at large. Everyone else got leftovers. Still, he rang and sent flowers daily after that, they went out together every night, and she said, "It was impossible not to fall in love with him." He made no attempt to hide his feelings, he loved Pilar and didn't care who knew it, even though he wasn't yet divorced. Pilar said, "I'd never known a more confident man, so comfortable with his own body. He never took a false step or made an awkward move. The nicest thing was that he seemed to be completely unaware of it. He was so attractive." Certainly he was more confident than he'd been in the past. The circumstances surrounding this affair were almost identical to when he had first fallen in love with Chata, but then he had been so unsure of his place in the world. He was now Hollywood's leading man, he had power, wealth, and was no longer dependent on one director, one producer or one studio.

He was his own man now and one emotional night, just two short weeks after her arrival in Hollywood, he begged her to stay with him, "I don't want you to go. I want you to take a chance on me. I love you and I don't want you to ever leave me." He pleaded his case well and she found herself willing to ignore the twenty four year difference in their ages, the other women who had shared his life, the fact that he was a man who didn't like to be alone, that he was a film star who put his work above everything, that she would only ever get the scraps he threw, she ignored everything when she decided to stay, "I don't think any couple has ever been more in love or needed each other more than we did that night."

But Duke was a complex man, full of contradiction; he was romantic down to his boots, deeply passionate, and at the same time, highly moral; traits which didn't fit together comfortably. Whenever Duke fell in love he wanted to marry the object of his desire. He constantly sought the perfect marriage, the perfect love. He loved and wanted to marry Pilar, but he was also put off by his previous failures. He couldn't bring himself to talk to her about it and he was in a tough spot. He was still not free from Chata either, and though public morals may have relaxed, living in sin was not acceptable, and the film industry remained particularly puritanical in its outlook. Although he was now in a stronger position, an open affair could still have ruined his career. Once more his quest for love had led him down a path fraught with danger, causing a surge of nervous tension that manifested itself in deep depression and intense jealousy. He suffered from insecurity, rooted deep in his troubled past perhaps, but which was re-ignited every time he saw his career under threat. Pilar witnessed that insecurity and realised that his self-assurance was just as fragile as the next man's when Marlon Brando asked to be introduced to her. Duke bellowed, "NO" and stormed away, dragging her off behind him. He had seen in Pilar his chance to have exactly what he'd always wanted. He grabbed hold of her and held on as tightly as he could and she understood that he was really nothing like the tough guy he appeared on screen, "He was far more romantic, his masculinity was mellower and yet deeper." She agreed with the writer who commented, "He never appeared in a fleshy, exciting way, as Errol Flynn and the like did, because his erotic potential was more substantial, was focused more deeply in the heart than in the genitals."

Once she had seen the insecurity she also recognised his need for the care so long denied him. He might play the rough and ready macho-man but that was not the man she saw. She understood instinctively the damage caused by his mother so long before, "He danced to his mother's unrealized dreams. She made sure the dance was painful, holding tight the strings of his emotions and jerking them sharply whenever she wanted to keep him in line." Once she understood his hunger and craving for praise, Pilar knew how to get her man. His mother had unfailingly rejected his every effort to win her affection, now she offered him the things he had been starved of, lavishing praise upon his head, constantly telling him how special he was. He thrived as a man.

He had grown up not knowing what was wrong with him, what it was about him that his mother found unlovable. All his adult life he had been sexually attracted to women and yet his mother's legacy left him terrified of them, afraid of the moods he couldn't fathom, afraid of their open expression of emotion. He guarded his own sensitivity under a strong, thick protective skin, rarely allowing anyone inside. But once he found Pilar it didn't take him long to realise it was safe to open up to her, she wouldn't hurt him. There would be none of the violence he had experienced at Chata's hands, none of the cold, indifference he had known with Josie, none of the scorn his mother had heaped on him. At long last, at the age of forty five, he found some personal happiness in the arms of a woman.

And on a professional level too things couldn't have been better. His political movies were making profits, they were acceptable to his audience. He had turned the corner. He resented being labelled a right wing extremist perhaps, but never realised it was the films he was producing himself that directly caused the way the reviewers treated him then and for the rest of his career. The critics didn't share his beliefs, they were unwilling to accept the heavy handed stories, unwilling to accept him as an actor, branding him instead an activist, a political animal, a monster of the Right.

In the early fifties non of that bothered him. He had Pilar and he remained Hollywood's biggest box-office draw. His standing then was such that when one very sophisticated political writer went to interview him at his home, she asked him one question and then, to his amazement, turned and fled. Later she laughed nervously as she explained, "When I looked up and realised I was actually talking to John Wayne ... the John Wayne ... I was speechless."

Marion (back row 3rd from left) aged 14, with members of the Glendale High School track team.

Marion(front row, 2nd from right) with Howard Jones USC Trojans 1928. Wardell Bond, a medical student is on the left of the 3rd row.

Marion, in typical Wayne stance, with Robert, 1911

The Big Trail 1929 "I was kinda pretty. I grew out of it in a hurry though".

Publicity treatment with co-stars Marguerite Churchill, Tommy Clifford and Champion the dog.

Duke & Josie get married at last 1933

Party at Ciro's

Waiting patiently for Marlene to make her move ... and she did!

Claire Trevor, Duke's co-star in Stagecoach commented, "He was a much more complex person than he seemed, with a quick-fire nature. My God, you had to be on your toes around him. He had no time for nonsense".

Ford saw the fluid body movement and feline grace but said that until 1939 Duke was too skinny and too pretty to do much with, "I offered him bit parts from time to time so I could keep an eye on him. He had some inner honesty that the camera couldn't miss".

Courtesy of the Academy of Motion Picture Arts & Sciences

© 1930

233

Duke and Chata in love ... for a while. She made his life Hell and he was soon looking for peace and tranquillity.

Ireland provided the perfect backdrop for Duke to have fun with great friend Maureen O'Hara during the filming of The Quiet Man. 1951

Duke and Patrick share a break. Pilar called her husband, "an idiot father."
"I'm proud of all my children," he commented.

In Rio Grande Duke was on his way to establishing the image in the minds of the Cinema going public.

In private he found the love he had been looking for with Pilar.

"No one smokes a cigarette like I do. I love smoking it's part of my identity."

236

He carried the weight of the world on his shoulders and laboured like anox-in-yoke to make The Alamo. Duke's finest hour, "I mortgaged everything but my soul to bring it together ..."

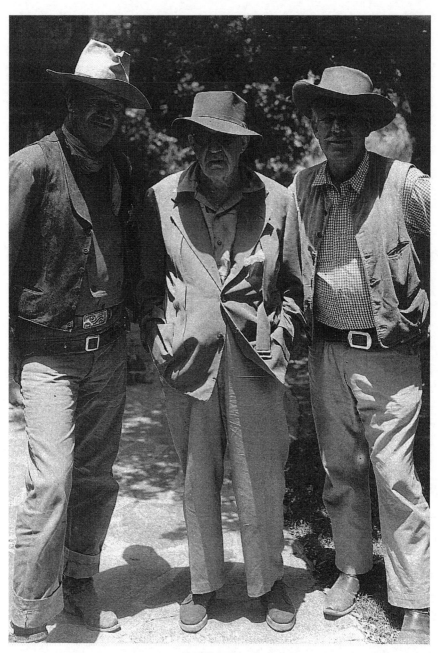

The Triumvirate.
Wayne, Ford, Bond

"Making a film is hard labour, and let me tell you when you're fighting in mud at 25 degrees ... you're earning money the hard way." But teamed once more with his favourite leading lady, Maureen O'Hara, Duke laughed, "I think the fun we had making Mclintock! came over well on screen."

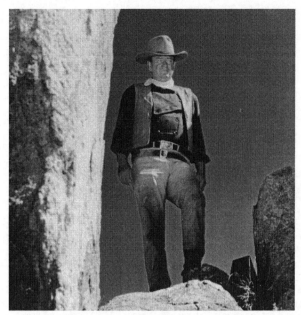

Doctors had advised Duke to rest for twelve months after losing his left lung to cancer. Bellowing, "I'm the stuff men are made of," he was working on The Sons of Katie Elder just three months after leaving hospital. The film was shot in Durango, Mexico at high altitude where people with two good lungs struggled to breath. Producer Hal Wallis commented, "In real life he'd now battled a deadly foe, beaten the odds and emerged victorious."

Flat out and in big trouble shooting the fight scene in icy water. Director Henry Hathaway stubbornly refused to either use a double or allow his star to wear a wet suit, "You'd look too fat. Don't baby yourself." Duke later admitted he'd made his come-back too soon.

Rooster Cogburn, a direct descendant of the traditional Wayne persona. "I never went into the field of endeavour that wins Oscars. It was an accident that I was in this picture and it was just a natural for me. Asking me to play Rooster was like giving me a handful of chocolate bars."

When his name was announced as Best Actor for True Grit, Duke whispered, "Beginners Luck."

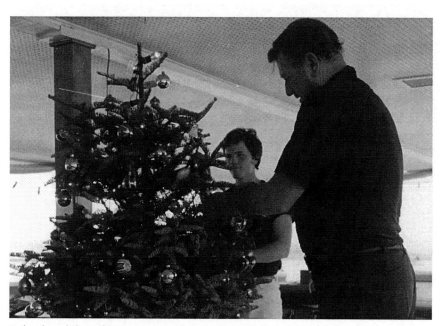

Duke aboard The Wild Goose 1976, Christmas in Mazatlan, Mexico, supervised by deckhand Jim Jacobson.

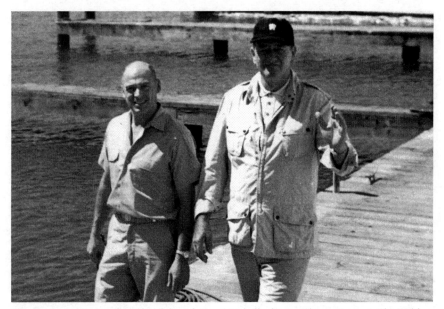

John Wayne at the Seattle Yacht Club with Ken Minshall who was the engineer on The Wild Goose for many years.

Wayne relaxing with son Ethan, Jack Gordean (Duke's agent) and wife Ruth, off Catalina Island.

Spare-time was usually chess-time, but Duke was rarely seen without one of his children, "Not only are his own children always around, but any number of grandchildren ... for God's sake. There's never been a time that one, two or even three of them aren't crawling all over him, even when he's playing cards or chess with the guys ... and he's a great picker-upper, a hugger, a kisser ..." O'Hara.

Duke's greatest pleasure was sailing The Wild Goose.

"It was as though an entire decade had gathered and swept over him." (Dave Grayson, Duke's long-time make-up man)

On April 9th 1979 Duke said all his emotional public "good byes" in the grandest style, at the Academy Awards Oscar ceremony.

Nobody should come to the movies unless he believes in heroes.

CHAPTER SIX

The Warrior Does Battle

The Alamo

"My problem is I'm not a handsome man, like Cary Grant. I have to be a director. I've waited all these years to be one. The Alamo is where I start. This picture is America and I hope that seeing the battle will remind Americans that liberty and freedom don't come cheap. Making it has made me feel useful to my country."

1952 saw John Wayne named Hollywood's number one box office star for the second year running and voted one of the most popular men in America. Many US towns ran several "John Wayne's" simultaneously, films where good triumphed over evil and where his image was powerful and all conquering. America loved him. He had reached the summit and was finally reaping top financial rewards. During the year he made *Big Jim McLean, Trouble Along the Way, Island in the Sky*, and *The Quiet Man*. Much of the pain he felt over his war record was eased in his anti-communist crusade, the Republican Party finally captured the White House, and he had Pilar. Politically, professionally and emotionally he felt close to fulfilment.

But as usual, life didn't run smoothly for the hero as he hit another series of challenges. In fact, his private life was in perhaps the worst state it had ever been in. He wanted to marry again, he didn't want an affair, but he needed Pilar urgently and couldn't wait. Whilst he fully intended having his way long before his divorce was finalised he did go to some lengths to hide the relationship. He discreetly rented an apartment for Pilar close to his own home. He enjoyed having her close at hand but still felt uncomfortable with the old dilemma. He knew that if he allowed her to move in more openly it could lead to the sudden end of his career. He'd taken chances with it before but was unsure about risking it now he'd reached the top. No matter how big he was he still felt too insecure to put everything to the test. There was another messy divorce to get through first and it didn't matter how well his films were doing in 1952, his private life left him far from fulfilled. The more professional success he knew, the more happiness that appeared on the horizon, the more bitter were the disappointments that followed. Chata was making things particularly difficult and the more embarrassment she caused him the better she liked it. She demanded a full blown divorce trial with huge media coverage; nothing he offered her moved her. He couldn't afford to take any chances at that delicate stage and he began staying as far away from Pilar as possible, spending long, lonely and frustrated weeks away on location, and taking pains not to get caught with her when he came home.

But get caught he did when Pilar blurted out that she was pregnant. She was surprised by his unexpected response, for whilst he was shocked he wasn't unduly unhappy about the accident. Of course he knew it would make life difficult when the news broke, and would probably affect not only his career but also the outcome of the impending trial. He would have preferred things done in the right order but he fully intended marrying Pilar anyway and he wanted more children, "I'll talk to my lawyer. I'll tell him to give Chata whatever she wants. I'll get the divorce sorted out as quickly as possible, then we'll go straight to Mexico and get married." Pilar wanted the baby and was sure from his reaction that he did too, but she was also certain that even he couldn't get rid of Chata in time for them to get married, give their baby his name or save his career, "I couldn't let him destroy everything he had worked so hard for. Chata was taking delight in being difficult, nothing Duke had offered had moved her before, she was unlikely to change now. She wanted to take him to court, wanted the scandal to hit the papers, wanted to hurt him in the most painful way she knew, by destroying his career."

It fell to Pilar to be the more realistic of the two and she decided to have the pregnancy terminated. "Pilar, you have to do what you think best. Whatever you decide I'll stand by you. If you want to have the baby, that's OK. I'll take my chances as far as my career is concerned, you don't have to worry about that. The only thing that matters is that I don't lose you." He made all the right noises, said everything she wanted to hear, but the fact was he was also scared, worried about the morality clauses he had signed and flaunted before. Pilar, sensing the fear, chose not to risk his happiness. Even then she understood that whilst he undoubtedly loved her, he loved working more and that because of the characters he chose to play the public confused his screen persona with his private identity. People would not be forgiving if he let them down and if they dropped him his happiness would be lost forever. In the end, she did what she thought best for him, but then, for a long time after, turned against him, blaming him for the decision she had taken. She could hardly bear to look at him. Duke, of course, hardly needed anyone else to make him feel guilty, he didn't need her to blame him, no one was ever as good as he was himself at guilt and blame. He was perfectly well able to torture himself. He wanted to comfort her, but when he tried to touch her she turned away. He could do nothing except hope and wait.

Not long after the abortion, as the Christmas holiday approached, Pilar agreed to sign a contract with Wayne-Fellows so she could obtain a permit to remain in the US. It was a time to forgive and forget, a time for fresh starts, a time when Duke made new promises. As always at Christmas he was transformed into an excited boy, a star who loved shopping for gifts for friends and family, a capable organiser of family get-togethers. He wanted them all to meet Pilar and she was introduced first to his mother. Things went unexpectedly well, with none of the usual arguments and stress that so often accompanied Molly's visits. Pilar made it easy for him to escape his life's greatest discomfort, she eased the tension around him, got on easily with Molly and gave him some welcome relief at long last. It was important that all his family liked her but Duke had no high hopes where his children were concerned, "Don't expect too much of them at first, they haven't forgiven me yet," he warned. She made a special effort to get on with them and was well rewarded when he told her she had given him the best Christmas present that he could have had, "For the first time in years I feel like I have a real home." She could hardly believe what he was saying and realised how little it took to please this superstar.

She decided to make up to him for the disappointment of the termination, for her behaviour and for all the less happy times he must have known. Her present to him that first year was the Christmas he longed for, she even offered to cook the dinner herself. On Christmas morning he found her washing the turkey in a bowl full of detergent. When she told the helpless Duke she was carrying out the instructions to, "Wash the bird," he laughed until he cried. She had never cooked before but luckily he was skilled in the kitchen and together they managed to prepare a reasonable meal. Things could get no better for him, the day represented normality and he never forgot the first time he shared an ordinary Christmas with someone he loved. Pilar already understood his needs and was willing to administer to them and he now became dependant on her for his every comfort. She offered him the things he most needed and provided some of the stability that he craved. Fortunately she also understood his obsession, made no demands on his time and allowed him to move freely between the centre of his existence, the movie world, and her world, the peaceful home life that he had yearned for. It was no easy task, and demanded much of her, he knew it and loved her for it. He became accustomed to the love and freedom she gave, and to the care she offered.

In 1952 his body of work represented a lifetime. He had grown before the cameras of the best, from a boy into a young man, into a mature, father figure, even into old age and death; the combined effect showed him to good advantage. Pilar knew nothing of his films and demanded to see them. He was happy to screen them just for her, "I've lived a long time without you, this is one way you can catch up." They showed her his past and allowed her into his life in exactly the same way they permitted his audience to share his reality. Now, as he played them, he told her stories about the making of each and about the people who had inhabited them with him. The first movie they watched together was *The Quiet Man*, one of his favourites. She sat in wonder, holding the man on the screen tightly, afraid to let him go. She had told him when they first met that she didn't like westerns, so he had chosen to show her one of his most powerful love stories first, but he teased her that from now on she would have to get used to shoot'em ups, "Because I make an awful lot of them." She watched his face, deep in concentration, as he ran his work for her approval. Even as he looked at himself on the screen with her there holding his hand, he was still carefully studying his performance, approving the things he had done well, hating his mistakes, constantly learning, analysing, dissecting, trying to understand why one thing worked and another didn't. His complete professionalism was demonstrated clearly and left her in no doubt where his heart lay.

At the time he was still going to Hollywood ceremonies alone. He wouldn't go with his wife and he couldn't take Pilar. Night after night he went off, dressed up, looking fantastic, and returned later staggering-drunk. On one occasion he came back with lipstick on his cheek. Pilar, like others before her, jumped to the conclusion that he had been out with someone else. Although he was furious in his denial she refused to speak to him for several days and returned the gifts he bombarded her with. Eventually, even though he was in the middle of his divorce and knew it was unsafe, he called at her apartment, "You're wrong, nothing happened, it was just someone who kissed me in congratulation. You're just going to have to trust me ... the last days have been hell for me Pilar. I just want you back ... please don't do this to me. I've already been through this so often, I don't think I can take it again." He was back in the old routine, begging for forgiveness for something he hadn't done.

And meanwhile Chata continued to do everything she could to humiliate him as the divorce loomed closer. The studio thought he would be safer out of town and he was shipped off to a desolate location to start shooting Hondo. They kept him there, out of harm's way for much of 1953. He wasn't permitted to take Pilar with him and he missed her badly. He did wonder though if his long absence might make her heart grow fonder, whether it would help her realise that she could take him at his word. He wanted to call her and get her to come out to join him but for many months his every step had been tailed by two private investigators who were working for Chata. They had followed him to Mexico, where they kept him under close surveillance. They were disappointed not to catch him with Pilar who had been packed off to Peru. Duke spoke to her on the phone every day, but even then great care was taken and he always used an assumed name. Subterfuge didn't suit him and he was like a bear with a sore head on location; he hated creeping around, and hated Chata for putting him through such anguish.

Duke was a huge and immensely popular star in Mexico. He returned there again and again to produce much of his best work. When local officials found out how upset he was about being followed around by the detectives they asked him if he wanted them to take care of things! Duke laughed, but rejected the drastic offer. Still when the two men, who spoke no Spanish, wired the telephone of the governor of the province by mistake, thinking it was Duke's room, they were both thrown in jail. Whilst he had certainly not wanted them "taken care of," he was happy enough to let them languish in the local jail. He got some peace for a few days until he heard one of the detectives had appendicitis and had received no treatment. Ward Bond, also on location, advised, "Let 'em rot." But when the detectives appealed to him personally he raced to the rescue, "The guy's sick ... I can't just leave him ... besides they were just doing their job." He paid their fines, had them both released and even paid their return air fares, "I was willing to return good for evil." Bond mused, "With those tactics I can just imagine what a bloody mess this trial's going to be."

Lonely Duke, away on location, was moodier than usual, increasingly miserable, grouchy and difficult for the cast and crew members to get on with. He tried to became engrossed in the business of making a movie but found it difficult. He complained bitterly about director John Farrow, saying the film became a Wayne-Fellows production because of his incompetence, "Farrow really didn't have a lot to do with it. We had set everything up before he arrived. He proved to me that he shouldn't be put in a producer-director position. That's only my opinion, and others might consider him a fine director. I had found all the locations for each scene, the story had already been written, and I'm not saying whether or not he was involved in camera set-ups or even directing the actors." Duke, already under pressure, found he had to deal with many tedious technical difficulties because of Farrow's short comings.

For some years Hollywood had been suffering a decline, partly due to the advent of TV, and of all the great stars, only he remained immune. Warner Brothers pointed out that there was nothing wrong with Hollywood that a dozen John Wayne's couldn't have fixed. His films were still guaranteed earners and all the major studios either concentrated on him, or came up with gimmicky ideas to draw people back to the cinema. One of the gimmicks they turned to was 3D, and even Duke decided to use it on *Hondo*. Despite his pulling power and his track record he never took success for granted. He was innovative and determined to hold onto his place, and if gimmicks were the way forward, he had to be on the front line, fighting there with everything at his disposal.

Filming in 3D was difficult and required many more retakes than normal, delays tended to be longer and equipment often broke down. Already on edge, disliking the director, separated from Pilar, a messy divorce looming, Duke was irritable and Warner Bros, kept pestering him to return one of their cameras. He wrote many bitter letters to the studio which was threatening him with breach of contract, and finally, in desperation, he snapped, "Perhaps the ten-picture deal we made isn't going to work. If you don't want to co-operate just call me back and cancel our relationship — I'm goddamned mad enough to." They allowed him to keep both cameras.

And if all the stress he was under was not enough, he also hated working with co-star, Geraldine Page. Duke who was unfailingly polite and renowned for his gentleness and generosity with leading ladies, couldn't stand her. He had originally cast her for the part himself, offering the successful stage actress the role over the phone, without a screen test. The script demanded someone attractive but he didn't want a sexy starlet to play the part of the woman abandoned in the desert by her husband. When she arrived in Hollywood, Duke's partner, Robert Fellows, saw her first and winced! She had terrible teeth and looked as if she had never heard of toothpaste. Her ugly smile might be covered up on stage but would be hideously emphasised on the big screen. When Duke finally met her he panicked at the thought of what the 3D camera would do to her and he packed her straight off to the dentist.

Working with her did nothing to soften his mood and everyone suffered as a result. It was unbearably hot in Mexico, he was uncomfortable, he had technical problems, the set had none of the usual family atmosphere about it, he was repeatedly called back to Hollywood to appear in court, and he needed Pilar. It didn't take much of Page to drive him completely over the top. Once filming got under way the fastidious Duke discovered the reason her teeth were rotten was a non-existent programme of personal hygiene. Mary St John said it was even possible to smell her around the set, "Do you want to know how bad she smelled? Page did not have the best morals in the world, and hard-up stunt men were seen stumbling out of her room every morning, but even Ward Bond wouldn't take advantage of her availability. That's how bad she smelled."

Her table manners matched everything else about her and disgusted Duke. One evening, as she sat eating mashed potatoes with her fingers, he stood up and tipped his own dinner over her head before storming away in a fit of temper. He said later, "And, I wasn't sorry." He certainly made no effort to apologise. The script required him to perform several love scenes with her and he confessed to Ward Bond, "Jesus Christ, I'm afraid I might puke the next time I have to kiss her. Maybe if I hold my breath it won't be so bad."

Duke may not have liked Geraldine Page, but as was so often the case, she was completely charmed by him. "He is a fantastic, fantastic man.

He's an enormous man. I have never encountered another man quite as big, rugged, strong, loud, critical, mean, short-tempered, quick to seek forgiveness and even quicker to give it, profane, intelligent, or supremely gifted. He has an irresistible charisma. I love him and would do anything for him. The best thing about him is that he will scream himself hoarse and then suddenly apologize and seek forgiveness. He'd get sarcastic with me when he was hung over or out of temper … and, like everyone else, I would be just about to say "I've had enough." He always sensed it and came over and sort of breathed down my neck, "Aw, Geraldine, you're not mad at old Duke are you?" … and I would melt and say "No" … I'd tell myself I was stupid to get taken in by that charm, but I just loved him."

However badly he behaved, it seemed people couldn't help responding to the John Wayne charm. Strother Martin, who worked with Duke a number of times said, "I always find it exciting working with him. I always know it's going to be a baptism of fire. He's rough, he's tough. But he's rough and tough with everybody. He's also sentimental. He's not a stand-offish man. He's a mixer with stand-ins, day players, bit players, stars, stuntmen, wardrobe people, electricians, the whole damned array of people on both sides of a camera that make a film. He'll never bite you behind your back. If he has something against you or something where he doesn't agree with you as an actor, you'll feel a chunk go out of your middle. He'll usually give you a hug at night though. He doesn't bear grudges. He respects hard work. He's ready to bust his ass, and he expects everybody else to do the same. There's never any lethargy on a John Wayne set. To be on a set with him is an electric experience, and nobody's going to doze off that's anywhere near where that man's working."

No one got star treatment on a Wayne set and all his crew were treated as equals. One night whilst they were making *Hondo* a storm blew up as the crew were moving equipment out of a dry lake bed. Hours later when Duke discovered they were not back he started worrying. He got the caterers up and helped them prepare coffee and food himself and took several bottles of tequila along to spend the rest of the night out with the stranded men. They ate, sang and told wild stories. And he was at his happiest out there with them. Page said, "The mutual affection between him and his crew was wonderful. He had natural leadership qualities and people would follow him anywhere, and through anything. Equally, he will do anything for them. He's terribly bright, terribly intelligent, and he learns so quickly. He just seems to know how to do everything … He has the most wonderful joke-appreciating laugh that is the warmest, the most spontaneous, the biggest most beautiful laugh. I have never heard a more spontaneous laugh. It's incredible." She even loved his profanity, and knew that much of his laughter out on the lake bed would be peppered by the foulest language. Duke, Bond and some of the stuntmen often played cards in the room next to hers, "All night there was an endless stream of it … you know it's like rhythm, like music … on and on it was fantastic."

Page fell deeply in love and had no trouble explaining his screen presence or her love. "He's a terribly honest man, you see. And that comes across, underlined by the kind of parts he plays. He always plays an honest man, and his own honesty feeds into it, and the simplicity of his acting. Big stars are a combination of their own personality and the parts they play, and if the combination of the two symbolizes something that's very dear to all of our hearts, we want to see them again and again, and that makes them stars."

Hondo was exactly that kind of role for him, it was vintage John Wayne, and Page was right, people wanted to see him again and again for he symbolized everything they held dear. The film offered escape from the conditions of life in a modern industrial society, took them out of their mechanised existence, away from economic dead ends, out of their own unhappy personal relationships, from political injustice and back to a time when men controlled their own destiny. His energy and power reflected the promise of a purer, more authentic existence in the story written by Louis L'Amour. Hondo Lane, US cavalry dispatch rider, was a worthy successor to the Wayne characters of a dozen previous westerns, and the film won positive acclaim from the critics, even though it didn't live up to Duke's own expectations. He felt the film was damaged by his 3D experiment and just one week after its release he launched a new, flat version of the film, which eventually went on to make money.

As soon as location work was completed he rushed home to rest. The difficult circumstances surrounding the movie had brought out the worst in him, and Pilar now witnessed his hard edge and his boiling anger, never too far below the surface, at close quarters. Plenty of people had warned her about his legendary rages and his fits of wild temper, but she'd never listened. When she briefly visited him on location she thought he'd gone crazy when he lashed out unexpectedly. What she actually saw was his dark side, always there, and only allowed to surface then because he was too exhausted to suppress it. His temper, like a flash of lightning, was there one second, gone the next, "I don't know what the Hell gets into me." He was quick to beg her forgiveness and he hardly noticed the power of his rage, or the damage he had done. Once he had cooled off Duke quickly forgot all about it and moved rapidly back to his more normal tender behaviour, but Pilar found it particularly difficult to forget, or forgive. Of course she, like everybody else, found him irresistible when he chose to be charming, when he was contrite after the anger had passed, when he began laughing again, but he hurt her more than anybody else because she was so ill-equipped to cope with it. Despite the fact that it was she who gave him all the things he had ever needed, she also bore the brunt of his temper and never knew how to handle his moods.

In 1954 Wayne-Fellows came to an abrupt end when Duke bought his partner out, saying, "Bob Fellows hadn't quite done the job." He called his new company Batjac, after the Dutch trading company Batjak in the film *Wake of the Red Witch*, "I didn't like the idea of my name being used for the company" — the typist who prepared the legal documents spelt the name wrong, but Duke never corrected the error.

Soon after forming Batjac he and Pilar went off on location to film *The Conqueror* for Howard Hughes, a film that later had devastating consequences, and which he knew he should never have become entangled in. It was written originally for Marlon Brando in stylised, ancient English; Duke made many elementary errors of judgement on the picture, not least of which was failing to check the script before going on location. The day before filming started he glanced at it and was horrified. He knew he couldn't do anything with the language and tried desperately, and unsuccessfully to get his scenes rewritten.

The script turned out to be the least of his problems and he found Susan Hayward, his co-star, like a line from the film, "consumed with want of him." It was the first time he'd openly taken Pilar on location with him and he spent most of his time fighting off the amorous advances of a drunken Miss Hayward. As ever, he maintained his politeness and Miss Hayward remained completely infatuated with him, "He was tough and he was strong, just like his screen image, but there was a tremendous gentleness about him. Of all my leading men, he was my favourite."

And she too proved to be only a minor irritant. Working on the film left many of the 220 people who joined him on location in Utah in 1954 suffering from serious and specific illnesses. Ninety one of them were later affected by or died of cancer and a radiologist said, deaths in the numbers that occurred in this group qualified as an epidemic. Pedro Armendariz suffered from cancer of the kidney in 1959 and finally committed suicide in 1963 after being diagnosed with cancer of the larynx. Hayward developed cancer of the skin, breast, uterus and brain.

The Conqueror was filmed in the Escalante Valley, where the Atomic Energy Commission had detonated eleven atomic bombs just a year earlier. The fireballs, two of which were described as especially "dirty" had covered the surrounding desert with a fine ash which had been absorbed into the red sands of the area and strong winds carried large amounts of radioactive waste throughout each of the valleys where filming took place. Levels of strontium 90 and cesium 137 remained high enough to set Geiger counters wildly ticking long after 1954. Crew and cast members were regularly covered with the thick dust which even caked their eyes and mouths. They were frequently blown clean with compressed air after a hard day on set. A further sixty tons of the red sand was carried back by truck for interior shooting, so colours matched outdoor scenes, and for another two months after they had finished on location they continued to wallow in the radioactive mix. In later years Duke's health suffered the consequences, at the time the critics berated his performance, "Wayne portrays the Mongolian conqueror as a moronic idiot!" Even he said, "It was probably the worst film I ever made, though it ranks alongside at least fifty others! Despite everything, I felt it could have been so much better if the producers had allowed me to have the dialogue altered." Rubbish or not, idiotic or not, audiences flocked to see it, and as ever a Duke film was a sure fire banker.

He was waiting, impatient as ever, for his final divorce papers to come through and he hoped to be free to marry Pilar in November 1954. He was under contract to star in *The Sea Chase* which was due to be shot in Hawaii that autumn. He asked Pilar to go on location with him again. He planned to marry her there the day his divorce became final. He didn't tell her his plans for the big surprise. Some months before the trip he had willingly agreed to have her dog, Blackie, shipped up from Peru. When the dog emerged from its crate he said wryly that the tiny Dachshund was, "funny looking." He added that although he didn't mind him being around he would not tolerate him eating off his plates or sleeping in their bed. When Pilar reminded him that he used to share his airdale's basket, he laughed, "Yeah, but he was special." At first Blackie didn't seem special. He was tiny and, even Pilar had to admit, funny looking, but he wormed his way into Duke's heart like no woman ever did. Everywhere the huge man went the dog was always at his heels. They were rarely apart from then on and Blackie became almost as important in his life as Pilar was. Before the little dog's arrival Duke had hated eating alone in the early hours of the morning. Now he and the dog shared breakfast and Blackie eagerly sat up at the table to drink coffee from a cup placed in front of him by rough, tough John Wayne, that same John Wayne who had said the dog couldn't share his plates! When he drove anywhere the dog went along draped around his neck. If Blackie didn't wake early enough to go on location with him, Duke sent his driver back to collect him later. At night they sat together companionably watching TV, dog perched on the master's lap where he fell asleep, securely held in huge hands. So much for Duke being unwilling to let a dog sleep in his bed. Blackie ruled John Wayne's home, his heart, ate off what he wanted and slept where he wanted, usually on top of Duke. It was a true, deep, long lasting and mutual love affair. Blackie, however didn't go with Duke and Pilar to Hawaii.

When they arrived on location Duke found that Warners had put them up in a hotel and he was hounded from sunrise to sunset by tourists and fans. Ever conscious of his image he didn't fail in his politeness, and it was entirely typical of him that he responded to every demand made of him. On the first night in the hotel he willingly signed hundreds of autographs, had countless photographs taken and talked to a never ending stream of people. He believed his fans deserved something of him. They had unfailingly stood by him when others let him down or turned against him, they never criticised him, and they continued to pay to see his movies, ensuring his continued success. He explained, "No one but the people like my films." Although he never forgot the debt he owed and politeness came naturally to him, he found the effort required of him in Hawaii tiring all the same, "Perhaps other actors can walk away from people and not be friendly and gracious. I cannot." But he had his plans for Pilar and they moved out of the hotel after a few days. Duke rented a private house close to the set. He made his surprise proposal and Pilar happily agreed to marry him as soon as filming was completed.

But Chata had not finished with him yet. She wasn't prepared to fade into the background and was determined to make his life hell. The trial was over, but things hadn't gone her way in court and she was mad. When she left the Encino estate she took Duke's prized fifteen volume set of American Indian photographs with her. She knew exactly where to attack him, how easy it was to hurt him, and she knew the loss of his books would leave him heartbroken. He offered her $1000 per volume in cash to return them. She ignored the request even though she badly needed the money, the chance to hurt him one last time was even more precious to her. She did eventually return them, one by one, throughout the next year, each one cut into thousands of pieces in fifteen brown envelopes. As she had expected he was devastated. He called her "One sick human being."

In late 1954 she contacted him one last time to beg for money. In the past he had told his lawyers to give her whatever she wanted, but this time he stubbornly refused. Somewhere deep inside he still felt guilty about Chata, he accepted some responsibility for the way things had turned out. Previously that had always ensured he gave into her demands, but he now believed the debt had been paid in full.

Throughout the trial Ward Bond did his best to talk Duke into staying single, "He was sick about Chata, well, now he's had two marriages fall apart, and he's even more sensitive about women than ever before. He should leave things well alone." It didn't matter what anyone said, Duke ran as fast as he could straight into his next effort at finding happiness, repeating a now familiar pattern of behaviour. As soon as he was free of one wife his first action was to marry again.

Toward the end of filming *Sea Chase* Duke's lawyer rang to say he was holding the final divorce papers in his hand. He turned to Pilar casually, "How do you fancy getting married today?" Very little daunted him and the prospect of arranging a wedding for the same day that his divorce came through didn't trouble him at all. "Just leave everything to me. You and Mary go and chose a wedding dress. By the time you get back everything will be sorted out."

They exchanged vows on the manicured lawns of the home of William Hill, territorial senator, at sunset. Local Hawaiians lit torches, sang traditional songs and danced fertility dances in the grounds that overlooked Keakoa Bay. At Pilar's request the word "obey" was dropped from the ceremony. "The others never obeyed me anyway," Duke laughed. It was a truly romantic wedding, and as he might have said himself, every image had perfect composition. After the ceremony they flew on to Honolulu where reporters asked where they were going to honeymoon. "Well fellas, Pilar and I have been travelling since the day we met. So we're going to honeymoon in our favourite place in the entire world. My bride and I are going home."

They returned to California for an extended honeymoon, and for many years after the sound of their laughter reverberated around Encino and the Hollywood hills. The quest was over, Duke had found his happiness at long last. Laughing with Pilar helped him forget the pain of earlier years, every element of his life was finally in place, he had arrived where he was supposed to be and was with the person he was meant to be with. The long search finally over, he relaxed and knew complete contentment. Peace replaced turmoil and the old rages, that had burned inside him for so long, subsided. For long periods he even managed to control his temper. Pilar told everyone her quiet man was, "The most tender man I have ever known. Sometimes he goes to extremes in being considerate with me. He telephones all the time, even when he's working on a picture."

Duke was as happy as it was possible to be, "This is what it's all about, what I've always wanted — a successful career, a wife I love and who loves me back, my family around me." He was forty seven years old and felt a complete man for the first time. He was deeply in love; one friend said it was possible to see how much when he looked at Pilar, "There was some heavy weather sometimes but it seemed they would survive everything to grow old and ever more content together. Watching Duke you felt you knew how strong was his love. When he talked about her you have to imagine that with the words *my wife* there was a melodic line below."

No matter how happy he might be Duke could not sit still, he had to carry on doing what he loved best. An inner energy drove him and left him unable to accept his new contentment, "Life can't stand still for anyone." He began spending more and more time scouring scripts, little caring how awful they were. He considered making any film he thought decent simply because he couldn't stand being idle. He said he loved being at home with his wife, that it was his favourite place in the world, but even now, he could never actually stay in it for any length of time. He was too conditioned by the rigours of the film world where he had spent a lifetime getting up at four am, into makeup by six and on set by seven ready and eager to start work. He was making anything that came his way, using the films as practice sessions and to keep himself occupied. He also made them to finance his dream. Most of the films he made then were considered dismal failures by the critics who took great delight in panning each one. They all agreed, he was washed up. He didn't care. They served his purpose and he hoarded the capital they returned against the day he would start work on *The Alamo*.

Pilar accepted that the movie industry lay at the core of his being. She put up no resistance against it and didn't harass him or make futile demands for things she knew he couldn't give. He talked about needing and wanting privacy, but in truth he was happy in his goldfish bowl existence. He hated being alone, even when he was alone with Pilar, and was always happier with others around them, either in public surrounded by fans, or in private when he invariably invited guests to stay over. Pilar took care not to let him know how much she minded never being alone with him. She wanted to be a true partner, she understood his need to be surrounded by people, and accepted that a man who dreaded being on his own couldn't run the risk of putting all his eggs in one basket. He always had other people in his life. If one let him down there was someone else there for him. But he had learned from past mistakes and he did put more effort into his relationship with Pilar; he never allowed himself to become too dependant, but he did give more of himself to her.

She hated the heavy Spanish furnishings left at the Encino estate by Chata. He now gave her a free hand with alterations. She ordered specially made reproduction early American furniture for every room, believing that if she could make him comfortable in his own home he might be happier staying in it with her. She had a vast bed designed and built from the foundation of a massive Old English bench on which Yorkshire farmers had smoked two hundred hams at a time in its past life. It was customised with arm rests, cigarette compartments, book racks, TV and radio control panels, several telephone lines, light switches for the whole house, remote control to open the front gates, and a backgammon tray built into the headboard. Although they were rarely alone in the house to enjoy the fruits of her work they did spend long happy hours snuggled up in silk pyjamas in the Old English bed, eating snacks as they watched TV on the screen built into the ceiling, or reading to each other. Pilar soon discovered the bed wasn't enough and that his home still served as a club for his friends. People called at all hours and the doors of the Wayne Estate were usually open to a constant stream of visitors.

John Ford, that monumental influence in his life, was a frequent visitor as he planned his next picture, *The Searchers*, with Duke. Pilar resented his frequent intrusion into her life, she also believed he limited her husband as an actor and ignored his abundant talent when he told her, "Duke cannot escape playing himself, he has to accept playing big rough men, simply because of his physical size. He isn't a good enough actor to do anything else and he should play to his strengths. I've never doubted him, but to this day, I wouldn't call him an actor. He is a reactor. Put him in a dramatic situation and he reacts to it as he would in real life. That kind of performance makes for fine, believable motion pictures. What he does isn't easy, it's hard work, but I know you can push him to the brink and he'll still come back for more."

For the psychological, brutal and realistic movie that Ford now planned, only Duke would do, no matter how good an actor he was or wasn't. He wanted to make a landmark film in Hollywood history, again in the magnificent setting of Monument Valley. He was determined Duke would play the role of the obsessed Ethan Edwards. And it didn't take much persuading to get him to go back to his spiritual home, he didn't have to be pushed into accepting a part that seemed to fit him like a glove.

When he and Pilar arrived in the Valley in June 1955 setting up location was business as usual for the Ford Stock Members and whilst it was the first time she had seen the three men work together, Pilar immediately felt the closeness that existed between Ford, Bond and her husband as they swung into their well-rehearsed preparations, "They seemed to work in the searing heat of the Navajo reservation without the use of words, each knowing instinctively what the other required. They might be abrasive toward each other but it was obvious they remained affectionate at the same time. They seemed to share a mystical attachment to the place and for some reason Duke expected me to love it too. He was ever the optimist. Even the Navajo didn't enjoy summer in The Valley!"

Ford had been anxious to film another western for some time, "Westerns are good for my health, spirit and morale." He had chosen the unusual story about Confederate veteran, Ethan Edwards, a man who returns home long after the end of the war, presumably after a successful career as a bank robber, with care and with Duke already in mind. When Ethan's family are slaughtered and his nieces kidnapped in a Commanche uprising, he sets out to avenge the murders and to rescue the girls. From the outset he is shown as having an obsessive hatred of Indians. Everything about him is designed to distance the audience from his attitudes. Throughout the film Ethan's rage deepens until he finds the mutilated body of the elder girl and it develops into burning hatred as he sets out to find his younger niece, Debbie. He allows nothing to turn him from his path and his stubborn commitment to the search pushes his war-damaged personality to the brink of insanity.

The dark film possibly reflected Ford's increasingly depressed state but Duke never saw the role in that light, "I loved Ethan and I loved playing him. A great deal of the work was instinctive, and I loved the fact that I wasn't just a good guy. I was kind of an anti hero. In every picture that I've done I've tried to have some human weaknesses and admit those weaknesses. They kept making westerns with me because my character was not too straight. A lot of the stuff I did, I did because I was under contract, and there we are. That's the way it goes. But Ethan was different. I loved him. People said he was lost at the end, that he could never become part of society, and perhaps that was how Jack saw him, but my way of feeling is that you could do a sequel, Ethan Rides Again. He has spent years of his life chasing down the people who murdered the woman he loved and her relatives, but you could start him off again. Naturally the chase has been the highlight of his life, he would take six months or so to regain his composure. He had been dedicated to a wrong cause, dedicated to vengeance, but I'm optimistic about the character. I don't see any reason why Ethan couldn't have snapped out of it, he loved the warm little human being, his niece, and he took her back to her own people. Right at that moment, because of the life he has led, no one is going to invite him in, but I'm sure that if he rode off into town and had a few belts, he would have thought about things, about his dead brother's homestead, about buying cattle. Somehow a man as strong as Ethan is going to get back into the swing. He isn't going to just quit. I think he is strong enough to carry on. That little girl was going to love him, and it would be a good life. He wasn't completely alienated like people said, or he would have killed her. Simply, I am an optimist. The ending of The Searchers is just a downbeat moment in a man's life, but I can always think what would happen to change things. I believe in the old thing where a guy looks in his stocking at Christmas and says, "Goddammit, I got nothin' but horseshit," but the other guy says, "Oh Boy, they got me a horse, but it got away! Yeah ... I'm an optimist."

Duke didn't feel alienated, he was aware he was doing a good job and he was as happy that summer as he had ever been. Harry Carey Jr remembered, "The minute we all arrived there you could tell that this was something really special, something different from anything any of us had known before. It sounds like I'm dramatizing but I'm telling the truth. The whole thing had a mood about it and Wayne was so powerful. He'd really done his homework. He became Ethan Edwards. I think it really was his greatest performance. I was mesmerized by the power of his performance. His acting brought tears to my eyes in the scene where he tells me my girlfriend has been killed. When Ford liked a scene he went, "Right!" Well, even he was satisfied and he went "Right!" after the first take. Everything was perfect but as Pappy sat back to light his cigar there was some mumbling behind the camera. Someone confessed that the cameras had stopped right in the middle of the scene. What had happened was that Ward Bond had arrived on set, unplugged the camera, plugged in his electric shaver and started shaving! Ford moaned we'd have to do it again but no one ever told him what Bond had done. I think he would have killed him. I was even more impressed the second time we did it. I was amazed at Duke's talent during the filming of *The Searchers*. When I looked up at him in rehearsal, it was into the meanest, coldest eyes I had ever seen. I don't know how he moulded the character ... He was even Ethan at dinner time. Ethan was always in his eyes."

Ford, at the pinnacle of his career, framed the closing scene in a doorway to reinforce Ethan's isolation. The shot was acknowledged as one of the most harrowing in film history and Olive Carey, Harry's mother, was reduced to tears as she watched it unfold, "All Duke had to do was walk up to the door, turn around and walk away, The End. He did so much more than that. I think he has the grace of Nureyev, he really is the most graceful man I've ever seen, his co-ordination is so fantastic. I love to watch him move around. He rehearsed the scene twice. After the five year search he had finally brought Debbie home. He stands alone outside on the porch as everyone else goes into the house with the girl. He is looking in after them longingly. The others move back into their close-knit community and Ethan is left out on his own, unable to rejoin society. His eyes showed his pain." Harry Carey recalled that Duke had a hangover when the scene was shot ... "There he was! The big man standing alone in the doorway ... he was to look in and then walk away, but just before he turned, he saw my mother, wife of his all-time hero, standing behind the camera, and as naturally as taking a breath, he raised his left hand, reached across his chest and grabbed his right arm at the elbow. It was a typical Harry Carey gesture seen by Duke in countless movies when he was a boy, he'd spent many a dime just to see that. He looked at my mother for a couple of minutes, then turned, and walked away into the loneliness of the desert. A sign should have been put up on the door of Duke's room at Goulding's Lodge, "In this room John Wayne got drunk before he shot one of the most famous scenes in motion picture history." It was filmed in the late afternoon. Ford didn't suspect anything special was going to happen when the cameras started to roll, but he loved the way Duke instinctively closed his picture. It was an unexpected and emotional personal tribute that touched my Mother's heart."

Duke hadn't realised anyone would notice, and he was surprised at the reaction, "Jesus, people noticed that? You know why I did this at the end of the picture? In the last scene Harry's widow had taken the girl in, and as they went by me I could feel the wind blowing on me, then I saw them all turn round. She and I had been talking about Harry and I saw her looking at me, and I just did it. Goddam, tears just came to her eyes. I played that scene for Ollie Carey. Turned out to be a great shot didn't it?"

Hank Worden played Mose Harper, a part Ford added to lighten the tone of the grim story. Hank had Duke to thank for a successful career as a character actor. They had worked together from the start at Monogram, "Duke helped me get a part in *Red River*, mentioning me to Mr Hawks. I had been a wrangler until then. He always asked for work for me and many of the jobs I got later were due to the exposure I got working with him. He was a first class friend, just the way he was in his pictures, and we often shared tents out on location in the old days. When we made *The Searchers* I bunked in one of the tents at the trading post in Monument Valley but Duke often came down there to eat with us, saying that our food was better than what was being served in the star's dining room. He turned up, threw his arm round me and said, "Hank, you old son of a bitch, what've we got? Let's eat." I have to tell you he called everyone he liked a "son of a bitch." If you were a SOB on his list, you were in. All his crew were sons of bitches and he loved them all. I've seen him on location talking to truck drivers, not big wheels you understand, and he'd be asking them about their wives and their kids. And he remembered all their names and all their stories and problems. We remembered him for his kindness and his courtesy in remembering."

All the members of the Ford Stock Company were working at the height of their popularity. The books of Zane Grey and Louis L'Amour were selling in their millions. Television was showing up to thirty five westerns a week. *The Searchers* could hardly fail. Still non of them anticipated the spectacular success of a collaboration that saw the picture hailed as the ultimate western. Film critic Andrew Sarris wrote, "Wayne acts out the mystery of what passes through the soul of Ethan Edwards in that fearsome moment when he discovers the bodies of his brother, his beloved sister-in-law and his nephew. He is invested afterward with the implacability of a figure too much larger than life for any genre but the western."

Ford's west had become a place of anguish for John Wayne. The hero had grown hard and his obsessive behaviour now bordered on insanity. Ford knew he could portray "the tragedy of the loner" to perfection, now he wanted to draw out a darker side. In all the films they had made together up to *The Searchers* the Wayne hero was always the saviour of civilisation. Now he became isolate, unwanted and rejected by society, a hostile, restless and impatient man, doomed to be a wanderer, he is "masculine, repressed, celibate, and brutalized" by civilization. Ford said, "What interested me most were the consequences of one tragic moment and how Ethan reacts to that moment, his search for the naked truth and the brutality of his actions. He endures everything the desert offers and in such a hostile landscape it was his own brute strength that determined his own, and finally Debbie's survival. We largely dispensed with language. Ethan was a man of strength and few words."

His face, movement, the cold stare of hard eyes, all tell of pain, endurance, and his commitment to see things through and Duke admitted, "I felt personally closer to Ethan than any other character I ever played." A lifetime of regret can be seen in Ethan's eyes at his first appearance in opening shots that establish him immediately as a man to be reckoned with. He is seen to be quick to anger, ready to explode, a timebomb. Hidden deep, but instantly visible when he glances at his sister-in-law, is one tiny spark of gentleness and warmth and it is obvious that he loves her. It is equally obvious that she shares his feelings. He gazes after her with longing as she lovingly unfolds and holds his coat against her body. Ford never makes clear what has happened between them before the war, "I don't think it came over very well that I was supposed to be in love with her. The story really called for a man that was fighting his instinct with reasoning that this was his brother's wife. That was the way I felt, though it wasn't in the script or anything, and with Jack, a lot of his work was instinctive, he came on with one idea, but maybe when he got on set he changed his mind."

Once his sister in law has been murdered Ethan's last shred of tenderness is lost and he becomes a totally hard character. Even the niece he has been searching for becomes his enemy, committing the ultimate betrayal with the Indian chief who kidnapped her. In the final scenes he steps back from the edge of insanity to recall that Debbie is all that is left to him of the woman he loved. She is terrified of him and expects him to kill her when he catches her, instead he holds her close against his chest and murmurs, "Let's go home Debbie."

French director and Marxist, Jean-Luc Godard said, "In that instant I realized the power and complexity of John Wayne." He had been determined to hate all Wayne films, and then he saw *The Searchers*, "How can I hate John Wayne upholding Goldwater and yet love him tenderly when he abruptly takes Natalie Wood in his arms in the last reel of *The Searchers*?" In no other film had he shown the emotional range that he now displayed and Mary St John said, "When he watched the rushes he knew he was giving a special performance."

At the time of its release few critics picked up its dark message or its splendour and it fell to a new generation of filmmakers to discover the classic. Reviews in 1956 only looked at John Wayne in another John Wayne movie, Duke doing business as usual, in itself that was hardly anything special. But the next generation of critics noticed that he had taken his Western hero to the very edge of evil, that he had pushed his accepted image way past the implacable, good guy of his earlier work and into another, darker realm and the Western gunman became an anti-hero for the first time. As cruel Ethan Edwards, Duke attracted a whole new generation of fans, youngsters who wouldn't have been seen dead at his earlier movies, but who now identified with his truculence and willingly adopted him as one of their own. Ethan's catch phrase, "That'll be the day" was turned into a song by Buddy Holly within weeks of the film's release. It remained at number one in the charts for months and the phrase emerged into American teenage vocabulary. Duke was surprised to find himself an accepted part of the youth cult along with James Dean and Marlon Brando.

On the whole it fell to younger film makers to recognise the quality and power of the picture. Whilst Howard Hawks said, twenty years after its release, "I rank it as the best colour picture that I've ever seen," it was the likes of Martin Scorsese who raved about it's grandeur, "The dialogue is like poetry! I see it once or twice a year," and Steven Spielberg who agreed, "I never tire of seeing it. It's John Wayne's best performance … It's a study in dramatic framing and composition. It contains the single most harrowing moment in any film I've ever seen."

On the home front too Duke made an announcement fitting his spectacular year. For months since their wedding, Pilar had followed him around from one location to the next, they had been exciting and fulfilling times for him, but less so for her. She was bored when he was working. She wanted a baby, partly to replace one lost and partly to fill the long lonely hours she spent on film sets. Duke also felt a baby would complete their happiness and was more than willing to oblige her. He had done his best with his first family, it had never been enough and now he knew a strong urge to make amends and to put past failure behind him. Pilar was offering him a second chance and he wanted to prove he could be a good husband and father. He took every opportunity that presented itself and a month after arriving in Monument Valley to shoot The Searchers, and just eight months after their wedding, Pilar knew she was pregnant again. She didn't tell him until filming was complete and they were back home. He was ecstatic when she shouted the news down the stairs to him. He ran up them two at a time, crying as he realised that yet again the Gods had smiled on John Wayne, "It isn't often a man gets a second chance in life. This time I swear I will do it right!"

The films he made during the fifties reflected changes in his own identity and he was increasingly portrayed as having hidden passion and eroticism, as a self-mocking, sometimes violent man who, appreciating his own huge image doesn't want to lash out as he is often forced to do. The toughness was a means of hiding his underlying vulnerability and in many of the films of this period he either draws away from violence, is seen to disapprove of it, or ultimately is killed himself. As an alternative to the graphic violence he so opposed, he regularly used his fists, and when he resorted to guns he lost as often as he won. When he failed it wasn't because of any lack of courage or endeavour, but because he was outnumbered, or because of circumstances outside his control. His strength lay in his willingness to accept responsibility, a willingness to die protecting those in his care, an ability to provide comfort and protection. His power of endurance and devotion to duty were constantly highlighted. His performances were marked by his actions and his personality rather than by words. As he aged and accepted more responsibility in his own life and the next generation of films reflected the emotional and physical changes taking place in the man. He provided the mould for the directors and his physical characteristics still gave them much to work with, even though he no longer possessed the hard muscularity of a true action hero. His stature now tended to display his sense of discomfort or awkwardness and his body was increasingly referred to in unflattering terms. At the same time he was better able to demonstrate the endurance that was so much a part of the characters he chose to play. He was big and tough and could still stand much abuse despite the loss of muscular power. His body, softer now, was perfectly suited to providing shelter and comfort, and in film after film he could be seen lifting women or children and holding them safely protected against a broad expanse of chest.

The dramatic changes abounded both in his film persona and in his private identity. Visibly older, the body was stiffer and heavier, and the eyes held hidden depths behind drooping lids. The parts he could play may have altered but they only reflected those changes happening in the man and the domestic path he now trod led straight to superstardom where he became the stuff of legend, the ultimate Hollywood film icon. He chose his own direction every step of the way, it led him to a secure place in the hearts and minds of the public but also carried him inevitably away from his beloved Pilar. He was driven, compulsively, obsessively, to make more and more films, always adding to the myth that surrounded and isolated him. When Pilar told him she was pregnant he was overjoyed but he didn't stop to think how a baby might alter their relationship. She began staying at home when he went on location, driven by her own obsession, as great as his, to raise their family. Changes were inevitable. For three years he and Pilar hadn't been separated, he expected and needed her at his side. When he made three films in a year he was away from home for up to nine months, during which time she had become vital to his comfort. He tended to work in remote locations suited to the kind of films he preferred to make. They were tough on him physically and demanded great effort, he was often left tired, uncomfortable and irritable. But he had his boundless energy that others didn't possess, and even as he approached his fiftieth birthday he could hardly control it. For those around him things were even more difficult, and Pilar began to find going on location exhausting and incredibly boring.

When she first realised she was pregnant she was as excited as he was but she instinctively feared that when the baby arrived things were going to get difficult. There was no way she would consider taking their longed-for child to the desolate locations where he spent so much of his time. She was suddenly torn by the realisation that even had she wanted to be with him all the time, she wanted to be a good mother to their baby more. For the first time she had the worrying notion that perhaps her children were going to mean more to her than he did, and knew that once he realised that he would be lost to her.

She kept her fears to herself and he welcomed the pregnancy as if he were a first-time expectant father, strutting round the house, drawing up plans for a new nursery. He thought his four older children would share his excitement but was shocked by the deafening silence that greeted him when he announced the news at a family dinner. Shrugging helplessly he moaned, "Well don't blame me. She's the one whose pregnant!" Pilar was furious to find herself the target of his children's displeasure, "Forceful though he was, he simply couldn't abide arguing with his children. He was always the one to back down in the face of family conflict. He could stand his ground in any situation except were his own family were concerned. He had his huge, furious temper that terrified many an onlooker, but he resolutely refused to be drawn into battles at home. He had lived through enough conflict in his life from his childhood onwards that now, whenever he could, he avoided anything even resembling an argument. At the first sign of trouble he simply turned his back and walked away. Strangely, he never got involved in disputes in his office either. Whenever voices were raised in his presence he beat a hasty retreat and disappeared until the unpleasantness passed." It was actually pretty typical Marion Morrison behaviour and he never grew out of the need to run from raised voices.

Still, he felt piercing shame. He had failed his wife when she had most needed his protection. The stunned faces of his children told him they were having difficulty swallowing his enthusiasm for a second family when he had done so poorly by each of them; his divorce from their mother continued to exact a heavy toll and Pilar continued, "He was Hollywood's leading man. He cast a huge shadow, and sometimes those closest to him got lost in its darkness. To his first family everything must have seemed so complicated; I was only six years older than Michael. The children of his second family would be the same ages as his grandchildren. Duke might still be able to keep his life in neat compartments, but we had difficulty conceiving the permutations of the relationships now approaching. He had defied the natural rhythms of life, and he was big enough to do that, but we were all left struggling along in his wake, we couldn't keep up with him, and we resented it." He simply ignored his children's attitude, left them to deal with their own feelings, and assumed they would come round eventually. They were adults and he had Pilar to worry about. He showered her with every concern, treating her like a fragile and precious doll, constantly checking that she felt OK. To her he appeared calm, reassuring, sheltering, comfortable, just like he was in his films … he was, she thought, smoothly in control of the situation … he was John Wayne, the man everyone could rely on … and then she went into labour.

They had gone to bed early. She had fallen asleep as he watched TV. When her waters broke he leapt out of bed shouting, "What do you want me to do?" He was neither calm, reassuring or smooth John Wayne, "He just fell apart and I had to ask him to calm down before he called the doctor. I was ready to go to hospital before he finished dressing. He couldn't fasten his buttons. The drive to the hospital, only half an hour away, was a nightmare. He had told me he could find it in his sleep. Duke was renowned for his bad driving, he pointed his car in the direction he wanted to go and put his foot flat down to the floor. As usual he drove too fast and somehow managed to get lost. When I teased him that he'd said he could find the hospital in his sleep he laughed, "I know, but I'm awake now and lost as hell!" At the hospital he behaved as if he was waiting for his first child, rather than his fifth. He paced the floor of the delivery room, stopped to hold my hand, turned white and then went back to his pacing and whistling — he always paced or whistled when he was nervous." His daughter, Aissa was born on March 31, 1956.

Duke was sure something was wrong with the baby when she didn't cry. The doctor reassured him, telling him she was fine, but he demanded, "Why isn't she crying, babies are supposed to cry." Pilar said, "He sounded as if he were ordering the Seventh Cavalry to charge. In the end a nurse picked Aissa up and made her cry. Duke smiled, satisfied at last, "Now that's more like it." He cradled his little girl until her cries subsided, Aissa said, "I felt my father's obsessive grip for ever more. His need to prove himself was suffocating. He loved me so fiercely and demanded so much back that it became almost impossible to breathe. He thirsted for love and wanted it above all things. His demand for affection was overpowering."

After being all but destroyed by his own childhood, failing in his first efforts at raising a family and also in two marriages, he now refused to let anything go wrong. He invested huge amounts of love in his "second chance." He couldn't explain to anyone why he gave so much, or why he needed and wanted so much back. He had learned to suppress his feelings and had long avoided open shows of affection, now he began to demand them from his wife and daughter. When the strong man clung to Pilar she didn't understand, "I had no idea why he wanted us around all the time, and in truth, I doubt if he knew himself." He shied away from explanations, all Pilar knew was that he made great demands on her after the birth of Aissa, "He behaved like an idiot father. I have never seen a man so entranced by a child."

For the last six months of her pregnancy he had refused all offers of work, explaining, "I just want to be home with my wife." However, once his daughter entered the world the idiot father soon resumed his old ways, accepting the role of Spig Wead for the picture *Wings of Eagles*, again directed by John Ford. Wead, who had recently died, put career and patriotism above the needs of his family, it was a role Duke understood well.

Work still came first, but Pilar said, "Duke and Aissa were addicted to each other. He was completely overwhelmed by her and she followed him around endlessly, staring devotedly at him whenever he was home. She particularly liked to watch him shaving in his dressing room." Aissa remembered, "It always smelled so nice, of him and of his soap. I hated to let him out of my sight." She was aware, almost from babyhood, of the hold she had over him, "Whenever I fell or hurt myself he would look sick to his stomach. He spent hours stroking my hair in his need to soothe me. At Warners he kept an old bicycle that he used to get around on. He let me ride on the handlebars until the day I fell off. He turned white with shock and repeated over and over, "Oh my God, Oh my God." He never rode it again." He enjoyed showing his princess off and although she was never carried round the lot on the bike again she still went everywhere with him, usually perched high up, safe on his massive shoulders, "He was strong and powerful and nothing could hurt me up there. When he was around life was safe. Nothing and nobody could threaten my world. I was John Wayne's daughter. Whenever he was home I crept into bed between him and my mother and lay listening to his peaceful snoring. It was just that he wasn't there very often."

After the success of *The Searchers* Duke's bankability increased dramatically and in June 1956 he signed a deal with Twentieth Century-Fox that shocked the industry. He agreed to star in three movies over the next four years for $666,666 a picture, "I'm glad the producers were stupid. They won't spend money to make new stars. They won't take a chance on these new kids, but they're more than willing to pay me a fortune." He was grateful he had been given his chance when he was still a kid, and was sorry those days were gone. His own rise had exactly coincided with the great developments taking place in the industry. He would have preferred to see a healthy, continued growth, with the studios developing new stars, as he still tried to do at Batjac, but he accepted it was easier and safer for the big companies to spend their money on his services. He thought it was short-sighted of them to pay him a fortune for a few movies when they could have more wisely invested in new, cheaper talent. He was glad to be personally secure at last, but worried about the future of a business that faced immense competition from outside.

Rich, famous and powerful, he was now used to getting his own way in Hollywood. At home he remained less successful, "I wanted to be the perfect father and husband but it didn't take long before all the old tensions and frustrations found their way back into my life." Just because he had a new family to love his priorities hadn't changed and, however hard he tried, he could never satisfy the needs of his family because he gave so much elsewhere. In 1956, just after the birth of Aissa, more offers than ever were flooding in; everyone wanted a piece of John Wayne and he was a busy man. He spread himself thinly and gave what he could, when and where he could. The demands of the industry put an inevitable strain on his marriage but as long as Pilar was at his side Duke was content. He didn't see why the arrival of the child he doted on should change things. He was passionately in love with them both and craved their company. He demanded their presence and found life tedious without them. At first Pilar gave in to his demands and took the baby and a travelling nanny along on location, but she felt increasingly unhappy following him around the world to various uncivilised deserts. She was torn by the dual demands he and the baby made on her. And he also began to face conflicting needs, those of his work and of his constant longing to be close to his family. The beginnings of the crack that would tear them apart had appeared. At the time he hardly noticed, he was so busy and so overwhelmed by love for his wife and daughter.

However much he loved and needed them he still couldn't contain his energy when he wasn't working and his restlessness invaded their peace. He made his family feel lazy when they refused to get up to share the morning with him, and they began to avoid him instead. Pilar said, "It was like witnessing a miracle. His eyes popped open at four thirty every morning of his life. Once he was awake he had to get up, he simply couldn't lie still. Unfortunately he also hated us all sleeping in and usually managed to drag everyone out by seven, bellowing at the top of his voice, "It's time to get up! It's seven o'clock in the morning! Come on!" Sometimes we pretended to be asleep, but we didn't want to bruise him by telling him to go away or to stop doing it. On the whole it was easier to get up than to hurt him. Anyone whose life he touched in any way, found him such an electrifying personality that he completely overwhelmed them, particularly in the morning."

The power of his presence filled and dominated the lives of his family when he was home, but left them empty and alone when he went away, the contrast of his coming and going was great; when he was there he was everything to them, and when he went he left a void that nothing filled until he came home. He came and went at will, passing through their lives and making demands which none of them had the energy to fulfil, and though they missed him desperately when he went, it was also the only peaceful time they knew. His comings and goings affected them all but Aissa suffered the most, "When I knew he was going to be gone before morning I cried bitterly. He always tried to comfort me, "Every night I'm gone Honey, I want you to look at the stars. Wherever I am, I'll look at them too. And no matter how far apart we are, we'll know we've looked at the same stars." I did that every night he was away. I longed for him to come home and make me feel safe again."

In 1957 when Aissa was still a baby he prepared to go off on location to make *Legend of the Lost*, a film involving two months of location work at an isolated oasis in the Sahara Desert, followed by a further twelve weeks shooting in Rome. He was going to be away from January to August. Henry Hathaway, the producer and director, had decided to shoot most of the film four hundred miles from Tripoli. Everyone, including the stars, were to sleep in tents. There were no radios or telephones available and there was just one toilet for the whole cast and crew. As Duke packed his bags and prepared to leave he told Pilar he wanted her and Aissa to accompany him, "It's going to be fun sleeping out on the desert in a tent. Please come with me." He was upset to find she did not think it was such a good idea, he was hurt by her rejection and began shouting that he wanted her there, that he was counting on her, "Damn it Pilar, you are my wife. The nurse is perfectly capable of taking care of Aissa, and I need you with me!" Pilar stood her ground in the face of his anger but she finally agreed to meet him in Rome for the last twelve weeks of production.

A few weeks into shooting Pilar received an urgent cable, "Please hurry here. I need you. I love you. Duke." She was filled with fear, something must have happened to him, he was a man of his word and they had made a deal, he was unlikely to go back on their agreement unless something serious had happened to him. He was always getting hurt during filming, "battered" as he called it, he took no care of himself as he struggled to make the action look realistic, and he still performed most of his own stunts. She was terrified something awful must have happened, and in fact he had hurt his foot and ankle and was hobbling around on crutches when he sent the message … but that wasn't why he sent it.

She rushed to join him in Africa. All through the flight she prayed he was alright, and as soon as she descended from the light aircraft felt relief to see him waiting for her on the landing strip. She rushed headlong into his open arms, thanking God he was at least able to stand up. When she asked him what had happened he smiled, "I just wanted you here so you could see the sunsets with me." She was furious, but he just laughed and turned on the charm until she agreed to stay with him and meet up with Aissa later in Rome, "The sunsets were spectacular, and he did everything he could to show me how happy I made him, but I was anxious to get home." Nothing made up for what he had done and nothing he said could dispel her growing unease or anger. He wouldn't be drawn into an argument and he refused to admit there was a problem; he had wanted her, and she was there … he didn't have a problem, the fact that she was unhappy didn't concern him then. She found it difficult to sleep in Africa, it was hot, uncomfortable, but mostly she worried about leaving Aissa. A doctor prescribed sleeping pills.

Duke was a massive star, a banker, his co-star Sophia Loren was a sex goddess, Rossano Brazzi a huge European star, the film was being directed by one of Duke's personal favourites, Henry Hathaway, and his own production company, Batjac, was involved. Nothing rescued it at box-office. It generated a small profit but nothing like the amount Duke had anticipated. His previous film *Wings of Eagles*, had also faired poorly and he was facing a situation he had never, even as a B-movie star, come across before, back-to-back disappointments. Complicating things further, Howard Hughes had finally released the film, *Jet Pilot*, which Duke had worked on many years previously. It was savaged by the critics. He was no more immune from the Hollywood syndrome of insecurity than anyone else. He was anxious and set off to Japan to begin work on the first of the films in the Twentieth Century Fox deal a worried man. If *The Barbarian and The Geisha* failed it would be disastrous. He liked to give value for money, he wanted his fans to enjoy his work; repeated failures implied they weren't.

The new film, directed by John Huston, fell far short of Duke's own expectations and he complained, "The experience was one of the worst in my career." When he was first introduced to Huston he was still full of expectation and hope but within days had come to loath the director. The feeling was entirely mutual. Huston hated Duke's politics, hated the John Wayne phenomenon, hated the man and he spent his entire time in Japan going out of his way to annoy his star. Duke, with great difficulty but complete professionalism, stayed calm and refused to rise to the bait.

Huston had himself chosen Duke to play Townsend Harris, the first American Consul to Japan, intending to "let loose" the huge actor against the beauty of Japan. But Duke was never happy working in an unstructured way, he relied on his director more than most and was used to the dictatorial Ford, Hathaway and Hawks, none of whom would let loose an actor for a second of a film. He wrote to Pilar, who had refused to go with him to Japan, "I have done everything but stand on my head to get near this man's thinking. I just have to hope and pray that he's good." She recognised the note of pleading and unhappiness and finally gave in, setting out to join him just before Christmas, after he confessed, "I can't work with the son of a bitch." He believed a director should direct, not spend valuable production time out searching the streets for arts and crafts. To make matters worse, the female lead was a real geisha who spent her nights with Huston. They both arrived on set late every morning; a cardinal sin in Duke's eyes who was intensely irritated by what he regarded as unforgivably unprofessional behaviour. He might have tolerated another man's weakness but he could never forgive Huston for giving him no chance to produce any kind of performance himself. This director, the complete opposite to the ones Duke so admired, continually rewrote the script and often worked without one. Whenever Duke asked to see the next day's lines he was told to go away and absorb the beauty of the area, and stop worrying about the part, "You can improvise." Duke couldn't work like that, mastering lines came easy, he liked to feel prepared and to know his moves and marks. He detested Huston, "He can quote chapter and verse on the price of a god-damned piece of Japanese porcelain, but he won't tell me how he wants me to do a scene. It's a little frustrating." For the first time since he had been making cheap westerns he had no idea how the film was going to look. When he saw the final cut he acknowledged its beauty but knew it was not going to be a good vehicle for him, "There wasn't enough action in it." Long before its release he worried it would go bust, and that, together with the other poor films he had been involved in lately, would probably mean it was the one that marked the end of his career. A less popular star would have been finished long before and his worries were well founded. In fact it broke even but gave him his fourth box-office disappointment in a row. Huston blamed him for the picture's failure, saying Duke made changes to it that he had not wanted. Duke offered a stinging retort, "Considering he never told me at any point what he did want, I consider his comments a little unfair."

The more he worried about his future the more he alienated an already fretful Pilar. She had gone to spend a few weeks with him in Japan but she worried about Aissa all the time and called home repeatedly to check she was alright. Eventually Duke suggested it might be better if she went home. She hadn't been back long when she was woken from a deep sleep by Blackie's furious barking. The house was on fire and by the time she snatched Aissa up, much of the second storey of the house was engulfed in flames. Before fleeing with the baby tucked under her arm, Pilar grabbed Duke's old cavalry hat. That was pretty much all that was saved and by the time the fire department arrived most of the first floor had gone and everything, including their wonderful bed, had been lost to the flames.

Ward Bond raced over as soon as he heard the news and took her, Aissa and Blackie next door to friend and make-up artist, Web Overlander's house. Pilar telephoned Duke but kept the call brief, knowing he couldn't break off filming, no matter what had happened at home and she asked, matter-of-factly, "How do you like single storey houses?"

He and Pilar had often laughed about her constant lament, "I have nothing to wear" when her cupboards were bursting at the seams. Now, in response to the call, Duke sent her a blank cheque and a note, "For the girl who really has nothing to wear." It was his way of telling her he loved her and badly wanted to be there for her. He was still having tremendous difficulty with Huston and he wanted to get home at the earliest opportunity. Because he was unhappy at work for the first time, because of the upset of the fire, and the thought of what might have been, because he found himself thinking about Pilar all day long, he stopped to analyse his own feelings, also for the first time. He wondered at the kind of love he now felt, deeper and more intense than anything he had ever known before, and the fire, traumatic though it was for Pilar, was also a life-altering event for him. The next day he made a highly emotional call his wife to talk things over. The cheque had been a jokey thing to calm his own nerves, but he was scared and by the time he arrived home he had sunk into a deep depression. Pilar did her best to reassure him. "No one's been hurt and the house can be restored." He was less sure about his career. At fifty he no longer felt at ease playing the romantic lead, and he needed an exceptional film now to repair the damage done by a series of flops. People wouldn't notice the rubbish he had been turning out with such annoying regularity once another good one turned up. He accepted he was at his best when he had no control over either script or direction, and that all his better work was done for the tough directors, and when Howard Hawks approached him with another Western, he jumped at the chance. He needed to develop his career, to re-invent the image and to start playing character roles that could carry him into a dignified old age. He had to devise a new persona that would allow him to remain a real man, but a real fifty year old man. Hawks' *Rio Bravo* provided exactly the vehicle he was looking for and his part in it became the one that opened the door to all his future roles.

Both Hawks and Duke had hated *High Noon* in which Gary Cooper's sheriff was deserted by friends, citizens and his new bride, when he faced a gang of killers alone. Duke said, "I didn't think a good sheriff would go running round town like a headless chicken, begging for help, and eventually being saved by his Quaker wife. Mr Hawks had prepared a script for Rio Bravo in direct contrast. My role in it called for more character development than action. The story centres around the town's jail house where I am holding a man I have arrested for murder." Sheriff John T Chance, every inch the hero Duke had been looking for, was an older man who believed romance and love had passed him by as he got on with the business of protecting the town's citizens. He represented moral, legal and emotional restraint, and his frequent violent outbursts could be interpreted as outlets for his bottled up desires. Into his life wanders female gambler, Feathers, and the transformation that takes place in Chance following their meeting was a story line tailor made for Duke. The new persona was readily accepted by film-goers who already knew John Wayne as a man who would never decry his fate, would never ask any one for help and who would certainly shy away from a pushy female, even whilst obviously longing for her comfort.

As he worked on *Rio Bravo* Duke was in affable mood and Hawks said, "He was a pleasure to work with. He could learn two pages of lines in three or four minutes so that was never an issue — he would just ask "What am I supposed to do in this thing?" All he needed was to be told, "Well you're supposed to give an impression of this and this." He didn't want to know the larger story line, and if anyone tried to explain he would say, "I don't want to know. I never like Hawks stories, but they always turn out good." For Hawks Duke was the perfect actor, "He never squawks about anything. He's the easiest person I ever worked with. Because he never says anything about it, he just goes ahead and does it." On the odd occasion when Duke wasn't happy about something Hawks was always willing to listen and take advice, "All he had to do was shake his head for me to ask what was the matter. I trusted his instincts, and as soon as I saw the worried frown I could be sure things could be improved. I'd sit him down away from the cast and listen to him. We'd go over the script, sometimes tearing it apart. I knew things were resolved when he suddenly beamed all over and said, "That works good." Hawks continued, "Wayne represents more force, more power, than anybody else on the screen. John Ford and I often discussed how tough it was to make a good western without Wayne. *Rio Bravo* was a good case. His persona provided the perfect foil for all the rest of the characters, because of his well-developed image as the toughest son of a bitch on the range, he does not have to win every fight, or dominate every scene. His mere presence, even offstage, is enough."

One of the toughest critics on the range said of the film years after its release, "If I were asked to choose a film that would justify the existence of Hollywood, I think it would be *Rio Bravo*." Still, the critics of the day all failed to recognise the importance of the film and once again he received no special plaudits for his performance in it. Duke was at least grateful that after four failures it did well at the box office, staving off his most pressing financial worries, and putting his career back on track.

Once again all should have been well in his world but, as was so often the case, as his star rose his private life disintegrated into chaos. Pilar was suffering from depression and the fire seemed to have shaken her more than she realised at the time. She felt particularly anxious when Duke was away, but was even more determined that she would not leave Aissa again. She knew Duke loved her more than he had ever been able to say, but had no idea why he constantly needed her to be close. He had never openly expressed his feelings for her despite the long distance calls from Japan, and it was not his style to talk about his needs. He was not prepared to speak the words that, in his own mind, left him appearing unmanly and weak. How could the toughest son of a bitch on the range possibly confess that he didn't like being alone, that he needed someone with him, that he was like a child afraid of the dark? Instead of explaining, he simply demanded Pilar's company whenever he went on location. She had no idea why he had to make so many movies, no concept of why he had to work so hard, she couldn't possibly understand the boredom that engulfed him, or the irritability that filled him when he wasn't working. His failure to put any of it into words led to their downfall. He left her torn apart and, as her depression deepened, she found it increasingly difficult to sleep. She became short tempered and irritable and went back to the doctor who had first prescribed sleeping pills to ask for more. Like so many Hollywood wives she began taking them whenever she felt stressed.

If she had no understanding of what drove him, he had no idea what was wrong with her. He couldn't understand unhappiness in people who had good lives. Admittedly he had often made a mess of his own but still he relished everything in it, the good and the bad. When things were going well he accepted and enjoyed the rewards, never questioning his good fortune, and when times were tough, he put his head down and charged headlong into the mire, doing the best he could with everything at his disposal. Life was for living, and he did it, as he did everything else, with full force. He couldn't cope with Pilar's misery. How could a woman with such a loyal, hard-working husband, a beautiful baby, a lovely home, and plenty of money be unhappy? Just as she could make no sense of what drove him, so he failed to recognise her increasing urge to find an identity of her own. Perhaps part of the problem was that he was so much older than her, he always called her, "My girl." But it was also because he was John Wayne, and too used to people jumping to do what he told them. Pilar was growing up, she no longer wanted to be his girl, she wanted to discover herself and his long-established lifestyle simply couldn't permit it. Inevitably trouble flared and soon after he got home from *Rio Bravo*, the heated arguments began. He didn't know why she was angry with him or what had happened between them, so he set about trying to please her, buying her gifts and doing things around the house that he would have done for no one but her. He was singularly unsuccessful in his attempts to win her over and felt confused and anxious when he managed to do exactly the opposite. He feared another failed marriage. Although he was wary of her newly acquired toughness and assertiveness he adored her all the more for it and dreaded losing her. There was nothing he could do, she seemed to have stopped loving him and in September 1958, when Aissa was just two, he announced a separation, confessing in tears, "The going has been pretty rough for us because of my picture schedule and the fact that I'm all wrapped up in my career. I suppose it will end in divorce."

He was wrong and within days they were back together again, he with a huge smile on his face, Pilar still worried and frowning because nothing had changed for her. He had made her promises to get her back, she knew he would be unable to keep them. He was already scheduled to start work on *The Horse Soldiers* in Louisiana that October, with John Ford, and as usual he expected her to go with him. Nothing had changed.

During a party at their newly restored home Pilar began to feel unwell and suffered a sudden panic attack. She had taken the last of her tablets and fled from the room in a cold sweat. Duke ran after her. He didn't know what was happening until she started to plead with him to go the local pharmacist, screaming, "You've got to get my prescription now." He was shocked, caught completely off guard, but he refused to get her any replacements, then or ever. When she tried to explain they helped her sleep he was furious, "Who the hell gave you this crap?" He called his own doctor who explained that Pilar was drug dependant and that she would need continual care until her system was clear. Everything fell into place; this was why she had been so distant and had been behaving so strangely. Now he understood, he could put things right. He believed he could look after her better than anyone else and he refused to have her admitted to a sanatorium. He promised that if she went to Louisiana with him he would get her through it, "I'll be with you every minute, every step of the way, all you need is a little rest. We'll take a vacation as soon as I've finished this one."

It turned out to be the worst location she had been on. Ford was in his most irritable, nasty mood and the whole cast found him impossibly difficult. Duke was kept busy protecting them all, taking the brunt of the worst temper tantrums himself. Pilar found it especially difficult, not only was she unhappy and craving her pills, but her strong husband who had promised to support her through the withdrawal, was suddenly reduced to a quivering wreck at the hands of his mentor. William Holden, co-star and a close friend of Duke's, didn't get on with Ford and after several weeks of watching his friend suffer, he took pity on him. He came up with a scheme to give him a break and told the director that Duke's teeth seemed off colour and that he should see a dentist before they filmed any more. He and producer-writer, Martin Rackin, whisked him off set and they spent a pleasant day drinking. Pilar was less than grateful for their intervention when Ford discovered the scam and she was left dealing with the irate director herself.

When Duke eventually got back it was to find a weepy wife and a furious friend who screamed abuse at him, pushed him around and for the rest of filming, watched him like a hawk. He carried out close inspections of the Wayne's room every night, looking for any sign of alcohol. Duke took to hiding his drink in the cameraman's room and sneaking around, trying to stay out of harm's way. He had no time to help Pilar who was now in serious trouble and his promise to be with her every step of the way proved empty indeed. In a desperate attempt to attract his attention she slashed her wrists and he was forced to accept that he couldn't look after her as she deserved. He chartered a private plane to take her back to hospital in Encino. Two year old Aissa remained with him and they grew closer and became even more dependant on each other.

Pilar thought him unmoved, cold, more concerned about the film than her. Once again he had failed her in her hour of need. He simply didn't know what to say and so kept his own counsel although he did phone home every hour to check her progress. Duke's biggest fear was exposed emotion; he suppressed his own feelings and kept them hidden from prying eyes. Now he found it unbearably uncomfortable trying to deal with her overt demonstration of unhappiness. She believed he didn't care, in truth he cared far too much.

A close friend of Ford's was killed performing a stunt during filming and the director lost what little interest he had left for *The Horse Soldiers*. He hit the bottle, drinking alone in his room each night, refusing to invite Duke in, perhaps believing he had enough troubles of his own, but commenting, "My era is drawing to a close. We're under attack from the permissive society and the studios aren't making enough of our kind of pictures anymore. It's a pretty bleak outlook." Duke said, "He looked as though he didn't care about anything anymore." He was haunted by the old man's face and words, and left location sure the director would never work again. He himself had always found ways to recreate an image to reflect whatever changes society threw up, the offers of work had never dried up for him. It was different for the creator of the star and as Duke rode toward his golden sunset, Ford became bitter and took to his bed.

Duke took his turn nursing the morose Ford through the next months and often sat with him through long, lonely nights discussing their problems. Duke understood Ford's better than he did his own and could easily imagine himself in similar circumstances, but his wife's depression remained a mystery to him. It was a difficult time for them all, Duke was seriously worried about both Ford and Pilar but he also had other pressing concerns of his own.

Despite the success of *Rio Bravo* he was again struggling financially and his investments outside the industry were in trouble. He had purchased four thousand acres of cotton land in Arizona in 1958 but the operation consistently lost money. He had a meeting with cotton brokers, Anderson-Clayton, who recommended he talk to Louis Johnson, who they considered to be the best cotton farmer in the world and happened to live in Stansfield, right next to Duke's property. When he met Johnson he took an instant liking to the farmer and asked him if he would manage his land, running both operations together. After agreeing a salary Duke went away, started work on another movie and forgot all about the cotton business. But Johnson was as professional in his business as Duke was and the first joint harvest he raised exceeded everyone's expectations.

Harvesting such a large crop presented unforeseen problems and he couldn't reach Duke to let him know that he needed to invest more money fast so he could get the cotton in. No one returned his calls, but he had been charmed by the sincerity of the film star, and instead of letting the crop rot in the field he personally guaranteed a loan for over half a million dollars to finance cotton pickers, trailers and extra fuel. When Duke heard what he'd done he could hardly believe his ears! He had been surrounded by con men or people only interested in what he could give them for as many years as he could remember; he was constantly spun schemes, dreams and promises of huge profits, few ever delivered. Johnson had made no promises, but had certainly delivered. He had bailed him out, and expected nothing in return, and Duke had found a man he could trust absolutely. He asked Johnson to manage his land for another year and in 1961 invited him to form a partnership, combining their acreage into one massive farm. Johnson was worried that Duke wouldn't be able to take the ups and downs involved and only agreed when he drawled, "What the hell, I've stubbed my toe before."

At exactly the time Duke was developing his own successful investment in Arizona, his relationship with his financial advisor, Bo Roos was rapidly deteriorating. The difficulties over the harvesting only occurred in the first place because some of Duke's cheques had bounced. When he learned about it he rounded angrily on Roos who promised to liquidate some of his assets to improve his cash flow. He quickly forgave Roos and again put financial matters to the back of his mind. They stayed there only briefly. $700,000 of his Panamanian investments were suddenly lost when he was unexpectedly embroiled in the political scandal surrounding his Panamanian friend Tito Arias, husband of Margot Fonteyn. A memo from Duke to the Arias family outlining his investments in the country was unearthed by the Panamanian Government. They believed the politically powerful film star was mixed up in a conspiracy against them and disbelieved his vehement denial of their charges. The FBI jumped at another chance to investigate him, but they, like the Panamanians themselves, finally concluded there was insufficient evidence to implicate him in anything. He survived the incident personally but his investments were doomed and it became impossible for him to trade there again.

Duke fretted about where he was going, about his money and how he could support all the demands being made on him. *The Horse Soldiers* had barely broken even, and of his previous six films only *Rio Bravo* had been successful. He might ignore his critics, but failing box-office terrified him and, influenced now by the depressed John Ford, he began to see a yawning chasm opening up in front of him. If what he had achieved in *Rio Bravo* hadn't been enough to guarantee succeeding box-office he was afraid he was now going to have to market himself as something other than an ageing action hero. It would require yet another re-invention or he would have to develop other lines of business. In 1959 he sat at the top of the heap, the most famous film star of them all, but after his disastrous run of failure, he believed he was washed up, that he'd been forced off the screen. The American public might adore its film stars, it never revered them. They were only ever as good as their last film.

It was not only his, Ford's and Pilar's worlds that were undergoing rapid change. The film industry, the United States, and the rest of the world too, were in the throes of transformation. He had already fought off the Communist in Hollywood but increasing liberalism was again surfacing in the movie industry. He hated the dramatic increase in sex and violence seen in so many new films; Westerns, like *The Wild Bunch* contained particularly graphic violence, pain and sadism. Duke hated the material coming out of Hollywood and believed it had to affect society in general, and the movie industry in particular. He began his crusade against modern trends.

Unlike the emerging new breed of film star he had always aimed to please and give value for money. He wanted his audiences' trust and affection, and believed his success in winning it was rooted deep in the movies he had chosen to make over the years. Public perception of his screen persona mattered to him, whereas other stars of the period were intent on appearing mysterious, difficult, and rebellious, they didn't care if the public liked them or not, "People have credited me with being a reactionary for years, but the only thing I'm really a reactionary on is the motion picture business, which was intended to be a medium of illusion. All these young actors and directors are trying to take the illusion out of it. I've knocked people on their ass, hit people over the head with chairs for years, but nobody ever said anything about it. Now they're specialising in it. They tape a piece of liver to you and blow it out so it looks like your guts are coming out. They want a realism that I think is unnecessary. Their attitude is realism against illusion. I don't say it's wrong, it's different than my conception, and all I know is that picture attendance has dropped off. It's no longer the American habit that it used to be. And it's obvious to me that it's because of the type of pictures that are being made. It doesn't take a soothsayer to figure it out."

And it wasn't only the film industry that was changing, political storms of unrest billowed in from the horizon to affect both his position in Hollywood and the American psyche generally. Everything he held dear was under threat again, and as in the forties, the only way he could cope was to stage a fightback. His war started when he took the decision to make *The Alamo*, a film that had already bordered on obsession for over a third of his career. He felt the time had arrived to give Americans the story of courage, sacrifice and devotion by the 184 men who gave their lives for freedom. He wanted to produce and direct a film that would "Shake hell out of people all over the world," that would be in stark contrast to the images of sex, violence and drugs that had become so fashionable.

Everyone in Hollywood told him he was crazy to consider getting involved in a film that no one would pay to see. Certainly no one was prepared to fund his dream. Jack Warner, a good friend of many years told him, "I don't think the fans want to see this kind of picture anymore Duke, forget it." The more they tried to discourage him the more convinced he became he was right. His friends told him it was lunacy to think about using this to make his debut as a director, but nothing would budge him, his mind was made up, and he refused to be put off. This was his dream, his full-force obsession, and with or without their help he was absolutely determined to make it. He had first become interested in the story after visiting San Antonio where he noticed tourists behaving as though they were entering a cathedral when they walked silently over the ground where the men had died. He read the letter of appeal written by Travis during the siege and explained, "Never before, or since, have a group of individuals signed a suicide pact in the name of liberty. This story has to be told." When he began the dogged fight to tell it he created the most lasting image of John Wayne, superstar, the image that endured and was remembered by the world as he lay dying twenty years later.

To bring the dream to life he first had to overcome immense personal and financial problems. He had already received the first warnings about his financial status when Bo Roos had to liquidate his investments. Since making *Stagecoach* in 1939 he had made millions of dollars which he handed straight over to Roos to invest against an uncertain future. In early 1959 he and Pilar went to New York on a shopping trip. All the bills were sent off to Roos to pay. Three months later when they were still unsettled Duke began receiving daily reminders. Eventually he called Roos, "Jesus Christ, Bo, would you please pay the bills. I look like a goddamn deadbeat!" Roos promised to take care of them straight away. Duke later mentioned the incident to Ward Bond who was immediately suspicious having recently heard rumours about the financier. He advised Duke to check things out and Mary was sent round to collect his investment portfolio. The files were virtually empty and when Duke met Roos several days later he asked, "Bo, exactly how much money do I have?" The answer alarmed him, "Well, not a great deal of cash. Your money's all invested in various business ventures."

Duke was angry, impatient and scared, "I know that. Just tell me how much cash I could raise if I had to." He knew Roos was stalling for time when he said it would take a few weeks to sort everything out, he lost all restraint, stood up, slammed a giant fist down on the desk and bellowed at the top of his voice, "For Chrissake, I've given you a fortune over the years. Its a simple question. What the hell have you done with my money?" Roos slumped in his chair, "It's all gone." At the very instant he needed his millions to finance his film Roos sat white-faced, telling him everything he had worked for had gone. Duke scrutinised every transaction Roos had ever made and was devastated to find he was left with just his home, some personal possessions, his production company, and some worthless properties. He stormed out of the office to call his lawyer. For a long time he couldn't believe his money could just have disappeared, but when a group of accountants poured over the figures they could find no trace of fraud, only gross mismanagement. Duke sighed his disbelief, "I'll be goddamned, I was sure he stole it, nobody's stupid enough to lose that much money." He had rarely given his investments a second thought, that was what he paid Roos for, but his money had ebbed away over a period of twenty years as more and more had been pumped into one disaster after another. Mary remembered, "Roos had a passion for business trips. He never bothered calling when Duke was home, but as soon as he was away on location he invented a reason to visit the set. When Duke was filming *The Barbarian and the Geisha* he spent a month in a Japanese hotel, having sex with local Geishas and eating in the finest restaurants, always at Duke's expense."

The only investments that had made money were the ones he was personally interested in such as the cotton farm, which many years later, helped restore the lost fortune. Right then he was all but ruined and forced to accept much of the blame himself, for Roos had not been alone in his negligence. When the head of CBS Television scolded, "How the hell could you give a guy millions and not ask any questions, never follow up on him? If you take him to court it will make you look like a complete ignoramus. Just forget about it and start over," Duke knew exactly what he had to do. And, despite feeling betrayed by a man he had trusted, he did his best to forget, to start over. Still the catastrophe couldn't have come at a worse time, occurring just as he was due to start work on *The Alamo*. Because he had been unable to get any studio to finance the project he had already invested as much of his private wealth into it as possible. Now he had nothing left to make the film he envisaged and he was forced back to the drawing board to consider new ways of raising capital.

As he planned his picture he stubbornly refused to listen to the arguments against it, he remained completely focused on his vision. However, he was forced to concede ground in one important area. He'd had no intention of appearing in the film himself, except perhaps in a cameo role, he wanted to dedicate all his time to creating a perfect vehicle. But finally, to win the financial backing he needed, he had to succumb to outside demands and take a leading role himself. Potential sponsors were certain that if he starred in it, the movie was unlikely to fail drastically at the box office. Without him it was likely to be a disaster that ruined not only him but them along with him. His complete dedication to the project, in the face of overwhelming opposition, was a testament to his courage, determination and integrity. He often laughed that no studio would touch the film unless he changed the ending! He loved the ending, which he said was, "A testament to man's courage, determination and integrity in the face of overwhelming opposition." He had already spent more than fourteen years trying to get the project off the ground, refusing to let it go and never allowing it to remain just a dream. He insisted on directing it, even though he had never previously directed anything, he knew what he wanted to see on screen and, from the earliest seed being planted, he had been unable to countenance handing it over. No one else could possibly capture his vision. And of course he wanted to be a director long before he ever wanted to be an actor, from the first time he stepped inside a studio, "I was only diverted from my course for the past thirty years," and it was only surprising that it took him so long to get to this point. It was also surprising that he chose such a monumental task for his first venture; even John Ford warned him to try something smaller to launch his new career.

Duke had been arguing with Herbert Yates since 1945 about making *The Alamo*. In 1951 he'd pleaded with him and Yates had finally given him the go ahead, telling him to talk to one of the studio screenwriters. But the producer was so set in his ways that, even when he was dealing with the biggest star in the world, he could only think in terms of low budget films. He offered to finance a studio lot for shooting. Duke's smile was dangerously sweet as he shook his head in disbelief, "I'm asking you to commit two million dollars so I can make the biggest epic ever filmed. I'm not talking about a goddam B-movie here. I've spent years looking for a suitable location for this film. I've got the perfect spot, a small settlement on the Pacific side of Panama. Looks good, realistic, authentic, and it's cheap. Come on Herb, what do ya say?"

Yates hated the smell of risk and he particularly disliked the idea of an expensive epic gamble directed by Duke Wayne. He might listen to him but he had no intention of letting the biggest draw in the game loose on such a hare-brained scheme or of putting any money into a film where all the heroes died. He had managed to keep his star hanging on at Republic by making promises he had no intention of keeping, and as long as he continued to make money, Yates was prepared to say anything he wanted to hear. But Duke had become increasingly impatient and difficult to handle after starting to make his own serious plans for the picture. He had been working on a screenplay with Jimmy Grant and Ford's son, Patrick, and finally in late 1951 he began issuing contracts for set construction in Mexico. When he looked back Duke realised how entirely typical of him it had been to rush headlong into things without completing all the feasibility studies, without checking what problems there might be, how entirely typical, that having lived with the obsession so long, he had been unable to wait another second to get things started once he had made his decision. How entirely typical it had been to think Yates would rush to give him money, and how typical that when the producer again prevaricated, "I'll think about it Duke," he had flown into the famous rage that led to the final separation from Republic.

All the time Grant had been working on the script he was employed by the studio and, legally, the screenplay belonged to Republic and not to Duke. He now found himself forced to crawl on his hands and knees, tail between his legs, to beg for it. He offered Yates anything he wanted, but the producer, as stubborn as the star, wouldn't give, or sell it to him at any price. He knew how badly Duke wanted the picture, here was the carrot to tempt him back. Grant, desperately trying to keep the peace between them before Duke blew a fuse and did damage to the old man, offered an amended script if he would agree to make the picture at Republic. He met a typically surly refusal; Yates had been offered the chance to share his dream on more than one occasion, now it was too late.

The next problem was even more drastic than the loss of the screenplay. When the Sons and Daughters of the Republic of Texas, the official custodians of the Alamo, heard he was planning to film their story in Mexico a loud howl of protest went up. To make a picture about the men who bought the hallowed ground of the old mission with their blood in Mexico, of all places, was sacrilegious. They told him sharply that if he went ahead he would alienate every Texan, he would get no financial backing for his venture there and no Texan theatre would ever screen the film. They were stating the obvious and he knew he had been really stupid to think he could make it anywhere except Texas and that, whatever other difficulties he might have to face, his dream was going to cost him a lot more than he had first anticipated. Still, what they said cast a seed, "No Texan would invest any money in such a venture ..." a small seed, just a grain of hope. He grasped at it and went back to the drawing board. If he shot it around San Antonio perhaps he could also finance it there ... He drew up a new proposal and went to talk to Texans.

Since the first stirrings of the idea he had been trying to sell it to the big studios. He never stopped talking about it and everyone in Hollywood was aware of his plans. By the mid fifties he had received some offers of help, but with each of those offers had gone the double condition that he star in the picture and didn't direct it. Duke of course was worried about ageing, about audiences tiring of him as an action star, he was worried about his future and producing and directing *The Alamo* was his cure-all. He stubbornly refused the conditions because he was determined to break into other areas of the business before he was completely washed up. He strode forward with determination, his personal power stirred everyone up, and the air in Hollywood became laden with his plans. He believed he had to go into directing. He had survived in the business for almost thirty years and had worked tirelessly because he loved it all so much. The industry was his life blood, and whilst he never liked to be called an actor — the term embarrassed him, and he referred disparagingly to most male Hollywood stars as "faggy." To survive in it he was willing to do anything and insisted, "My problem is I'm not a handsome man like Cary Grant. I may be able to do a few more man-woman things before it's too late, but then what? I never want to play silly old men chasing young girls, as some stars are doing. I have to be a director — I've waited all these years to be one. *The Alamo* is where I start."

By the time he started building the set for the film he was fifty, and he was right, he didn't posses the face of Cary Grant. His was a western face, sculptured by adversity, it was wrinkled, weather-beaten and hard, the bright blue eyes were narrowed by his years in the sun and deeply embedded in those wrinkles. The nose was Roman, the jaw was strong, the mouth heroic. His was a lean, tough face that reflected his years, reflected the pursuit of a dream, and showed his single-minded obsession and his unwillingness to bow to adversity. His was the face of Ethan Edwards, Thomas Dunson and John Stryker, characters obsessed, strong, unwilling to bend or give up, they were all John Wayne, and he was imbued with the strength and stubbornness of each. He heeded nobody and his craggy, fifty year old face was set as he shook his head, "No, I'm doing it myself," and as he repeated "No," over and over again to every entreaty, to his sons who warned him it was too big, to his agent, lawyers, business advisers, movie executives, to everyone who pleaded with him not to do it. If he couldn't get the support he needed in Hollywood he would have to arrange it elsewhere.

Through the disappointments, the lack of trust and belief from every side, one person stood steadfastly at his side. Pilar heaped encouragement on him and urged, "You can do this." In spite of their recent problems she now lent her support and strength, and actively pushed him to follow his dream. She let him know that she believed in him and told him how proud of him she felt. Things didn't get much better than that for Duke. He loved her intensely and never noticed the massive toll *The Alamo* placed on their already faltering marriage.

He had no control over his obsession. He tried to explain it to the media but the words came out wrong, "This picture is America. I hope that seeing the battle of the Alamo will remind Americans that liberty and freedom don't come cheap. This picture, well, I guess making it has made me feel useful to my country. I think it's important that foreign countries know about this aspect of the American struggle for freedom. I hope our present generation of Americans, our children, will get a sense of our glorious past, and appreciate the struggle our ancestors made for the precious freedoms we now enjoy — and sometimes just kind of take for granted." If people thought he sounded like he was making a Fourth of July speech, they should have remembered he was bankrupting himself to make the film, he had committed every possession he owned to it and had destroyed long, steady relationships with Yates, Republic and many other associates as well.

When he saw how popular Walt Disney's *Davy Crockett, King of the Wild Frontier* was, Yates planned a dirty campaign of revenge against the star who had walked out on him. He decided to make his own film about the Alamo with a huge budget on location in Texas. Neither Disney nor Yates could upset Duke who hardly bothered lifting a laconic eyebrow, "Yates tried to steal my idea, he came up with *The Last Command* which was a quickie. 'Nuff said."

After leaving Republic to form Wayne-Fellows Productions Duke had signed the famous deal with Warner Brothers, but even though they threw money at him, they were still unwilling to put anything into *The Alamo*, and deliberately left any mention of his pet the project out of the lucrative contract. With no studio backing, Duke was completely on his own with it and he began making as many movies as he could, working at a frantic pace, trying to fund the picture from his own resources. He was still very much in demand and he rarely turned an offer down during this hectic period. Grant, meanwhile started work on a new screenplay, producing four expensive re-writes before Duke was satisfied. The cost of each one upped the final budget and forced Duke to accept that no matter how hard he worked, he would never be able to earn enough to make his vision and he began the long chase to obtain independent financing. No matter what he was working on, he never stopped pleading or begging, never gave up knocking on doors to ask for money. Every rejection felt personal but his determination intensified along the way, "I have everything I own in this picture — except my necktie. I have gambled everything, all my money, my production company, my home and my car … everything … including my soul." And when he looked back it was with horror at the risks he had taken, and with enormous pride that he eventually brought it off.

The financial package he put together was revolutionary. By 1956 he had fulfilled his contract with Warner Brothers and was negotiating a new deal. When they continued to ignore *The Alamo*, he looked at other studios and found what he was looking for at United Artists. The contract he signed was poor, not as good as the one he already had at Warners and he got none of the concessions he might have got elsewhere … but they offered to put up $2,500,00 for his film and to distribute it. They agreed he could direct and produce it himself if he would play Davy Crockett himself. Suddenly everything was possible and he jumped at the hand they held out even though he had to agree to lower percentages on the other films he appeared in for them, "I made a bad deal for myself because I wanted to do the picture so much."

UA expected Batjac to invest an equal $2.5 million but he didn't want to risk his company. He had budgeted the film at $7.5 million and needed outside investors, the more he raised independently, the less pressure there was on Batjac. At least he now had a big studio behind him which might attract other sponsors. Whilst he put the finishing touches to the financing he continued looking for suitable locations and liked what he saw in Brackettville, the sleepy little village where Yates had made *The Last Command*. Happy Shahan wrote to Duke offering to let him build his set on his 22,000 acre spread, "We argued about it until 1957. We always argued and it took me two years to convince him that this was the best place to do it." Shahan wanted to be the general contractor and to retain ownership of the set after filming was completed. Unusually Duke had hesitated but eventually agreed to his requests. On the day the agreement was signed Shahan introduced Duke to Mexican, Chato Hernandez, who he had chosen to supervise construction. Duke asked Hernandez, "Do you think you can build the Alamo?" Hernandez replied solemnly, "Senor Wayne, can you make a movie?" Duke laughed, nodded and asked no more questions, "That's good enough for me."

He was still $1.5 million short of construction costs and needed another $5.5 million to shoot the film. All of it had to be raised from private sources but, with every other element in place, Duke guessed it wouldn't be too difficult to raise the rest of the money from wealthy Texan businessmen. For some time he had been tapping their patriotism, eagerly explaining that a story of such universal appeal couldn't fail, especially now he had a big backer and had already signed several big stars. He personally appealed to Texan Governor, Price Daniel, asking him if he could put him in touch with "some wealthy men who would be willing to risk their money in a good cause." The seeds, planted when the Texans attacked him for wanting to film in Mexico, were about to come to fruition. Governor Daniel was eager to help and provided a list of prospective investors. Duke insisted on doing all the leg work himself and, armed with his personal introductions, he became a dedicated salesman, working night and day, selling a dream. And he was amply rewarded when money started pouring in from local oil and cattle barons. Many of them sent notes with their cheques saying they didn't care whether they got their money back or not, so long as he made the film he promised. He quickly hit his $5.5 million target and in 1960 revealed the final breakdown of his backers in Variety Magazine; UA invested $2.5 million for ten percent of profit, the McCullough brothers; $3 million, Clint Murchison; $2.5 million, the Yale Foundation; $1.5 million, he and Batjac made up the balance. The final cost of the movie was reported to be $12 million and Duke's personal investment in it was huge.

He hired Walter Ybarra, an art director he had worked with many times before and who was renowned in the business for saving production costs, to help him design and build the set. Over a six year period they had made several trips to San Antonio to take precise measurements of the buildings that would be represented in the film and together planned the most authentically detailed film set ever created. Consideration of camera angles meant some accuracy had to be forsaken but on one point neither Duke nor Ybarra would shift. The whole set was to be built from authentic adobe bricks and labourers were brought from Mexico to make the twelve million bricks needed to construct the two hundred thousand square feet of permanent buildings to effectively recreate San Antonio as it looked in 1836.

Immediately building got under way six wells were drilled to ensure a good water supply ran through the twelve miles of underground water and sewage lines that were laid. Five hundred acres of corrals were erected. Fourteen miles of heavy duty roads were built to cater for the increased traffic to the area and a large air strip was put down so film could be flown out daily to be developed back in Hollywood. Even an indoor set was created. Duke's insistence on accuracy held up shooting for a year in a delay that gave him time to make three more films, the proceeds of which were all ploughed straight back into *The Alamo*.

For ten years he had been talking to the stars he wanted to sign for his picture. He was only interested in the biggest names such as Clark Gable and Burt Lancaster, but when neither was free he made the unusual choices of British star, Laurence Harvey to play William Travis and Richard Widmark for Jim Bowie. Duke wanted to create a family feel to the production and he signed old friends and his son Patrick for the other parts, he even persuaded Pilar to allow Aissa to be in it, and Michael served as assistant producer. He and his eldest son had many heated arguments over casting, and great tension built up between them, "The arguments were on an hourly basis. We were always at it. It's just a natural thing, nothing to do with being father and son, it had to do with being a star and a producer. It was always combat over whether we could spend money or not. My father would ask me what I was doing, and I would answer "I'm producing this film."

Duke was drained and physically exhausted before he even started pre-production in Bracketville. He had set himself a punishing schedule; when he wasn't involved in the shooting of *The Barbarian and The Geisha*, *Rio Bravo* or *The Horse Soldiers* he was on the phone doing deals, badgering, wheedling, organising, or flying down to his set to oversee the work going on there. Apart from all his other concerns he also had to give some thought to how he was going to play Crockett. He had no director to offer advice so he spent time studying original letters and talking to local historians about the character. He found a warm, witty man, full of fun and devilment, a man with a vision who had left his wife and children to search for land and prosperity. He was a man Duke readily understood, "Crockett never ate on an empty stomach nor drank on a full one. That gave me an idea how to make a human being out of a legend. Actually I suppose Travis would have been a better part for me but I didn't want to go hogging the picture."

Shooting began on 9th September 1959. He had gathered three hundred longhorn cattle, leased sixteen hundred horses, housed a permanent crew of 342 people, had costumes prepared for six thousand extras, the catering company kept 41 full-time workers on the set, and during filming some 190,000 meals were served. Duke ensured everyone was well fed in his own terms. He ordered 120,000 pounds of steak, roast beef, veal, hamburger and sausage, 500,000 eggs, 400,000 bottles of milk and 1.5 million rolls. Patrick said, "Watching my father at work was revealing. He ate, slept and dreamed *The Alamo*."

Everyone involved was left shattered by the monumental effort, but for many it remained the most exciting four months of their lives. Mary St John commented, "I had to leave my husband behind for those four months, but everything was Duke's total responsibility and that meant he had to have me with him. Everything about it took on epic proportions and we did so much night work we often had dinner at midnight. All the others would be out fighting the war, and I don't think anyone but me and Duke knew what had to be done so they could all eat. He was so considerate of the crew." Pilar added, "He wasn't making a movie, he was on a crusade. And I fell in love with him all over again. He invested all his heart and soul in it but the toll on him was tremendous. He was everywhere at once, arranging props, correcting the extras, praising people. I felt frightened for him. He went through such anguish." In fact he found the organisation relatively easy and he felt enormously rewarded as he saw things coming together. He enjoyed walking around his set at dawn watching the dream come alive in front of his eyes. His voice could be heard everywhere, barking out orders as he passed. He continued his daily consultations with Ybarra who said, "Duke had a great eye for detail and for film composition, though he was never given the credit he deserved."

At Batjac he had gathered together the finest talent in Hollywood, and he was as confident about his employees as he was of his own ability, he didn't mind who got the credit so long as every detail was just right. He leaned heavily on his son, Michael, and although they might have argued hourly, Duke trusted him to get his orders carried out. Still, he wasn't left entirely without headaches, and Linda Cristal, his co-star, said, "He was working for results and he didn't go in for diplomacy. When he exploded his fury scorched many. He and Richard Widmark had some thunderous confrontations."

Widmark was notoriously difficult to work with and Duke soon found the rumours he'd heard were understatements. When he hired him, he placed an advert in *The Hollywood Reporter*, "Welcome aboard, Dick. Duke." When the two first met Widmark told him moodily, "Tell your press agent that the name is Richard." Duke stared down at him, lit a cigarette with the greatest deliberation and waited for his temper to subside before murmuring softly, "If I ever take another ad, I'll remember that, Richard."

Two days into shooting, as he sat down to dinner with his family, Widmark burst into the room shouting he was quitting because he felt miscast. Duke, at his most dangerous, said quietly, "Richard, I want to have dinner with my family. We can discuss this later." Widmark continued to insist they talk then. Duke finally slammed his two paws on the table and stood up to order him out. Whatever the difficulties, he couldn't afford to lose Widmark. If he walked out production would be delayed whilst a replacement was found and with costs running at $90,000 a day, he couldn't risk loosing even an hour. After finishing his dinner he strolled across to Widmark's cabin. Raised voices could be heard for some time before Duke finally threatened legal action. Widmark, forced to back down, became extremely difficult on set, and constantly criticised Duke's efforts in front of the rest of the cast. After three weeks of such treatment Duke, who had been trying his best to stay calm, blew his top, chased Widmark across the set, threw him up against a wall, and promised physical violence to go with the lawsuit. His outburst had the effect of calming them both for a while, though no one could have ever have described them as friends.

Tension ran high throughout filming, but the murder of actress LaJean Ethridge in Bracketville was only the worst of the many disasters that beset production. She and her boyfriend, Charles Smith, had signed on as extras, but Ethridge was given a better part and Smith, jealous of her success, plunged a twelve inch knife into her chest. The under-pressure Duke reacted like the egocentric director that he wasn't, bellowing as his frustration boiled over, "Jeeeesus Keee-rist. This is all I needed!" In his defence he was struggling through a tidal wave of problems, smoking up to six packs of cigarettes a day and hardly eating. He was pushing all the crew hard but was toughest on himself. Later he felt regret, remorse and of course, guilt, at his reaction to the death of one of his team.

The location and the work proved stressful for them all. Most of the cast and crew had never seen an area like it, with its scorpions, rattlesnakes and cockroaches. The heat and humidity were unbearable, with temperatures soaring to 84 before ten in the morning, but it wasn't the dry desert heat Duke was used to, and in his buckskin costume and coonskin hat, sweat poured off him. He frequently had to change his clothes twice before even getting in front of the cameras himself. He lost eight to ten pounds every day and suffered from a burning, dry sore throat. He drank water constantly, but it made no difference and he was often dizzy and weak, suffering the effects of dehydration. Finally he got rid of the hat which rubbed his forehead raw as his skin peeled away under it. Like everyone else, he was extremely uncomfortable, unlike everyone else, he had constant worries and production problems to cope with. Fortunately he also had his extraordinary energy and whilst he worried about everything somehow, down in Bracketville, Duke was a happy man. He was where he had wanted to be for so long.

One of his main worries centred on his daughter, Aissa, not then four. She was untrained and was sometimes frightened by the noisy action going on around her. Throughout filming he gently encouraged her and she eventually completed her scenes to his satisfaction and pride. He ranted and raved in his loudest voice at everyone else, but never lost patience with his girl and his tenderness toward her surprised outsiders who didn't know him well. Whenever she finished a scene she looked at him and asked, "You're proud of me aren't you Daddy?" After her constant question Duke found himself faced with all his main actors asking him the same thing as each scene was wrapped. He appreciated the joke and it never failed to bring a smile to his face. He smiled a lot on location and particularly enjoyed bi-sexual Englishman Harvey's sharp sense of humour. The tough guy fell about laughing when effete Harvey minced through the cream of Hollywood's stuntmen to tweak his cheek and call him, "Dukey." Happy Shahan said, "Duke was having fun. There was a big heart beating in that frame and all kinds of people responded to his warmth."

Though he smiled a lot and was clearly enjoying himself there was always something going wrong in spite of all his careful planning. There was always someone demanding his attention, always something requiring his decision. Eventually, inevitably, he tired and became irritable and difficult. The hundred and twenty cigarettes a day he was smoking probably didn't help, and they certainly contributed to his painful throat and persistent cough. He collapsed each night into a restless sleep around midnight and then got up at four to start drinking coffee, light his first cigarette and get ready to face the problems of another day. Pilar said, "For the next two hours, before he went off to start shooting, I listened to his barking cough. I was worried for him. He sounded like he was tearing himself up. I pleaded with him to see a doctor." He asked how she thought he could afford to break the schedule, and he even angrily refused the cough mixture she offered, saying it made him tired. He was chain smoking, lighting each cigarette from the last. He was well aware of the damage he was doing to himself but needed the comfort as he suddenly began to fear he might have taken on too much.

Duke demanded perfection of himself in front of the camera, but now, as director, he was looking for effort to equal his own from the rest of the cast. He led by example but the demands he made on the others were all but impossible to meet. Because he was so tired he became intolerant of mistakes and shortfalls, and was quickly fired up. One afternoon, as he tried to direct a complicated scene, he was distracted by voices behind him, he tried to ignore it but eventually flared, "Jesusfucking Christ! Shut up back there!" He spun round to continue the blast only to find the culprits were a party of nuns on an excursion to Happy Shahan's ranch! He turned red, felt dreadful, apologised profusely and went back sheepishly to continue the scene.

Everybody was concerned about the strain he put himself under, but Pilar discovered they worried needlessly, "He had memorised not only the whole script, but the page references as well, knew by heart where every word appeared, and he had no need to even refer to the script through the whole filming process. Each day he carried in his head a detailed vision of every shot he wanted. Each night he figured out every camera angle for the next day. He went to set prepared for every eventuality — barring murder, and all the other unforeseen misfortune that happened." The cast and crew respected what he was trying to do, they understood the difficulties he faced and responded by giving that little bit more too.

Of all the problems he faced, the worst arrived late in the day in the person of John Ford. The director had been sitting around at home, bored and depressed, when he decided to visit Duke's location. He wrote to his friend Michael Killanin, "I hope to go to Texas and cast a paternal eye on Duke Wayne. This young and ambitious lad of fifty six years is writing, producing, acting and directing *The Alamo* with the excessive budget of five million bucks." He turned up three weeks into shooting announcing he was taking a little vacation with them all. Back in 1950 when Duke first mentioned his plans to the press it had been assumed that Ford would direct the film, and the rumours had never died. But *The Alamo* was his film, and Duke believed his whole future rode on its success. Having Ford drop by unannounced threw him into a no-win situation. If the film was unsuccessful the critics would blame him, if it was good the same critics would attribute it to Ford, so the last person he wanted to see in Bracketville was Coach, "I'm directing this picture; it's my picture, good, bad or indifferent — I'm gonna rise and fall with it; it's costing a lot of money and I've got the money and I don't want anybody else to run me. If I'd wanted Jack to direct it Batjac could have signed him and it would have been made ten years earlier with any of the studios who rejected my idea out of hand."

Ford was full of advice for the novice and naturally tried to take things over. On the day he arrived he followed Duke around, peered over his shoulder, pulled up a chair next to the camera and began telling everyone what to do. At night he wanted to play cards and drink like they had always done before. Although Duke could just about manage a shower, a massage, and dinner with his family before falling into bed, he was deeply concerned about the old man. He understood how much Coach needed to feel wanted on his massive project and there was no way he could bring himself to ask him to leave. His soft heart wouldn't allow him to reject the man who had given him everything; he simply could not be disloyal, under any circumstances. He kept remembering how bad Ford had looked when they finished work on *The Horse Soldiers*, and now, though it shattered him, and annoyed Pilar, he sat up playing cards and talking into the early hours. Duke had watched John Ford fall apart, now on the set of *The Alamo*, he began putting him back together, bringing him back to life, making him feel wanted and valued.

It wasn't easy and Ford nearly drove Duke mad in Bracketville. He heard constant criticism of his efforts over his shoulder as he tried to concentrate, "You didn't do that right Duke. You can do better than that ... And your walk there ..." He confessed to cinematographer, William Clothier, "I don't know what the hell I'm going to do." The cameraman suggested letting Ford loose with a second unit. Duke smiled his relief, asked Jimmy Grant to write some extra scenes, and sent Coach off happy with a cameraman and Michael as his assistant. Michael was ordered to keep Ford away when work was being done on any of the main scenes and not to let him talk to any of the stars. Between them they kept Ford occupied for weeks looking after the Mexican extras. When he eventually went home Duke wrote thanking him for his help. Very little that he'd worked on ended up in the film and Clothier maintained that Duke had never intended that it would, although it cost him an extra $250,000. He spent a quarter of a million dollars of the money he had struggled so hard to raise to keep John Ford happy, telling his son, "Look, let him do anything he wants, I'll pay. I don't care what it costs, I am not going to let him feel rejected. I'd rather spend another million dollars than hurt his feelings."

Clothier later became irritated about the rumours that the battle scenes were Ford's work, "I saw Duke sweating and striving, day after day, saw the amount of weight he lost — a total of about thirty pounds. *The Alamo* is entirely his movie. His ideas. His directing. Santa Anna's army approaching the Alamo was Duke. Everything was Duke's — except the horsefalls. Cliff Lyons directed most of those. But where eight or ten horses and riders jump right over the camera that was Duke's work. He directed them jumping through canon fire, rifle fire and all the clasps. Dammit to Hell, when those sixteen horses leap over the wall of the fortress — John Wayne directed that and John Ford wasn't even around. He placed the men. Told me how to light it. Told me the effect he wanted. Told the stuntmen how to move and when to move. John Wayne directed *The Alamo*. All the way. Could have been one of the best directors in Hollywood if God had not made him such a star." Clothier, known as "Wayne's cameraman," worked long and hard on the film but said no one worked harder than Duke, "He knew the script backwards. He knew every line better than the actors did. In the morning we would have breakfast together and go out onto location and discuss every shot for that day, and which we were going to start with. He knew the script so well and what he wanted so precisely that he was never seen to refer to the pages of his script and more than once he ruined Davy Crockett scenes because he was mouthing the other guy's lines to himself. I'd motion to him and he'd go, "awww", we'd cut and have to start again. Duke knew himself that he had severe limitations as a director but his crew and actors seemed to accept that he knew what he was doing, and responded with style." The word on the set was, "Duke can run all over you and knock you down, but he will always come back, pick you up, dust you off and say, "Sorry," in that sheepish way he has." Most recognised his generosity and he seemed able to command the deepest loyalty from his employees, "He was just as likely to make a joke when something went wrong as he was to chew someone out over it."

He had a good eye for composition, knew which shots would work and how to create mood, but he had little talent and no patience for explaining to other actors how he wanted them to move. He tried to demonstrate what he wanted, but Duke worked fast and was prepared to carry on till he dropped in his effort to get something just right. He demanded the same of others. Most didn't match his requirements and the combined demands of producing, directing and acting all but overwhelmed him, and them. Mounting production costs put him under constant strain and caused him to try to work even faster than normal. He could always be heard shouting at someone. He simply didn't have the time to quietly explain what he wanted. He barked out his orders and expected everyone to understand and follow them to the letter. Ken Curtis who starred in films with Duke over many years said, "He was great at action. But directing actors, I was not all that pleased with him. All he told you to do was his mannerisms, but his mannerisms were unique, and others could not easily copy them. When anyone tried to emulate his body movements they appeared contrived." A smile was even seen on the face of Richard Widmark when Duke called out, "Goddammit, be graceful, like me," he couldn't think of another actor with the grace of John Wayne.

Initially Duke had planned to film in Cinerama which he knew would have been magnificent for the action sequences. But he had learned his lesson from the experiments on *The Big Trail* and *Hondo*. Cinerama required specially constructed theatre screens which would have made it far too expensive and would also affect distribution. He opted instead for the new 70mm Todd-AO process, which had been so successful for *South Pacific*, and which didn't require expensive adaptions, "We found an exciting manner for opening the picture to take advantage of the wide-screen process." Clothier had five Todd-AO cameras set up every day, and before each scene was filmed he and Duke visited the cameramen to review their assignments and block every shot. The final scenes involved thousands of actors, extras and horses, all moving in furious battle sequences. All five cameras had to be perfectly synchronized. Duke wanted shooting complete by December 20th because that was when the rains were due; he and Clothier were so successful that he was able to send everyone home on the fifteenth.

The original budget of $7.5 million proved inadequate in the extreme. Just as he was about to shoot the final scenes UA contacted him to advise him he was running $400,000 short, and that they had no more money to give him. He had already pledged his own salary from the film to cover any shortfall. Even that would not be enough and he was forced to dip into his own pocket again just to finish those last impressive shots. He took out a second mortgage on the family home, sold property in Mexico, and borrowed the rest against his personal possessions. His debt was such that until the film grossed $17 million he wouldn't see a penny profit, but he believed he had made an epic story and said, "It was never about money for me. It was about a group of men who believed in liberty enough to die for it. It was about them and it was about my soul too. It was right that I gambled everything on it. My whole well-being was at stake."

Aissa later said, "I think *The Alamo* became my father's own form of combat. More than an obsession, it was the most intensely personal project of his career." It was where he explained himself, his passions, lifestyle, patriotism and even his failed marriages, it was his "Open Letter" to America, and it told more about him than it did about Texas in 1836, "It was the first time in my life I'd been able to express what I felt about people."

He later discovered that UA had lied to him. They'd had the extra money all along, but had decided not to use it, knowing he would come up with it himself even if he killed himself getting it, knowing he couldn't leave his dream unfinished. Though the risks he took scared him, he always felt the money he had ploughed into those last scenes was money well spent, and twenty years after its completion most directors agreed that John Wayne's battle scenes from *The Alamo*, were some of the finest ever shot.

When filming was over Duke had lost thirty pounds in weight as well as a personal fortune, he was exhausted, left shattered by the whole experience. When he got back to Hollywood it was to find 560,000 feet of film waiting to be edited. He looked at the monumental task still ahead of him with some trepidation but had enough confidence in the first footage he saw to realise that he had fulfilled his ambitions. He decided against resting and rushed straight into the editing suite with a specially gathered team. It took a further month to get the exact image he wanted then he flew straight on to film *North to Alaska* with Henry Hathaway, a film he had long been contracted to do. Whilst he was away he allowed John Ford to see the director's cut. He contacted Duke to congratulate him on the huge hit he was going to have on his hands.

Even as he worked in Alaska he was still involved on a daily basis with Batjac and *The Alamo*, polishing it, making sure everything was perfect for a launch date in August 1960. And although he was tired he knew it was already time to start making personal appearances on behalf of his film. He had been involved in everything to do with it and he couldn't hand it over now just because shooting and editing was finished. He personally controlled publicity, he set up the photographic shots of the paintings he had selected for the opening credits, and he worked closely with Tiomkin on the soundtrack, explaining in detail exactly how he wanted key scenes underlined. All day, every day, over the next months he was up to his neck in some chore relating to *The Alamo*. He never took a second to recover from the effort he had put in on location in Texas. Finally, on June 8th, he ordered a negative to be cut in its final form which ran 192 minutes together with the prints to be processed from that negative. He felt drained and ill, but devoted a further ninety days to a gruelling schedule of publicity tours. He badly needed to rest, not just his body, which could take more than most, but his brain too. He could hardy think anymore and just wanted to put his head down on a pillow somewhere. But there was to be no rest; he organised the premiere of the long awaited dream himself, planning the most spectacular night in motion picture history, a night fitting his film. In mid-September he was due to start another thirty day personal appearance tour and he prepared the schedule like a front-line general.

He took no risks as he prepared a massive, patriotic and politically conscious advertising campaign. He hired Russell Birdwell, publicist for *Gone With the Wind*, to help design a programme to suit his needs. Birdwell linked the film to the Cold War and asked Richard Nixon to help promote it. Nixon, anticipating Wayne's support in the forthcoming Presidential election, was eager to assist. Hollywood had seen a recent shift in political mood, the anti-communist crusade had lost steam after the failure of McCarthyism in 1954, and whilst fear of the Soviet Union had increased as the Cold War reached its height, paranoia over domestic subversion had all but disappeared. The Hollywood liberals of the forties were re-emerging unopposed, and Communism remained a real threat in Duke's mind. In May 1960 he let everyone know his feelings, publicly criticising Frank Sinatra for using a screenplay by a blacklisted writer about Eddie Slovak, the only American executed for desertion during World War Two. Sinatra, infuriated by the interference and the resulting bad press, was forced to sack the writer. Later in the month when the two met at a benefit for children they almost came to blows, and friends only just managed to separate them before punches were traded in front of the surprised children. The ensuing publicity didn't worry Duke, he used it to full advantage to advertise his views on the dangers of Communism and his film at the same time.

When he was finally satisfied he had done his very best he turned his future over to the American public, scheduling the premiere for San Antonio at the end of October 1960. In July, whilst he was filming *North to Alaska*, he and several crew members sat down to a poker game which lasted long into the early hours. By 8 am the next morning the fifty three year old who had not had a day off in months was on set, in make-up ready for the day's action. Filming, however, was delayed until the rest of the card players straggled in, red-eyed and exhausted. Duke shouted loudly across the set, "Well, here come the kids. I had to tuck them in last night." He added under his breath, "The country's going soft." And America, it seemed, agreed with him. Toughness and heroism in the face of an external enemy became a central issue in the presidential election campaign, issues exactly reflected in *The Alamo*.

Duke naturally supported Nixon's tough anti-communist stand against Kennedy's more liberal approach. He disliked all the Kennedys, believing they were soft and unimpressive because they had never had to work. He saw them as self-serving people who lusted after power, and had no moral vision. He referred to John Kennedy as a, "Snot nosed kid who couldn't keep his dick in his pants," — his own agent found girls for the Kennedys whenever they were in Hollywood! He also believed much of Kennedy's prize winning *Profiles in Courage* had been ghost written by Theodore Sorenson. One week before the Democratic and Republican conventions, Duke spent $152,000 on a three page ad in the Fourth of July edition of *Life* magazine. It was the first time such an ad had ever been placed. It was written by Duke and Birdwell, "Very soon the two great political parties will nominate their candidates for President. One of these men will be assigned the awesome duties of the White House ... In this moment when eternity could be closer than ever before, is there a statesman ... who knows that the American softness must be hardened? ... There were no ghost-writers at the Alamo. Only Men." The advert was an unprecedented and quite phenomenal success. It also whipped up a political storm. Several times reporters asked Kennedy if he thought Duke had aimed it at him. He avoided answering. As the opening date for the launch of the film approached Duke stepped up the hype, announcing, "Nobody should come to see this movie unless he believes in heroes."

He arranged some secret previews of the film throughout the country to test audience reaction whilst there was still time to make adjustments if necessary. In Denver a 900 seat theatre sold out days before it was shown even though the title of the film had never been mentioned in any advertising! He couldn't have wished for a better response. In Denver he received a standing ovation from fans who cheered all the way through the special screening. After the film finished the audience was asked to complete a questionnaire and to return the cards to Batjac offices. The replies, which indicated a huge hit, were even better than Duke had hoped for. He decided on the back of them that no fine tuning was necessary.

The strain of the year's work had begun to take its inevitable toll, "I've got a helluva cold. I'm starting to fold and I need to sleep for about thirty hours." In the months since filming finished he had filled every day with promotional activity, he'd attended meetings, appeared on TV and radio, talked at press conferences and gone to every award ceremony, lunch and dinner, he had constantly been on the move until, by September, he hardly knew where he was or what the time was. His cough and throat deteriorated and when he finally saw his doctor he was ordered to cancel all the remaining dates of the promotional tour so he could go home to recover in time for the October premiere. He was told he was suffering from acute bronchitis.

On Monday, October 24th 1960 crowds lined the streets of San Antonio, despite a heavy and unusual rainfall, to catch a glimpse of John Wayne as he travelled from his hotel to the theatre. When he arrived it was to a huge cheer and he told his fans, "It's mighty wonderful of you to turn out in rain like this. We've done the very best we could with the picture. I hope you all get to see it."

The audience in San Antonio had paid $50 a ticket to see the film but the reaction to it was exactly the same as when it had been screened at the sneak previews, with the crowd of dignitaries shouting all the way through it. They reserved the loudest and longest cheer for the first appearance of Davy Crockett, and when it was all over Duke received another standing ovation. He had done everything he could, and now he waited; he was quietly hopeful, but hardly dared expect any praise from the critics. The reviews in the Texas papers were generally good although some mentioned historical inaccuracies and commented that perhaps the film was over long. Duke was already in London for the English premiere by the time the first East Coast reviews came out. Again and again they criticised the length of the film. After London he flew directly to Rome for the Italian premiere, and from there he went on to Africa to start work on *Hatari*, another Hathaway film. He had no time to attend the biggest show of them all, when *The Alamo* finally hit Hollywood, his home town.

More and more reviews came out as the film hit each big American city. Some were good, none were great. They generally praised the message of the film and the battle scenes. Some said it would sweep the Academy Awards, but as usual his own performance hardly rated a mention. He was disappointed by the early reaction, even though he had expected nothing better, but he was worried by the luke warm comments in the trade papers. They were only average at best, with *Variety* saying his portrayal of Crockett was stiff and tense, that he acted like a man with $12 million on his conscience. Deep down he recognised the truth of the criticism but the words stung nevertheless. Even his leading lady now took a shot, complaining that he had seemed preoccupied throughout filming, "During the love scenes his eyes were open, but the shutters were down."

One critic, repeating that it was too long, went on to say it was also boring. Duke could accept all the political hits, all the personal criticism, but couldn't bear to think of his work of art as boring or embarrassing. He took the reviews personally and was devastated. He had been counting on good reviews to help him recoup some of his financial investment. He had to save the film quickly before it got lost and he raced back to the editing suite where he spent four days re-splicing, cutting almost 30 minutes from the film before releasing it to any more theatres.

In fact, as was normally the case with his films, what the reviewers said made little difference, and in the first few weeks business was brisk. Within two months it had earned two million dollars. Not bad, but nowhere near the $17 million he needed to break even. The 1961 Oscars became critical, and from his base in Africa he launched his first attack, stepping up Birdwell's original campaign. *The Alamo* received six Academy Award nominations — Best Sound, Best Song, Best Cinematography, Best Score, Best Supporting Actor (Chill Wills), and Best Movie; success in any category would help receipts.

Duke hated the "garbage" that Hollywood was producing, saying the industry was now, "polluted with perversion." He frequently lashed out at the filth he saw on screen, "My picture is all about men and women who were prepared to stand up and fight for the right to live decently. The other nominated films are about corruption, greed, and perversion." *Elmer Gantry, The Apartment, Sons and Lovers, Butterfield 8* and *Never on a Sunday*, contained everything he hated most and he became increasingly outspoken against them. *Spartacus*, starring Kirk Douglas, called for a different line of attack, its story about a slave uprising against Roman masters, was untouchable. It was however based on a book written by Communist, Howard East, and the screenplay was ghost written by Dalton Trumbo, one of the Hollywood Ten, who was still blacklisted. Although Duke's ad, "There were no ghost-writers at the Alamo," had been a sideswipe at Kennedy, it was a more direct attack on Trumbo and Douglas. *The Alamo* carried an obvious political message, but so too did *Spartacus* and Duke used the Oscar campaign to let people to know how he felt about Douglas using a Communist to write a film about revolution to be screened across America.

As the campaign gathered momentum the Left stepped up their attack and Duke shot back from the hip; it was standard, routine and acceptable fare. But Birdwell's own battle of words was less responsible. By March he was out of control, leading to much embarrassment in the Wayne camp and Duke himself sensed that Birdwell's responses to the Press appeared desperate and petty, "I felt sickened by the whole thing." He wanted to back away and allow the hype surrounding his film to die down in the run up to Oscar night but Chill Wills, nominated as Best Supporting Actor, escalated things further as he almost single-handedly, managed to make Duke's work of art the laughing stock of the industry. The actor had spent a lifetime in B-movies, he was well aware he would never get another chance to win an Oscar, and he took out his own two-page ad in the trade papers, listing hundreds of members of the academy and saying "Win, loose or draw, You're Still My Cousins, and I Love You

All." Groucho Marx issued a sharp reply, "Dear Mr Chill Wills; I Am Delighted to be Your Cousin, but I Voted for Sal Mineo." Wills, who didn't get the point, bought more space and against a backdrop of the film's cast printed the message, "We of the Alamo cast are praying — harder than the real Texans prayed for their lives in the Alamo — for Chill Wills to win the Oscar ..." It was signed, "Your Alamo cousins."

Duke, horrified, rushed to place an immediate disclaimer, "I wish to state that the Chill Wills ad ... is an untrue and reprehensible claim. No one in the Batjac organization or in the Russell Birdwell office has been a party to his trade paper advertising. I refrain from using stronger language because I am sure his intentions were not as bad as his taste." Groucho Marx had the last laugh, writing that for John Wayne to criticise Mr Wills for bad taste was like Jayne Mansfield criticising Sabrina for too much exposure. Blinded by his own love of America, as much as by his hopes for the film, he remained personally convinced that he had made a noble and worthy statement and had allowed a campaign to develop that suggested a vote for The Alamo was also a vote for the United States. He had compounded mistake after mistake and perhaps the biggest was his failure to realise that no one liked having their arm twisted. He failed to spot quickly enough that his eagerness had rubbed people up the wrong way, but as soon as he saw the Wills advert he smelt impending doom, "From the morning the ad turned up there was just a pall, like something had hit town."

Out in Africa he contracted flu and became extremely ill. He was physically and mentally all in. Suddenly, and unusually, he was overwhelmed by self-doubt and a sense of terror. He suffered a panic attack, and on the spur of the moment, sold his stake in the film back to United Artists. Eventually it went on to make enormous world wide profit but Duke, who saved his sanity by selling his stake, never saw any financial reward for all the years of devotion and superhuman effort.

As he sat through the 1961 Oscar ceremony he witnessed the fall of The Alamo again. The Apartment won Best Picture, Peter Ustinov won Best Supporting Actor, and the only Oscar his film took was Best Score by Dmitri Tiomkin. He went home empty handed to lick what he feared were fatal wounds. No matter what he told reporters that night, he felt both humiliation and disappointment. He had devoted fifteen years to a film about honour and decency, now he felt sick to his stomach on, "The day indecency triumphed." Elizabeth Taylor and Shirley Jones both took Oscars playing prostitutes and Burt Lancaster won his as a flawed preacher, "My politics definitely interfered with the fucking critics but, sonofabitch, after all that work I thought we'd win something. It was a damned good picture." He was defeated ... but hardly surprised.

After twelve months *The Alamo* had made $14 million. United Artists went on to release the film several times and by 1970 it was one of the most profitable films in Hollywood history. They did well out of their deal with Duke, who emerged able to repay his debts, but without a penny to his name and hardly owning the shirt on his back, "I couldn't even buy a pack of chewing gum without a co-signer!" When he sold out to UA it was to protect Batjac and ensure the future of his production company, but at that point he walked away from the dream that had consumed him for so long. He closed the door behind him. He had done his very best and took some pride in his achievement, but the price had been too high, he had been all but devoured in his obsession, "Financially the film didn't really fail, it made fifteen million the first time round. Of course I didn't make a cent because I made a bad goddam deal. I know the rumour was always that it was a bomb, but listen, I've only directed two pictures, both of them did fifteen million first time around. Show me another director who's done that."

The critics continued to laugh at him and his film but they never understood his dream and ignored his intent, instead they dwelt on what The Alamo wasn't, "I saw the story as an ode to an heroic era, I aimed it at a generation that didn't believe in heroes anymore." In the process he at last became the man he'd always wanted to be. Few film makers had ever had to fight as hard or as long as he did, against such overwhelming odds. He'd jeopardised his health, well being, his wealth and his reputation to make his testament to heroism and its production became his crowning glory.

Duke sold his set back to Happy Shahan. It was turned into a Western film set and tourist attraction. He had already sold his stake to UA. Neither action recovered his losses and his only solution was to throw himself into another orgy of work. He was staring ruin in the face and his wife commented dryly, "The trouble was he had trusted too many people and put his confidence in people who let him down. It was his biggest fault and was why he got hurt so many times. Right then he was extremely vulnerable. He was ill and tired but he couldn't afford to rest and through the next years he had to work at a frightening pace. It was a hard time for him."

Shortly after selling out to UA he discovered they had been holding spare production capital back from him all along. He felt cheated and immediately broke away from them. He never worked with them again and they ultimately paid a high price for crossing him. But Duke was fast running out of friends. He had already ended his business partnership with Bo Roos and alienated many people in the industry who had previously liked him. He found he now had many enemies, all intent on bringing him down. Unbiased observers felt much of the damage was self-inflicted and of long standing, the result of his anti-Communist activities and Duke conceded, "Well, there might be a little truth in everything you hear, and the Alliance thing was used pretty strongly against me. I sometimes feel lost. The critics didn't work on *The Alamo*, they worked on their feelings about me. They kept saying the picture was a failure, well, Christ, it was far from a failure."

In itself it didn't fail, but neither did it give him the security he had been looking for. Hollywood made it plain on Oscar night that he would never be recognised as a director and he was forced to accept that the world saw him as a cowboy, soldier, or sailor. He had to resign himself to the fact that he would have to take action parts for as long as they were offered. He had no way of knowing then that the offers would continue to flood in, or that his financial security was safe in his own hands. He had never been a man to look back or bemoan what might have been, now all he could do was carry on as though nothing had happened, "I'll just keep working."

Anti-climax after fifteen years of hard labour, public humiliation over his effort, ill health and exhaustion, fear about how long he could survive in what had become a hostile environment, panic about how he could put his finances back in order, all contributed to an overwhelming sense of black depression. And then the most bitter blow of all landed. One week after *The Alamo* premiered in San Antonio Ward Bond suffered a heart attack and died in a Dallas hotel room. The years of bleak, unabated gloom began and on that day his eyes filled with the haunted sadness which rarely left them again.

Many years later he was asked what he thought about the advertising campaign for *The Alamo*, the hound-dog sadness was on his face as he spat out pithily, "It hurt us. Hurt the way the film was accepted." It also turned him into a media-generated political enigma when, in truth, he was a film star obsessed only with the business of making films. He spent his every waking moment involved either in film making or trying to create some kind of order from the chaos that was his life. After *The Alamo* he was weighed down by emotional and physical inertia and his heart and mind were fully occupied. He could spare little of his depleted energy in the political arena. On the other hand he was intelligent and interested in everything going on around him. He read the papers avidly and watched TV. He had opinions about how the country should be run and he enjoyed expressing them. He reacted to the situations he saw emotionally and, because he was a film star, his outpourings were always widely reported. The Press loved the larger than life image he had created; almost everything that came out of his mouth sold copy, and almost every word that escaped was reported to the world. Because he had often been asked about, and been widely quoted on political matters, people assumed he had a real and deep interest in politics per se, and was possessed of a political sophistication he always denied. He unashamedly said what he felt at a given moment, hardly sophisticated stuff, but his comments were always good news to a media more than willing to use them and him. He was fully aware he was used to sell papers, he anguished over misquotes, and often told himself he should take more care. He then waded straight into the next interview.

If the repeatedly self inflicted wounds didn't hurt him enough there were plenty of others waiting in the wings to lend a hand. Soon after Bond's death, Darryl F. Zanuck, a man Duke considered a friend, unexpectedly launched an amazing attack. Zanuck moaned to the Press, from his home in France, about on-going problems in the American film industry, complaining about the stars who were busy setting up film corporations of their own. He saw men like Brando, Douglas and Duke at Batjac as usurpers to his power. He unleashed a viscous blast, blaming them for Hollywood's ills, "Actors are now producing, directing, and writing; they have taken over Hollywood completely, together with their agents. What the Hell — I'm not going to work for actors. I've got a great affection for Duke Wayne, but what right has he to write, direct and produce a motion picture? … Everyone is becoming a corporation and you can't talk to individuals any more. You can't work as I used to, assigning one man to a story. Everyone has a percentage of everything. As a result they end up with nothing. Look at poor old Duke Wayne. He's never going to see a nickel. He put all his money into finishing *The Alamo*."

Duke, deeply hurt by the comments, immediately lashed back at producers who ran away to foreign countries to make pictures! He used no ghost writer when he sneered, "So Zanuck has decided to stop working for actors has he, and is shedding crocodile tears for poor old Duke Wayne and his Alamo? Please inform him that as far as old Duke and his picture is concerned — which was made, by the way, in the United States — it has made just under two million in three months in thirteen theatres and has ten thousand more play days to go." Whatever he said in public, Zanuck's unprovoked attack, coming as it did so soon after Bond's death, affected him badly. It was a final crushing blow and one from which Old Duke Wayne didn't recover for a long time.

At home his family found him mean, moody and distracted. He hardly bothered to talk to anyone and was rarely his usual smiling, whistling self. When he met his fans he continued to do the business, disarming them with joviality and politeness, but that was just an act he happened to be very good at. He had sunk into a mood of profound crisis after exerting the most enormous amount of energy to capture a prize that had eluded him at the last gasp. And now, with the death of his best friend and the blows raining down on him from all sides, he realised that perhaps the prize wasn't enough anyway and, for the very first time he wondered if there was any point to his artificial existence. He had found a wonderful new life with Pilar, he was deeply satisfied in his love, he had a new family, he had made his dream film. Nothing compensated for his loss. Despite all his achievements, which he knew to be great, he remained unfulfilled. He felt unsure of himself, didn't know what to do or where to turn to find relief from the sadness that gnawed at him. Death had stolen his friend and darkened his world. He couldn't escape the terrible pain that had to do with going into battle and not winning, with being badly wounded but left alive to fight another day.

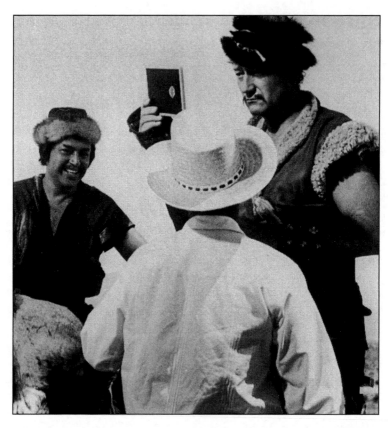

Goddam! I'm the stuff men are made of! Working makes me feel like a worthwhile citizen. I can't retire. I intend to stay in the saddle until I drop.

CHAPTER SEVEN

The Warrior's Supreme Ordeal

"I loved smoking; it was part of my identity. I'd smoked all my life, I grew up with a cigarette in my mouth."

His plane touched down ten minutes late at London Heathrow. He was tired after the long flight from Los Angeles. He had often stayed in England, home of his own hero Winston Churchill, where his fans were every bit as loyal and devoted as those in America, and he liked to visit. He was rarely attacked by the Press on a personal level and, on the whole, British reviewers tended to give him an easy ride. Now he hoped the critics would see *The Alamo* in a favourable light, their reviews had become vitally important to him after the savaging he had received at the hands of the American Press.

Still casually dressed in a T-shirt, as he had been at home in Encino, he was hit by the icy northern hemisphere air as the aircraft doors were opened. He had misplaced his jacket but as he stepped out of the plane he was immediately warmed by the greeting that met his eyes. It was a universal welcome that he had never got used to and it never failed to move him. A slow smile spread across his face as he began the task of shaking hands. The grin stretched wider at the welcome more normally reserved for Churchill himself.

A man from British customs was waiting patiently, "Mr Wayne, I have made special arrangements for your luggage, if you'd like to follow me," he smiled up at the rugged face which appeared to have been rearranged in countless bar-room brawls, and he thought there was only one other person in the world he would have gone to so much trouble for ... and his name was Churchill ...

"Mr Sutton," Duke drawled, draping the mighty weight of his arm across his shoulders, in a friendly, trademark gesture, "thanks." He added with a shiver, "Cold tonight isn't it?"

Mr Sutton could not believe that this man, his hero, had remembered who he was from his last trip, and had also recognised the favour that had been done for him, "Yes sir, it is, don't you have a coat with you?"

"Seem to have misplaced it. Never mind."

His bags were cleared through customs in double quick time and Duke knew no other celebrity ever had such a smooth passage into Britain. He was relaxed and happy, if a little cold,

"Mary, we're missing a trunk. The only clothes I NEED are in it. Where is it?"

"I'll go see." He smiled after his devoted secretary as she scuttled away to find the baggage containing his dress suit and, he hoped, a warmer jacket. If he couldn't get warm on the outside it struck him that if he could find a drink he could warm up his insides a little. He looked around hopefully and spotted the studio officials sent to meet him, "Ah, just the men I needed." he said handing the young executive a roll of notes from his pocket, "I'm cold son, go see if you can find me a bottle of Wild Turkey will you."

"The bar's not open Mr Wayne, and anyway, we'll be out of here in a few minutes."

"OK," Mr Wayne drawled in his softest voice, but with eyes turning to steel, "a few minutes is all I need to have a drink … if I could get one. I'll go look for one myself … but I don't think the studio are going to appreciate my disappearing off into London alone." He started to pace up and down the length of the lounge, muttering to himself and rapidly loosing his fragile temper, commenting, as he often did, "A man could get a bill through Congress quicker than he could get a drink around this place."

He was well aware it would be no easy task for the boy to find a drink so late in the evening, but smiled as he saw him returning with a bottle in his hand.

"Duke, we can't find the trunk. It may not even have been put on the plane at all. Mr Sutton has gone through everything with a fine-tooth comb, but it's not in the airport now."

"Alright Mary, thanks for looking. I'll sort something out tomorrow, can't go to a Royal Gala in a T-shirt."

The studio executive unhappily handed over the bottle of Scotch and a glass, "This was all I could get Mr Wayne … why don't you just let me get you to the hotel, and then I'll sort out whatever you want … oh and if the case doesn't turn up tomorrow I'll personally see to it that you are correctly dressed … and if you feel cold in the car I believe there is a fur rug in the back … Mr Wayne?"

"Yes son?"

"I'm really sorry about tonight. I did everything I could to get you in and out of here smoothly. I don't know what went wrong."

The icy mountain melted immediately, "It's OK Tom, really, I'm just tired and cold. Let's get to the hotel."

He might have forgiven Tom but he was far from happy to be told he had to give an interview on the way. He got into the back of the car that he was sharing with two reporters, huddled his weary frame into the huge fur rug and poured himself another large Scotch. The Press men sat waiting quietly as he made himself comfortable for the twenty minute drive to Windsor. They were nervous and he was well aware of it. He rested his head back against the leather seat and wished he could sleep. He couldn't of course and he smiled resignedly, knowing he had to go through his paces again because it was expected of him. He opened tired, aching eyes, "You fellas want some scotch?"

Both shook their head and waited, "Well, you've got twenty minutes — ask whatever you want."

"Mr Wayne, I've seen a studio news sheet saying a mountain in Utah is being named after you — is that true?"

He nearly fell off the seat. It was a new one on him, and he roared laughing, "That's great. I'd not heard that one. That's really funny. No one has told me that one before." He added more seriously when he saw they didn't share the joke, "No I don't think that's true." He lay back again, lost in thought, wondering if any one would ever share a joke with him again. Though the reporters continued to probe he only answered briefly, nodding his head from time to time. Mary, sitting in the front with Tom, sensed the sudden change in his mood, noticed again how unusually subdued and withdrawn he had become since Ward Bond's death. Though he occasionally flashed a broad smile he was certainly not his normal self. He asked no questions himself and looked out of the window at the passing scenery. When they climbed out of the car he wandered slowly into the hotel with Tom, then turned to wave goodbye to the newsmen before ambling off to the comfort of his room. Mr Mooney, the first reporter, ran a line through his head, "A place where Duke could rest his saddle aches," it was a good line. He said to no one in particular, "He's got a contagious laugh. I LIKE him."

Mary was at the reception desk arranging all Duke's comforts. She heard Mooney talking and turned toward him, she felt impelled to rush to defend her boss when his colleague commented, "Yes, but he gave us nothing."

"He's just tired boys. Come back in the morning and..well I can't promise anything, but you could try talking to him then." They hung around, not daring to risk missing an interview now. Mr Mooney was nothing if not dogmatic. The opening words of his report were already prepared, "In today's world of showbusiness, giants walk the earth, stars shine, and superstars are available as guests on talkshows. Living legends receive standing ovations when they come out of retirement. But then, stomping along, cutting a wide path through all the lesser lights, is the greatest legend of all. He is still working, still going strong — John Wayne — superstar, icon. His shadow dwarfs all the others as he rolls past them, like a tank overtaking the ox-cart, he is the all-time box-office champ. Pictures of young Duke reveal the sensitive, brooding, intense character hidden deep inside the rough exterior ... There is about him an inner poetry, buried deep, left somehow undeveloped. He can convey the rugged beauty of the wild west and still the violence he so often portrays is not out of place ..." He was pleased with the words he had put down before he even met Wayne, words chosen with care to describe the superstar. Now, after sharing the back seat of a Rolls Royce with him for twenty minutes, he would have to find the words to convey the message, "I LIKE the man."

At two in the morning Mooney's devotion to duty was rewarded when the man in question ambled into the lobby. Dressed casually in an open-necked denim shirt which hung carelessly out of blue jeans, his feet stuffed into a pair of thick woollen socks and unshod, Duke still looked every inch the icon of Mooney's imagination. "Still here fellas? Come on then, let's talk," he offered genially as he sank his weary body into the depths of a huge leather chair and rested his feet on the table in front of him. He was still clutching the whiskey bottle, he waved it toward them, "I was looking for some ice."

Mooney couldn't believe his luck. He had waited because he hadn't wanted to move far away from his hero, sure there was a story to be had, hoping to be the one to get it. "But Mr Wayne it's two o'clock. Aren't you tired? I can wait until morning."

"Yeah, well I can't. I'll be busy tomorrow. It's been a long day and I'm beat, but I can't sleep so I thought I'd take a look around, see if I could find some company … and there you boys were. I've had a rest, but at home it's still evening, I wouldn't even have had dinner yet. I'll be happy to talk now." He talked at length about films, his acting technique, he even demonstrated the "pass system" explaining, "When you're filming you miss like this." A huge fist brushed Mooney's cheek, "A hit is a miss. I never hit a man since I came of age. All I do is hold 'em a little. Hold 'em kinda hard," and the line shot into Mooney's head — "Lest he should be mistaken for a pacifist, when he holds kinda hard he can lift a man right off the ground." Duke was still talking, "Hitting or missing, making a film is hard labour, let me tell you when you're fighting in mud at 28 degrees and the Texas wind comes over the prairie at you — you're earning your money the hard way. The Western is America's folklore and it deals with simple ideals. I've played plenty of different parts but they still say everything I do is the same. I guess I've just got a strong personality that keeps showing through. I'll just keep talking shall I? Or did you want to throw the odd question my way?" He smiled.

"You invested a lot of your own money in *The Alamo*, will you get it all back do you think? Are you solvent?"

"Helluva good question, and I can't answer it. I guess I'm all but broke right now, and it's all my own fault. Made a lot of bad investments. Hell, I've owned more restaurants than you've eaten in. Gold mines, oil wells, I was known as Dry-Hole Wayne in the oil industry. People say I had bad advice, but I can blame no one but myself, I should have known better.

Now I'm letting my own family take care of my interests, and I can command big money for my work. I guess I'll be alright. I love my life, there's no better way to make a living. That's why I'll keep making westerns. You get the sun, lots of action, fresh air, scenery and for some reason none of the bickering that you get back in the studios. The men I work with are all outdoor guys. Greatest guys in the world, I have a great time, and I love every minute of it. I don't chase girls in my pictures any more. I wanted to mature so people would accept me. Of course in real life it can happen … I'm twenty two years older than the girl I'm married to now … I was a star before she was even born. But people don't like to see an old guy making it with a young girl on screen, so I won't do it. Course, you don't need a love interest in a western …"

"Mr Wayne, why have you never got involved with TV?"

"Oh, really because I'm still making good money doing pictures, you know doing the thing I love best. But hell, you're right, I've been offered lots of series. *Gunsmoke* for instance. But I didn't want to do it. Jim Arness was under contract to me but I let him go do it. Being an actor myself I couldn't make money off him, I released all my actors from their contracts, I felt too embarrassed to make money out of them."

"Why did you want to direct *The Alamo*?"

"I just believed in it and thought I could do a good job. I still think I did a good job, even though the critics in America say it's too patriotic. Hell, of course it is. That was the whole point, you just can't be more patriotic than giving your life for your country. I suppose I won't make a cent out of it because I made some bad deals so I could make it as I wanted it. I am proud of what I did."

Mooney was worried that perhaps Mr Wayne would be irritated by his questions, he must have heard all of them before. But he answered each one with patience and gave no hint that he was tired or bored. He looked relaxed and there wasn't the slightest suggestion that the whiskey was having any effect on him. They talked until the bottle was almost finished, but Duke still gave no sign that he wanted to end the interview. Mooney found the man who had killed off all-comers from *Stagecoach* to *The Alamo*, a film in which he had been killed off, full of the most astonishing humility, friendly, open, good-humoured and above all, polite. He had been expecting the typical Hollywood creature of artifice, but had found instead a man larger than his own image, "I like him," the reporter thought again. He watched him intently and considered the intangible air of sadness that hung about him, and which was especially noticeable the more he relaxed. Mooney found his patience incredible, it was three in the morning but he showed no sign of flagging. He brushed over politics, but happily talked about sex and violence in the business, commenting once again that he would never do any of that stuff. It was the reporter who tired first, and as his eyes began to droop he knew the last line of his report would read, "The image of the man is that of a dogmatic Puritan with the fiery righteousness of Moses. The man I met was warm-hearted, an almost reticent legend who obviously likes people too much to be iron-clad in his approach to them. Above everything else I found him to be a gentle man … and I liked him very much." Great stuff …

Duke smiled as he watched another fall by the wayside. Always the last to collapse, he again assumed the responsibility of looking after "the children." He called to the night porter to bring a blanket and covered the weary reporter with it himself. He padded off back toward his room wondering what he could do now; he wondered if Pilar was home, what would she be doing now? Was she missing him? He wished she and the kids had come with him. Energy seethed inside him, making rest impossible. He picked a book up he had found in Los Angeles … he'd just look at it, see if it gave him any ideas for a picture.

Some days later, after waving a fond farewell to England where his beloved film received every plaudit he had hoped for, he flew on to Rome and then, finally back home to his family and the increasingly savage attacks by the American Press. The excitement he'd had for the project had died along with Ward Bond. He needed to put it behind him, he needed to recover his strength, and Duke, ever the optimist, believed something would come along to replace *The Alamo* in his heart. Nobody could replace Bond, but he consoled himself, "At least I still have my family, my friends and my health."

He was about to lose each of those things as, first, his friends, his health and then his beloved family began to slip away. In a strange twist of fate his friends, the inner circle, seemed to die in rapid succession. Ward Bond hadn't been the first to go. Duke had known and loved Grant Withers for thirty years; they had shared many a daring escapade together, but as Duke went on to find fame and fortune, Withers turned into an incompetent drunk. The laughter had stopped as he passed through five disastrous marriages and his life became a long list of arrests for drunken driving, car accidents, and wife-beating. For years he lived on the edge of disaster with Duke always doing what he could for him. In the end what he did proved inadequate. He never understood that others couldn't cope with the excessive amounts of alcohol that he consumed, and although he continued to drink too much, when Withers died he was forced to look back to ask, "What if?" He had always believed that the drinking they all did was harmless fun. Duke was a happy drunk who mistrusted those who didn't indulge, but his friends paid a tragic price for the fun they shared with him. No matter how much Duke drank he was always able to get up and go to work the next day, was always able to fulfil his responsibilities. He couldn't understand why Withers couldn't do the same. He simply didn't have the same constitution and on March 27th 1959 he left a note asking his friends for forgiveness, swallowed a bottle of pills and drank a quart of vodka. Duke, weeping openly, blamed himself for not being sensitive enough, for not doing enough. The death hit him hard but what followed was worse.

Ward Bond had been, at fifty five, just two years older than Duke, when he died. They had grown up together, shared the worst of times together, and been sitting at the pinnacle of their careers together; Bond starring in the hit TV show, *Wagon Train*, and Duke completing *The Alamo*. Bond had not handled his long awaited stardom well after living too long in Duke's shadow. He loved the attention he got away from the star and accepted every Hollywood invitation that came his way, stubbornly ignoring his friend's advice to slow down. After Wither's death Duke was especially sensitive to the health and welfare of his friends, and was particularly worried about Bond, who loved going to parties and was using a cocktail of amphetamines and other drugs to keep pace with his newly acquired celebrity.

Bond's last episode of *Wagon Train* was directed by John Ford and starred Duke in a cameo role in his only dramatic TV appearance. Starring "Michael Morrison," the show was screened posthumously. Duke rushed straight to Dallas when he heard about the death, to accompany the body of his best friend back to Los Angeles. Crying once again, he read the eulogy at the funeral, "We were the closest of friends, from schooldays right on through. This was just the way Ward would have wanted it — to look out on the faces of good friends. He was a wonderful, generous, big-hearted man." Duke was inconsolable and much as John Ford was upset himself, he was seriously worried about the state Duke fell into as they went to tip Bond's ashes into the Catalina Channel. Bond had requested a sea burial saying, "I have loved lobster all my life, and I want to return the favour." Duke laughed when he heard that, but cried throughout the ceremony. He cried again later when he discovered the gun, with which he had accidentally wounded Bond so many years before, had been left to him. Their friendship had been a rare commodity in the jungle that was Hollywood and Duke knew he would never find anyone to replace Bond. He missed him badly and sat alone for days, desolate and refusing to talk to anyone as he looked back, remembering the past, "There will never be another Ward Bond. I remember telling him, a hell of a long time ago, that he was too damn ugly to be a movie star. But I was wrong. He was beautiful where it counted, inside." He wept uncontrollably and contemplated his loss.

He had great difficulty coming to terms with the concept of ageing and death and suddenly, with the loss of Withers and Bond, he found himself facing his own mortality alone. The members of the Ford clan handled their grief in their own way but of them all Duke was the least equipped to cope. Ford himself turned to the Catholic faith, but Duke could find no solace there, he had always shunned organised religion. He might have drowned his sorrow in a wild drinking spree but Jimmy Grant had turned to Alcoholics Anonymous, and his other drinking partners were all cutting back. He didn't know where to turn to find salve for the wounds that followed so hard on the heels of his personal savaging by the Press and his depression was compounded by the deflating sense of anti-climax he inevitably felt after completing his life's obsession. Mary St John said, "He looked as if someone had cut out his heart." He couldn't eat or sleep as he tried to come to terms with everything, he felt useless, angry, embarrassed and out of control.

And the pain didn't end there. Bev Barnett, Duke's shy, honest, softly spoken press agent and close friend, was the third to go. Duke, badly injured by life, cried, "God, I miss him. His death is so hard to take." Everywhere he went there was a visible aura of defeat about him and Mary went on, "The emptiness he felt was tangible."

His family began to worry when he lost interest in his work and even five-year old Aissa sensed something was terribly wrong, "He became distant, empty and angry." She noticed the first real change to their close relationship on the set of *The Comancheros*. She had never felt threatened by him in any way; whenever she had been naughty it was her mother who shouted at her, and her father who put things right. He had never shown the slightest aggression toward the girl he called his little princess. She had a small part in his new film and was supposed to deliver her line after playing with his tie, as he held her in his arms. She said the line but forgot the tie. He shouted at her in his sternest voice, "You're supposed to play with my tie, Aissa. Come on, get it right." She was shocked by the anger she saw in his eyes and refused to be comforted when he apologised profusely. Too young to understand that he had been lashing out at life in general, she was old enough to sense that things would never be the same again.

Immediately after *The Alamo* he still had "his friends, family and health." The friends were rapidly disappearing, he soon noticed the inevitable changes taking place in his family and, at the same time began to be deeply troubled by the cough that had started in Bracketville. He suddenly felt old, ill and unable to overcome the insecurities that plagued him. He wanted to be held and comforted and he started demanding evidence of love from a family he sensed was growing away from him. He understood Aissa was growing up, developing her own interests and was less dependent on him, but he hated the fact that her spontaneous demonstrations of affection had suddenly stopped. When his urgent need to be smothered in warm family love went unfulfilled he couldn't hold on to his fiery temper. His outbursts of anger were often delayed and his daughter said, "He bottled up his emotions, their release often came in the form of misdirected rage." No one could predict what would set him off, but his wife and children knew they didn't want to be around when he was angry and they began avoiding him; the very thing most likely to upset him. When he lost his temper with anyone other than his family, the rage was even worse, and his speech became peppered with obscenity he wouldn't dare use at home. Once the anger subsided, which it usually did quickly, he was full of deep and sincere remorse, and he repeated over and over, "Oh my God, I'm so sorry, I'm so sorry."

As in his youth, his physical presence, enough to intimidate the very boldest, became a problem, and even his own children cowered away from him. The screen image might be somewhat threatening but the man behind the image took no pleasure in any situation were all he saw in front of him were cringing white faces and he tried hard to avoid confrontation. Still he crashed around in pain, and drove away the very people he needed most; he knew it, but was powerless to stop himself. The harder he tried to put things right, the further away they drifted, and the louder he shouted.

His wife recognised the fragile and gentle soul behind the fury but even she began to turn away, "I could feel his pain but could do nothing to alleviate it." She wanted him to slow down and relax, to take life at a more normal pace. She let him know that to keep her he had to give more of himself and his time, he had to cut back on his work schedule. In a weak moment he admitted there was more to life than work. Still, a film set was the only place he found relief, and the knowledge that she expected him to ease off frustrated him. How could she suddenly demand that he start living a different, normal life, when nothing in his life had ever been normal, when life had made him anything but ordinary? She was asking him to break a lifetime's habit, demanding that he gave up his sure route to happiness. His self-esteem had been entirely tied up in his need to hustle since he was eight years old and an outside force, greater than himself, had spurred him on ever since he first found his salvation in effort. Sometimes he felt so exhausted that he would have given anything to be like other men, to be able to switch off and slow down, like his wife wanted. He knew it was impossible. He was still running as hard as he had done at any time in his life, powered by a complex mix of emotional, financial and professional needs.

He accepted the love of his fans gratefully, demanded love from his family, put his head down and bullishly charged at life, finding it impossible to relax no matter how much others wanted him to, or how much he himself needed to. Two wives and four children had already been sacrificed at the altar of his profession and experience warned him that if he didn't cut back on his work load now he would lose all the things he valued most. Experience meant nothing and, ultimately, the man who had a constant need to be surrounded by the love of his family was doomed to face the sad fact that he drove them away with his restless, unrelenting energy, his dedication to his craft and constant sense of economic insecurity. He feared his fortune was on the edge of collapse and his wife got used to hearing him lament, "We'll all be hurting if I don't make this movie!" She also knew money wasn't the root of his compulsion although he complained constantly about the increasing line of people who depended on the "next movie." The line never got any shorter and he continued to struggle to ensure no Wayne or Morrison wanted for anything. But she looked at his exhausted face and suspected an imminent collapse. His stubborn refusal to listen to her warnings annoyed her and led to increasing friction at home.

For him though, the bouts of black depression were interspersed with some of the best moments a human being could have experienced. One of the best came when Pilar announced she was pregnant again. He took consolation in her news, interpreting it as a sign that life went on. John Ethan Wayne arrived on 22 February, 1962, and Duke was delighted with his new child. He even managed to smile as he sat and watched Aissa play with baby Ethan. Although the recovery was long, the vacuum left by the deaths of his friends was slowly being filled. His son's arrival went a long way toward healing the wounds and lightening his mood, and Pilar was relieved when she heard him laughing at the baby's antics. The knowledge that he had once again created a tiny, helpless life that depended on him, stirred up familiar urges. The need to get up on his feet and be the provider again became so strong that he couldn't deny the call any longer. The dark times had lasted five long years but now, despite the cough, and Pilar's serious warning, he struggled up to go back to work.

In 1962 an article by Dean Jennings appeared in the Saturday Evening Post headed, *The Woes of Box Office King John Wayne*, declaring, "John

Wayne is finished." Jennings painted a picture of a man washed up by life, a man with erratic and deranged notions, who had only ever been a cowboy actor, who was now doomed to continue playing such parts to support his wife and growing family. He summarised his career as a failure, saying that here was a man whose future held no beauty. He said nothing more than Duke himself thought, but as soon as he saw the article something snapped and he found the courage to rouse himself to go in search of a beautiful future to prove the critic wrong. He had wasted enough time, worried too much about who thought what about him and his films. The time to move on had arrived and once again he used effort to turn a period of profound personal crisis into one of remarkable professional success.

He absolutely refused to be drawn into the trend of making films full of violence and sex and decided instead to continue making "John Wayne" movies. He heard people talk about him as if he was a dinosaur and was stung, but he was not extinct and said, "As long as people still pay to see my pictures I'll continue making them the way they want them. I'll only finish when they say, "Oh, do we have to look at that old sonofabitch again?" And, despite the critics, a new generation of film-goers now turned onto his films, "I hope I appeal to the more carefree times in a person's life. I'd just like to be an image that reminds someone of joy rather than the problems of the world. Luckily so far, it seems the youngsters consider me an older friend, somebody believable and down-to-earth." He refused to lie down and die, and no matter how ill he felt after completing *North to Alaska* he was soon racing half way round the world to make *Hatari!* with Howard Hawks in Africa. Duke had accepted the offer to work with one of his favourite directors without any thought that once again he would get no rest between films.

Most of the picture was to be shot on location out on the Serengeti where, during the day temperatures soared passed one hundred degrees and at night were close to freezing. Duke had anticipated no more fun without his old friends around but he enjoyed his time in North Africa in spite of everything. He loved the vast landscape of Serengeti, as beautiful in its way as Monument Valley, "You wake up and hear the savage sounds of the animals and your hair curls." His wife and children had gone on location with him, he got on well with the rest of the cast, and he loved Hawks who still let him do his own stunts. He was allowed to sit tied to the front of the car lassoing the wild animals himself, and he found great relief in the tough physical activity. Hawks understood perfectly what he needed, "I gave him no script and the chase scenes, the charging rhinos and the crashing jeeps in the film were shot just as they happened. Duke got himself into all sorts of real trouble and was almost tipped out of a jeep when a rhino unexpectedly rushed at it. His sense of exhilaration came across well in the picture."

Whilst the slow recovery continued in Africa, his future still troubled him. He had to accept that *The Alamo* was not the first stepping stone to him becoming a director. He was ageing fast, felt increasingly unwell, and all around him stars of his own generation were dying or retiring; Humphrey Bogart (1957), Tyrone Power (1958), Errol Flynn (1959), Clark Gable (1960), and Gary Cooper (1961), Cagney retired and Cary Grant announced that 1962 would be his last year in films. Duke told his wife he couldn't afford to retire or die!

He did though find enough money to finance another personal dream. John Wayne, cowboy actor, had wanted all his life to be a sailor. His love of the sea was enduring and he had, for some years, owned the 75' *Nor'wester*. Now, after long coveting her, he purchased *The Wild Goose*, a 136' mine sweeper. He rarely wanted or bought anything for himself, but The Wild Goose was different and the minute he heard she was for sale he snapped her up and began alterations as soon as he took possession. At sea he could take refuge from the glare of Hollywood, he felt safe to be himself, and after buying the Goose whenever he wasn't working, he was at sea or pottering around the decks of his boat in the harbour. Most winters saw him sailing down to Acapulco and summers cruising up the coast to Alaska. The boat was his proudest possession and he loved her, but she was also another huge expense. He had to keep making films now to pay for her upkeep.

As he sailed, fished and relaxed, he took stock of his life. Lying on the decks of his new boat he began to redefine his image and plan his next moves. Before acquiring her he had been confused, worried and depressed, but somehow, dozing contentedly at the back of *The Goose*, his thoughts became clear, uncluttered by fear, and he finally accepted that his future was as a film star not a director. He had to look for roles that centred on the image of a strong man, a man still capable of righting wrongs, but which at the same time allowed the hero to soften and age gracefully. He began searching for fatherly or even grandfather figure parts that suited his strengths and into which he could relax. Over the last years he had become increasingly sensitive to his image, he repeatedly turned down roles that went on to be great successes, saying he would not have been right in the part. Now when called on to act opposite a woman, he shed the sexual image of his past and adopted a more mellow approach of mutual respect and affection. He knew exactly what suited him, how to play the role and he guarded the new persona jealously. Offers began flooding in and his mood brightened perceptibly, "What the hell, the sun's going to come up tomorrow morning whether I'm pissed or depressed. I'm gonna get up with it and get on with my life."

The sixties, a time of deep depression followed by studied redefinition, turned out not to be a stultifying period leading to the death of the dinosaur, but rather, one of hyperactivity. In thirty months he starred in some of his best films including *The Man Who Shot Liberty Valance*, *Donovan's Reef*, *McLintock!*, *Circus World* and *In Harm's Way*. He had worked all through the dark years but now his performances were invested with renewed vigour. Best of all, he was even able to get revenge over the friend who had hurt him the most, Darryl Zanuck. When Zanuck started casting hundreds of soldiers and leaders for his war epic, *The Longest Day*, the first person he called was poor old Duke Wayne, on whom he had poured so much scorn. Suddenly Duke found himself flavour of the month, needed to play a wonderful manly, American leader, a part he had made his own. Zanuck rang him to tell him what he had in mind and was left in no doubt about what he could do with the part and the movie too. Duke offered no reason for his rejection, and though Zanuck guessed his comments had hit him hard after *The Alamo*, he had no idea that he had taken them so much to heart. He tried to explain that his remarks had been misquoted, he appealed to Duke's well-known patriotism, and told him he could choose his own part.

"No" Duke slammed the phone down.

Zanuck smiled and refused to give up, he rang straight back to offer a cameo role; he offered him anything he wanted because he needed Duke's name to sell the picture. Zanuck was kept dangling when Duke agreed to do a cameo for a quarter of a million dollars. The producer pleaded, but for once Duke didn't buckle, he had not had so much fun for a long time. He never expected him to agree his terms, he didn't particularly want a part in the film, but it gave him the sweetest feeling listening to Zanuck beg. It was a shining moment when they finally agreed terms. Duke spent four days working for his money. "Poor old Zanuck," he remarked with a huge grin, "I shouldn't have been rotten I guess … I always liked that son of a bitch. A good chess player. A good poker player. Loves pictures. Good studio boss. My idea of the kind of guy Hollywood needs. But I was goddam mad at his attack on me. I didn't like being pitied by him or anybody. But you know it was nice when I got over there on location, old Zanuck was decent to me. He was so pleasant I kinda wished I hadn't charged him so much money. It has to be the most expensive interview a movie producer ever gave. Should teach us all to keep our mouths shut more often. What the hell I needed the money, and

I didn't think Zanuck would give me the quarter of a mil … served the bastard right."

He still needed money badly, but Paramount was about to come to the rescue, offering him $600,000 a movie for ten pictures, with a six million dollar lump sum in advance, an irresistible package to a man with a fortune to recover. Slowly but surely he was climbing out of trouble and now, through sheer hard work, he began to amass a new fortune. As he approached his sixties he was working harder than ever, and was about to pay a heavy price. All his next films saw him away on distant locations, in Africa, Alaska, Hawaii for *Donovan's Reef*, Utah for *The Man who Shot Liberty Valance*, Arizona and Mexico for *The Commancheros* and *McLintock!*, and Spain for *Circus World*. The shadow of cancer hung over him but, as he travelled the world, he never suspected he was dying on his feet. He felt ill and was troubled by the nagging cough that gave him no rest, but nothing could stop him working, "He laboured with the perseverance of an animal in a yoke," Zolotow wrote in his biography. He had made promises which he would not break, had signed the massive deal with Paramount, he still had debts to repay, and running the *Wild Goose* was costing a small fortune. He never mentioned what he considered to be minor aches and pains, and very few people knew how much effort he was putting into each day. Pilar commented, "He's very good because you don't know he's in pain. Like when he fell off a horse and the next week he said, "I think I'd better see a doctor because I've been aching for seven days," Then you realise he's been in pain and said nothing about it, he had broken two ribs, and it was murder getting on and off a horse, but he never let on. He doesn't let much bother him, and he would never let a thing like bust ribs keep him out of a film. My husband may not be a boy anymore but he thinks he is, and he acts like one. He's so active. He doesn't waste a minute of the day. He won't stop for a moment."

Still, despite his refusal to moan, she began to fear something was seriously wrong. His cough was getting worse and his voice sounded raw and ugly. She noticed during his brief visits home that he was obviously uncomfortable and quieter than normal. On location he concentrated on his work but offered little of his usual humour. Only out at sea did his family catch occasional glimpses of the husband and father they had known and loved. There he was able to relax and was more willing to talk and to listen to their concerns.

Pilar was worried about him but John Ford required his services again, ill or not. He had been planning *The Man Who Shot Liberty Valance* for some time and was determined to have Duke working on it. By that time the star's fee was far higher than Ford wanted to pay, he constantly niggled him until he gave in and agreed to play the part of Tom Doniphon at a reduced rate. Duke sensed that Ford was angry with him about something and the old man had taken it into his head that he was trying to avoid him. Duke wrote, trying to clear the air, "I don't know who you heard over the phone when you called my home, but it was certainly not I … I talk to every Tom, Dick and Harry who calls. I certainly would not be too tired to talk to a man whom I consider my best friend — that I have a feeling of blood kinship with." The letter didn't fix things and Ford had remained distant. In the end Duke felt he had to accept the part to put their relationship back into some kind of order. Ford's grandson, Dan, said, "My grandfather continued to direct Duke's life."

As Duke emerged from his period of depression, Ford was sinking into the vacant hole he left behind. He wanted to shoot the film in a murky black and white to give it a dark, old fashioned look and feel, that reflected his own mood. He had lost his belief in the value of community, he no longer felt like celebrating civilisation or American values. Initially, when he first broached the subject with Duke, he was full of enthusiasm and fire but he lost interest in the film almost as soon as shooting began. His mood made life difficult for all the actors involved but he was especially tough on the favourite son who found himself in the direct firing line again. He was particularly nasty with him, despite having pestered him to join the cast, and Duke was furious for allowing himself to get roped in. Onlookers felt Ford pushed him to the brink of ending their relationship on the set of *Liberty Valance*. Perhaps if he had not still been feeling so raw he would have ignored the director as he normally did, instead he became surly and aggressive himself. Fortunately James Stewart, one of Duke's closest friends, was the other star of the picture, and he afforded Duke some moments of light relief. He said, "John Wayne was probably the biggest star in the world, yet he retained the qualities of a small boy. He had an enthusiasm for life that would make a high school football star envious. And he never changed. As a man he was exactly the boy he started out. And as a friend … well, you just wouldn't want a better one, once a friend, always your friend." That friendship was now heavily leaned on and Duke even managed to raise a laugh when, near the end of filming, Ford turned on Stewart for the first time. He threw over his shoulder, as he made good his own escape, "You thought you were going to make it through, didn't you! Ha, ha."

Much of the filming was completed on a sound stage in 1961, "It was a tough assignment for me because dammit, Ford had Jimmy for the shit-kicking humour, O'Brien playing the sophisticated humour, and he had the heavy, Marvin. Christ there was no place for me. I just had to wander around in that son of a bitch and try and make a part for myself. And he let me too. I mean he just, goddammit, he forgot I was around. He made it kind of rough on me. I never thought it was a case of whether Doniphon belonged any longer … I didn't take it at all that Ford was saying there's no place for that type of character. I don't think Jack meant it as such either. And in the long run the girl would have had a more pleasant life with Jimmy. She'd probably have been happier if she'd married me though … more exciting say. I'm probably more optimistic about Doniphon's character than other people were, I didn't think he was alienated. I think that the character really wasn't a well-rounded, developed character. He was good as a tool for a certain time." He found Tom Doniphon uncomfortable to play and Ford's behaviour didn't help. All the cast were in awe of him, he terrified some, and was hard on all of them, but actor Ken Murray confirmed, "Working on the film became a misery for Duke." Many felt it was Ford's way of getting back at him for not using him on *The Alamo*, others believed he was jealous of Duke's increasing success compared to his own sudden decline. Once he started shouting at Duke about one thing, he carried on throwing an endless stream of venom at him. Even in 1961 he continued to bring up his failure to enlist, and reminded him over and over again that both Stewart and Woody Strode, had both been real war heroes. Duke, highly embarrassed, deeply hurt and offended, rarely spoke on set. He also lost his temper easily and at one point almost came to blows with Strode, not the real target of his anger, after he nearly lost control of a team of racing horses. Strode said, "Duke couldn't get the horses to stop but when I tried to help he pushed me away." Duke eventually fell off the wagon. He was unhurt and Strode had been eager to trade punches with him, mad that he had endangered both their lives. Ford, witnessing the incident, finally realised how badly he had stirred Duke up. He was well aware that his best boy wouldn't retaliate against him, but it was equally obvious that he was taking his spleen out on everyone else. When, many years later, Duke was still complaining about the treatment he got on the film, Mary St John attempted to comfort him, venturing hesitantly that Doniphon was full of ambiguity. He snapped back, "Screw ambiguity … I don't like ambiguity. I don't trust ambiguity."

Many film reviewers felt the same way, though over the years the picture grew in stature until it was eventually accepted as a masterpiece, representing Ford at the apex of his career. He and John Wayne had made some remarkable films together, shared many adventures and much fun, they had also taken many a knock along the way. By the time they teamed up for *Liberty Valance* they had almost reached the end of the road, and

Ford's lament, the last western they made together, was the conclusion to a spectacular association. Eventually, despite the tension that existed between them throughout the sixties, Duke accepted that what they achieved had been remarkable, "We had great days. I generally don't look back, but it's pretty hard not to when there were guys like Ward and Jack around. You don't meet them everyday." Duke didn't like to look back. He wanted to move on but, as so often in the past, his periods of depression coincided with those suffered by Ford, and certainly whilst working on *Liberty Valance* he sank again, his mood once again affected by that of the director. Neither was left untouched by the changes occurring in Hollywood, changes that now sent them down different paths. Ford was about to give up, John Wayne was going to fight on and leave his mentor far behind.

They made only one more film together, *Donovan's Reef*, which was completed in 1963. Both were determined to make the picture despite all the usual pre-production problems, and when financing was pulled out at the last minute Ford decided to go ahead and make it himself. Duke guessed he would not get many more chances to work with Coach, and after *Liberty Valance* he wasn't even sure he wanted to anymore. Now he planned one last fling, an epitaph, to make up for the misery of their last experience and he anticipated a nostalgic trip back in time to the good old days. Instead the project ran into serious trouble before they even left for location and it turned into yet another difficult assignment. Jimmy Grant was fired, and Frank Nugent, who wrote *The Searchers*, was asked to come up with something quickly. The resulting script was weak. Duke also believed the film was badly cast, "I should never have been used in that one. I was too old." Once they arrived in Hawaii Duke found Ford more irritable than ever. He had become fiercely protective of the old man and he watched over him constantly, ensuring he was alright. He took over much of the direction himself and rarely left Ford's side. The film was not hailed as a classic and Duke later accepted it was a less than fitting end to the Ford-Wayne collaboration.

In September 1962 the whole Wayne family went to Arizona to make *McLintock!* Duke had not enjoyed his last couple of pictures but now had a great time working on a film that teamed him once more with his favourite lady, Maureen O'Hara. It was a family affair and combined many of the old Ford regulars. Michael got his first solo production credits, Patrick and Aissa both had roles, Andy McLaglen, son of Duke's old friend Victor, directed, and even Ford turned up to help out when McLaglen fell ill. There was a sentimental feel to the location and Duke said, "Some films are tough to make and you can work harder but not get such a good result. I think that the fun people had making *McLintock!* came over well on screen. It's not that it's a great film, it is entertaining." He worried how his fans would take to the light-hearted comedy; he feared they would go in expecting a typical shoot-em up and come out disappointed. He didn't need to worry and the picture was well received.

McLintock! was one of Duke's earliest attempts to set down his personal view of life on film. He went to extraordinary lengths with it and spent a lot of time, trouble and money getting things just right. He even had one of the last surviving herds of long horn cattle in the country brought in, had an authentic railroad station built in the desolate area north of Tombstone to add authenticity, and arranged to borrow a nineteenth century train, complete with engine, passenger coaches and box-car from Paramount Pictures. He hired 287 Indians from all over Arizona including Sioux, Crow, Apaches and some of his Navajo friends from Monument Valley. When the 14 Navajo chiefs arrived Duke quipped, "Hey, didn't I kill you 12 pictures back?" They all laughed, but in fact *McLintock!* was a statement from Duke marking the sadness he felt at the passing of a noble civilisation.

Ford had first noticed the special chemistry that existed between Wayne and O'Hara during the filming of *Rio Grande* in 1950, and of course, later in *The Quiet Man*. She was Duke's ideal woman; she laughed, drank and cursed with him, and he found her irresistible. She was one of the only women he ever felt truly comfortable with, the only one he ever went out of his way to keep company with. Duke always fell in love with passive, demure, Hispanic women, and his problems started when they began to express themselves more. But Maureen O'Hara was like no other woman he ever met, able to stand toe to toe with him, and as powerful as he was himself. He called her *Big Red*, or *Herself*, and often spoke about how things might have been if they had married. Fortunately for them both, it was an honest friendship that never turned into anything more. Mary remarked, "They are the strongest two people I have ever known. They would have been like oil and water as man and wife. They were better off as friends." O'Hara said, "People assumed there was a great romance between Duke and me. There wasn't. We loved and respected one another and we knew we were good for each other on screen." All the films they shared were special, the magic that existed between them clearly visible.

In *McLintock!* they had a fine time, both especially loving the scene where the whole town brawls on the edge of a fifty foot hill with a mud hole at the bottom, into which they all inevitably slide. The first stuntman to try sliding down into the mud fell and cut his head, and the others then demanded extra danger money to perform the stunt. Duke was disgusted, it was already costing Batjac $50,000 to shoot the scene. He stood at the top of the hill and bellowed, "Well then, I guess that means I have to do it, you white-livered chicken shits! It's about as dangerous as diving into a swimming pool, and Maureen and I will prove it." Miss O'Hara shouted back, "That old bastard wants me to slide down the hill with him, but I won't do it." She did it, as Duke beaming, took her by the arm and dragged her down with him laughing, "That's my girl." Temperatures suddenly dropped to 42 degrees and a cold wind blew up as they worked, but neither of them was about to quit.

The film also featured Yvonne De Carlo in her first picture for four years. She was married to Bob Morgan, a stuntman who had lost a leg in an accident whilst working on *How The West Was Won*. As soon as Duke learned of the hardship they were suffering he insisted on rescuing De Carlo from the night-club circuit by finding her a well paid role in his film. Chuck Roberson, who played the marshal said, "If Bob had been able, right then, I'm damn sure Duke would have written in a part for a one-legged man … Somehow he managed to lend a hand without damaging anyone's sense of dignity."

After completing *McLintock!* and playing a cameo role in *The Greatest Story Ever Told* Duke and his family set off on their traditional trip to Acapulco where he spent some peaceful months away from his hectic routine. Though the town was full of the rich and famous, he steadfastly refused to get involved in the social life of the resort and rarely went to parties. He was, however, friendly with Merle Oberon and accepted an invitation to her villa. The Wayne family lazed around the pool whilst Duke talked or played cards with other guests. His children enjoyed playing with Oberon's adopted family. On one occasion three year old Ethan dived into the pool. After a lifetime at sea with his father, he already swam like a fish, but President Johnson's daughter, Lynda Bird, worried for his safety, dived after him and began dragging him to the side. An angry Ethan shouted for help, "Daddy, why is this crazy lady jumping on me?" As it turned out Daddy had to rescue them both as her paper dress started to dissolve in the water. Some time later Duke was shocked to receive a warm invitation to a reception at The White House for the king and queen of Thailand. Ethan, who was included in the invitation, was assured no crazy ladies would throw themselves at him. Duke muttered, "I can't go, I'm a Republican." Pilar smiled and said, "I'm sure they know that dear," but she added with determination, "and I don't care what you are, I want to go."…they went. On the way to The White House a nervous Duke told his wife, "They probably just asked us because of

Lynda. Hell, everyone knows what I think of the Democrats. We'll probably be seated behind a pot palm." When they arrived Pilar was thankful to find her staunch Republican gracious, assured and polite as he shook hands with all those Democrats. They were both surprised to find they were not seated behind a pot palm but at the main table, treated as guests of honour.

Whatever he was doing, and wherever he was he always longed to get back to sea and soon after acquiring the *Wild Goose* he began dreaming about sailing her across the Atlantic. His next scheduled film, *Circus World* was due to be shot in Spain and provided him with the perfect excuse for his voyage. September 1963 saw him sailing down the coast of Mexico where he fished and relaxed for a couple of weeks before continuing on to Panama. He sailed the *Goose* through the Canal and across the Caribbean to Bermuda and then straight across the Atlantic. The boat became home for the duration of his stay in Spain, and he enjoyed many unexpected and uninvited visitors whilst he was there. He stood on no ceremony and everyone was welcome aboard the Wild Goose. Friends dropped by all the time during what turned into one long, happy party. Grace Kelly arrived one night long after the Waynes had retired for the evening. Duke started running round the bedroom shouting, "Jesus" at the top of his voice, as he tried to throw some clothes on.

As soon as filming got under way the party ended abruptly. Hathaway, though a friend of Duke's, was as tough in his own way as Ford, and equally brutal. He delighted in challenging actors with the hardest physical effort and when Duke worked with him he had little energy left for socialising, "We worked nights for months. I generally fell into bed at about five in the morning." Duke found little pleasure making *Circus World*. It was the first time he had acted with Rita Hayworth, he said it would also be the last! He found her difficult to work with, she was temperamental, unprofessional and rude; she played a drunken has-been in the film and Duke commented that she was much the same in real life, she was always late, had difficulty remembering her lines and was exactly the type of star he detested. On the only occasion they went to dinner together in Spain she was so nasty to the waiter and other diners that he was acutely embarrassed and tried to make up for her behaviour by spending his entire evening signing autographs, leaving an over-generous tip, and sternly warning every member of his family, "Never think anyone is better than you, but never assume you're superior to anyone else. Try to be decent to everyone, until they give you reason not to."

Working with her was the least of his problems, and he was lucky to escape with his life as the climax of the film was shot. The scene involved the big top catching fire, panicking animals, and Duke, as Matt Masters the circus owner, trying to save everything single-handedly. When he first heard what Hathaway had planned he tried, for once, to get a stuntman to do it. Chuck Roberson, his double, was away working on another film and the director said he had no choice, he had to do it himself. It took Hathaway five days to shoot something he was happy with, and in that time artificial and real fires were lit and re-lit. Duke, in the thick of the action all the time, spent those days breathing in thick black smoke and fumes. When Pilar complained about the risk he was taking he flared up, saying he was only doing what he got paid for. Still the work exhausted him and when he got back in the evenings he didn't even bother eating before collapsing into a restless sleep. The smoke he had inhaled prevented him getting much rest and he lay coughing violently all night. Pilar ordered him to see a doctor but he refused and reassured her, "It'll be better once I've finished this."

In fact things took a dramatic turn for the worse when the fire he was working close to suddenly whipped out of control and Duke, who had his back to the camera, didn't notice what had happened. The director and crew fled from the tent, but although Duke was aware of the increasing heat and smelt the burning seats, he carried on working until he could no longer breathe. When he finally turned it was to find he had been abandoned to the raging inferno. Even though he'd been uncomfortable he'd carried on, waiting to hear the word "Cut" before giving up, John Wayne didn't run unless he was directed to run, "Hell, I can't even sleep unless I'm told to by the director!" Once he realised what had happened he furiously threw the axe he had been using across the set and stormed off, his singed hair and eyebrows still smouldering. He went back to his hotel and didn't reappear for some days. He sulked and refused to talk to anyone, angry — not because of the danger he'd been in, but because no one had even caught his brush with death on film and he was going to have to go through it all over again.

The night of the fire he started coughing up blood, his eyes were red rimmed, he could scarcely talk, and Pilar, shocked at his condition, pleaded with him again to get checked over. His health was deteriorating rapidly, but he still refused, saying he was too busy. He promised to go for a check-up if the cough didn't clear by the time they got home. He went back to work and no one ever heard him complain about the incident again. The fire footage Hathaway eventually got was acknowledged as some of his most spectacular work, but it was Duke who paid the price. No one in Spain had any idea of the terrifying truth nor of the damage that had been done during those five days, John Wayne was invincible, too big and strong to be ill. Those who heard him coughing then were certain he'd only sustained temporary mad minor injuries. That was also what he hoped and his wife prayed. In fact he had inhaled so much smoke that his lungs were severely and permanently affected and he never fully recovered. His chain smoking habit had done untold harm, but the fire speeded up the inevitable. His condition worsened daily and even he began to worry at the sight of the blood he brought up.

Meanwhile as the world shook the day President Kennedy was assassinated, John Wayne trembled at the news, "It seemed so much worse because we were away from the United States. I just wanted to go home." He was deeply disturbed, hit by the enormity of the event despite the fact that he had never liked Kennedy as a man and deplored his politics. The dream trip, that had started with such exhilaration and high hopes, had turned into a nightmare. And it was going to get worse.

He and Pilar were having frequent and heated arguments on location. She had always ignored his impatient blustering, knowing her silence infuriated him. Now, for the first time, she shouted back at him, returning fire with fire. He was shaken, suddenly reminded of terrifying fights with Chata, and he rounded on her in a fearful temper. His reaction and his language surprised him more than it did her, and he became withdrawn, shy and hesitant, not knowing what to do to make things better. He didn't understand why she had attacked him so unexpectedly, never guessing it was because she was so worried about him. He shouted and made her the direct target of his venom because he felt ill and was too scared to confess just how bad he felt. He saw no point in frightening her and he edged away as he tried to protect her with empty reassurances. He planned a relaxing trip back to California and was confident the sea air would clear his chest, certain things would soon get back to normal.

On March 21st 1964 further tragedy struck as his boat was anchored off the tip of Baja, California. Four young crew members wanted to go ashore and they set off in the skiff through choppy waters toward the nearest town. Still drunk the next morning, they headed back out for *The Goose*. One of them fell overboard and as the others tried to save him the skiff capsized. Three drowned and only the boy who couldn't swim and clung to the upturned boat survived. Duke, filled with a dark sense of gloom and bitter self-reproach, took each death personally as he spent the last days of the dream trip arranging funerals. He'd spent his life shielding and protecting others, ensuring the safety of everyone in his care, the fact that three of his staff were dead just had to be his fault. He hid himself away in the wheel house, he wanted to be on his own and avoided everyone, only joining his family briefly at mealtimes. Finally, when he could stand it no longer, he cut short his stay and flew home to Encino. He could find no rest there either and he was relieved when the time came to set off for Hawaii, where he was under contract to make *In Harm's Way* with Patricia Neal and Kirk Douglas.

For some years he hadn't had the luxury of being able to turn down bad roles as he felt the compulsion to make good his financial losses; as a result, by the mid sixties, he felt trapped in a professional rut. He was tired out by the continual need to push himself making films he felt personally dissatisfied with, and he agreed with the critics who pointed out that after thirty years of film making he had become stale. Even he felt bored with the old John Wayne image and knew he needed to find something fresh. As it turned out he had to do very little; the image was altered for him, not in any way he could have anticipated, or wished for, not in any way he could have wilfully created.

Though he continued to ignore Pilar's nagging and promised to go to the doctor after finishing Otto Preminger's picture his hand was eventually forced when Paramount needed him to attend a routine medical check for insurance purposes. He underwent routine tests at Scripps Institute and, surprisingly, received a clean bill of health. He was given cover for the film despite the one-centimetre shadow of death already clearly visible on his left lung. He carried on coughing, happy it was nothing serious, and went off to make a film requiring little physical effort but, for the first time, his persistent cough caused delays. He was furious at his increasing weakness.

In most of his last films he had been displeased to find himself playing a middle-aged man chasing younger women. He particularly disliked the kissing and bedroom scenes in *Hatari* and said he felt more foolish than virile, and he had decided not to play such scenes again. *In Harm's Way* was his first attempt at a different type of role, playing opposite Patricia Neal, an older woman. Neal hadn't seen Duke since they worked together on *Operation Pacific*, "He'd been through a lot since then. He was a better man for it." And Duke discovered some rare chemistry, "God, I thought the love scenes with her were just great. Otto had a fine picture going for him, I thought the story played beautifully, right up to the end of the battle, when he insisted on using miniatures, after that you can't believe in one thing. I look like I've gone through the towering inferno, wrapped up in bed. It doesn't mean anything, because no one could believe those battle shots. The finish was just so poor, and I know Otto is going to hate me for saying that."

When Hollywood had first heard that Wayne, Douglas and Preminger were going to be working together, a disaster was predicted. Many of the cast did find Preminger difficult as he strutted around shouting, "I am the man with no hair, who shoves around people with hair." The self-confessed bully and hater of actors was merciless but Duke somehow managed to escape his wrath, "I know he's supposed to be a sonofabitch but he had my respect. He was terribly hard on the crew and on those people he thought were sloughing. But this is a thing I can understand because I've been there and I know that if a fellow comes on and he's careless and he hasn't thought about his … well, I just come ready, that's all, and he appreciated that. I was usually there ahead of him on the set, and he couldn't believe it. But that's how I always work. So we got to have a really nice relationship … except there was no way to tell him … goddamm, he wanted to have his picture taken on all those miniatures! You know, a film can't be a success once it loses its credibility. That's why I don't try to outrun Paavo Nurmi, nor outplay some 6'11" basketball player, I keep within my own limits so that my audience can accept me. I get kind of anxious about that."

Just as Duke obviously respected Preminger so the director commented that he had never worked with anyone who had so intuitive a sense of the camera as the star, "I was surprised at his ability to gain maximum effect from any situation. He was the least ego-ridden man I ever met. It was unusual to work with a star who was unconcerned about anyone stealing his lines. He had a deep interest in making movies, he loved everything about the business." Preminger gave Duke a wider latitude than he offered anyone else, and was almost fatherly toward him. Like many who had heard he was a right wing monster, Preminger expected Duke to be rude, brash and primitive, and was surprised to find almost the exact opposite, "He was an urbane and civilized human being; well-read, sensitive and gentle. What professional discipline he had, in make-up by 7am every morning, staying until he was dismissed, and often long after he had been dismissed. There are stars who disappoint you when you first meet them, but John Wayne was even taller, more majestic, than I expected him to be. He had none of the usual tricks of a star's temperament. When a take was spoiled he simply always thought it was his fault and he apologised to everyone involved. In fact he rarely made mistakes when the cameras were rolling. He never argued with my decisions, he listened attentively and accepted correction and direction without comment. He listened to every suggestion and did his best to follow it."

Wendell Mayes, who wrote the screen play, enthused, "Wayne never blows a line and when the other actors blow theirs he stands patiently waiting for them to get it right." Despite their political differences, Kirk Douglas agreed, "The perfect movie star is John Wayne … he brings so much authority to a role. He can pronounce literally any line in a script and get away with it." One line was so corny that Douglas waited, amused as Duke tried it out, "I wish to have no connection with any ship that does not sail fast, for I intend to go in harm's way." Douglas held his breath, "But you know what? He said it, and he got away with it. Now that's John Wayne. No one else could have done that line and got away with it." Hollywood had predicted a disaster but the three men worked professionally together and proved the pundits wrong.

The director was worried about Duke's hacking cough but was reassured when the star told him it was just a cold.

"Do you have any fever?"

"Oh a notch or two above normal, but Hell, it's nothing, Otto, nothing."

In fact getting through each day was proving to be a tough assignment and as far as Preminger was concerned, the fact that he was obviously sick throughout filming was further testament to his pure acting ability. Pilar had gone to Hawaii with him and was scared, "He rarely complains. He amazes me. He is addicted to danger, but he scares me and I worry all the time. It keeps me up nights. I wish he would take things easier. I'm so afraid of losing him. He is blind and indifferent to hazard. He takes too many chances and we fight about it all the time. I wish he would see a doctor, but he won't ... there's nothing I can do ..."

The *Hollywood Reporter* commented favourably on his performance and admired his "Tremendous masculinity, his massive physical strength and his casual acting," but in the four months that had passed between filming *Circus World* and *In Harm's Way* he had aged considerably, he no longer looked strong or fit, his eyes were watery and clouded, he looked older than his fifty-seven years, and he'd gained weight despite the fact that he was off food. He admitted that even walking across a room left him shattered. He found it difficult to breathe and was aware of a strong and rapidly increasing pain across his chest.

He had promised Pilar he would go back to the clinic after finishing *In Harms Way*, but then changed his mind again and told her he would go after completing *The Sons of Katie Elder* instead. She stood strong and insisted, "No — You are going now." Duke caved in and drove himself down to Scripps Clinic, "He was like a little boy about attending the clinic, he hated hospitals and doctors. He detested the loss of privacy and control when he entered the clinic. He usually forced me to go with him and have all the same tests that he had. This time he went alone." He had arranged to meet old friend Louis Johnson after the physical was over to go to the races.

The unusual thoroughness of his medical surprised Duke. Tissue samples were taken and various other tests were carried out. The probing, draining, repeated blood tests and X-rays annoyed him. He was suddenly overwhelmed by a sense of fear, and he wished Pilar had gone with him. Lately they had been arguing ferociously, but he trusted her, loved her, and knew she wouldn't let him down if there was anything seriously wrong with him. He felt old, ill and deeply troubled. On paper he was still all but broke and the future of his family rested on his ability to remain one of the top ten box office stars. He left the clinic at the end of a harrowing day of tests worrying how he could support them if he could no longer work because of ill health.

When he reported back into Scripps the next morning for his results a dark shadow crept across the sky, hiding the sun. The receptionist told him he needed further X-rays and a number of shots were taken from several different angles. Two hours later a surgeon gave an ashen-faced Duke the stark details of his illness. He was told he had a one in twenty chance of surviving lung cancer, "I think I might have been treated with a little more humanity." He felt cold and vulnerable sitting all but naked in a hospital gown, as the doctor tried to decide how far it had spread, "I had flu when I was about eight. I had an appendicitis operation. I'd had some trouble with an ulcer. Now I felt like somebody had hit me across the belly with a baseball bat. It wasn't just the fear of death, although there's that too. When the doctor taps you on the shoulder and says, "you've got cancer," the sun sure doesn't shine any brighter."

He called Pilar from the hospital, knowing she was waiting for news, "How to tell my wife, my mother, those kids who are the joy of my life and who'd never seen me sick? I'd always been big, healthy, somebody they could kind of depend on. It's ... the helplessness. I couldn't see myself lying on a bed, not able to do anything for myself, no damn good to anybody. I felt like a jerk." He decided it would be too cruel to tell her over the phone and he lied that all was well.

He set off for home in his old green Pontiac station wagon that was almost as famous as he was, and the custom-built model with its raised dome drew plenty of attention as he turned out of the hospital grounds. People stood to watch and wave him on his way up the Pacific Coast Highway, oblivious to the devastation that had left him reeling. Normally, when he drove he pointed the wagon where he wanted to go, put his foot flat to the floor, and weaved in and out of traffic. Pilar and the children thought his driving was so bad they never volunteered to sit in the front with him, preferring instead to huddle together in the back with their eyes shut. This time he drove slowly, with care and deliberation, as he planned his next moves.

Even driving home, facing a bleak future, he hungered for a cigarette, "It sure was agony. The doctors had told me I had to stop, and I was going to do as I was told, but it wasn't easy. My mouth was dry and I ached all over. I'd smoked all my life, I grew up with a cigarette in my mouth. But now I had my family to think of and I was running scared. So I was going to quit ... but even on that drive home it was murder. I had the most terrible craving and it felt like I was being dragged through Hell backwards. But I intended becoming a non-smoker, I was going to stick with it. I guess it's never easy." He had smoked since he was a young boy and for over forty years had averaged three packets a day. Aissa said, "I never saw my dad without a cigarette in his hand." When he was under stress he got through six packs of unfiltered Camels a day, lighting each cigarette from the one he was putting out, "I loved smoking, it was part of my identity." The mannerisms he used were peculiarly his own; he held his cigarette deep inside his hand, his huge palm obscuring his face when he took a drag, "No one else smokes a cigarette like John Wayne."

As he continued his drive along the coast his hands trembled on the steering wheel, "I even craved the sensation of tearing the cellophane wrapper, unfolding the tin foil, and pulling out that first one, putting it between my lips, lighting it and inhaling deeply. These were sensations I loved and had become used to over many years. There had been many times during my years making movies that I could have died. I was thrown off and under horses, I had jumped out of windows and off roofs. I had been living on borrowed time for years ... when that rhino charged in *Hatari*, during the fire in *Circus World*, when I jumped from the roof in *McLintock!* ... I could have been killed so often ... I ruptured a disc in my spine in *McLintock!* and was left in agony. I've had lots of serious injuries, I've bust my ribs, ankles, I've torn tendons, had my nose smashed. What the hell did just one more cigarette matter?" Even as he was hit by the impulse to stop and buy one last pack he began coughing, pictures of his young dependant family sprang to mind, and he couldn't do it. He drove on until he reached Newport Bay where he could see *The Wild Goose*, his pride and joy, anchored in the distance. No, he had a greater love, and the thought that he might not be able to work struck him again. He had contemplated his family, his life, and his boat on the long drive from the clinic, and now it hit him ... work ... would he ever make another picture? If he couldn't fall off roofs or horses any more, if he couldn't make movies he had no future to contemplate and he might just as well be dead.

He drove on, more slowly, scared of arriving home where he knew he would have to face Pilar's questions. He had hidden the truth over the phone, he wouldn't be able to do it face to face. He rehearsed his lines, "Everything will be alright. I know the man upstairs will pull the plug when he wants to, but I don't want to end up my life being sick. I want to go out on two feet, in action. I'm not ready. Everything's going to be alright," he repeated it over and over. Nothing could touch him, he was John Wayne, the guy who faced and beat all-comers, the man with the huge appetite for life with the enthusiasm of a young football star, he was the man who took everything in his stride; he smoked too much, drank too much, ate too much, worked too hard, loved too hard, he was John Wayne, "Christ, how can I live if I can't get up at four in the morning, drive to work as the sun comes up, get into make-up and costume, how can I live if I can't chat to Jack, or Henry or Howard. How am I going to make it? There's so much to do."

And then he had a brilliant idea! "If I can't have a cigarette, I'll have a drink every time I want one instead." He had already entered the outskirts of town but there were lots of bars before he got home and he stopped at a small roadside café. It was against everything he believed in to drive after having a drink, he was a fanatic on the subject, and he had an arrangement with local police who took him home whenever he had been out drinking. Nevertheless he was fairly smashed by the time he got back, "Yeah, I was scared. Real scared. I realised I'd been self-centred, had never given my family the real consideration I should have. I guess we're all like that. I'd taken so much for granted. When they told me I had cancer I realised I wasn't worth much without the people around me that I loved. At first I sort of gave in. I cried. I sobbed. I needed Pilar's courage and support but I was scared to tell her, I was scared to look her in the eye." When he walked in, he looked at the floor instead and mumbled, "I've got a little problem Pilar. The doctor says I've got a spot on my lung, but don't worry." They had been married almost ten years, he was afraid they wouldn't be celebrating any more anniversaries, "I wasn't even sure if the next day would be my last. I wondered if this would be the day I'd see the sun for the last time, the day I'd have to say goodbye to Pilar and the kids. I was afraid to tell her how I felt."

On September 3, 1964, two weeks after the initial diagnosis, he met surgeon John E. Jones at Good Samaritan Hospital, "The cancer is quite obvious. We have a fine surgical team here." Duke couldn't hide any longer, "OK, When? I'm contracted to make *The Sons of Katie Elder* in November. Can surgery wait?" Jones told him to either reschedule the picture or forget surgery altogether. He had told no one other than Pilar that he had cancer, now he had to confess to Henry Hathaway, who was directing the movie. At the time almost every form of cancer was a death sentence but Hathaway himself had survived cancer of the colon. He talked to Duke at length about what he now faced; he reassured him about his chances of recovery but also warned him not to expect it to be a piece of cake either, "Surgery will be as painful as hell, but everything's going to be fine Duke."

At home he became increasingly introverted. He refused to discuss the future, made no arrangements and wouldn't discuss his illness, he made no special effort to see any of his friends, he kept himself to himself and felt isolated as the days before the operation dragged on, "I was tough to get along with. I'd discovered I was fallible and my body was craving tobacco. Pilar was the real strength then. She forced me not to give in and stuck with it when I wanted to surrender. I guess I should have talked to her about it more. People should talk. But like so many others I was afraid of the very word cancer, I didn't want to say it … to any one."

Pilar knew him well and understood how he felt, "Duke was a chain smoker. I never saw anyone smoke as much as he did. It went on constantly and I don't know how he gave up something that meant so much to him. I knew he was scared about having cancer, but I think not getting his tobacco hurt him much more. Even if he hadn't been so unwell I would have expected him to get snappy if he wasn't smoking. I tried to be understanding, but sometimes he pushed me to the limit."

The two weeks waiting for the operation were torment for them all as he did his best to hide his fears. In the end he stopped communicating altogether, he was afraid to let his guard down as he tried to protect the inner man. He acted tough and was left unable to share his anxiety or even to acknowledge it himself. On the only occasion he let the mask slip he confessed to Pilar that his constant coughing reminded him of the unhappy boyhood nights when he had listened to his father, who had tuberculosis. He told her that feeling ill was torture to him, but so was being made to talk about it and he begged her to leave him alone to deal with things in his own way.

Before going into hospital he'd been undecided about what to tell the press. His agent, Charlie Feldman, warned that his image as the tough, virile, action man, would be harmed if people knew he was suffering from lung cancer. Duke found falsehood difficult to sustain but Feldman, his son Michael, and his son-in-law Don La-Cava, who now handled his business affairs, all advised him to keep quiet about the impending surgery. They told him no studio would hire him once they heard he had cancer and he didn't feel well enough to argue the point. He wanted to tell the truth but once he saw how the people closest to him were reacting he guessed the studios would also panic. He didn't want to survive only to find himself unemployable, and because he knew he couldn't survive without work, he became trapped in an image of strength that he no longer possessed. He had to be seen to be invincible, audiences had to believe he was a man immune to life's ravages. He'd invested so much energy into creating the image that every role he was offered reflected the stereotype and John Wayne, weakened cancer victim, as vulnerable as the next man, could be forced out of Hollywood. He had no alternative but to live his life according to the image. He reluctantly agreed to say nothing and Feldman took matters into his own hands, telling the Press that Duke was going into hospital to have an old football injury repaired.

"Everything is going to be alright," he whispered to himself as he walked nervously into the Good Samaritan Hospital on September 16th 1964. He laughed and joked with staff and behaved in the only way he could; the toughest son of a bitch in the West had arrived for the showdown. Pilar stayed with him in the bleak hospital room, afraid to be away from him for too long. She also guessed that he must be afraid, even if he couldn't give voice to those fears. Neither slept the night before the operation, and a million unspoken thoughts ran through Duke's mind, but as he was wheeled away to theatre he gave his wife a warm kiss, a John Wayne smile and a cheery wave.

The scalpel of Dr Jones entered his chest just under the left breast. It ran a full twenty-eight inches up under his left arm and into the middle of his back. Muscles were separated, ribs were cracked and one was removed to expose his diseased lung. An average four packs of cigarettes a day for forty years had done their inevitable damage and Jones uncovered a dark grey inflexible organ with a large tumour present in the upper lobe. It was self-contained with a well-defined border. The doctor was hopeful the cancer cells hadn't spread. He removed most of the lung and surrounding lymph nodes in a procedure lasting over six hours before finally emerging from theatre to tell Pilar things had gone well, and that he believed Mr Wayne would go on to lead a "fairly normal" life. She smiled gratefully, aware that there had never been anything even close to normal about her husband's life and that there was no way he would ever be able to lead a fairly normal life, "My husband was a rare man! He simply couldn't live as other men did."

At first he lay unconscious and heavily sedated, but as he emerged from the anaesthetic the days became a living nightmare for the rare man concerned. Pilar was terrified by the sight of her heavily bandaged husband who was attached, completely unmoving, to various machines, "He was so pale, vulnerable, and helpless. His breathing was even more ragged than before. He appeared like a small child and there was nothing there that reminded me of my strong husband."

When he finally opened dazed eyes he looked at her and smiled meltingly. She gave his hand a squeeze to reassure him, "Everything's going to be alright, you're going to be fine." He started coughing and continued to do so for the next two days, and instead of being fine he sank steadily. Every time he moved he was in agony, "I was in intensive care and every time I coughed I thought I was going to die. I hadn't expected to wake to so much pain." The cough, worse than ever, tore his sutures, dislodged the drainage tubes and damaged the remaining, already badly injured lung sacs, which burst with the pressure. Air began leaking directly into his chest cavity then out into surrounding body tissue. His head, neck and torso began to swell up as large amounts of air filtered into the layers of his skin, blowing him up like a balloon. He was racked by pain and his neck became so swollen he could hardly breathe.

In one of his brief lucid moments he was told that his brother had also been diagnosed with lung cancer! Duke was devastated. He had long since forgiven Bobby for being the favourite son and as his success grew he had done everything he could for him, persuading people in the industry to give him work and continually bailing him out of financial difficulty. Bobby never had the same drive, steadfastness or determination as his brother, he had no desire to be a film maker either, but Duke loved him anyway and enjoyed having him around.

On September 22 Dr Jones attempted further surgery to repair what was left of Duke's lung, his windpipe and to drain the life threatening oedema. He didn't expect his patient to survive the ordeal. Although Duke hung on grimly he later admitted, "I was more scared the second time around. I was sure I wasn't going to make it. I didn't feel so uptight about having the cancer removed, but the operation for the deem scared me. My windpipe was also twisted. When they had to operate to put things right and sew me up a second time ... well, when I saw the look on Pilar's face I figured, "Jeez, I must be just about all through." I didn't want to die, but what frightened me most was the idea of ending up a helpless invalid, the idea of having people start to feel sympathy for me rather than love ... I couldn't take that. You know, pity isn't for me."

John Ford flew in from Hawaii as soon as he heard how ill he was. He sat at Duke's side for hours and told Pilar, "You know he is like a son to me, I couldn't bear it if anything happened to him." Duke was struggling to breathe and hardly had the energy to speak, but he was happy to lie quietly listening to Pappy talk about the old days, dreaming about the pictures they'd soon be making together, "Coach, I'll be up and on my feet before you know it. I'll never be ready for that rocking chair, they're for the dying ... as soon as I can get out of here I'll be ready to work again."

They never did make another film together, their days as director and star were over. Other things had changed too, but as Pilar watched them talking she little guessed the man she had loved and been married to for over ten years was lost. Duke hadn't died perhaps but the man she had known had gone forever … "He'd reappear for weeks or months at a time, but he'd never be back to stay. The operations changed him forever."

She called him remarkable, but he wasn't superhuman, and at first he was scarcely managing to cling to life. Still, the image wasn't false and Duke possessed many of the same qualities he so often portrayed on screen, his personal endurance proved steadfast and strong during those days and he held onto life with determination, refusing to give up. Eventually the swelling began to subside, he grew stronger and, inevitably, irritable, restless and fretful. Once he had been told the cancer had not spread to the lymph nodes, and had been contained within the tumour, he smiled and said he wanted to go home. He hated being in hospital, hated the lack of privacy and, above all, hated the feeling that he had lost control of his most powerful asset, his body. He hated being touched and prodded by a series of strangers, and particularly disliked being cared for by women other than his wife. He began resisting the doctors and sometimes even threw things at his nurses when they ventured into his room without his permission. He demanded Pilar take over his care. When he emerged from heavy sedation after his second operation he was unprepared for the excruciating pain; he complained he felt as if he'd been cut in half. He couldn't put on his tough act any longer and Pilar was the only person he trusted to see him in such a weakened state. He had always needed her comfort and now, following the trauma of near death and the pain that accompanied his survival, he demanded her full attention and refused to be helped by any one else. He was scared about what was happening to him, scared about his chances of a full recovery, and when he first caught a glimpse of his unbandaged body he was horrified by the full extent of the damage. His worst fears were confirmed when he viewed the raw scar and the deep indentations down his left side where his ribs had once been. He doubted that he would ever work again in an industry that really only valued his powerful body and he needed Pilar's constant reassurance that all would be well. He was modest about his accomplishments, but he had taken pride in his athletic ability. Now he felt robbed of every bit of strength and energy and he hated having to admit he needed help or care.

As soon as Pilar was satisfied that he was getting stronger and was going to survive after all, she felt an urgent need to spend more time at home with the children. Eight year old Aissa, who still followed her dad round the house because she couldn't bear to be separated from him, was missing him badly. She knew he was ill and imagined the worst. The longer he stayed away the more upset she became, and the greater was

Pilar's need to spend some time with her. Each evening, as soon as Duke fell asleep, she raced home to report his progress to the kids. She had usually no sooner walked into the house than the phone rang and one of the nurses told her he was awake again and pleading for her. He had only ever called her "Pilar," he had never used pet names for her, but in hospital when he wanted her he asked for "Mom." She took it as an indication of how weak, helpless and completely dependent on her he felt. He had always done everything for his family, she had never had to do anything except enjoy his company. He had provided everything in their lives, he had been the carer and the doer, always in control. Now suddenly Pilar found herself responsible for his well-being in a shocking role reversal. They both found the situation difficult. He hated being dependant, and she was exhausted by his dependence. The only other time in his life he had ever needed anyone to care for him was, as a child, when he had longed for his mother. She had turned her back on him and he had learned to take care of himself. Fear of further rejection had left him unable to express his own needs, but now he found had no choice and he was angry about it and embarrassed to be lying helplessly in bed. He was irritated when Pilar mentioned he was lucky to be alive. He didn't feel lucky, he felt worse than he had before going into hospital. His cough was agony where it had only been troublesome before. He felt as if he were choking all the time and nothing eased his discomfort, no amount of pain killer seemed to help. On top of everything else, making him so very miserable was the constant demand his body made for another cigarette, he told a nurse, "It's so hard. I feel like I'm being murdered."

Signs of improvement came slowly. The intravenous drips were removed, he began eating solids, his colour returned and he was finally allowed to sit up. He came back to life rapidly as soon as he could take short walks around the hospital. He was at last told he could go home to recuperate if he promised to take things easy and do nothing strenuous for at least six months.

The morning he was discharged he insisted on dressing himself. It took a long time, and just that small act of independence and defiance frustrated him. He was shocked to discover his clothes didn't fit and he worried that people would immediately notice how thin he had become. He buttoned his shirt to the throat to hide the dramatic weight loss. He was pushed into the elevator in a wheel chair but before reaching the ground floor he stood up, "I'm going out of here on my own two feet." His determination didn't surprise his wife but she winced as he pulled himself upright.

He knew the Press would be waiting for him and he dreaded that first meeting. He smiled broadly as the lift doors opened, "Nice of you fellas to pay me a visit." He stood for some time, shaking hands and patiently answering a barrage of questions, "There's nothing wrong with me that getting out of the hospital won't cure. I haven't had a heart attack, and I don't have cancer. I just want to go home." Pilar held his hand tightly, in awe at his power. Only minutes before he had hardly been able to catch his breath, now he stood on legs that trembled with the effort and she knew then just how good an actor he really was. He told the reporters he felt great before finally excusing himself to walk in best John Wayne style to his waiting car, he didn't falter until he got inside. Then he lay back, moaning and asking for the oxygen mask that would never be far from his side again.

Once he got home he was angry and frustrated to find he was expected to go straight back to bed. He had anticipated that as soon as he arrived back in Encino his life would return to normal, that he would miraculously feel better, and be able to breathe freely again. He badly wanted to be up and doing things. When he walked through the door his children raced to hug him. The pain was unbearable and Pilar, watching him intently, knew he was struggling, "He wouldn't stop for a minute, but I could see how fatigued he was. I made him go to bed and as soon as he put his head down he was sound asleep. Even though it was the last place he wanted to be, he was so tired that for those first days he spent his time just staring up at the ceiling, he didn't have the strength to get up again." If the kids were disappointed when he left them to stagger off to bed alone, he was devastated, he feared he would never be whole again, "I never got over the feeling that I was living on borrowed time after that."

He had been shocked when he reached his room to find, not his own giant bed, but another hospital one, with two oxygen tanks standing next to it and he raged, "What's all this crap doing in here? Where's my own bed?" Pilar ran up after him to remind him he had to sleep in a sitting position, "You won't be going back to your own bed for some time Duke."

If he had nothing else he had enormous will power and slowly but surely he battled back from those early disappointments and eventually he was able to give more time to his children. His daughter, who was aware he'd had an operation, kept asking to see his scars. He promised to show her as soon as the bandages were removed and one night he shouted her to come to his room to see. The purple, vivid scar, running right around his body horrified her. She feared he was about to die after all, no one could survive being cut up like that, not even her dad.

Throughout 1964 the health of John Wayne became the hot topic in town and within six weeks of his operation he knew the rumours flying around were worse than the truth. He hadn't told other family members the full extent of his illness, but he had already made the decision to confess everything to his fans; hiding the truth from them felt like betrayal. He wasn't worried about how they would react to the news and he felt secure in their affection but he was terrified that the Hollywood producers would turn against him, afraid he would no longer be able to do the business. The moguls all knew he would die rather than let anyone down, but now he might just die on them. How could he ever deliver the goods again, how could they ever take another chance on him? Even he couldn't provide guarantees, he didn't know himself if he was going to survive. He looked so ill that the story about an old ankle injury just didn't work and he hated the cover up. The lie had seemed small and insignificant to those who gave it out, but he knew it wouldn't be to the Press once they uncovered it, "Maintaining lies consumes too much energy. I have none to waste." He didn't want the studio bosses to see him disabled but he didn't want to be exposed as a liar either. His whole image was based on the assumption that he didn't lie. He had to tell the truth to relieve his discomfort.

The LA Herald Examiner was the first with the news that John Wayne was recovering from the removal of a malignant chest tumour. Mel Shavelson who made *Cast a Giant Shadow* with him, remarked, "The important thing was whether the sheriff would survive the shot in the back. Cancer will never be the same after its encounter with Duke."

Although he had finally got the truth off his chest, it didn't mean he wanted the world to know every detail of his illness. When he first went home to his Encino estate he was still loudly declaring that he would allow no one but Pilar to touch him, he would have no nurses in his home. Being the man he was, the star he was, it was hardly surprising that he didn't trust outsiders to look after him, if anything went wrong with his body the press would be like a pack of blood hounds, willing to pay a fortune for information, they would probably pay a fortune for a story anyway, whether there was any truth in it or not. He felt vulnerable and weak, and he only wanted people around him he could rely on. He didn't want his every yelp of pain reported to the world. Pilar would keep his condition to herself, his doctors wouldn't talk, but he could trust no one else. His body was a valuable property and he didn't want anyone to know the extent of his scars, even though he had allowed his daughter to see them. He didn't want the graphic details or photographs printed on a daily basis. He wanted to maintain some dignity.

He had been told to rest for six months. He was far too impatient to sit still that long, and his powers of recuperation proved remarkable. He lay in bed and lounged around the house, bored and restless, for three weeks before forcing himself to begin the endless pacing up and down as the craving for tobacco worsened. So far he hadn't touched another cigarette. No one ever heard him complain, but Pilar once caught him in an unguarded moment staring down at his empty hand, "I feel like something's missing," he confessed. It was tough and he had nothing to distract him from the overpowering hunger, he was bored with television, bored with reading, bored by enforced inactivity. He could spare no more time recovering, he had to get back out there.

Get a good story out of doors, let in some fresh air and sunlight.
Give the cameraman a chance to photograph something besides
walls and doors.

CHAPTER EIGHT

True Grit on the Road to Durango

"I have to learn to live without a lung and the sooner I get back to work the better. The Sons of Katie Elder is a typical John Wayne Western, so you know I have to be in good health to do it. I didn't get famous doing drawing room comedies."

He told Pilar he was flying to Durango, Mexico, on January 3 1965, to start filming *The Sons of Katie Elder*. Durango was, in every way, a setting fit for a traditional John Wayne western, a high desert 6,500 feet above sea level, with a backdrop of awesome mountains, a land torn apart by deep, dark ravines, each thickly wooded. He still had trouble breathing and yet he planned to go to make his first picture after the removal of his lung to a location where the air admittedly contained no smog but was thin, crisp and dry, and where people with two healthy lungs were shocked by the difficulty of inhaling oxygen. He told his wife, "Every time Pappy started another western they'd say, "There goes senile Ford, out west again." I guess they'll say the same thing about me now, but I don't give a damn. I have to do this."

He felt he had been sitting around too long, and despite Pilar begging him not to go and pleading with him to give himself more time, he was determined, "I have a point to prove ... especially to myself. I need to get The Wound off my mind ... and I can't stand being idle ... I feel like I can't afford to waste even a minute." He told Pilar brusquely, "I've loafed around long enough and I'm going to Durango." He was still often exhausted and he frequently had to go to his room to gulp down oxygen from the green bottles he hid away there and he knew it was going to be really tough in Mexico. That was the whole point, if he could work and survive there he would be alright, he could carry on as though nothing had happened, he would be able to put The Wound out of his mind, it would be healed.

His doctors had told him he needed complete rest for at least six to twelve months, but the speed of his recovery amazed them and his family. Once he was up on his feet they all knew he would be impossible to hold back. He walked further and further every day and his muscle tone soon recovered with the exercise, his colour improved and he regained his huge appetite. Life began to get back to normal and just three short weeks after escaping from the hospital he insisted on going sailing. He drank and fished a little, and began to feel better. It was as he relaxed aboard the *Wild Goose* he first decided to go public about his illness. Those closest to him still advised him to keep it quiet, but on December 29 he called a press conference at his home. He told the gathered reporters the full story and spared no detail. He had decided there was a good, strong image in showing that John Wayne had beaten cancer and coming clean also went some way to putting him back in control of his own life, "I wanted to tell the truth right from the start but all the statements were given out while I was doped up under sedation. By the time I got on my feet, the damage was done ... My advisors all thought it would destroy me, but there's a lot of good image in John Wayne licking cancer — and that's what my doctors tell me … I had the big C, but I've beaten the son of a bitch. Maybe I can give some poor bastard a little hope by being honest. People should talk about it, but the trouble is they're afraid of the word. I want people to know cancer can be licked … I guess I'm a lucky guy, I feel great now. On January 3, I'll go to Durango, Mexico, to start *The Sons of Katie Elder*. It's a typical John Wayne western, so you know I have to be in good health. I didn't get famous doing drawing room comedies." He went on, "My doctors tell me I was saved by early detection. Movie image or no movie image, I think I should tell my story so that other people won't be afraid of cancer and will see a doctor so they can be saved by a check-up." The medical profession were happy he brought cancer out in the open and commended him for speaking out.

The Press announcement turned him into the country's most famous cancer patient and public reaction to the news was extraordinary. Through 1965 he received over one hundred thousand letters from cancer patients and their families, "People have written from all over the world. Their letters are different … warm, personal, like letters from old friends. At first I had almost given in, but I had so many letters from fellow sufferers urging me to fight … and their courage … their hope … well they gave me the strength to fight for myself. Now I want to do something in return." Inevitably, given his nature, he pushed himself too hard in the attempt. He was invited by every cancer society in the country to sit on their board, he found himself in great demand on talk shows and he maintained a steady stream of interviews advising people to get checked out. He was always there supporting and encouraging, telling those who had cancer detected not to give up hope.

Inevitably public adulation and interest in his well-being led to incredible tension and he began to find things a struggle; cancer was rarely far from his thoughts, he had his own regular three-monthly check-ups to get through, and whatever he might say in public, he harboured a constant fear about recurrence, pain, suffering and death. Then suddenly his old friend Jimmy Grant died of lung cancer. He couldn't forget what had happened, nor could he put it behind him, "The cancer societies want me on their campaigns. They're welcome to use my case, but I don't want to make a profession out of this. Before I know it I'll be "The Man Who Had Cancer." Thanks to the Man upstairs and my doctor I've got my life back and I want to go on living — that's the whole point." He didn't want to dwell on the past, but found himself continually called back as his health became a constant talking point. He tired of it and became more determined to get on with making the next film.

Privately his doctors were not only amazed by his survival but by the fact that he was seriously planning to continue making a living riding horses at high altitude, fighting and doing his own stunts, and that he continued swilling a fifth of a bottle of tequila a day. They were inundated by letters from people suffering from lung cancer requesting John Wayne's operation — they had seen him interviewed on TV and marvelled at how well he looked. Harassed doctors had to explain they were just NOT John Wayne, and they couldn't make John Waynes of them. Biographer, Maurice Zolotow, wrote that he appeared to be supernormal; how else could he have gone on to make films at fifty seven, possessed of only one lung, always on location, many in far away places, and requiring the greatest physical effort, "He could do it for he exists on another plane."

Duke was now trapped in the legend and, no matter the cost, he found he had no choice but to carry on playing the part of John Wayne. It was a virtuoso performance, and whilst he might have existed on another plane to devoted observers, he was in fact an invalid who had difficulty walking, who still coughed heavily, and who frequently needed oxygen. He bought a golf cart to use around the grounds of his home so he could still go outside with his children. He was not prepared for outsiders to know the full extent of his disability, he only told them what he wanted them to know.

Apart from his physical weakness he also kept the severe and debilitating depression, another legacy of the operations and illness, well hidden. He had suffered several bouts of depression in his life but things took a drastic turn for the worse before he finally set out for Durango. He was emotionally drained and he wrapped himself in dark and sombre thoughts and refused to let anyone in to help, even the wife who had devoted herself to his recovery, and who was hurt now to be shut out. Duke knew she was angry with him but felt that, having given every ounce of strength to surviving, it was unfair of her to expect more from him. He didn't want to talk to her about how he felt and he resented her probing his deepest wounds. He wanted to forget what had happened, wanted to feel strong again and, more than anything else, he wanted to be the man he had been before. Deep in his heart he already knew he never would be. The knowledge terrified him and left him quick to flare up, and they fell to arguing again at the time he most needed peace.

He told her he believed the only way forward was to put it all behind them, to make a new start in a new home far away from the sad memories, close to his beloved ocean, and of course, to get back to work as soon as he could. He wanted to start enjoying life again. Pilar had her own thoughts about what he should be doing to get better but his plan for survival included getting back on a horse to fulfil promises made long ago, in a different life. Pilar said, "I was furious with him. He was in such agony but he simply couldn't stop." He didn't need her to tell him he was being stupid, that he must be out of his mind to go back, painfully reminding him, as though he needed to be told, that he could hardly walk, that their children needed him, and that he would be killing himself if he went off to Durango. He was angry at his own weakness and even more angry with her for drawing attention to it. He ignored the pain and the weakness and he ignored Pilar's entreaties; just fourteen weeks after his two operations he was back at work!

Somehow his miraculous survival created exactly the new image he had been searching for before disaster struck. Hal Wallis, the producer of Katie Elder, said, "In real life he'd now battled a deadly foe, beaten the odds and emerged victorious. Duke acted his part to perfection and his courage and fighting spirit made him an even greater hero than he'd ever been on screen. His fans were awed and he won a host of converts."

He invited the Press to watch his comeback. His film sets had always been open and, no matter how desolate or isolated the location, they never failed to show up to watch Duke at work in his natural element. This time they turned out in droves to witness the efforts of a fifty seven year old who had lost forty pounds, whose right shoulder was immobile, who still suffered the painful effects of the ruptured disc in his spine, a man with only one lung and a tremendously painful fresh scar running around his left side, and on top of that, a man going through the agony of tobacco withdrawal.

Making *The Sons of Katie Elder* had become vitally important to that man, but his performance before the cameras of the Press was equally so. Old friend Henry Hathaway was directing the picture and he also took control and managed Duke's re-entry into the public eye. He was sure that hard work was the key to ultimate recovery, "Don't baby yourself," he told him, "or you'll become a psychological cripple. The way to get over what you've been through is to forget it ever happened and get on with your life." It seemed like good advice from a fellow survivor of cancer and was exactly what Duke wanted to hear, and the words he heard from Hathaway allowed him to ignore his wife's stern warnings, "Aw, what does she know?"

On the flight down to Durango he had to use the oxygen mask constantly, and when he emerged from the plane he was unable to catch his breath in air that was too thin for normally healthy people. He had ignored Pilar to his cost and was now forced to concede her wisdom, "I guess she was right all along." He shouldn't have gone until he was fully recovered and now he was about to fall flat on his face in front of the world's gathered Press. Every painful movement let him know that he should have heeded her. His whole left side and arm ached unbearably, and the scar felt raw and stingingly new. Still, he was there, face to face with dozens of reporters and photographers who were waiting to greet his return. He knew they were also there to check out his every step, every wince of pain and every wheezy breath he drew. When he had first walked away from Encino he had been determined that everything would go to plan, but as he stepped from the plane into the blast of flash bulbs exploding in his face he was hit by the unexpectedly frosty atmosphere of high altitude. He turned deathly white and the photographers caught his expression which was later described on every front page as "haggard." The world wanted to know if he could still ride, fight and rid the world of bad man, if he was still John Wayne. If he faltered in front of the media men now, the career he had built on the foundation of endurance and heroism in the face of pain, was over. Somehow, driven by that knowledge, he managed to stay on his feet and get through his initial arrival at Durango.

He was equally determined to get through the film, however tough things got, and Hathaway, who knew how important it was for the star to survive the ordeal, planned being anything but gentle with him. The director was well aware as soon as he saw Duke that he had made the effort too early, but now he was there he had to get through it or he would never try again and he would be finished. He should have been at home in bed, heeding his doctors, instead he was working in freezing conditions and fighting for his life against an increasing feeling of weakness, with the press watching his every faltering step. Their reports went not only into the entertainment pages, they hit the front pages too, his survival was big news, but if he died in Durango it would be even bigger news.

When he first arrived in Mexico he had a bad cold and kept his oxygen close at all times, but he felt happy to be back doing what he did best and was relieved to have found an outlet for the pressure that had been building up inside ever since his escape from hospital. He was particularly pleased to be working with Dean Martin again. Martin had the knack of making him laugh, he shared his zest for living, his love of alcohol and films, and he helped Hathaway bring Duke back to life. They spent most of their evenings drinking and singing their hearts out and Martin commented, "Anyone else would have laid around feeling sorry for themselves. But he just doesn't know how to be sick … He's recuperating the hard way."

Duke believed in what he was doing; if he hadn't been sure of himself, he would never have invited the Press to witness his comeback, "The operation hasn't impeded anything except that I get short of breath quickly, particularly here at higher altitude, that slows me down. I still intend doing all my own fights and all that stuff. I'd probably do a bit more if I had more wind. I still do more than my share. Nobody else does anything more than I do, whether they're young or old. I don't have to assert my virility. I think my career has shown I'm not exactly a pantywaist. But I do take pride in my work, even to the point of being the first on the set in the morning. I'm a professional." Wallis said, "In Durango he amazed me. He showed no sign of weakness. He did all his own riding. He roped steers and did the fight scenes without a double."

And he was desperately trying to enjoy himself. He wanted to have some fun and forget the horrors of the last months. He laughed and joked with everyone on set, for long periods he even managed to suppress the cough, but those who knew him best saw the changes and noticed the distant look and the forced smile; Duke might be back in the saddle where he belonged, but he was not the same as before. There were fleeting moments when he couldn't keep the act up, times when he was too tired to do anything but sprawl out on his bed, and times when the mask slipped. But his future happiness depended on how things went in Durango and he put every ounce of his energy into making *Katie Elder*.

His distinctive voice took on a strange cragginess in the thin air. He couldn't sit his horse properly and he was well aware he looked awkward and uncomfortable rather than tall in the saddle as in the past. Every movement was agony but Hathaway refused to pity him or make any allowances. He had always been hard on his crews and stars and he knew Duke would soon realise if he was given any special treatment, so he resorted to Ford's tactics of being especially tough on him. Perhaps he hadn't been fair, but he believed it was the best way to get Duke through what he faced. The film was full of action and Duke had known when he first accepted the part that he would be required to perform several difficult stunts, of course he hadn't been ill then, but he had given Hathaway his word and now, however bad he felt he had to go through with things. Many of the shots could have been given to a double, but neither man had any intention of using one for even the toughest scenes, despite the fact that Duke had a long history of getting injured doing his own stunts. He never complained about his aches and pains but he did find one sequence particularly rugged. He had to jump off a wagon into an icy river whilst manacled to another actor and carry out a long gun battle in wet clothes from under a bridge. Chuck Roberson, Duke's stunt double, pleaded with Hathaway to use him, he saw no sense in killing the star, but the director refused every entreaty. He wouldn't even permit him to wear a wet suit under his costume like the rest of the cast, "You're too fat Duke and it will be noticed." Poor Duke was occasionally heard laughing feebly as he pretended all was well in his world, and as he tried to prove, perhaps to himself, that he was still the man he had always been. He did everything in his power for Hathaway but it was also an attempt to forget what had happened, it was his own way of getting his life back on course. It took five cruel days to produce shots that satisfied Hathaway but Duke managed to joke with newsmen who caught him warming up after one icy take with a drink of what locals called *la gaselina*, a 120 proof liquid, "Goddamn! I'm the stuff men are made of!" They watched in awe as he threw his head back and, closing steel blue eyes, shuddered against the cold. He was standing proudly bare-chested, his spare tyre exposed, displaying his scars for all the world to see and photograph, "That's it boys, that's where they cut me up to get the Big C." It wasn't his style to talk openly about what had happened to him, but they had presented him with a golden opportunity, and they could do him and other cancer sufferers a service, "I decided that if I continued saying something about cancer, showed them what had happened to me, it might stop some poor slob putting a gun in his mouth." He told the gathered pressmen the very things he refused to talk to Pilar about, showing the livid scars he would rather have kept covered, so others might benefit, but also to prove the point, "I'm the stuff men are made of!" The story they wrote after his dazzling display in Durango made him the stuff of legend. When they caught him in that one off-guard moment he was quick to seize the chance, convinced his future depended on them and the image they printed. Only a few days later a photographer took a picture of him gasping and struggling to breathe as he held his oxygen mask to his face. Duke exploded with rage and furiously demanded the film. He knew the instant he blew up that his reaction was a big mistake, the last thing he had wanted was to appear desperate. After cooling down, he wandered over to the motel dining room where the crew and press were gathered. He approached the group of photographers and said in a loud voice so everyone could hear, "I'm a grown man. I ought to be able to control myself better than I did today. I'm sorry. I know I came back too early, but I had to. I can't stand being idle. I have to work." Hathaway offered his own explanation for Duke's unusual behaviour, "It knocked him to be sick. He suddenly found out he was vulnerable. The humiliation has been the hardest thing for him to recover from. It's not his image that's been hurt, it's his pride."

Everything had been planned for his comfort in Durango, he had his own make-up man, his own trainer to massage aching muscles with a foul smelling oil, causing Hathaway to joke, "Old actors don't die, they just smell that way!" No one dared smoke around him, though he never asked anyone not to. He had an unlimited supply of cough drops, chewing gum, and he cleaned Durango out of his favourite peppermint wafers. Then, as soon as he stepped back in front of the camera, his mood brightened perceptibly. He was back in control and able to push every worry about his physical condition to the back of his mind, it was business as usual.

Pilar hadn't gone to Durango but she was so worried about him that, two weeks into production, she flew down to join him. To the Press he appeared much as he always had, "What went into his mouth might be different, but what came out wasn't noticeably so." The prying eyes missed the odd grimace of pain when he pulled himself into the saddle, but his wife knew he was far from well, far from his best, and she knew he would push himself too hard, knew he was likely to die giving this performance. Even so, when she arrived in Mexico she was shocked by his appearance. His condition had deteriorated rapidly since she had kissed him goodbye in Encino and he had obviously not kept his promise to look after himself. At first he was overjoyed to see her, grateful she was there to support him through his toughest ever assignment. Then she began nagging him, "I trusted you to do the right thing. This can't be right Duke. I've never doubted you or your ability until now. You're being crazy. You're too old and ill to be staying in a seedy hotel room with bottles of oxygen for company. Nothing can be worth what you are doing to yourself, to me and the children. I just want you alive and home, safe with us. Your image isn't worth dying for." It was the last thing he wanted to hear, he needed tender words of love and devotion, he wanted her strength to lean on. He didn't want her to remind him about his weakness again, he wanted reassurance that he was still the man he had always been, the same father, lover, and most importantly, the same star he had been. He had gone to Durango to prove that and he snapped, "Mind your own business, you take care of the children and I'll make the movies." She didn't think the image was worth dying for, to him it was everything. Having a wife and children he idolised and a film star's lifestyle had never been enough for him. He had to find a way to get his life back, or die looking.

Duke and Pilar clashed again over a scene Hathaway was planning where he had to be pulled into a frozen lake and then stand fighting in the water for three or four minutes, soaked to the skin. Once again no double was to be used and he was determined to go through with it. Pilar refused to watch him film the scene, but three year old Ethan stayed on set with Mary St John to watch his dad. Hathaway, not wanting to risk more than one take, had multiple cameras set up to capture the action from every angle. Thick ice had to be broken from the lake's surface before Duke could be pulled into the water by his three co-stars; he later admitted sheepishly that he had been crazy, the water was much colder than he had anticipated, "My body went numb immediately, I landed in the water badly and couldn't catch my breath as I surfaced. I felt panicked when I hit the air." Somehow he managed to carry on, determined to finish the scene. He heard a frightened scream in the distance, but had no idea it was Ethan, crying "Daddy" in terror. Hathaway allowed the action to continue even though he knew the boy's scream had been picked up by the microphones. He knew Duke wouldn't be able to get through a second take, and well remembered his fury after the fire scene in *Circus World*. When he finally clambered out of the lake his body was shaking uncontrollably, he was gasping for air and his mouth was turning blue as his good lung started to collapse. He was aware of the press corps advancing toward him. This was exactly what they had come to see; not his success, not his effort, not his recovery, they had come to see him die! He thought he might be about to oblige them, and then, Hathaway and Martin were at his side, pushing the photographers away. Oxygen was produced, a blanket was thrown around his shoulders, and the crisis passed quickly.

Mary, watching the scene, holding Ethan's hand, said, "I had always thought of Duke as indestructible, but I guess lung cancer had been something out of his control. He was in the greatest pain after they cut it out, there was no way he could avoid it, every time he coughed or moved. His recovery was slow and painful. When he decided to carry on making the film he told me, "I've got to learn to live without that lung, the sooner I start the better." Making *Katie Elder* was just terrible for him. With normal lungs in good condition it was hard to breathe. When they dragged him into that icy water what they wanted of course was to catch Mr Wayne's expression, that was why no double could be used. They did the scene but it nearly killed him, he came up gasping and it was caught on camera, and they kept it in, they never cut that!" Mary understood his determination better than anyone, "I watched him strive over so many years, and I knew that nothing would stop him, no matter how badly he hurt. He had to prove himself to the people around him, the people that mattered."

Once the director wrapped everything up there was nothing left for Duke to do but go home and wait to see if the public would accept him, wait to see if the moguls would offer him any more parts. And in the meantime he planned to get back into shape, to work even harder after a reporter irritated him by commenting on his spare tyre, "I admit I'm balding, I admit I got a tyre around my middle. What man of 57 doesn't?

Big news!" He began lifting weights and tried to go back to scuba diving and swimming but found it difficult and frustrating to exercise at all. When he went diving he couldn't inhale enough oxygen from his tank to enable him to go very deep and he was forced to re-surface after only a few minutes. He ripped off his mask and screamed his fury, "Goddammit! I'll never have any more fun."

By the time *The Sons of Katie Elder* premiered in August 1965 America was under the cloud of Vietnam and its people were living in a changing, threatening society. Many were desperate for their old heroes, symbols of their traditions, and they were longing to see John Wayne back in the saddle. He offered comfort and protection from the fears of their normal lives. They loved *Katie Elder*, the Duke was safely back in a world where there were no doubts or uncertainty, where men could make their own rules and live by them. He wasn't finished, he was only just starting out.

At home too, he was looking for a new start. Even before going off to Durango he had told Pilar he hated living in Encino. His bedroom with the green bottles and austere bed reminded him of his ordeal and, with so many of his friends gone, he no longer saw any reason to stay so close to Hollywood. Pilar often found him forlornly wandering round the house or staring sadly into a room, haunted by the ghosts he saw there. When the estate was broken into by a fan he decided the time had come to get out. He saw it as a positive move, the final part of his recovery and he was sure that getting closer to the ocean would do him good. Pilar was weary of Los Angeles and the movie colony herself, tired of his world and the unfair demands it made on every member of the Wayne family. Together they chose Newport, where he already moored his boat, as the ideal place to go to.

They talked about moving for months, but two days before Christmas 1964 he walked in and stunned Pilar, announcing he had sold the estate to Walt Disney's daughter. His sudden and unexpected action, taken without a word to her, reduced her to heartbroken tears. He didn't have a clue why she was so upset; she had already agreed she wanted to move, he never dreamed of consulting her about accepting a good offer for the property. She was angry about his high-handed action, upset that she seemed to have no identity of her own, she was Mrs John Wayne and he made every decision in their lives. She had allowed him to dominate her life, now the worm was about to turn, things had to change. She was swift in exacting her revenge. When he was away filming in Durango, she bought a new family home in Newport Beach, without even telling him about the purchase. She expected fireworks from him when she confessed but he took her news calmly enough, apparently happy about relinquishing some responsibility, "I've always liked Newport Beach. I'll be happy there if you are." Illness had definitely changed him and, Pilar thought, in some ways for the better.

Whilst he had accepted the house purchase, Pilar had become increasingly worried about the other changes she noticed in him. He was less open, more withdrawn and his temper, always fiery, became almost uncontrolled as his frustration with life and death built up. Her concern led her to discuss his outbursts with his doctor who explained that patients who had suffered as he had, sometimes did undergo a complete change of personality. Whatever the cause, she found the changes hard to swallow, "Before the operations he was the strongest, kindest and most loving man I had ever known, with the sweetest, gentlest disposition." When he left hospital he was unreasonably angry and irritable, and their warm relationship was badly affected. Still, whilst the problems between them grew, they were only part of a complex web of emotional and personal difficulties that beset the lonely Duke.

The children were growing up, bringing all the trauma of adolescence into his life. They no longer wanted to spend all their free time on location with him, they saw no great privilege in being dragged halfway round the world to sit in a dusty motel waiting for him to appear. They wanted to stay home with their friends, they wanted to play at the beach, they wanted to be like other children, and Pilar sided with them, "I had no desire to watch him punishing himself, always trying to prove himself, knowing he would fly into a rage the moment I made any comment." During one of their more fraught moments she screamed at him, "What's the matter with you? Have you lost your mind as well as your lung?" He stared at her, stunned, not understanding the woman in front of him, a woman who had never questioned him throughout ten years of marriage, and he was suddenly scared. He felt a lot older than her. He was sick and struggling. He wanted the old Pilar back, he wanted the girl who haunted his dreams, not this woman who had become a stranger to him. It hit him hard that his adored wife seemed lost to him when he needed her most. In a six month period he had battled cancer, sold his home and made another film. During those months life had been chaotic for the whole family but Pilar struggled the most and she felt she had undergone an ordeal as great as his own. She thought he should have been more tolerant of her needs. She hoped that in time he would revert to being his old loving self and that their lives would settle down as he began to accept the many changes he faced after moving to Newport. She was whistling in the wind and whilst she and the children settled in and soon made new friends, he felt more and more isolated there. Pilar began building her new independent, adult identity once she escaped the pressure of Hollywood. She took up tennis, launched her own business, the Fernleaf Café, and she left the Roman Catholic Church to convert to Christian Science. She all but excluded him from her new life and, in so doing, she destroyed all his hopes for the future. That he should survive cancer and save his career after such a mighty struggle, only to find he had lost his most prized possession at the last moment seemed ironic, and entirely typical.

Newport Beach, that rich, upper-class area of Orange County, should have been the perfect home for John Wayne, and he certainly loved the new house that Pilar had chosen on Bayshore Drive. It was less private than the Encino estate, but his new patio faced the ocean, providing a perfect view of Balboa Island out across the bay. He sat out there whenever he could, often for hours at a time, watching the sea and the boats sail past the end of his garden. The stretch of water soon became a favourite haunt for tourists but they never troubled him, and he often waved happily for their cameras and shouted out hearty greetings to passing fans. He should have felt contentment, instead he was full of all the old familiar restlessness.

Alterations to the house had started and he had always enjoyed big remodelling projects before. Pilar was sure everything would be OK between them once he became involved in her plans. She was excited about the house and he joined in, trying his best to be who she wanted him to be. He said nothing about his feelings but nonetheless he feared for their future, he was scared he had already lost her, despite his best efforts. When he returned from filming *Katie Elder* he hardly ventured away from her side, he huddled close and listened to her ideas for his future, "I want you to take life a little easier Duke." He did what he could because he wanted to keep her. He sat still as long as possible although inevitably, on occasion, his restlessness broke through. Pilar expected it of him and tolerated the nervous tension because it was so much a part of his character. Still, it pleased her to see him relaxing out on the patio instead of pacing fretfully around it. He liked to please her and went to great lengths in his effort to hold onto his prize, even agreeing to attend a few dinner parties in Newport with her. In his heart he knew the strained peace wouldn't last, it was too difficult for him to sit around the house, and although he had signed no new contracts he could sense the urge to work welling up inside, even if his wife failed to spot it. He began exhibiting all the signs of a caged animal with increasingly frequent outbursts of frustration and temper; Pilar admitted, "Almost dying hadn't altered his priorities." And they both stared at defeat. Even if the man she had loved had gone forever, this man's need to work had not diminished with him.

There was no way he could take things easy whatever else had changed for him. And things were different; his voice had altered, seeming harsher than before, friends noticed the far away look in his eyes, he was more withdrawn, more guarded. The changes were hardly surprising, it would have been more surprising if he had emerged unscathed. Pilar didn't much like the man who had survived, and she couldn't understand the anger that burned in him; he had nearly died, but he had recovered, why was he still so bitter? Many years later, when it was too late for them, she came to realise that he had been angry with himself, not her, unable to forgive himself for not being the superman everyone expected him to be. His brush with death had forced him to face the fact that he was only human, and that he shared all humanity's frailties. His temper was only one of his many weaknesses and in 1965 Pilar was not willing to put up with them. She wanted her husband back whole, the way he'd been, but in fact she wanted more than that, she wanted to develop her own identity, so recently discovered. She had been happy to play the role of Mrs John Wayne whilst he remained happy and strong, but now, on top of his acquired aggression, she found his sadness and weakness a huge strain. He wasn't fun anymore and she was dissatisfied with the position she held in his life. Just as he was restless and quick tempered, Pilar was unhappy and distressed by the way things were turning out. She felt cheated and directed the displeasure she felt with the man he had become against his most treasured possession, *The Wild Goose*. She began skipping the sailing trips whenever she could and when she did go with him they argued all the time. He was once overheard angrily whispering, "Well, you don't have to make it so godddamn obvious to everyone that you want a divorce." She moaned at him, "You don't know how to treat a woman." He just moaned. He had heard the complaint so many times before, he accepted the truth of it. Each of his wives had felt deserted by the man they loved, and he felt equally let down, first by Josie, then Chata and now by his adored Pilar.

When she refused to go on location with him, refused to sail with him and went out playing tennis or to church instead, he took it as a sign of disloyalty rather than recognising her unhappiness. He loved her but took the changes he saw as lack of interest in him. He was filled with dread, afraid she was about to leave him for a younger, healthier man, and now he was no longer fit, the age gap seemed to make a big difference to their marriage. He assumed her coolness meant he no longer satisfied her. The insecurity he felt was shown in small and unusual ways; he had never been vain but he began wearing his toupee whenever she was around and when she asked him to stop smoking the occasional thin cigars he had taken to, he gave them up straight away. He didn't know what she wanted from him, but he was sure she was slipping out of his grasp, "Damn it, I bend over backwards to please her, but no matter what I do, she just doesn't seem to care anymore. I really don't know what the hell to do." He had been the one who had suffered the ravages of cancer but she had emerged the more damaged and he didn't know how to make her feel better. They blamed each other and neither understood why they were being driven apart. They both wanted things back the way they had once been but could do nothing about the changes that had occurred in their developing personalities. The very things they had each loved in the other had evaporated, they were left little more than strangers. They both stubbornly refused to give up hope and when Pilar converted to Christian Science she managed to persuade him to go to church with her. She wanted him to see for himself why she had become so deeply involved in religion. He went with her but sat fidgeting throughout the service, just as he had at his mother's side a lifetime away, and when he finally escaped the torture he moaned, "I can't sit still that long Pilar!" She knew he hadn't heard a thing, nothing had reached him, he was far too strong minded to need to go to church, "I believe in God. I don't need to go to church to prove it or to hold a conversation with The Man Upstairs." Church was off the agenda.

He missed the old Pilar but still enjoyed playing with his children when they consented to go sailing with him. He turned to them for the excuse he needed to have fun, he enjoyed playing Monopoly or cards with them, and was happy to spend an entire day fishing off the back of the boat with Ethan and Marisa. Not too far below the surface he had retained something of the child about him and the skipper of *The Wild Goose*, Bert Minshal, said, "His enthusiasms were big and his pleasures many. The simplest things gave him the greatest amusement." He kept live anchovies for bait in a salt water tank on the deck and he could often be seen with his arm in the tank manoeuvring a rubber shark in a Jaws-like attack on the tiny fish, laughing helplessly. He also enjoyed swimming with his children and he taught them all a healthy respect for the sea. In some ways he taught them too well; for years they refused to enter the water unless he led the way, working on the theory that if there were sharks around they would go after him first. When he entered the water he glided around, completely submerged for some time, then broke surface to bellow at the top of his voice, "Jeeezzusss Christ!!!! It's COLD!" The kids giggled at the ritual before diving in to show their frail father how warm it really was. His general comment, "You kids are too tough for me," left everyone laughing before they began their favourite game, trying their best to drown him. They scrambled onto his shoulders and pushed his bald head under as each of them endeavoured to become king of the floating mountain. Frequently he laughed so much he nearly did drown as he choked on a lung-full of salt water. He rigged a make-shift diving board to the bow of *The Goose* and all the crew and family took it in turns to show off. One day when the skipper stepped onto the board in front of his boss, there was a loud crack as it snapped under his feet, sending him splashing into the water in an undignified heap. When he surfaced it was to the roar of Duke's laughter, "Gee, Bert! I wish *I* could do that."

Bert agreed that the changes in him were obvious after 1964, "He was more volatile with a temper quick to erupt," but he added, "He was just as good natured as before, still full of fun. He wasn't one to hold grudges. He could and did blow up with a fury that was sometimes surprising ... but once he calmed down it was as if someone had pulled the burning fuse from a bundle of dynamite."

Pilar rarely went along to join in the fun. Duke missed her company badly, but in spite of the difficulties in his personal life, surviving the onslaught of a sure-fire killer had turned him into a legend of mythic proportion. He had been a high-flying Hollywood star for many years, but his stardom accelerated rapidly into superstardom as the story unfolded. As the image grew and burned more brightly, those closest to him disappeared deeper into the shadow he cast and were left far behind as he was turned into an icon by the media. All seven of his children were aware he was special, they had always understood that the time he could give them was limited, but now even those times became fewer as public demand for him grew. His wife and children had difficulty coming to terms with this super-being who had little in common with the husband and father they had known before cancer struck. John Wayne had survived to ride the range stronger, more powerful than ever, but the last remnants of Marion Morrison seemed to have been lost to those who cared about him most.

His family might have resented his superstardom, but he resented it more deeply himself, he felt isolated in it and he suffered the consequences as profoundly as they did. At least they had each other, he had no one to turn to, no one to share his feelings or his fears with. Who but another super-icon could possibly understand what he was going through then? He had left Hollywood to move to the beach and he no longer had easy access to the clubs or bars where he might have been able to talk things over with Sinatra or Martin. All his closest friends were gone and since moving to Newport he had made few new ones, and none that were involved in the movie industry or were likely to understand. He was more lonely than ever at a time the whole world seemed to adore him and longed to associate themselves with his strength and were clamouring to see his powerful image. Again, the irony of his situation wasn't lost on him.

As he outpaced his family his options in life seemed to be reduced. He was obsessed with the business of making films and from now on he turned his full attention to the fans and they got the best of him, he had little left for anyone else. He dedicated himself to them and remained unswerving in his loyalty. In return, his new persona won their committed devotion and was carried to new heights and also to its conclusion. He hadn't purposely created it, all he had done was manage to live through a terrible ordeal and the new John Wayne was very much the invention of those members of the Press who had gone down to Durango to watch *Katie Elder* being made. His legion of fans perceived him as tougher than before, more courageous, more enduring. Duke laughed cynically, here they were talking about him as though he was immortal, when his illness had made him all too aware of his own mortality, they had turned him into an icon at the very time he had been forced to acknowledge his own humanity.

He had been sitting around worrying about things for too long and it was getting him nowhere. He shook himself, he needed a familiar distraction, it was time for movie action. Having somehow managed to survive the trauma of *Katie Elder*, he was feeling stronger and when old friend Howard Hawks offered him another chance he jumped at *El Dorado*, his third film of 1965. At first glance it was just another "John Wayne" but it went far beyond that, telling a tale of male friendship, disability and growing old. McLeod, Duke's adversary in the film, though on the wrong side of the law, is an idealist and believes in the professional honour of the gunfighter. Duke as Thornton, another gunfighter, knows there is no such things as professional honour for a gun man, there is only pain, suffering and eventually, death. He has no illusions. His friend, the sheriff is a drunk, his girlfriend has a damaged reputation, his own life is full of pain after being shot in the back. His gun hand is often paralysed, the result of the bullet still lodged near his spine. The lives of Thornton and the sheriff are threatened, and their only hope is to work together. Both men are experienced and survive only because they are willing to use any dirty trick available in the fight. *El Dorado* ends with the two friends limping down the street together, both wounded, both alive. The film meant everything to Duke whose own goals were much the same; getting his work done anyway he could, and staying alive to fight another day. And audiences loved it. Within a year it had taken $12 million.

After his financial disaster with Bo Roos, Duke needed a new business manager. He didn't have the time or the inclination to sort the mess out for himself, but he did need someone he could trust; if possible, a member of his own family, to act on his behalf. He targeted son-in-law Donald La Cava, husband of his daughter, Toni. La Cava already worked at Batjac and intended going into production, but Duke decided he was the ideal man for the job, and he put him in charge of his money instead. He had no financial background and Duke had no high hopes of him, he just wanted someone he trusted looking after his interests, "I don't expect you to make money. Just be dammed sure you don't lose any more."

He turned his attention away from illness and loneliness to concentrate on rebuilding his collapsed fortune. He had lost almost everything he had ever earned and was still in serious financial difficulty. He knew the only way to recover his position was through hard work and during 1965 and 1966 he turned out a high number of films, all of which made a lot of money. He personally commanded $1million per picture plus a percentage of profit and he felt he was finally earning his just rewards. He believed that between his hard work and La Cava's careful banking things should begin to look up.

In October 1966 he flew to Dallas with Pilar to do some early Christmas shopping. On the journey he scanned a variety of catalogues for ideas. He loved to shop, and it was often the arrival of a new store catalogue that triggered a wild spree. He had been fascinated by them since he was a small boy, "When I was young I used to dream that one day I'd have enough money to order everything in the catalogue. They became an obsession with me." As an adult he continued to enjoy pouring over their pages, deep in thought, marking off anything he fancied or noting down ideas for gifts. Once his choices had been made he usually asked Mary to order the things and send off his money. He rarely bought anything for himself, but he selected an endless stream of gadgets, novelties, paperweights, nautical equipment, kitchen items, shoe racks, flashlights, anything that caught his fancy. He sent away for so much that unopened boxes had to be piled high, stored in warehouses on the dock. The packages remained stacked there until he gave them away, usually to members of his crew or staff. Many of them disappeared, but he never cared, the fun was in searching the catalogue in the knowledge that now he could have whatever he wanted. Once he had paid the cheque he lost all interest in his purchases.

In Dallas he and Pilar spent thousands of dollars. They enjoyed wandering through the stores looking at furniture, smelling perfumes, handling accessories. Duke never took armed guards along as other stars did, he simply ambled round smiling, and hardly noticed the amazed stares of other shoppers. He rarely got into conversations but was happy to wish everyone "Good day," or "Howdy," as he stood in line to pay for his goods just like a regular human being. Pilar said, "He was actually very good at shopping. He could accurately judge the sizes of friends and children and he unfailingly chose colours that suited them." He swamped his acquaintances with gifts and anyone who got a surprise package from some strange foreign destination would be right to assume it was from him, they would know he had been out shopping and thinking about them. Duke went home from Dallas having spent well over thirty thousand dollars.

Throughout November the bills piled up in La Cava's office. Eventually he drove over to see his father-in-law, "How could you spend so much money? You don't have that kind of money. How am I supposed to pay these?" Duke replied stonily, "There goddam well better be money to pay them. I've turned over millions of dollars to you ... there goddam well better be enough." His blood froze the instant he saw La Cava's face, the scene was all too familiar, he had been down this same road before. Unpaid bills had first alerted him to Roos' failure, surely his own family couldn't have done that to him again? He was rocked to his foundations, but there certainly wasn't enough money in the bank to pay October's bills. He had slaved his guts out after his operations to restore his finances, he had earned millions since 1964, yet here he was once again, with nothing left. LaCava was fired on the spot, but in fact detailed investigation showed things were not as bad this time as before, and his investments at least were all doing fine. All the profits he'd made over the last few years had been ploughed into his successful Arizona cotton farm, and he wasn't in the red, he simply had no cash available to pay for the shopping binge. He would just have to keep on working to pay these bills, and in some ways the disaster gave him just the excuse he needed to carry on doing what he wanted to do anyway.

Duke had made one new friend in Newport. Frosty, a white Samoyed, had replaced Blackie in his affections after the death of the little dachshund. He missed him almost as much as he missed all his other lost friends, but even as a puppy, Frosty had Duke just where he wanted him, and knew exactly how to get his own way. Early every morning as the boss took his breakfast alone on the patio, Frosty growled and nipped his ankles until he picked him up, sat him at the table and served him coffee and scraps of bacon. Duke enjoyed the company of dogs and at one time kept four at his Bayshore house, though he complained, "The whole bunch couldn't corner a rat if each was armed with a Colt .45." Visitors had to fight their way through a tail-wagging, slobbering welcoming committee. He loved all of them, even though his gardeners and visitors generally didn't. The grounds of his home were littered with the remains of his newspapers lying in chewed-up soggy heaps, the bushes and shrubs were torn up and piles of waste were left all over the lawn. Duke laughed when welcoming guests, "Christ, watch where you walk, I've seen horses that crap less than those dogs." He was often found gazing longingly into his neighbour's perfectly groomed grounds muttering, "Makes mine look like a goddamn jungle. Still, I like the more natural look!"

He was still not particularly comfortable in his new surroundings and he continued to miss the people who had shared his work and his life for so long. Until they moved to Newport his free time was dictated by his career, he read scripts, attended meetings, spent hours with John Ford or any other director or producer who happened to be in town. In Newport he felt torn out of the only life he had ever known or wanted.

He had gone to Newport to be close to his beloved ocean and now it and *The Wild Goose* remained his best escape from the monotony that plagued him. He was free to be himself there, could hide from prying eyes and cameras, and he didn't have to put on the John Wayne act out at sea. He could allow his increasingly fat stomach to protrude out of an open shirt, he could leave the hairpiece on the side, and drink tequila until it poured out of his ears. He delighted in sitting with his crew, trading stories with the men who had been with him the longest, mostly he enjoyed just listening to them. When Pilar didn't sail with them the stories became X-rated.

And she went with him less and less frequently, telling him his beautiful minesweeper felt like a prison to her. Now when Pilar took herself off to play tennis he wandered down to the port on his own, pottered around, made suggestions for improvements to his boat, planned overhauls, or sat talking with other boat owners, but he remained sad and empty without her by his side.

Then, in the late sixties, he again turned to politics, taking some pleasure immersing himself in some gentle activity. He said politics and politicians came way down his list of priorities, but in fact he had more than a passing interest in both. He steadfastly refused all offers of public office in the choicest of terms, but on the other hand, he was always willing to give his wholehearted backing to any candidate, either of the Left or Right, who took his fancy. For a man with no interest he dedicated many hours to writing long complex letters to various politicians, offering suggestions for their campaigns. He wasn't a man to mince words or gestures, an attribute that frequently plunged him into hot and deep water, now he found himself out of step with American popular culture and attitudes. Many felt his patriotism maudlin, and he acquired the label "reactionary." Whilst he remained a champion to some, people became afraid to claim the dinosaur as their own. The instant he started another flirtation with politics he again found critics everywhere and despite his much publicised ill health and the warmth of the public reaction to it, many believed his outdated attitudes held no validity in the modern world. Surgery had cut short his efforts on behalf of Senator Goldwater, but by 1966 he felt strong enough to start campaigning again, this time on behalf of Ronald Reagan. When his old friend became the target of a viscous hate campaign Duke worried about the effect it would have on Nancy and he wrote to her offering his solid support through whatever came her way. She retained a deep fondness for him in return for the help he gave her and her husband over many years and said, "John Wayne was the most gentle, tender person I ever knew."

His boat and his renewed interest in politics were valuable distractions to him when he was bored, but he also suddenly and unexpectedly began receiving vast numbers of scripts and offers of work, and from the late-sixties onward he started rediscovering some of his old enthusiasm for life. Then, just as he was restoring his own life, two thousand soldiers were sent off to Vietnam, and he was thrown into the middle of yet another controversy, another battle, another war.

On a hot day in August 1965 he and Mary were strolling through the grounds of the USC campus, relaxing and talking about how it had all changed since the days when he was a student there. As they stood on the lawns outside the library he became aware of a commotion close by. Some students had set up a table and posters protesting about the war in Vietnam. They were heckling a young marine as he walked past. Duke's interest was caught by the soldier whose chest was covered in medals. He noticed he had an arm missing, and guessed he had been at the college to sign on to go back to school. He rushed over to escort him back to his car, and he thanked him for serving his country. He waved as the boy drove away. Mary, glancing at her boss's face, realised that all hell was about to erupt. She couldn't prevent him storming over to the table where the students sat amazed as he slammed both fists down, yelling in a voice shaking with rage, "You stupid bastards! Blame Johnson if you must, blame that sonofabitch Kennedy, blame Truman or Roosevelt, but don't blame that kid. Jesus, his arm's gone!" As he backed away he murmured, shaking his head, "What the Hell is happening to this country." Later he commented, "I think the American public is getting sick and tired of what these young people are doing. But it's really their own fault for allowing the permissiveness that's been going on for the past 15 or 20 years. Our entire society has promoted an "anything goes" attitude in every area of life and in every American institution. The front pages of the newspapers are encouraging these kids to act the way they are. I deplore what happened at My Lai, but I could show you pictures of what the Viet Cong are doing to our people over there. But for some reason the papers don't report that."

He was full of rage as he realised the things he believed in were under threat once again from the inside. Eisenhower said that if Vietnam fell to Communism it was only a matter of time before all the far east fell; the Domino theory. If Vietnam was the place where America had to make its stand against that threat, Duke for one supported the policy of war, "It's obvious to me, because I've been there, and to the young veterans coming home, that there is a lot to say that the media hasn't told us. Those young men own a piece of that war, and they know what they're talking about. We should ask them about it. They maybe didn't want to go, and maybe the government wasn't justified in sending them off to an undeclared war either, but I sure don't know why we send them and then stop the bombing so that they get shot up that much more. We could easily stop them getting guns from Chinese and Soviet Communists, but we do nothing because we're afraid of world opinion. Why in hell should we worry about world opinion when we're trying to help out a country that's asked for our help? I don't say the American government should decide what kind of government they should have over there. I just don't want the Communists to decide either, and if we hadn't gone to help out that's just what they'd do. I honestly believe there is as much need now to help the South Vietnamese as there was to help the Jews in Germany. And I figure if we're going to send even one man to die, we ought to be in an all-out conflict. If you fight, you have to fight to win. And the Domino Theory is something to be reckoned with too. At some point we have to stop Communism, it might as well be right now in Vietnam. There is the fear that Russia will go to war with us if we stay in Vietnam, but I don't think Russia wants war anymore than we do."

The American government had given its word to protect Vietnam from the advance of Communism, and to Duke breaking that word would be criminal. Whether he was right or wrong, whether the government was right or wrong, his belief in keeping faith with a promise made was fundamental. Loyalty and courage were the basis of his identity; he believed he was the sum of what his country had made him, if America couldn't keep its word he was left with nothing. He had made many mistakes in his life, had done things in which he took no pride, but as an older and hopefully wiser man, he believed he ought to set the younger generation a good example. As always he took no lame measures, he did it full force and hoped some of the kids would listen. Loyalty, courageousness and keeping faith with promises made were uppermost in his mind when he said, "I don't know a better way to go through life than guiding others — getting the best out of them, pushing them to do better than they thought they could — and all in the framework of fair play and mutual trust. We were coached into leading legal lives by parents who loved us and who knew the rules of the game of life. The secret was coaching. The other secret is one generation setting a better example for the generation that's pulling up fast. In that area, I plead guilty for not doing more on the positive side. I've tried — but in looking back, maybe I could have tried harder." Pilar responded, "I don't know how anyone could have tried harder than he did, especially in later life, when almost everything he did was chosen specifically with the purpose of setting a better example. It is hard to think of anyone else who was so willing to risk everything to set the example that he believed in, to take an unpopular stand to say what he believed in."

He was offered a part in *The Dirty Dozen* and though he loved the story he rejected it, saying, "I've got my heart set on making a film about Vietnam, I want to show people in the US that we are at war with international communism." The only way he could support the American soldier was to lend his celebrity status to the cause, making a film in his honour, paying tribute in the best way he knew. He began a rallying crusade, focusing his attention on an idea for *The Green Berets*, the film he had set his heart on making.

In 1963 Robin Moore wrote to the Pentagon asking for assistance in writing a novel about the new special force that symbolized military excellence, the Green Berets. The resulting book, published in 1965, sold three million copies. Although it was a best seller the war was so unpopular that movie makers steered away from a project they considered too controversial, "political" usually spelled box-office disaster. But Duke was unafraid of controversy and he bought the movie rights for fifty thousand dollars. He wrote to President Johnson telling him about his plans to make a film that would inspire patriotism and asking for his support in the project.

Johnson was intrigued by the idea and asked Jack Valenti, his domestic advisor, what he thought. Valenti replied, "Wayne's politics are wrong, but insofar as Vietnam is concerned, his views are right. If he made this picture he would be saying the things we want said. I recommend we support him." The decisions all taken, Duke promised they would be pleased with his movie. Once again he had a cause, and there was no room for ambiguity in his heart, "If you go over there, you won't be middle of the road."

Pilar knew a frightening sense of deja vu, she had witnessed the damage he did to himself with *The Alamo*, now she was terrified for him but knew it was useless to argue, "When Duke had something to say, an Act of Congress couldn't stop him." Once again he was starring, producing and directing a picture, explaining, "I wanted to direct the film, like when I did *The Alamo*, because it was quite obvious to me that no one would tell the truth of why we were there. I'd been over there and I knew that the people of South Vietnam were being treated very badly. I tried to put that in the picture. Whether I succeeded or not I don't know. I didn't want anybody else to do it because it was something I was interested in and I wanted it told as I had seen it over there."

All the big studios ran scared. They had been unwilling to support *The Alamo* with him at the helm, and he knew there would be no money available for *The Green Berets* either, but he was convinced Hollywood misjudged the country's mood. Duke was sure this was a story that would do well financially. He set the film's budget low at $6.1 million to attract backers, and set off on a now familiar treck round the studios to plead his cause. He did a deal with Universal but when they pulled out, he suspected for political reasons, he turned to Warner Brothers who offered to distribute it and give him a little money toward costs. Pre-production got under way and by the time he began casting everyone in Hollywood was talking about it and wanted to get in on the action. Batjac had to close its doors to agents and Duke was able to hand-pick his stars.

In 1966 he was invited to Fort Bragg where the Green Berets trained. He was given star treatment there and came away full of enthusiasm, convinced he was going to make a great movie. He went on another tour of Vietnam, giving no prior warning of his visit. Within days of his arrival he was unable to leave his hotel without being mobbed! He talked to soldiers in small informal groups, getting close to the men, standing in war zones where snipers bullets hit the turf yards from his feet and visiting the hospitals and camps.

Producer Paul Keyes went with him and was awed by his drive, "He kept going from six in the morning until eleven at night. I was forty-two, had two good lungs. I was in good condition but I couldn't keep up with him. He had in him some peculiar drive which was beyond understanding. On his orders, we went as close to the firing line as we could get. We went by plane-helicopter-boat. He talked to sailors in the holds of boats where temperatures reached 145 degrees. He was airlifted to aircraft carrier decks by ropes dangling from helicopters. I remember one day at Pleiku, we were going over in a chopper. They radioed us to get out fast as an attack was in progress. Duke said the hell with that. He was landing. We did. They were attacking. Duke stepped out. He walked around the area. He introduced himself. Some of the GI's had loved him since they were little, they had grown up on Wayne pictures and suddenly here was Sergeant Stryker. Some of them just started crying. They couldn't believe it was really him. And Duke would start blubbering as well. This is what he wanted to do. Sometimes he used prepared gags, mostly he just walked around, shaking hands with strangers."

Whilst he was there he was hit by a severe eye infection and he had to be treated in hospital. The only spare bed was in the psychiatric ward. The man in the next bed looked depressed and Duke tried to cheer him up, "Hi, I'm John Wayne. Your Doctor tells me you're doing fine." The man laughed hysterically and Duke went to fetch a nurse. When she went across to the man he told her, "That guy is really crazy, he thinks he is John Wayne!"

The Green Berets would be the only pro-Vietnam film made during the war. Before he started work on it Duke patiently listened to all the arguments for not doing it. Nothing dissuaded him. He had won a sympathy vote after his battle with cancer, his friends warned him he would be stirring up trouble and antagonism in Hollywood if he went ahead and made this film. He had opposed the election of Johnson in 1964, had opposed sending the army into Vietnam, he didn't like "Johnson's no-win policy," he thought America should bomb Vietcong supply lines and blockade their harbours, he didn't approve of sending men out to fight the war Johnson was sending them to. But the fact was those men were fellow Americans and they were doing their duty to the flag. Meanwhile in American towns and cities the anti-war protests were escalating and intellectuals were burning the flag he honoured out on the streets. He couldn't stand by and watch that whilst American soldiers were dying for it. He couldn't forget what he had seen with his own eyes and he was haunted by visions of lonely, confused soldiers doing what had to be done. No matter how logical the argument against it might be, he had to make his film, "I owe it to them."

Duke's son commented, "At the time it was all very controversial, but dad knew it would be a money maker. The controversy helped what was actually only a formula movie. They wore different uniforms but the story was the same as any story told about World War Two. It was just a group of guys and how they reacted to different situations. In this case it was set in Vietnam. But it was a very difficult film to make and I can't tell you how many trips I made to The Pentagon, just to get the scripts approved. They kept saying, "You can't put that in the film," and the script they finally approved wasn't as good as the original one." Final approval came from the Pentagon on March 30 1967. It was at that time Universal backed out, saying the approved script was the worst writing they had ever seen. Duke turned to Jack Warner, who signed the deal because Duke begged him to trust him, promising it would make money. The picture wasn't about box-office for him and he said, tongue firmly in cheek, "This picture is naturally from the hawk's point of view, but it isn't a political statement, it's made strictly for entertainment purposes." The fact that he deferred his salary made it a most personal political statement.

The movie couldn't be shot on location but Pentagon officials allowed Duke to make it at Fort Benning instead. Almost as soon as filming began there the weather turned cold and he found himself in a race against time, struggling to beat the onset of Autumn, which would turn his Vietnamese jungle brown. Already deep in production problems, he continued giving interviews to a Press intent on goading him into making statements which, when taken out of context, as they always were, made him appear a sadistic idiot who gloried in the shedding of blood. Richard Warren Lewis, Contributing Editor of *Playboy*, and a man hostile to Duke's image, later interviewed him, probing him about the picture and his stance on Vietnam. The finished article ran ten pages and Duke, well used to difficult writers, had fallen headlong into a trap. By the time the interview hit the stands Duke was the last remaining Hollywood superstar, grudgingly acknowledged by Lewis as a top box office attraction for 19 consecutive years, a man who had earned his studios more than $400,000,000 — more than any other star in motion picture history. He also scoffed, calling him a "profit without honour" because of his "squareness," his politics, and films like *The Green Berets*. Lewis visited Duke's "11 room, 7-bath" Newport home and wrote, "Wearing a realistc toupee, Wayne at first appeared considerably younger than he is: only the liver spots on both hands and the lines in his jut-jawed face told of his 63 years. But at six feet four and 244 pounds, it still almost seems as if he could have singlehandedly mopped up all those bad guys ... his sky blue eyes, though somewhat rheumy from the previous night's late hours, reinforced the image." Duke later confessed mournfully, "I don't even remember why I agreed to talk to him at all."

Lewis had approached cautiously; asking standard questions about the state of the film industry. They talked about his childhood, his favourite films, and then Duke was steered into politics, the state of America, and finally, Vietnam. Lewis led, but Duke had never been afraid of alienating a few people, he had nothing to hide and believed he had the same rights as every other American to air his views. He blamed the liberals for, "perverting the natural loyalties and ideals of our kids, filling them with fear and doubt and hate and downgrading patriotism and all our heroes of the past." And when Lewis asked him what he thought about Angela

Davis, the black radical philosopher at UCLA he replied, "I don't want Angela Davis inculcating an enemy doctrine in my kid's heads. I wouldn't mind them being taught the basic philosophies, the theory and how things work practically." He was chased him away from reasoning and started off on something else. Lewis was delighted with every response, he pushed the buttons and Duke said what he thought; nothing could have been easier. When he was taken down the line of welfare Duke said that though he had gone without the odd meal he blamed no one else for that, and expected nothing from any one else. When he was asked about his privileged position he agreed, "I am privileged. But I don't feel the least bit guilty about having worked my ass off to make a good living. You just can't sit around bellyaching because someone got a break and you didn't." He had never had any patience or sympathy for people who complained all the time about their lot in life, and it didn't matter to him what race, creed or religion those people were, "I don't feel guilt about the fact that five or ten generations ago these people were slaves. Now, I'm not condoning slavery. It's a fact of life, it happened."

Lewis had great fun, pushing him, getting a great quote, pushing harder, getting another Wayne pearl of wisdom. He asked about the plight of the Native American, "This may come as a surprise to you, but I wasn't alive when the reservations were created ... what happened a hundred years ago in our country can't be blamed on us today ... what happened between our for fathers is so far back ... right, wrong or indifferent ... that I don't see why we owe them anything today."

And so it went, until Lewis finally asked if he thought America had lost its dignity, if he was gloomy about the future of the country, the answer shocked him. "Absolutely not. I think that the loud roar of irresponsible liberalism will be quieted down by a reasoning public. We built a nation on the past, it can't have been so bad. We have to look to tomorrow. Tomorrow ... the time that gives a man or a country just one more chance ... its just one of many things that I feel is wonderful about life. As a country, our yesterdays tell us that we have to win not only at war, but at peace. So far we haven't done that. Sadly, it looks like we'll have to win another war, to have a chance at winning peace. All I hope is that in our anxiety to have peace, we remember our clear and present dangers and beware the futility of compromise, only if we keep sight of both will we have a chance of stumbling forward into a day when there won't be guns fired anymore in anger."

Lewis was surprised by the unexpected eloquence, it was time to wrap things up, "In retrospect, would you have wanted your life to have been any different?"

"If I had it to do over again, I'd probably do everything I did. But that's not necessarily the right thing to do."

"What legacy do you hope to leave behind?"

"Well, you're going to think I'm being corny, but this is how I really feel. I hope my family and friends will be able to say that I was honest, kind and a fairly decent man."

There was no mention of image, nor of his films, nor even about how fellow Americans might see him, he was only concerned with friends and family. Again Lewis was surprised because it was so obviously a gut reaction to the question, as all his answers had been … unguarded, open, and very unwise.

When the issue came out shops ran out of copies. Duke's phone never stopped ringing, with callers either heaping praise on his head or abusing him. He had anticipated the reaction but felt he had been unfairly treated, goaded into making rash answers and not given time to explain himself. Years before he had complained that whenever liberals asked his opinion they shouted him down before he could get two words out of his mouth, he felt the same way now, but Mary said that on the whole he was happy at the public reaction … "Well, at least I still get a reaction. My philosophy became public property some time ago. When you're in the public eye you're always on the spot. I try to remember that at all times. There's nothing I can do to stop it. I'm often forced into a position where I talk … I'm given leading questions that I feel I should answer. After I do it for one reporter, another comes up and says, "You said so-and-so, what did you mean by that ?" Pretty quick I'm in trouble and there's no way out … But I'm not intimidated … Actually, here's how I felt about it … I got a lot of complimentary letters about the article. Still, I wish they'd deleted some of the words I said in it … you know we were just two men sitting in the den. But they're right down on paper … nothing I can do now. But before I'd even read it I'd heard they were leaving every word in. My wife called to ask if I'd seen it … I said, "No," … I waited … then she said it was good … phew, I got off the rough part of it … because she was the only one I was afraid of. The material, what I said, I meant, and I don't intend to explain or complain. Anyway, people got over it in a hurry … better than I did anyway! I just had to hang on and tough things out."

Duke may only have been concerned about his wife's opinion but from the day *Playboy* hit the street he was unmercifully caricatured, misunderstood, dismissed by the liberals, and attacked with venom and brutality by the Press. He was personally more tolerant and forgiving of human mistakes than most of them were toward him.

By the time the filming of *The Green Berets* commenced he was under immense pressure, he faced a multitude of production problems and felt under attack at every turn. The weather was cold and damp. His eye infection flared up again. His back hurt. He lost his appetite as he had when making *The Alamo*, and he was coughing violently again and often using oxygen to aid his breathing. One of the stars, Edward Faulkner, said, "He was under terrible pressure and, sure, he lashed out on a number of occasions. He had a temper, but he only ever attacked people he thought weren't giving a hundred percent. He was giving 110 or 115% himself. He did intimidate people, but he respected those who worked hard and could stand up to him. He didn't like "yes" men. He was an absolute, complete professional. Yet I thought he was also a decent man. He was one of the most generous, big-hearted men I have ever known." Everyone who worked on, or visited the set, were incredulous at his power and determination as he got on with directing, producing, starring, checking scripts, stunts, props, checking everything. When he fell behind schedule he started shooting scenes through the night, personally working fourteen hour days. His lonely figure was often seen stalking back and forth across windswept hilltops as he planned each scene, a raincoat slung across his shoulders, and his green beret set at a jaunty angle as he barked out orders to the cast and crew. He was lost in a world of his own, his mind far from profit and loss, friends and enemies, his wife and even their children. David Janssen, another star, said, "He was like a man possessed by a demon that had him in its grasp. How he summoned up the physical and moral strength to go on like that for over three months, in the condition he was in, I had no idea."

He had been sure about *The Alamo*, but it had not been the success he had hoped for. He was sure about this too, yet was now astute enough to know that nothing in life was certain. If the critics could hit *The Alamo* as hard as they had, he could only guess what they were going to do with this one. Still he believed in it, and when he stood alone on the hillside making changes to the script, getting things together, forgetting his body and thinking about his own vision of beauty and truth he really didn't care what they did with it. He was making it honestly, saying what he wanted to say.

In 1968 Renata Adler, a sensitive, thoughtful reviewer, was hired as the movie critic at the *New York Times*. No one, least of all Duke, anticipated her savage attack, "*The Green Berets* is a film so stupid, so rotten and false in every detail that it passes through being fun, through being funny … through everything, and becomes an invitation to grieve, not for our soldiers … but for what had happened to the fantasy-making apparatus in the country … it is vile and insane. On top of that it is dull." Duke smiled,

"The critics were condemning the war, not the picture. Renata Adler was almost foaming at the mouth because I showed a few massacres on the screen. She went into convulsions. She and other critics wouldn't believe that the Viet Cong are treacherous … that the dirty sons of bitches are raping and torturing. However their comments ensured the success of the movie. Luckily for me they overkilled it. It might have taken the public longer to find out about the picture if they hadn't made so much noise about it. And I agreed with them that it was a shameless propaganda film. It was an American film about American boys who were heroes over there. Yes, in that sense it was propaganda. That little clique back there in the East has taken great personal satisfaction in reviewing my politics instead of my pictures. They've drawn up a caricature of me. It doesn't bother me; their opinions don't matter to the people who go to the movies, never did."

Of course their opinions bothered him very much. Perhaps they never hurt his pocket, but Duke, the man, had always wanted to be loved and was hurt when he wasn't. Later reviewers and critics came to see more in his films because they stood isolated in time from the politics of his era, those critics respected his saltiness, grandeur and loneliness, respected the honesty of his achievements on screen and only the image he created mattered. It was the reason TV continued screening his work, the reason his career could still go on after the battering he took over *The Green Berets*. He spoke disdainfully about awards, especially the Oscar, but he was hurt not to have received that symbol of respect from fellow members of the industry that he loved. After the hammering of the picture he was sure he would never receive one, "I'm not hurt and I'm not angry. I'm aware that I'm unpopular in the industry because my political philosophy is different from the prevailing attitude. But I don't reply when they gang up on me, because I think political street fighting is unprofessional. Yes, I sometimes feel lost, but my convictions are my own and I'm entitled to them. The films I choose to make are a matter for my own conscience. There is little I can do to satisfy the critics."

He received frightening hate mail after the film's release and the Press dug up past failures and personal problems to show him as a brute, lacking intelligence. But his belief in both his own, and his country's actions didn't waver and although, inevitably, he wearied of defending his stance, he still gave his time unstintingly and did his best to answer every criticism thrown his way. Eventually, once he realised that many people chose to misrepresent him, and there was nothing that he could do about it, he said, "If I depended on what the critics had to say about me, if I depended on their recognition I would never have gone into this business. It really doesn't bother me when they are disparaging."

Pilar begged him to retire. He was washed out, bone tired, but he reaffirmed, "I can't retire. I would die. I'll not stop until they just don't want me anymore. Working makes me feel like a worthwhile citizen." Retiring would have been giving up on himself. He talked briefly to her about buying a property in Mexico, where they could go to escape the world, where he would be able to relax, somewhere she would be happy. She laughed telling him he'd have to improve his Spanish, but knew he wouldn't bother, because they would never be going to live in Mexico. And she was right, because his life was set for another astounding change of direction.

Politically, he had taken a massive side step to defend President Johnson and the war. He had seen LBJ standing alone, as he so often did himself, against a domestic siege, and said, "I think our film will help re-elect LBJ, because it shows that the war in Vietnam is necessary." However, with or without the support of John Wayne, Vietnam destroyed Jonhnson's presidency and he wasn't re-elected. Another period of great change and turmoil was beginning; Martin Luther King was assassinated, followed by the black riots, Bobby Kennedy was shot, and *The Green Berets* was released with its weak script, doctored by The Pentagon, into a period of severe civil unrest. It was attacked as if it were the cause of the war, instead of one man's reaction to it, and Duke was targeted as *THE* primary cause of the war, when he hadn't even supported it. He was also lucky, the political backlash gave him millions of dollars worth of free advertising, and Duke was grateful for it. He was sure that middle Americans, the true patriots, would come to his rescue again, back his judgement against the Adlers of the world and turn his film into a huge box-office hit. Within eighteen months receipts were up to $20 million. Foreign rentals took its earnings even higher.

In 1970 the "hardhat demonstrations" exploded as many ordinary workers gathered to express their love for their country. They waved flags, sang songs, and many carried Duke's picture. *The Green Berets* had tapped into their feelings; they were the very people who had grown up watching his movies, and despite the poison pen letters he became even more popular with vast numbers of American citizens. He thought the time for political change had arrived. Johnson had gone and he believed Richard Nixon was the best man to be next president and he lent him unstinting support to help him get elected. Once in power Nixon began a phased withdrawal from Vietnam, at the same time, sending troops into Cambodia to eliminate the communist bastions there. Duke was delighted by the message Nixon was giving. Punish the communists and then bring the boys on home. All Americans were relieved that the war was ending, he was no exception.

In January 1971 he was out celebrating with Frank Sinatra, Dean Martin, Sammy Davis Jr. and Ronald Reagan at the Memorial Auditorium. During the evening three hundred anti-war protesters gathered outside in the hope of forcing a public confrontation. When it was time to leave the police asked the stars to go out of the side exits, warning them that the crowd outside was hostile. Duke, hardly the man to slink out of a side door, refused, "The hell with that, I'm 63 years old, too damn old to run away from a bunch of kids." Since the 1920's he had portrayed men of courage in the face of an external enemy. He had long been seen as the protector of American values. His screen persona, by the time he made *The Green Berets*, had already assumed mythological proportions, based on that reputation. He simply could not walk out of side gates. The others left as requested but he ploughed headlong into the crowd which soon engulfed him. He asked them politely not to push, but when one of the protester's flags nicked his nose he lunged after him. It was the old man of 63 who had to be restrained by a security guard, not the protester, who fled in the face of Duke's fury. What he'd have done if he caught the boy even he didn't know, he might have "held him kinda hard!"

The movies John Wayne made now struggled to keep up with *HIS* image. It had been that image that persuaded many young men to join the army in the 1960's, and influenced the whole generation of men and officers serving in Vietnam. Still, the image was severely dented by the war, and often the boys who joined up because they wanted to be John Wayne, forgot his persona often died for his country. Just before *The Green Berets* was released Richard Schickel wrote, "For some of us who have grown up in his shadow, measuring our changing personalities against his towering constancy, Wayne has become one of life's bedrock necessities. He reminds us of a time when right was right, wrong was wrong, and the differences between them could be set right by the simplest of means. Most men of his paunch have given up righteous violence in favour of guileful acquiescence in the world's wickedness; the Duke is still banking away at it … an unconscious existential hero." Vietnam had shown a whole generation that wrongs couldn't always be put right by the simplest of means, well, not unless you happened to be John Wayne, and even he admitted life could be a struggle.

Until the release of *The Green Berets*, whilst he was recognised as a huge film star, he was still known primarily as a cowboy who always fought for good, after its release he became much more than that. On one hand his career was destroyed, on the other he was turned into the most popular working class hero America had ever seen. He had thrown down the gauntlet, had opened himself up to the bitter attack he knew would surely follow and the liberals behaved just as he expected them to. His own behaviour was also typical, pure John Wayne, right, wrong or indifferent he stubbornly refused to back down or apologise for one word of the film. He could not be sure what the outcome might be, but he was absolutely certain about his own stance.

As a grand old man of 63 his friends and family told him he was too old for all the stress he brought on himself. They begged him to take up golf or tennis, to take a well-earned break and allow the rest of them some peace. They told him what he already knew, that he was far from well and needed to slow down and allow himself time to recover. He had so much, his land in Arizona, his boat, his wife, children and grandchildren, and at last, new friends to replace those he had lost. They all advised, "Duke hang up your six-shooter and throw the spurs away. It's time to retire." After his two operations he had amassed goodwill and love from his public, he agreed, he could have sat back then, illuminated in that and his achievements for the rest of his life. But he answered every well meaning advisor with the same words, "I can't retire. I would die." Like the ox in harness that Zolotow called him, the need to work consumed him. Away from the movie industry he would not have to face hostile reviewers or critics, or have to read threatening, abusive letters, he could have rested his aches and pains by the ocean instead. But whilst he appreciated the adoration of his fans, any one who knew him at all, understood it wasn't a desire to be loved that drove him, and now, the very scale of the attack following *The Green Berets* meant he could not sit back, he had something to prove. It was not adoration that pushed him on, nor the need to please his fans that drove him, it was the stern words of the fiercest critics who reviled him.

Many of those critics said the film didn't work because the Wayne persona had lost the ferociousness of Stryker, Edwards or Dunson, there was none of their hidden bitterness in Colonel Kirby. He had acquired a more tender and protective quality, there was less of the hurt man, damaged by life, to be seen. The gentleness had always been there, the aching vulnerability clearly present in Dunson, now though it seemed to seep into every corner of his being, and all his ruthless harshness was softened, the raw emotion smoothed away. Pilar and cancer had made a more accepting soul of Duke and he could never again play the ruthless loner whose sadness and pain lay hidden deep in shaded eyes, and Colonel Mike Kirby, adrift in Vietnam, was his last attempt at such a character.

He had always possessed an amazing ability to bounce back from life's disasters, he had made and lost fortunes, he made bad films and been slated for them, he made some great ones too, and been slated for them, he got cancer and survived. Come what may, John Wayne struggled back to take all the gifts life offered, "Tomorrow is the most important thing we have." Sometimes it took him a little longer to get over a set back, but somehow he always managed to put his losses behind him. Every time he was knocked down, he got up again and seemed even bigger than before. When he lost one fortune, he just worked that bit harder to recover it, when one film flopped he tried harder on the next one, when one wife stopped loving him he moved on to the next. He was as driven now as he had always been, as desperate to face the challenge that tomorrow brought as when he started out along *The Big Trail*.

The master of change was already preparing the next re-invention. This one, like the last, was rooted in a fight for survival, but not in ill health. He was entering his fifth decade in the industry, he should have been close to the end of his chosen road, but the next series of characters, against all the odds, became the most successful of his illustrious career. He agreed he had changed as a man and now saw the world differently, as did his audience. To survive required evolution, and whilst he had to remain familiar to his fans, it was time for change. He went back to the drawing board and began piecing together the new patriarchal character that he had indeed become. He sketched an older man, still striving in the crusade against evil, a man who remained in the service of community and it was through this characterisation, brought miraculously to life in *True Grit* that he was transformed into the true mythic hero of all western legend. Embodied in Rooster Cogburn, the first of the new group of characters destined to make his fiercest critics sit up and take notice, it became the defining role in his life and the one that belatedly won everything for Duke that his admirers believed he was due.

Just before making the film Duke became interested in another capital venture. He had lost untold thousands of dollars in poor investments over the years, but when he came across an invention for separating oil and water in a ship's bilges he decided to take a chance on the local company that was developing a process to prevent ocean pollution. He read everything he could about the discharge of bilge water into the sea and spent many happy days promoting the company, investing heavily, enjoying a personal input into a project that he took on almost as his own. He was bouncing back again ... but the best was coming up behind fast.

Many people who read the novel by Charles Portis believed he based the character Reubin J. Cogburn on John Wayne and when Henry Hathaway first came across it he immediately called Duke to tell him to get hold of a copy fast, "There's a great part here for you." And as soon as he read it he knew his old friend had been spot on and he said, "I wanted the part of Cogburn so much I could taste it." His company offered Portis three hundred thousand dollars for the movie rights, and Duke was confident he would get it.

But Hal Wallis, the independent producer working out of Paramount, had other ideas and more financial clout. He went to five hundred thousand to leave Duke devastated by the loss of what he suspected would make a first rate movie. When he had considered his position he decided it was too good a story to miss, there was no time to waste on anger or frustration, and instead of bemoaning his fortune he rang the producer to beg, "Come on Hal, just give me a chance at it." Wallis had made *The Sons of Katie Elder* with Hathaway and Duke, and had been looking for another property in which to use the two of them together again for some time. He refused to sell the movie rights but had never considered offering the part to anyone else. Completing the deal was easy and they had no problems, Duke was offered one million dollars and thirty five percent of gross, he accepted and the agreement was signed. Henry Hathaway went with the deal.

Both producer and director were well aware Duke liked to have scripts re-worked to suit himself, but they warned him that this time he was going to play the part as it was written, "We're not going to have any of your moralizing or preaching on this one." When Duke was handed the final script he was amazed by its brilliance, "It was the best thing I'd ever seen." Cogburn was to be based directly on the book, rough and ready, a man who took a wench when he wanted one, got drunk when he wanted to, and fought just because he was in the mood to fight, a man who was as much as a sinner as a saint. There had never been anyone like Rooster on the screen before, and Duke agreed to stick scrupulously to the novel, playing him almost exactly as ordered, although there were some heated debates and a little give and take on all sides before the creation was complete. He had been in the business over forty years, he knew every aspect of movie making, and he expected people to listen to him. Things were different in Colorado. Wallis wanted him to wear a moustache and an eye patch, but Duke objected, saying his fans paid to see him, "Not some sonofabitch who looks like a pirate in an Errol Flynn movie." Wallis compromised, letting the moustache go, but insisting on the eye patch. He knew his star would need careful handling and that only one or two directors were capable of keeping him under control, he crossed his fingers and prayed Hathaway was one of those. He was another tough director and when he overheard Duke protesting about the patch, he warned, "Listen, Duke, I'm in charge of the picture and you're going to have to do what I say. Cogburn can win you the Oscar if you'll play him true. So quit bitching about it. Anyway you won't have to go on a diet. I want you big bellied at 260 pounds." Duke gave up, there was no point hitting his head against a brick wall, "It's sure as hell my first decent role in twenty years, and my first chance to play a character role instead of John Wayne. Ordinarily they just stand me there and run everybody up against me." And he admitted that not having to diet was a massive bonus.

In the autumn of 1968 a fat and happy John Wayne met up with Henry Hathaway in the Colorado Mountains to make a masterpiece and produce one of life's rare moments when every element falls neatly into its right place. Duke emerged from it as a superhuman presence, finally becoming the superman that he had cursed himself for not being after his date with death. He had been ordered to rest after *The Green Berets*; battling against constant criticism had tired him out, but the sights and sounds of the Colorado mountains refreshed him and breathed life back into his weary soul. He took refuge up there and began to feel better. Hathaway had no trouble with his star and was unusually gentle with him in return. He screamed and bellowed at everybody, all the rest of the cast and crew were fair game, but he never raised his voice to Duke, who seemed to know instinctively what was required of him. The director wanted this to be an especially good experience for him because he'd seen the damage *The Green Berets* had done and he longed to make things better for him. He'd looked so ill when he turned up on location that he hadn't the heart to treat him roughly; he spoke to him in quiet confidential whispers and allowed him get on with the business he knew best, confident that Duke was invariably right about body placement and nuances of meaning in a script.

Over the years critics accused Duke of being formulaic. He fuelled their criticism by saying that he didn't act, he reacted, repeating it so often that they came to believe he possessed only limited talent. Now he had been given a once-in-a-lifetime chance to prove his ability. On the surface the character possessed similarities to many others he had played down the years. Rooster was a classic frontier hero, an autonomous man with no woman, family, or ties. But as Duke made one of the longest speeches of his career, telling Mattie he had a wife and son who had left him, but that, although he misses them, he would rather have lost them than his independence, members of the cast and crew applauded, knowing they were witnessing a very special performance. Duke said, "It was the best scene I ever did, it gave me great personal pleasure." His portrayal of the drunken, swaggering, kindly, warm, and above all, courageous US Marshal, was so clearly a product of his own acting ability that even critics who only months before had written him off forever, were suddenly able to see him clearly, maybe for the first time. Obviously here was a virtuoso of the film world, an artist who knew exactly how to arrange moves, how to raise a single eye to unbelievable effect.

Hathaway had cherished Duke's ability over a thirty year period. He, more than any other director, had coaxed out his more amiable side, the side that so many others missed completely. Together, on this one special occasion, they combined to produce a shining moment and, many said, to make the best western ever. Apart from his one long speech he actually had few words to say; he had to drink, shoot, pursue, and fall off his horse. But his performance went deeper than words could have taken him, and he conveyed the character of Cogburn simply, in gestures and intonations.

Pilar watched as another of his favourite sequences was filmed out in a meadow of autumnal brilliance. Duke sat tall in the saddle telling the four outlaws confronting him that he plans to either kill them or see them hanged. "Bold talk for a one-eyed fat man" their leader sneered back. Duke's horse was already at full tilt as he shouted his most famous battle cry, "Fill your hands, you son of a bitch," and, with the reins in his teeth, pistol in one hand and Winchester in the other, he charged hell-for-leather straight at them. It was the first time anyone ever heard profanity from John Wayne in a picture, "In my other pictures, we've had an explosion go off when I said a bad word. This time we didn't. It's profanity alright, but I doubt if there's anyone in the United States who hasn't heard the expression. We felt it was acceptable in this instance. At the emotional high point in that particular picture, I felt it was OK to use it."

Over many years he had portrayed characters unaffected by eating, drinking, or smoking, but in Rooster the laws of nature had clearly taken a heavy toll. He is old, fat, one-eyed, hardly able to get up in the mornings. He can't hold his liquor and falls off his horse after a long day's ride, too drunk to get back up and says, "We'll camp here tonight." Unlike his other unencumbered characters Rooster falls under the spell of young Mattie, he cares about her, and in looking after her, begins to lose the independence he cherishes. Rooster was strong, funny, subtle and at all times believable and, although Duke had no hand in script development, he was a direct descendant of the traditional Wayne character. He invested Rooster with the warmth, comfortable masculinity, and dignity that was all his own, he was the heartbeat of the character. As Pilar looked on in wonder Rooster came to life before her eyes, spinning his Winchester in his hand as he rode toward his adversaries with all his skill. He rehearsed the climactic scene over and over again, helping the rest of the cast to get it right. She was worried about him working at such high altitude. He was the oldest member of the cast, and even the younger members moaned they couldn't catch their breath. The difficulties of filming the scene where the five men performed a tricky manoeuvre on horseback and the long hours necessary to choreograph it perfectly were tough on everyone. On the day it was finally shot it was bitterly cold. Hathaway repeatedly called, "Action," in his determination to get the best image of Rooster, riding alone but undaunted, against an enemy that far outgunned him. At the end of the day, Duke asked how it looked. The director asked him how it felt, and laughing, Duke replied, "Damn good." Hathaway told him that was how it looked. He had caught Duke's most triumphant moment in all its autumnal glory and knew what it had taken out of the star, "Yeah, I'd say Duke had more guts than the average guy. He did another scene where he had to pick up the body of a dead villain, a 200 pound man, and carry him over his shoulder like a baby for fifty yards. He did it, bad back, one lung, at altitude. When we finished he was exhausted. No other actor would have done that, because he was actually walking away from the camera, and he didn't need to do it. He did it for authenticity. It knocked the breath out of him and it took him a long time to come out of it. He sat on a rock struggling to breathe. Duke just doesn't have to do things like that anymore, but there was never one complaint out of him about anything."

After finishing filming just before Christmas he took a month off to rest at home. In January 1969 Hal Wallis drove down to see him, "I knew we had a winner Duke." He had seen the rushes, "It is extraordinary … Familiar as I was with the script, I often laughed out loud viewing the film." Just one year after *The Green Berets*, *True Grit* opened at Radio City Music Hall. The same critics who had said they could never take Wayne seriously again now lavishly piled praise on a great moment of American cinema, calling his performance in it a triumph, by far the best of his career, and just twelve months after writing him off they actively hyped him for the Oscar. Everyone was talking Oscars except Duke, who didn't even dare to hope, " I never really went into that field of endeavour. I think to get the critics interested in you for an Oscar, you have to be in a certain type of picture. It was an accident that I was in this picture. It was just a natural for me."

Paramount promoted *True Grit* as his "Fortieth Anniversary in Pictures" film, and to make it special they scheduled three screenings just for the movie community before its official release. Duke felt especially worried and nervous about those shows; the approval of his peers meant a lot more to him than the barbed words of the critics. Each performance was met with thunderous applause. The biggest stars in Hollywood all agreed it was by far his best work and when the critics finally had their say even they agreed. Vincent Canby, who had hated his last film, wrote, "The last scene in the movie is so fine it will probably become Wayne's cinematic epitaph. Curious thing about *True Grit* is that although he is still playing a variation on the self assured serviceman he has played so many times in the past, the character that seemed so grotesque in Vietnam fits into this frontier landscape, emotionally — and perhaps politically too — Hathaway obtains from Wayne the richest performance of his long career." Duke's Cogburn was called, "A flawless portrait of a flawed man."

Everyone was eating out of his hand, a strange but welcome feeling for him. Andrew Sarris wrote, "And there is talk of an Oscar for Wayne after forty years of movie acting and after thirty years of damn good movie acting. Wayne's performances for John Ford alone are worth all the Oscars put out ... Indeed, Wayne's performances in *The Searchers*, *Wings of Eagles*, and *The Man Who Shot Liberty Valance* are among the most full-bodied and large-souled creations of the cinema ... *Rio Bravo*, *El Dorado*, and *Red River* for Hawks are almost on the same level as Ford's, and *Hatari!* is not too far behind ... Then there were the merely nice movies ... finally there are the leisurely Hathaway movies. It would be a mistake to assume that all he can play or has played is the conventional western gunfighter. There is more of Christian submission than pagan hubris in the Duke's western persona. Relatively "liberal" types like Henry Fonda and Paul Newman have been considerably more conspicuous than Wayne in the matter of flaunting virility and swaggering about with six shooters at the ready ... Wayne embodies the brutal implacable order of the West, less with personal flair than with archetypical endurance. He is more likely to outlast his opponents than to outdraw them, and ever since *Stagecoach* he has never hesitated to use the rifle, an instrument more efficient, though less phallic, than the six-shooter. Ironically, Wayne has become a legend by not being legendary. He has dominated the screen even when he has not been written in as the dominant character."

"The perfection he created in Ethan Edwards is echoed in Rooster Cogburn. They have in common the essential form of John Wayne, the continuos identity of the western hero, the loner, the rugged individualist who serves the community without being part of it. And this is the public conception of John Wayne as well. As Rooster he adds new shadows. The broken-down marshal is a mythic creature of folk legend. He is the ironic descendant of Wayne's own heroic past, roused once more to action and adventure and love. The "knight" is summoned by a call to duty. Every time Wayne embarks on such a journey he faces an important spiritual struggle, just as he faces the external struggle with the villain. In creating the mythical, symbolic, American hero, Wayne always incorporates something of himself into the characterisation."

Hardly a sour note sounded. John Belton went on, "What's remarkable about Wayne in *True Grit* is that, though his part is self-conscious and self-parodic, his performance is not. He plays Cogburn straight and without tricks. He has come out of the classic mould of acting. He always gives a clean performance. Where Brando creates *The Godfather* with the aid of make-up and mumbling, Wayne portrays Cogburn in spite of the eye patch. He always finds a single gesture to express what he wants with simplicity, surety and clarity. For Wayne every gesture is effortless, he has non of the neurotic mannerisms of other actors. His every move is pure, natural and intuitive, giving each performance a slow, fluid grace. The final scene of *True Grit* is both absurdly comic and heroically grand. It can only work because Wayne, the actor, is totally committed to what he is doing, totally absorbed himself. Only Wayne could have carried off an otherwise unplayable scene."

Richard Fleischer praised him, "This was true stardom." Duke could hardly believe what he was reading. He was pleased and flattered by the attention. After *The Green Berets* he had been shown as a brutal and harsh man; the interviews he had given had done little to dispel the image. Now, suddenly, he was a sensitive, college-educated, skilful actor. They had always used words like "tough" "leathery" and "stupid" to describe him, now they were calling him a man of real emotion, a man easily moved to tears, a man who by his own admission had shaken with fear. That at least was close to the truth!

He was due to go to the clinic for his regular cancer check-up. He dreaded going each time, and lay sleepless for weeks before each visit. Now he was going for the five year examination, the one that would tell him if he had really beaten the disease, and the nervous tension he felt was even worse than usual. He always hated the way the doctors talked about remission, recurrence and about the length of his future although their previous reports had been good if cautious. This time he expected to be told cancer was present again, "Every time I have to get a check up it runs through my mind about how I'm going to tell my family this time, without being too dramatic. Every time is like waiting to be hit in the body by a hard left hand. There's no other way I can explain it. It's rough. You know I've got seven kids, and fifteen grandchildren, and I nearly know most of their names" he smiled, but added, "it's really rough thinking about how I'd tell them ..." He expected to be humbled by cancer. He had just been named Hollywood's top attraction, surely The Red Witch had to be waiting for him and he couldn't fail to spot the irony of the possibility of winning his first Oscar as he was being slowly suffocated by a lung tumour.

When he walked into the clinic for the results of his tests it was to find his doctor smiling at him broadly. He was swept by overwhelming relief; he was disease free, clinically cured. He still needed an annual check up, but he was assured there was little chance of his dying of lung cancer.

Long before the Oscar nominations were announced he was already back at work. In February 1969 he was working on *The Undefeated* when his horse stumbled and fell, throwing him badly. He broke two ribs and badly bruised his left side. He took several days off, and went home to recover. Filming went on without him until he returned well taped, uncomfortable but willing to continue shooting a scene that called for him to ride a horse at full speed into a Confederate position. His bad luck continued when his stirrup came loose, "I fell right under that god-damned horse; I'm lucky I didn't kill myself." This time he dislocated his right shoulder, an injury that forced him to ride with his arm held close to his body to reduce the pain.

Rock Hudson, Duke's co-star, had been anxious about working with the embodiment of American masculine strength. He knew Duke was aware of his homosexuality and was worried about how the macho man would react to him. On the first day on location he sat watching Duke apply natural lipstick in a small mirror. When he turned to face him he smiled, "Well, I hear you're a good bridge player." Throughout that day's shooting he kept telling Hudson how to walk and talk to obtain the best effect. The next day Hudson returned the favour, giving unwanted and unhelpful advice to Duke, who eventually laughed, "It's OK, take it easy. I like you." Everyone knew Duke hated being around gay men, or "men in striped trousers" as he colourfully described them, but he never let that get in his way when he worked with a fellow professional. The two got on well and often played bridge together in the evenings, "What Rock Hudson does — in the privacy of his own room — is his business. He's a professional on the set and a real gentleman — and he plays a hell of a hand of bridge."

Duke was putting the finishing touches to his next film, *Chisum*, when he first heard he had been nominated for an Academy Award. Pilar, who still hated going to Durango, happened to be spending a few days on location with him there when the news hit town. He tried to brush it off, telling her, "You can't eat awards, and you sure as hell can't drink them." He was convinced he wouldn't win and he didn't even dare to hope, but getting the nomination would at least ensure the success of *Chisum*. "Well, of course, I knew *True Grit* was going to go … even with the critics. Once in a while you just come across something with such great humour. The author caught the flavor of Mark Twain, to my way of thinking. You know it wasn't really parody. Rooster was basically the same character I've always played. And the film wasn't the best one I ever made either, *Stagecoach*, *Red River* and *The Searchers* were all better. But I knew it was going to go. I never expected to win the Oscar though." The other nominees had much to recommend them, Dustin Hoffman, Jon Voight, Peter O'Tool, and Richard Burton were all actors of the highest calibre. Many thought that if Duke won it would be an award honouring his lifetime's effort as much as this performance and Hollywood expected him to emerge the victor. Rooster Cogburn was a grandfatherly figure and even the Hollywood liberals could accept him in that light; he may be politically and socially outrageous but grandfathers were allowed, even expected to be.

The nomination revived interest in him, and offers of work started flooding in again although he had already agreed to make *Rio Lobo* with old friend Howard Hawks. He signed a contract to work on it before even seeing the script because it gave him another chance to work with Hawks and Yakima Canutt. Duke sensed he was going to fall at the final hurdle, so he couldn't afford to relax. As long as he had a project he had to keep going and he scanned every script that came his way.

On April 13 1970 filming on Rio Lobo was well under way, and he had to fly into Los Angeles from location, accompanied by make-up man Dave Grayson, for the award ceremony. Pilar had travelled up from Newport and found a nervous wreck waiting to meet her. He rambled fretfully for hours, telling her he was sure it would be Burton's night. The more he talked, the more he seemed to accept, and prepare himself for ultimate disappointment.

Richard Burton and Elizabeth Taylor were staying at the same hotel as the Waynes, and on the morning of the ceremony Duke and Elizabeth Taylor set off early together to rehearse their part of the show. He tried to appear calm and was unusually quiet as he attempted to distance himself from all the hype and also from the hope that somehow refused to be extinguished. Pilar arrived at the Dorothy Chandler Pavilion later in the afternoon and once Duke spotted her he couldn't suppress his excitement any longer, he ran toward her and held onto her tightly, taking comfort in her presence.

When they returned in the evening for the ceremony he heard the mighty roar of approval from waiting fans as they drove up and the warmth of the welcome shocked him. He said nothing but clutched his wife's hand tightly. She knew from the pressure just how nervous he was and during the ceremony her fingers turned white and numb. When she glanced up at him though she was amazed to see not the slightest sign of nerves on his face, he looked supremely confident, a man at ease; only her crushed hand belied the performance. He let go of her briefly to go to take part in the early presentations. When he returned he whispered to her that he could hardly breathe, "My heart is pumping so wildly." Barbra Streisand was presenting the Best Actor award, the whole audience silently waited for her announcement, and Duke wasn't the only person sitting with baited breath. He sat completely rigid as she opened the envelope, stared at the name of the winner for some time, then smiled, "And the winner is John Wayne for *True Grit*." He was surprised, shocked, and for some time remained frozen in his seat. He licked dry lips before standing up to pull his jacket together and moving swiftly down toward the stage. When he embraced the delighted Streisand, his eyes brimmed over and he was red-faced and embarrassed. Now all the world knew that the sentimental Duke could be reduced to tears, and though many were shocked to see Big John Wayne crying like a baby, Pilar was not at all surprised at his reaction. He hadn't prepared a speech and he whispered to Streisand "Beginners luck," before turning to face the audience to speak straight from the heart. He wiped a hand across his eyes to clear the tears and gasped, "Wow. If I'd known that, I'd have put on that eye patch thirty five years ago." The craggy voice broke, he brushed more tears away, "Ladies and Gentlemen, I'm no stranger to this podium. I've come up here and picked up these beautiful golden men before — but always for a friend. One night I picked up two; one for Admiral John Ford and one for our beloved Gary Cooper. I was very clever and witty that night — the envy of Bob Hope. But tonight I don't feel very clever, very witty. I feel grateful, very humble and I owe thanks to many, many people. I want to thank the members of the Academy. To all you people who are watching on television, thank you for taking such a warm interest in our glorious industry. Good night." Simple, to the point and to those fans who had stood loyally by him through thick and thin, keeping faith with him despite his politics and his critics. He was honoured by them and by the industry, and he wasn't too proud to say so.

Hollywood rose as an entity to roar their approval of the man who had loved their "glorious industry" so much that nothing had ever made him turn his back on it. All the set backs, old antagonisms, and political hatred were washed away as the audience refused to sit down and continued cheering long after he had hurried backstage, clutching his Oscar, to join his family.

He and Pilar were stopped by *Chicago Sun Times* reporter, Irv Kupcinet as they stepped outside into the night air. In one of Pilar's rare TV appearances she was asked if she had been nervous, "I think I lost about seven pounds the last two days. Now that it's all over, I'm just so delighted." Duke put his arm around her and strode off toward a waiting car. Inside, it wasn't Duke who held the prized trophy, but Ethan, who pretended to be a soldier, shooting at the crowds with it. When they got back to the hotel Pilar and the Burtons started the celebrations without the winner who spent the next two hours with an eager Press, posing for pictures, answering their questions politely. He was ready for a drink when he finally arrived at his own party. As he walked in he overheard Burton complaining that he should have won the Oscar. Duke placed it in his hands, "You're right, you should have won this, not me." Burton handed it back, shaking his head, and the serious drinking got under way, Duke had a lot of catching up to do.

The following morning Duke had to get straight back to location to carry on filming. When Dave Grayson went to pick him up to take him to the airport he found a happy, smiling Duke, still very drunk from the night before. He hadn't even been to bed but he told Grayson, "I couldn't feel any better than I do right now." As soon as they landed in Tuscon he telephoned Pilar to make sure she and the kids had arrived home safely, then he asked in a tense whisper, "It really happened, didn't it?" She confirmed that Oscar was waiting for him in his den.

When he drove onto the set in Old Tuscon Duke was a little hurt that everyone had their back toward him, no one waved to him or greeted him. The whole crew was standing around doing nothing, until, at a sign from Hawks, they turned to face him. Everyone, including Duke's horse, had an eye patch on, someone waved a ten foot high replica of Oscar and another, a banner proclaiming, "We Love Ya, Duke." He started crying again as the assembled cast and crew clapped and cheered.

When the exteriors were finished the cast returned to CBS studios in Hollywood to complete the interior shots, but Pilar didn't join him in Los Angeles. He stayed alone at a hotel and confessed that once again he was having marital problems. After winning the Oscar he had asked her to go back to Tuscon with him to continue the celebrations. She refused, telling him she didn't want to go on location anymore, "I've got a life of my own now Duke. I'll see you when you get home." It was a cruel, if long anticipated, blow to a man now armed with an Oscar and a clean bill of health.

Just six weeks after winning his coveted Oscar and finishing *Rio Lobo*, another heavy blow landed when he was hit by yet another death in the family. When he received the news that his brother had been struck down by lung cancer he took the death very badly, coming as it did only four months after his Mother had died. He had spent all his life with Bobby hanging on his shirt tails, as a child he had taken his little brother everywhere with him, and later he had carried him into the movie business with him. Bobby had never had any real interest in the work but had always enjoyed the lifestyle that went with being John Wayne's brother. Once again Duke was seen weeping uncontrollably at a funeral, "I didn't do right by Bobby in bringing him into this business. He would have been happier if I'd bought him a hardware store. That would have been more meaningful than what I gave him." But Robert had never complained about the easy and prosperous life his brother had provided. Bobby had loved Duke dearly, had always enjoyed his company, wherever Duke was Bobby had found fun and pleasure in his shadow. Duke had done fine for his little brother.

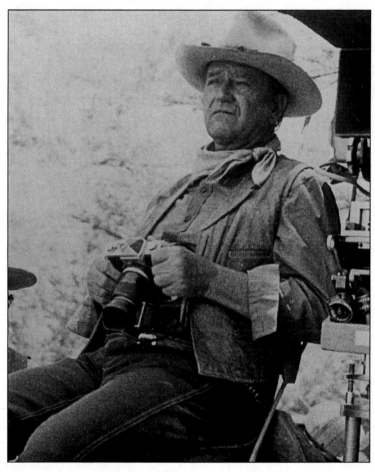

If I had my life over, I'd probably do everything I did. That's not
necessarily the right thing.

CHAPTER NINE

Home is the Hero

"I enjoyed it all so damn much. A man just couldn't have known so many dear people in one lifetime. I had one helluva time. Out there doing the things that keep a man fit ... Yeah ... I had one hell of a good life."

Winning the Oscar put extra money in the bank and Pilar asked him again to retire on the back of his success and begin to take life easier. He was damaging his health by his insistence in carrying on but he had already told her he wouldn't retire and, in the face of her opposition, he embarked on a whole series of films for Batjac in Durango. He finished making *Rio Lobo*, and then in quick succession *Big Jake*, *The Cowboys*, *The Train Robbers* and *Cahill, US Marshal*. He explained why he had to go to Durango, a place he described himself as *really rough*, "Look, when I started out things were different, there was less bureaucracy. We took a cameraman, a grip, a couple of assistants and we went out and made a picture. If there were no houses we'd get a tent, somebody'd go get the food and we'd survive alright. But now ... well ... the logistics are so different, so difficult. I can't just go out and do it where it's rough anymore. We can really only work in Mexico ... some parts of Colorado or Arizona maybe. Then we get a shot set up and a plane goes over, and we all have to sit around for fifteen minutes waiting for the con trail to disappear. You don't realise how much production time that wastes in a day ... we have to work there now, or nowhere ... I have to go."

And, in fact, he was at his happiest when he was roughing it. He yearned for the old days when movie making had been simpler, for the days when he had been one of the boys, chatting with Yak, sitting out under the stars drinking from a shared bottle, days when it had all been fun, "We never went out to make a classic. We tried to make the best picture we could with what we had to work with. We kind of captured companionship and we made the most of it. And it was delightful. These last few years everything has become built up so it's hard to find locations like we used to, and if the locations are gone so too is the comradeship. If there's a road to a location there's a motel. We don't live in tents and eat in a commissary anymore. And at night, everybody goes their separate ways. We're losing the closeness we had."

He told Pilar it was the only place he could make the movies he wanted to make, but he also enjoyed going there, it reminded him of times lost and gone forever, days he couldn't recapture however hard he tried. Dan Ford said, "I don't know what drove him to work so hard to make so many bad movies. I think he just enjoyed the whole process, whether the picture was good or bad. He and my grandfather wanted to be on set, involved in the camaraderie. Making a movie is a grinding, difficult process and it feels so good when you have got it done." But none of the Batjac Westerns he made down there did particularly well. Most scarcely broke even and, as each film struggled, it seemed the day he had been dreading for forty years had arrived. On the back of his greatest moment of triumph, his fans suddenly deserted him. In America *The Godfather*, *The Exorcist* and *The Sting* fared well as the youth culture, generated in the sixties and raised in an atmosphere of civil unrest, youth rebellion, Vietnam and drugs found new heroes. They had no connection with, and felt nothing for, frontier values. The morality of the western shoot-out meant very little to them and for the first time the John Wayne image seemed to have nothing to offer.

If he had been angry before, he now became engulfed by a rage he could scarcely contain. Much of his venom was directed against modern trends in the film world, a world from which he felt increasingly excluded and which was turning out westerns like *The Wild Bunch* which starred several of his friends including William Holden and Ben Johnson. In its graphically brutal opening scenes innocent women and children are slain by the "heroes." Duke could see no marked difference between right and wrong, good or evil, and he hated it. He was disgusted with his friends and the producers for succumbing to modern trends. He refused all compromise and instead became swamped in nostalgia, dwelling on the past and raging about how it had all been lost. He stubbornly clung to the image he had so lovingly created, refusing to bend with the times, increasingly rugged in his determination to make what he called, "The John Wayne Thing." When he discussed films like *The Wild Bunch* he all but foamed at the mouth. The western mythology that he treasured and had so carefully nurtured over the years was being turned into a nightmare from Hell. The cruel and violent modern films were vehicles expressing the tension and anger of modern times, but they didn't reflect western tradition as he saw it, "I haven't seen many films lately that appeal to me. They're so corrupt, or the approach is so cheap that I walk out after the first reel. These days they want to show it all to you, they want to shock you, and shock's all right, but the whole picture shouldn't be all sweat and hair."

The anger boiled over at odd times, unexpectedly, and was often misdirected. P. Kluge, writing for *Life*, believed it was his own long association with the mythology of the nineteenth century which so alienated him from the twentieth century fascination with violence, "Once he gets going Wayne paces his study back and forth. He's flushed and he's breathing hard — for the first time you remember that he has just one lung. He's filled with distress at how things are turning out ... He leaves the study and paces the green carpet edging his patio swimming pool ... you try to calm the roar ... but there's no stopping him ... When we remember him, we will not see an ageing movie cowboy pacing in anger at the edge of the Pacific. We will see him when he was a younger hero, on horseback, in the Monument Valley of 30 years ago. We will picture him a proud figure in a bright and clear landscape ..."

Duke didn't care about the message the new films were trying to put across, the violence was simply too graphic for his own taste, "Movies should be the stuff of illusion, and these pictures shatter all illusions and dreams, they leave no place for escape, no place for hope." The modern taste for vulgarity and violence lay outside his comprehension and he didn't understand why Hollywood was pandering to the country's worst instincts. He could often be found gazing out over the water of the harbour that lapped his back lawn, shaking his head mournfully, longing for a return to old fashioned values, and for some self regulation from within the industry. He had been a supporter of the Production Code which tried to do just that, but when it was made defunct he commented pithily, "Men of bad taste were then allowed in to make pictures. Perhaps I'm just too set in my ways to ride with the times, but I hate what they are doing to the industry I love." He believed the public would get tired of the fare pouring out of Hollywood and he deeply regretted that the Golden era was drawing to a close.

He had been away on location almost constantly after *True Grit*, always in isolated spots, always angry, increasingly withdrawn, lonely and unapproachable, very unlike his old self. He had a lot on his mind and he needed the support of his family. He was, Pilar recognised, sinking back into depression and despair, hit hard by the deaths of his Mother and brother, by the horror that Hollywood had become, by the changing world over which he had no control. She could not reach him any longer and knew the man she had loved was lost to her. Too often he allowed his temper to run unchecked and it wasn't only his wife who dreaded the sound of the Wayne roar. Once, on location, he called to Dave Grayson, his personal make-up man. He didn't hear and carried on his conversation until Duke leapt up in fury and threw a chair across the set. Though it hadn't been aimed, it struck Grayson on the arm and he charged over to confront his boss, "Why the hell did you do that?"

"Well, I called and you deliberately ignored me!" Duke said, as stunned by the incident as Grayson.

Duke, who could be perfectly charming when the need arose, broke the tension, joking "kiss me." Although the incident blew over quickly Duke continued to apologize for his behaviour for the next three days, suffering as much as those around him from his ungovernable temper. Grayson said, "Duke was a man of very contrary qualities, he was naturally humble, without a trace of vanity, and yet it was vital for him to look good in front of others. When I ignored his call, I guess he felt exposed to ridicule, suddenly undignified in front of the crew. He threw the chair to re-establish his macho image." And Grayson might well have been right, the image was vital, but that didn't stop him torturing himself for his behaviour, "In apologetic mood, Duke was like a big, vulnerable kid, charming and ingratiating. He couldn't hold a grudge against anyone for long, and those who really knew him couldn't hold a grudge against him either."

The arguments continued to rage around him as he left home to begin work on *The Cowboys*, a film in which he was starring but had no controlling interest. It promised to be a whole new experience as his co-stars were all young children, and he was to be brutally murdered two thirds of the way through it. He pleaded with Pilar to go along with him on what he expected to be a tough assignment. She told him she had other, more important things to do. He was hurt, disillusioned and bitterly disappointed, "Dammit, you're my wife and your place is with me."

During filming he made a brief visit home. Grayson said when he returned he was very distressed, "He looked as if he'd had enough whiskey to anaesthetise a horse. He had obviously not had enough though because the tears fell unchecked as he sat at the mirror having his make-up applied. He was too drunk to bother trying to hide them." He had been talking to his lawyer, arranging a maintenance settlement. He had fought against the inevitable for some time, it wasn't in his nature to give up but the bitter tears he cried on the set of *The Cowboys* told their own tale of personal defeat.

If he was forced to admit he had failed in his third marriage his career seemed to have picked up again. The movie-going public was looking for something different and he accepted he had to adapt again, without giving in to modern tastes entirely. He set about subtly changing his movie persona in the Mark Rydell film, a picture that proved to be another turning point in his career. The young director had acquired the story as an unpublished novel and originally had no intention of casting Duke, "The prejudicial attitudes I had about John Wayne made him just about my last choice for the role, but Warner Brothers wanted him. I reluctantly sent him a copy of the novel enclosing a note telling him I wasn't looking for a co-producer or co-director, but that I might have a part for him. I flew down to Mexico to meet him. He absolutely disarmed me with his graciousness and warmth." And he needed Duke; Warner's had agreed to increase the film's budget to $6 million if he accepted the part, the largest amount allocated for a film made in the US in 1971 and further testimony to his pulling power, "Wherever his hand falls, the black ink flows, a rare sight these days." Of all the movies being produced in

Hollywood then, only "John Wayne Westerns," a genre in their own right, were still guaranteeing a sizeable return on investment. At the time when the vehicle of stardom was dying on its feet audiences were once again won over by the belief that a Wayne film, however mediocre, was worth going to just for the pleasure of seeing him tie his horse at the hitch rail.

Rydell insisted on surrounding Duke with his own crew and young, trendy method actors but he was astonished by the way the star responded, "He worked slavishly with no reservations. We didn't allow him to use his conventional wardrobe or anything like that. He at first bristled, but soon embraced the challenge and tried to show that he was as good an actor as any of them. In fact he did instinctively what Actors Studio people learn as a craft. He brooded over his role but used to say "pshaw" to our acting talk."

Rydell knew Duke had the reputation of chewing up young directors and spitting them back out again, "Once he started a scene calling "action" without my permission. I was at the top of a crane at the time and I yelled down at him, "Don't ever do that again," I had completely lost my temper. When he finished the scene he got in his car and left. All the crew assumed I would be gone the next day ... I was horrified by my lack of tact. I had told him off in front of a lot of people. I returned to the production office very disappointed with myself. There were four messages waiting for me, all from Wayne. He invited me for dinner. I thought he was going to tell me the film was over. In fact he was the most charming I had ever seen him and from that day he called me "Sir." He told me I treated him in a way he responded to. I reminded him of Ford. He explained that although he had a reputation for being difficult it was just his way of testing people. If a director was weak he was prepared to walk all over them. He was a constant surprise. Here was somebody I disagreed with on almost every level and yet he was most affable, warm and gracious and I couldn't help but respond to him."

In the film Duke played a character forced to hire a group of schoolchildren to help get his herd to market. Rydell said, "He was a giant both physically and in terms of his work but he wasn't threatened in any way by working with children. The kids climbed on him like he was a playground, there just for their amusement. They loved him. And their affection was more than returned. He took an interest in each of them, talked to them and offered fatherly advice and unlimited candy." Duke found them a bonus on that lonely set, he enjoyed working with them and they distracted him and made him smile again. They accepted him as just one of the boys and never treated him as the star. He appreciated it, "In this one I play a sixty year old rancher with eleven kids under my wing and I try to get us all through a cattle drive. No actor in his right mind would try to match the antics of 11 kids on screen. But you know what — it's been the greatest experience of my life!"

Throughout the filming of *The Cowboys* he was plagued by the Press who still found every move he made newsworthy. He sat patiently, if a little bored, through scores of interviews, shrugging aside questions he didn't want to answer, stringing together words he had often used in the past but which still satisfied most of them, and occasionally enjoying moments of unexpected banter with them. This time it was harder, he felt less inclined to talk, they found him a little distant, and he smiled sadly as he said, "I've had the most appealing of lives. I've been lucky enough to portray man against the elements at the same time as there was always someone there to bring me the orange juice. I never had to choose between adventure and comfort!"

Many of the films he made after *True Grit* rejected any kind of domestic life and were more often about abstinence, and his character in *The Cowboys*, Wil Anderson, became a focal point for the tragic figure of the man who gives his life for the enrichment of the next generation. He worked hard creating Anderson and was so successful that one writer called the murder scene, "The most shocking moment of violence in the Nixon era. It is as if the Statue of Liberty had been toppled. More than any other, the moment marked the demise of the heroic westerner. From that time on all that remained were fragments of the legend." Many felt the film might be a fitting last episode for the legendary cowboy. Duke could hardly agree, the whole point of the exercise was to keep working, to create a character and a performance so fine that the studios would continue to see him as a banker despite the difficulty of getting him insured. He was, however, worried about how the death scene would be interpreted by the fans, the studios and the critics. Everyone involved in the project dreaded broaching it with him. It called for a brutal fight, witnessed by the boys and ended when he got shot in the back. Rydell planned the bloodiest sequence ever in a John Wayne film, knowing full well how strongly he opposed graphic violence. So far the director had navigated the choppy waters well and had managed to avoid all the pitfalls associated with working with Duke. He put off discussing the scene until the very last moment and finally asked Dave Grayson if he could broach the subject. Grayson warned ominously that it would take four men to get Duke into such bloody make-up, three just to hold him down whilst he applied it. Everyone expected the reaction to be volcanic but when Grayson finally found the courage to tell him he was subdued and resigned, "Well, alright. Go ahead. Put the stuff on," although he added with determination, "But I won't tolerate bodies opening up and liver flying out all over the place." On the morning it was to be shot Grayson applied the evil wounds to his face, and slopped blood down the front of his shirt, and when Duke caught a glimpse of himself in the mirror he smiled sarcastically, "Why don't you put a little more on me?" It hadn't taken four of them to hold him down, just plenty of free-flowing booze and Grayson recalled Duke was in mellow mood as he left his trailer, "He filmed the entire scene through a drunken haze."

Years later Duke still insisted, "He didn't need that stuff all over me. If you had just seen me bust the guy's head against the tree you would have realised that he was mad at me. But they made us wet and snotty and the audience is saying, "Wait a minute, what's going on here?" Before they get into the mood for me to play a death scene, I've played it and it's over. I pleaded with Rydell, "Just take a shot of me in the sand, any goddamn place. Boom, guy goes down, cut." The reaction of the kids to my death was also wrong and alienated the audience. I think Rydell knows he made a mistake, but Hell, I got good money to do what he says. Only one man can paint the picture but it's kinda sad when you think what it could have been if the scene had only been played right. The audience couldn't cry because they weren't in the right mood. ....I just don't understand why that happened. But I do know they blame me when it turns out like that. Kinda sad. And I know it could have been so good."

His breathing problems worsened dramatically as he struggled through the difficult schedule. Mary said, "He was still in so much pain eleven years after losing his lung. It was really tough for him. I'll never forget him coughing his way through the dust storms in Santa Fe. His problems with the thin air became serious and any effort caused him to breathe so heavily that the crew were unable to tape his microphone to his chest as it picked up too much wheezing and panting as he struggled. He was in such misery."

In fact even those who would not normally have been sympathetic toward Duke were worried by his dogged insistence on doing several difficult riding scenes himself. Rydell allowed him to continue as long as he could, and turned away when he became so winded he could just about remain standing. It hurt Duke's pride badly to have to give in but Rydell was happy enough with his consistent performance and felt irritated when other actors' erratic readings forced him into a re-take, "It took great effort on his part just to curtail his rapid gasping but he always hoped no one noticed how weak he was. His health was the hot topic of gossip amongst the crew and everyone present was acutely aware that he was walking around with just one lung. They were all extra careful where he was involved, anxious to get everything right first time. I did everything I could to lessen the strain on him."

Rydell began the project an unwilling admirer but later admitted, "Duke is an individual man, like the character in the film. He was also a stunning shock to me. I went in prepared to do battle, to "handle" him, but I found one of the most incredible professionals I have ever met. He knew he was in alien territory but he was always ready, always listened to reason, he never let our differences get in his way, and because of him we finished way ahead of schedule. As soon as he knew anyone was in trouble he was the first in there, helping out. It's very unusual for me to be charmed by such a man. But I knew he had to have something to have captured world interest for the past forty odd years. All it took was a week in his company to realise that his qualities are quite remarkable. He is sharp, with a wit and ability to make the most pungent observations. I found myself listening to him and learning. The key to his success, I think, is that he is so secure as a man you don't have to worry about stepping on his toes. At first I was terrified of him. To begin with he is just so BIG. But he was obviously so happy to be working, so happy to be before the lens, you could detect the unmistakable eagerness on his face as soon as it was his turn to get up and step into the lights. I guess he was a little frustrated not to have any control over scenes and props but he gave no trouble. It was fascinating to go out in public with him, after all he is one of the ten most famous people in the world. In the middle of meals people would come up to demand his autograph and he was unfailingly courteous, never appearing to resent the imposition on his time or privacy. I never saw him turn one person away. John Wayne is far more flexible than is commonly allowed." The other stars in the film agreed and Roscoe Lee Brown added, "I came prepared to dislike him but I found an intelligent, courteous and well-read man. He's literate, genuine, a compassionate human being who can spend hours discussing Shelley and Keats with liberal left-wingers. Duke had everyone eating out of his hand. He was so articulate and sensitive and totally unselfish. The Great Dictator turned out to be a lamb."

The critics loved him in the movie, "Old dusty britches can act." Molly Haskell, a well known feminist wrote, "The Wayne I shall always cherish is the humbled and softened hero. It is Wayne the gentle patriarch, the last of what I hope is a dying breed, that I love ... indeed it is difficult not to!" His fans hated it and were unwilling to watch their hero murdered only two thirds of the way into the film. They stayed away and it made little money for Warners but Duke marched on toward the conclusion of the legend, the humbled hero of *The Cowboys*.

And ironically, he only managed to survive at all in films set in modern urban landscapes. His fans hadn't rejected him, they still longed for the image of the loner, righting all wrongs, but not in the setting of the western. The city had become the domain of the outlaw and was where the weak needed the protection of an Ethan Edwards. Duke's first chance at such a role came when he was offered the part of Harry Callahan, in Dirty Harry, the cop who broke the rules in the pursuit of justice. He was busy fulfilling his many other commitments when he turned it down and Clint Eastwood grabbed it to go on to fame and fortune. He came to regret his decision and when he saw the film he knew he had made a terrible mistake, he realised *Dirty Harry* was John Wayne, removed from the old west and placed down in the city; "How did I ever let that one slip through my fingers?" He attempted to capitalise on the idea, making *McQ* in 1974, and *Brannigan*, released the following year. Both films came too late and both were hit hard by the same critics who had so loved *The Cowboys*, both just scraped a profit, whereas *Dirty Harry* generated $18 million.

Even though his last films had made little money he remained immensely popular with his fans, and despite his general decline the seventies saw him awarded honour after honour. He felt grateful and humble and spurred on. His critics had never managed to slow him down, neither could he now sit back in the glow of the accolades. His destiny had never lain in the hands of others, never been a matter of chance, nor luck, but had always had more to do with his own self-belief and fanatical effort, "They offered me $75 a picture and I jumped." Now he was winning awards and earning a million dollars a picture he was no better able to relax than he had ever been. He was not a man to await the next moment, he had always actively hunted each one down. The pursuit had been lifelong, unrelenting and he had chased his fate with a single-mindedness that left little room for anything or anyone else. His strength of purpose, determination and willingness to continue the chase at all cost, were the qualities that separated him from all the others aspiring to Hollywood immortality. He simply had to keep moving and was never happy unless there was a target to aim at, a challenge to overcome. Awards meant little to him and in the early seventies when he was asked why he had wanted to be a movie star he answered, "I didn't. I wanted to be a director, but they offered me too much money ... God ... I sometimes made $500." The interviewer persisted, "But why do you keep working?"

"M.U.N.Y."

"No! How much have you made?"

"Quite a bit." Duke hesitated before hanging his head and confessing, "But I haven't kept a whole lot of it. I've been better at making it than keeping it." It was a sad reflection of how he viewed his situation and when he was asked later why he kept working when he didn't have to, when he had already won everything, he responded angrily, no longer amused, "What makes you think I don't have to work? Have you checked my financial statements? If you did, you'd know that if I'm going to continue to live this way, I do have to work. Awards don't pay the bills. Maybe I should be in a position where I don't have to, but I'm not." He continued to suffer the severe cash flow problems that had long plagued his life and by the seventies he was still forced to work hard.

He even began accepting offers to do television commercials in an attempt to pay the bills that the awards didn't. He had long disliked the intrusion of television in his career and felt degraded to be forced to accommodate it so late in his life. Early in 1977 he signed a deal to advertise a headache remedy in an episode that took on nightmarish proportions. His fans thought the idea of John Wayne needing anything for a headache was ludicrous, and he too felt it tarnished his image. His own identity had been submerged in the "John Wayne thing" long since, he hated the idea of appearing weak before others, and it was not long before he backed out of the arrangement. He promised himself he would never get tangled up in another. It was one promise he broke. He was desperately short of money and feeling very insecure when Great Western Savings approached him offering $350,000 a year to advertise their company. As old age approached and offers of work began to dry up he'd not really slowed down much, he still felt the burning, restless energy and no matter what he told others, it was that, more than a need to earn money, that continued to drive him. He poured himself into one venture after another, including the commercials.

Pilar was engrossed in her own life and they no longer even shared a bedroom. She told some friends it was because of his snoring, others that he was impotent. Whatever the reason there was very little physical closeness between them anymore and he missed her warmth. Until cancer struck they often danced with each other at home, kissing, cuddling and always holding hands, oblivious to everything and everyone else. They frequently swam together late at night, or took themselves off to their specially made bed straight after dinner where they changed into silk pyjamas and lay close, watching TV, reading, or just talking and laughing for hours. To loose that closeness was devastating to the man who could never get enough love and affection. But once Pilar had turned to her new religion she could no longer smoke or drink or even share the love they had known in that huge bed, and whether he liked it or not she took herself off to the guest room. He raged that Christian Science ruined their marriage and took all the fun out of his life. He was hurt when she drifted away but equally, was too proud to explain how he felt, to ask her to give her religion up or to go back to being his old Pilar. Instead he complained bitterly about small things like the length of her tennis dress, shouting that it wasn't seemly for the wife of John Wayne to go out in such a short outfit. He felt threatened and insecure but knew in his heart that the changes in her were the direct result of his overwhelming need to work and had little to do with Christian Science. Between 1939 and 1972 he had made an astonishing average of over two films a year, putting in six to nine months of each of those years away on location. He often worked sixteen-hour days, attending meetings and conferences, doing vast amounts of promotional work, running his production company and carrying out the day to day tasks required to keep his career up and running. The result had been frequent spells of severe illness, exhaustion and depression, and hardly controlled temper tantrums. He was well aware that he was difficult to handle, extremely demanding, and that his wife and children now found him uncomfortable to be around. But he missed them and wanted them back, and would have done anything for them. He hated the changes taking place in his life and longed for security and continuity. Both Marion and John Wayne, the man and the star, felt lost, tired and unwell.

He began flying round the country visiting old friends, spending the little money he had trying to fill the emotional voids in his life. He loved to go to the ranch near Springerville where he and Louis Johnson still ran their successful partnership. The two men remained close and every Thanksgiving Duke attended the cattle sale at Stanfield where he enjoyed mixing and relaxing with the cattlemen who expected nothing of him, made no demands and accepted him as one of their own. They gave him no special attention and he loved it. In 1974 at a party held by Johnson, Duke fell into a swimming pool and when one of those present shouted, "Shit, he can't walk on water after all!" it was the film icon who laughed the loudest. All his life he had enjoyed the easy companionship of male friends, liked being one of the boys and being with people who allowed him to be a man rather than an untouchable star. He appreciated the way the cattlemen teased him and laughed at his status. He knew he was accepted when they began playing elaborate practical jokes on him. The jokes went both ways and he was well equipped to fight back. On one occasion he got two of the cattlemen drunk and persuaded them to invest $2500 each in a non-existent enterprise. He took their money and gave it to another friend who was going off on his honeymoon! It took three years for them to get even but they did it with a vengeance that surprised him. They began placing fictitious bets on a horse and bragging to Duke about how much they were winning on it. Finally, when Duke could contain himself no longer, they "allowed" him to buy a share of the animal for $12,500. At the next Thanksgiving cattle sale Duke was discussing the merits of the horse but soon realised that no one else had heard about it. He was just becoming suspicious when Johnson let everyone in on the joke.

He found it easier being around men. He always suspected women were trying to take advantage of him, "They usually just want a piece of me. They frighten me." He was self conscious, always careful, always on guard. He idolized them, needed them to complete his life, but still they made him feel uncomfortable and guilty. His mother had always made him feel bad, as had one wife after another, for one thing or another, he took few risks as a result. And it wasn't just his women that gave him problems; sometimes even his children made him feel guilty. He continued to worry about the kind of father he was but his friend Maureen O'Hara said, "Have you ever been on the set of any of his pictures? Not only are his own children around … but any number of grandchildren. For God's sake, there's never been a time that one, two, or three of them aren't crawling all over him, even when he's playing cards with the guys. They are on his lap, his shoulders, around his legs, and he's a great picker-upper, a hugger and a kisser."

He wanted to spend more time with them, and it was only when he started making demands on their time that difficulties occurred. Both Aissa and Ethan felt he was too easily hurt when they did not want to be with him. When his second-chance children were small they loved being with him, loved the attention and care he gave. But in trying so hard to be a good father he managed only to alienate them and make them all feel uncomfortable. In 1970, when he got home after completing *Big Jake* he wanted to take the whole family away on *The Wild Goose*. Aissa, then fifteen, wanted to stay with friends. He tried everything he could to get her to go, begging and cajoling, and finally becoming angry and flying into one of his towering rages, "Oh, you'd rather be with your friends than with me. I'm home from making a movie and you'd rather be with them." The demands he made put up the very barriers he had been so desperate to avoid.

He had never found being the father of teenagers easy. They wanted to wear what they wanted to wear, to go where they wanted to go, and to do what they wanted to do. They didn't care about John Wayne's image and didn't understand that they could destroy it either. It was even harder for him to accept the needs of his second family than it had been with the first because he was so much older. He came from a different generation of fathers and these rapidly growing youngsters frustrated and bewildered him where once they had given him only the utmost pleasure. He had loved the holidays on the boat when he and the kids spent relaxed hours swimming and playing. He simply couldn't accept they had grown away from him, as all children must. Pilar complained bitterly about his need to possess the people he cared for, and patiently tried to explain that he was smothering her and the kids, "My beautiful nineteenth century man couldn't adapt to the seventies." He didn't understand and continued to fight tooth and nail to keep them all close under his protective wing.

He had successfully manufactured a stunning array of characters to satisfy the changing demands of the cinema-going public but was hopelessly lost when it came to pleasing his wife. He was overwhelmed by the discovery that she no longer found him attractive. He had never paid much attention to his thinning hair or his weight, he had been steadfastly opposed to the idea of cosmetic surgery and hated the world's preoccupation with his looks but now he was afraid of loosing his wife to a younger man. He confessed his anguish to the captain of the *Wild Goose*, saying that nothing he ever did was enough for her. He moaned that he loved her, was afraid of loosing her, but that he felt the age gap was to blame for her coolness toward him now, "Damn it! I bend over backwards trying to please her, but no matter what I do, she just doesn't seem to care … I really don't know what the hell to do."

He was adrift and couldn't get close to the family he loved. His relationship with Aissa became particularly fraught. He wanted to keep all his children wrapped in cotton wool, safe and protected. Aissa wasn't interested in protection; she was a teenager growing up in the rebellious sixties and seventies and she wanted to take risks, she wanted to make her own way in life and was angered by his clumsy attempts to help. She lost all faith in her old fashioned father and rejected the legendary John Wayne values of truth, honour, right and wrong that he had pushed at her, wilfully breaking as many of his rules as she could. She, like her mother, felt the urgent need to escape his overbearing influence, she didn't wanted to be an extension of John Wayne's life.

He was sad, confused and concerned, he didn't know what to do and he also became increasingly angry with her. He didn't understand what he had done to make her so desperate to get away from him. He'd given her everything he could, just as he had her mother. Pilar tried to explain that if he just loosened his grip everything would be alright. But not only was he unable to let go, he didn't want to. He was a generation older than most fathers of teenage children, and he was stricter than most. When the other local kids went barefoot to the beach he gave his famous lecture, "John

Wayne's children wear shoes and socks." When his teenage daughter cried her frustration it served only to spur his rage, "Why do you cry when I yell at you? Because you can't go out with bare feet? Jesus Christ!" He shook his head in disbelief, "What the hell's going wrong?" Pilar had all but destroyed him, now he had to face the fact that his precious daughter wished she wasn't his and rarely even used the name "Wayne."

Sometimes though, his reactions to their exploits were unexpected, like the time he discovered Aissa was using diet pills and amphetamines. He had repeatedly begged each of them not to shame him in public, "I worked fifty years for my reputation, I worked damned hard. If you get caught doing something wrong, or if you're with kids who are doing things wrong, it will go right in the papers. You'll ruin all that hard work as easy as that. You'll ruin me. So really think about it before you do anything stupid." Aissa thought about it every time she smoked pot or ran barefoot to the beach. When she was finally caught out he didn't rage but told her quietly instead, "Aissa, I love you very much. The people that gave you that stuff, they don't love you the way I do. You can take their word that this stuff is good, or you can listen to me when I tell you it's bad. Who's word are you going to take, someone who's loved you all your life, or someone you met two days ago?"

He was fighting a losing battle and couldn't recreate times long gone. The kids and Pilar resented his effort to be the husband and father he wanted to be. They looked forward to him going away on location as much as they had dreaded his going not so long before, at least when he was away they got some peace and could run their lives as they wanted to.

Part of the problem with his younger children was related to the guilt he continued to feel about the older ones. It could be seen in many of his later films where most of the characters he played had trouble with women and children, where he is alienated because of his work, which is either dangerous or takes him away for long stretches. He consistently demonstrated love and a willingness to sacrifice himself for his family whilst being unable to live within a normal relationship. On screen he said exactly how he felt about that. He might argue with or shout at Pilar but he found it almost impossible to discuss his innermost feelings with her, he was unable to express pain, disappointment or fear, he was even uncomfortable around those who did. He was much more successful at exposing his emotions before the camera. Taken out of himself, put down on a set in costume and make-up, he could reveal himself and react freely to any situation. Love, fear inadequacy and insecurity were obvious and his apologies were offered profusely. He hoped those he wanted to talk to were listening for he had no other way of communicating with them. Very often the messages were aimed directly at his children and Andrew McLaglen, director and friend, said Cahill in particular was, "A deep statement of feeling from the heart to all seven of his children." Duke himself tried to explain, "Movie goers interact with their idols through an idealization of the screen presence tied to an awareness of the star's private life. I felt justified using my screen image to reflect my private life, of using the movie to make contact with all the elements of my life." He used "The John Wayne" movie for his own ends, manipulating the vehicle to express his own personality, desires and needs. When JD Cahill tells his elder son, "I've been gone a lot of times when you kids really needed me. And I've missed a lot too. Missed watching you two grow up. I think about it a lot. On every job. But even before that job was finished another one seemed to crop up … I don't want what I'm saying to sound like excuses. There is no excuse for negligence." Here was Duke talking to any one of his children. He had many flaws but he worked hard at being a good father. He desperately wanted his children to benefit from his lifetime's effort and was tireless in his attempt to provide them with the financial security he hadn't known himself. He didn't believe that made him a negligent or bad father, only a busy one.

He had ventured to Durango once again to make *Cahill*, saying, "Down here we can still tell a story about human frailties, about a lawman and his kids who become criminals, children neglected by their father because he is always too busy doing his job. We can get down to the nitty gritty of what's wrong today. It didn't have to be a western at all, but somehow the beauty of the West gives it a spaciousness and an earthiness."

Most of the locations he worked on were still open to the Press and he continued giving interviews to anyone who wanted to talk. Whilst he worked on *Cahill* he spoke to as many reporters as possible, there was nothing like a good trade paper report to stimulate interest in a flagging career. He had started smoking cigars again and it was noticed immediately, "Yeah," he responded scowling, "I try to hold it down to three a day and not inhale, but it's hard. Once you've been a smoker it's hard to stop inhaling, and I catch myself!" Politics continued to be a source of irritation and sometimes, after perhaps half an hour of trying to divert them, he stalked away to his chair where he would slump exhausted and tried to recover his temper without giving offence. Once he cooled off he might wander back to give more answers to unimaginative questions. Microphones were frequently pushed under his nose as he was asked about the problems with the young today. His face burned as he snarled, "I don't see anything wrong. It's you people who make a lot of a few bad ones. They're no worse than they have ever been, only today they get more attention. We spend a lot of time telling them about their rights, but we don't talk to them about their responsibilities."

Left to his own devices he concentrated on the good things in life, always seeing the best in people, young or old, and as soon as he was asked about his own children he still melted and turned into a real softie. He was happy to dwell on them, his pride in each, despite their problems, obvious, "I do tell them about responsibility and what we expect of them. My Dad wanted me to be a man, and that's what I hope for my boys too. I am proud of my girls. The most important advice I can give them is to follow their own conscience, trust their own judgement and don't let political parties or other institutions tempt them away from what they know to be right. I tell them not to sacrifice their moral standards and to take a strong attitude toward life, stand up for what they believe in. I don't tell them what to believe in. There's that hour before you hit the sack at night, when you're alone. That's when you have to think over your past and that helps you shape your future, your attitude to other people and situations. In that hour you can think about self-respect. I believe if you lose sight of that you loose everything. That's what I believe and it's what I've tried to teach my kids too."

Once he started reminiscing they gleaned many a good new story from him, "My dad told me he had been forced to play the piano, so he told me I could choose what I wanted and I picked the banjo. There was a fella called Fat Stockbridge at Glendale who could really play and my Dad arranged for me to get lessons. Trouble was I was so mixed up in all the school activities that I never practised and when Fat and I got together he'd end up playing dirty songs. In college I pawned the banjo to go away for a weekend and that was the end of my musical career." None of them knew John Wayne played the banjo! The few writers who understood he mellowed as soon as politics were off the agenda got by far the best of him, and those who hung around after the others had drifted away were sometimes allowed to catch a glimpse of the real man. If they thought to ask him about music he smiled gently, "For my dough Sinatra's stuff is best. I guess I'm a little sentimental, but some of the things he does are so beautiful. I love Country and Western too, I like Charlie Pride." He enjoyed relaxing in the setting sun talking about music and the kids. He might have been struggling to breathe all day at altitude, hollering directions to other actors, camera men, lighting technicians who couldn't deliver what he wanted, he might have been driven to despair by some of the sycophants who hung around, but come the time of day the hangers on all went home he enjoyed nothing better than sitting talking, enjoying another cigar. He always allowed one last question before sauntering away to dine alone in his trailer, "When do you plan to retire?"

411

He smiled, "Never. I intend to stay in the saddle until I drop!" And there was his message for Pilar. She wanted him to give up the cigars, to stop working, she wanted him to relax and reap the rewards of his effort. She wanted him to change. He might apologise to his children for what he knew was negligence but wives were a different matter entirely. She had known from the outset the demands of his work, and he would not apologize or ask forgiveness for any seeming neglect toward her. In that, Pilar was no different to his previous wives. He had always wanted each of them to be with him all the time. He had never wanted to be apart from them, and was prepared to give each of them the world, but he expected them to be willing to share the life of John Wayne. His mother's unhappiness had stemmed from his father's inability to provide a decent lifestyle for her. None of his wives could level such a complaint against him. He provided each with all the things he thought his mother would have wanted. In return, he expected to be loved on his own terms, it was the price to be paid for his complete devotion. His friends said it was possible to see how much he loved Pilar when he talked about her. He talked about her all the time.

No matter how much he loved her he had little patience with her new religion, tennis, friends, or any of the other things that took her away from him. He thundered that if he couldn't have the old Pilar back she might as well leave him altogether. Things were out of control and he shouted his disappointment. He never stopped loving her but by the early 1970's he was very angry with her. He no longer considered her a real wife, at least not the one he had chosen to marry. He couldn't talk about it, couldn't clear the air between them, and they drifted further and further apart, until the rift became fatal.

In 1973 he announced his third marriage was over. He told reporters it was his fault, that the problems had arisen because of his work schedule, "Pilar and I can't seem to get an understanding between us anymore," he added, "I can get along with everybody. Why the hell can't I get along with women?" He acted tough and spoke in a cold detached voice, he hid his fears and no one saw John Wayne cry because he had lost the woman he loved. At least, no one on the outside saw, but after a particularly bitter fight with Pilar he told Aissa, "Your mother and I are having serious problems. I love her so much, I love you, I love our family, but I have to work — you know I have to — it's hard on your mother. She doesn't understand …" He was a mess, he hadn't shaved, and tears ran unchecked down his stubbled face. He sat for a long time talking about the old days, the people he had already lost, and about his fears for the future. Who was going to protect John Wayne from life's hardest knocks?

He was devastated by yet another failure. But this time he had done his best, he knew there was nothing more he could have done to make this marriage work. His priorities had never altered, but, almost overnight it seemed to him, Pilar wanted him to change. When she asked him again to retire she was asking for something he couldn't give. Without work he was a lost soul and he saw only hours of loneliness stretching ahead of him if he gave in to her demands.

He did try to cut back in a half-hearted attempt at compromise, it wasn't enough and Pilar warned him that she would be moving out of their home. Before carrying out her threat she made one last effort, pleading with him to go with her to see a marriage counsellor. The idea of talking openly to a stranger filled him with disgust, "I don't believe in all that mumbo-jumbo. We are grown people and we ought to be able to settle our problems ourselves. Couches are only good for one thing. You never understood my need to work. That's all that's wrong between us and I don't need a counsellor to tell me that."

His wife left and the house fell silent. His children didn't take sides but knew how badly he suffered. He needed them more than ever and Aissa said, "I'd never seen him so torn up, nor so lonely. We visited him frequently and tried our best to help him out." Pilar expected they would get back together and knew he still loved her. She hoped they would be able to work things out. Mary told her he sat alone crying for three days after she removed her belongings. She had gone when he was away filming knowing he wouldn't let her go had he been there. It was December, the time he most enjoyed sharing with his family. She knew she was destroying his vision of happiness and how disappointed and hurt he would be. But, although he was a sorry sight throughout the holiday period, life didn't really change that much for him during the first months after the split. He had never spent much time at home. He still didn't. Just because Pilar was no longer living at home he saw no reason to change his normal life's patterns. He stayed away a little more, and worked even harder. All the time he was away he could pretend nothing had happened. He talked to her on the phone from location, just as he always had, and he supported each of her new ventures. If anything, although he felt adrift, he was more open and friendly with her than before. Still, he hardly looked forward to his future with anything other than the deepest anxiety and he bitterly resented the fact that Pilar wasn't there to ease his way into old age.

The children were certain their dad couldn't make it without her and were sure he would ask her to go back to him. Of course they didn't know much about his colourful past. Historically when a wife became difficult she was replaced. He only loved one woman at a time, but he had to have a woman in his life and now he badly needed a replacement.

In the early 1970's faithful Mary St John, the woman at his side longer than any other, decided it was time to retire. She personally interviewed and hand-picked the small, dark, bubbly and intelligent Pat Stacy and then set about training her to work for a demanding, but very loveable boss. From 1972 she phased herself out of his life and allowed her replacement to take over. Pat worked out of his Batjac office at first and it was over a month before she was introduced to him, "I was surprised by his warmth, his sense of humour and his obvious gentleness." The thirty-two year old was instantly attracted by his unassuming and kind manner and gradually relaxed in his company. More than that, she developed a crush on him and her eyes followed him hungrily whenever they worked together. Duke, of course, was instantly aware of her feelings, it was not uncommon for new members of staff to react to him in that way, and although he knew the impact he had on people, he never took advantage. He smiled, remained open and friendly but didn't say anything untoward. He didn't want to embarrass her. Whenever he caught her staring at him or jumping to perform trivial tasks he laughed and tried to ease the situation with humour. He introduced her to his wife and children. They all appeared so affectionate toward each other that she had been working for him for some time before she began to realise all was not well in the Wayne household and sensed his depression at the way things were turning out. And there was his replacement, waiting, ready, willing and able to pick up the pieces.

She began working at his home two days a week but was kept completely busy as his secretary; their relationship was all business. He gave no indication that he was looking for anything other than an efficient secretary and he remained completely impersonal toward her. But as Pat learned more about him she came to understand his needs and his fears; he became less the superstar boss, more a man in need of help. It was as inevitable as night follows day that he became involved with her but he took pains not to get too close too soon. He was scared to admit that he was attracted to a woman who was even younger than his wife and at first he was almost brusque in his dealings with her. He was unsure of himself but it wasn't too long before he began to actively seek her company.

He was looking forward to starting work on his next venture, *McQ*, due to be shot in Seattle. Once more the Press was hot on his heels; Duke abandoning his natural environment of the Old West was newsworthy and they wondered if they were witnessing the end of an era. His name was synonymous with the Western where he rode tall in the saddle. Had things changed, or was he playing the natural descendant of John T. Chance, taking the next logical step in bringing the American hero up to date? Wasn't he a little long in the tooth for a new twist?

"Well fellas," he drawled, "I guess it was just time for a change."

He was grateful that all the questions were about his pictures; thankfully none of them had scented the dramatic events taking place in his private life. He had been married so long and seemed so blissfully happy that they assumed things were going to stay that way. They never thought to question it. He had made exactly the same mistake himself. He was not his usual amiable self for the pack of news hounds. Filming was falling behind schedule, he didn't like the story or the script, he was restless and on edge. As soon as the cry went up, "The sun's out!" he raced to get in front of the camera, eager to get it over with. They were running late and all he had to do was play chess or listen to newspaper men commenting, "Why would a two-fisted hombre like Duke leave the wide open spaces to take refuge in a police station?" Well the two-fisted hombre was fed up and he hadn't particularly wanted to leave the wide open spaces. More chess, lunch, lines, sun in, sun out, more talk with the Press.

"Why the sudden change Duke? Isn't this a come down?"

"Certainly not. You have the wrong idea son. This is a promotion. *McQ* is a modern counterpart of all the lawmen I have ever played. Only the scenery is different, and it's nice, I don't have to fall off a horse. *McQ* is the same as *Cahill* or *Big Jake*, he's a tough old bird who doesn't indulge in the frivolities that other detectives like. Not that he's a dirty policeman or unfeeling. But I have done civilian films before. I do own suits you know!"

When the sun set on another frustrating day he retreated to *The Wild Goose*, at rest in the harbour, where Pat was waiting to smooth things over. It was the first time Mary hadn't accompanied him, the first time Pat took up her full responsibilities. She was excited to be working alone with him and he caught her enthusiasm, she was like a breath of fresh air. And slowly, as the days passed, his mood lifted. He began to feel a little better, less raw, less frayed.

During filming he was delighted when Pilar dropped by unexpectedly, then was just as suddenly thrown into despair when she told him she wasn't staying because she had a tennis tournament to attend. She wanted him to look after their youngest daughter while she was away. "If that's the way you want things," he murmured. That was the way she wanted it. He felt as though he had been discarded and from that moment on he made little attempt to hide his attraction for his secretary. On the evening he was to attend the premiere of *Cahill, US Marshall* in Seattle, he invited her to go along with him. He was more informal than before, he joked and talked affably, and things were about to change. That night he took her for dinner after the show and they had a lot to drink. When they got back to *The Goose* he guided her toward his room without saying a word. He had already left for work when she woke the next morning but the crew showed no surprise when she sidled out of his room wrapped in one of his towels.

He remained friendly and relaxed toward her, he seemed to be easy and comfortable, but he didn't invite her back to his bed. He liked her because she eased the dull ache Pilar had left behind and she amused him but he felt guilty about what he'd done. He felt he had used both her and the situation.

When they got back to Newport life returned to normal. He became moody and withdrawn, and, missing his family badly, he toyed again with the idea of reconciliation. He made a half-hearted attempt to talk things over with her but Pilar was no longer prepared to live according to his dictates, "He would have given me anything money could buy. The only thing he couldn't give was any degree of independence. He was no nearer understanding women toward the end of his life than he'd ever been." Though deeply wounded by her continued rejection and, knowing his marriage hung in the balance, he blustered to the Press, "She can have a divorce any time she wants." The self assurance was a façade. He had always turned to work to ease his burdens but nothing he did now wiped out the loneliness he felt.

The only moments of relief he knew came from Pat who was willing to do anything for him. She offered an uncomplicated relationship and was perfectly happy to give up her identity to share his, she enjoyed his company, she idolised him. And although Duke never stopped loving or wanting Pilar, and continued to talk highly of her, he felt abandoned, confused, and missed having female warmth in his life. He turned to Pat and she stayed at his side, comforting him through all his next, most difficult years. He and Pilar never divorced and he never openly declared any other relationship in his life.

Pat only wanted to be with him, she was happy to play hostess to his friends, she worshipped him and would willingly have married him had he asked. He never did, he thought she was much too young, and more importantly, that he was much too old for another marriage. He openly took her out but told everyone they were friends and professional associates. His image always firmly at the back of his mind, he never let her stay overnight at his house, and said, "Sure, I've taken her out a couple of times. But there's no particular romance … I'm past the age of romance. I'm getting smart enough to know."

The death of John Ford had left him deeply traumatised and the last thing he had wanted was to loose Pilar as well, but in Seattle he resigned himself to the inevitable. Mary St John explained, "Mr Wayne misses having a woman in the house. He's very much a family man. He's also a one woman man. He tried very hard to save the marriage to Pilar. I'll say that for him."

In 1972 he was distracted from his personal heartache by the call for a strictly defined code of decency in Hollywood. Duke, who hated so much of what was being turned out, saw the code as being too close to censorship, and when the industry called for his support against it he gave it unreservedly. He argued against the proposals made by the Californian conservatives in several radio speeches and when their plans were defeated they turned against the darling of the Right, for his part in their downfall. But he was only dabbling in politics and his interest came to an abrupt end in 1973, the year of the Watergate scandal.

As the news first broke he switched the TV channel back and forth, sometimes watching more than one set at a time. He shouted at the screen, flying into a rage and throwing things, "Those bastards have to be cute to know ahead of time what the president is going to do." Nixon was a personal friend and when he said he had no involvement Duke saw no reason to doubt him. All through 1974 as the incident unfolded he stood by the beleaguered President, calling for reporters to get off his back and let him do his job. He believed in the system and was sure Nixon stood above reproof. When he resigned in disgrace, up to his neck in lies, Duke, who had gone out on a limb for him, could hardly believe it and was deeply shocked, "Damn. He lied to me."

Until 1976, when he began campaigning on behalf of Gerald Ford, he kept a low profile in the political arena. When Jimmy Carter came to power he didn't dwell on the disappointment of another Republican failure, and was delighted when the President-elect invited him to the pre-inaugural festivities in Washington. Carter, it turned out, was a great John Wayne fan! At the gala, Duke congratulated him graciously, "I am privileged to be present and accounted for in this capital of freedom, to watch a common man take on uncommon responsibilities that he has won fair and square by stating his case to the American people ... I'm considered a member of the opposition, the loyal opposition. Accent on the "loyal." I'd have it no other way." Later that evening Carter left the receiving line when he saw Duke enter the room and the Republican and the Democrat had a long friendly talk. Duke was impressed by Carter's sincerity, it made a refreshing change and gave him heart for the future.

The two men were political opponents however and they maintained a lengthy, albeit consistently polite, correspondence. Carter was always one of the first to congratulate Duke when he won yet another award. They forged an unexpectedly warm friendship and shared much common ground. Duke proved time and again that he wasn't a doctrinaire conservative, often to the despair of the Right. He came in for heavy criticisms over his stance on the Panama Canal Treaty, when he sided with Carter. America had seized control of the Panama Canal Zone in 1903, and Roosevelt admitted he stole it. The zone was a strategically valuable piece of territory controlled by the US, which effectively cut Panama in half. By the 1960's the Panamanians were vociferously demanding their land back. Resentment against America escalated and in 1964 exploded in the "flag riots" when some Panamanian students tried to raise their flag at a high school inside the American zone. This led to a fight with American students in which 21 Panamanian students and three Americans died.

The canal became less important to America once they began to maintain separate Pacific and Atlantic fleets and Duke lent his support to the left, offering his aid to President Carter. When negotiations were successfully concluded, he wrote to the Panamanian president to congratulate him. The letter threw him into another political minefield, and hate mail began pouring into his office once again. He was called a traitor and a commie bastard by the right wing, he admitted, "I really caught hell over that one!" The Republicans felt their hero had deserted them in their hour of need. He was shocked by the depth of the anger unleashed against him by those who had called themselves his friends. He was hurt when they spoke about him as if he had sold out, but he refused to back down and stubbornly clung to beliefs based on his extensive reading and his own understanding of the situation, "Giving back something that is no longer important to America would give a sense of nationhood to Panama, as well as a sense of gratitude to America. Also it would be an act calculated to protect national security and eliminate a painful vestige of colonialism. It would improve US relations with South America." Leading Republicans had found an issue which could have brought Carter down if Duke had added his weight to the cause. He'd let them down and now he found himself out of step with the right wing and with old friend Ronald Reagan. When the treaty was finally ratified, by just a one vote margin, President Carter wrote to thank the man who claimed to have no interest in politics for his effort and his steadfast support.

The name John Wayne did not appear in the 1975 top ten box-office star list for the first time since the 1940's, "I guess it's a sign everything must change, everything has to come to an end. Only a goddamn fool would think that anything is forever." He was injured in a way no film critic had ever managed to wound him. Then in 1976 his declining status was brought home even more painfully when he was not asked to present any award at the Oscars.

Duke had never given in to anything in his life, he had adapted to ill health, financial difficulty, continuously recovered from critical beatings and had been resilient in the face of every family crisis. But now he faced the most savage enemy of all, old age. He found its advance difficult to deal with, "There's no such thing as growing old gracefully, it's all deterioration, decay. You just can't give in to it." He had to carry on, doing the best he could. He had abused his body all his life and in 1976 he bragged that he had never really been ill. No one understood how his body had stood up to what he did to it, he had remained illogically healthy despite smoking up to six packs of cigarettes a day, washed down with any alcohol he could get, and eating foods loaded with fats. He had always worked too hard, rarely got sufficient sleep, and was always involved in any devilment to be found. He was about to pay the price.

His problems could be traced back to a cold day in New England in 1974, where he stopped off on his way to London to film a Glenn Campbell special and take part in a talk show to promote *McQ* and the upcoming *Brannigan*. In 1973 the editor of *The Harvard Lampoon* had sent a tongue-in-cheek innovation, "You think you're tough. You're not so tough. You've never dared to set foot in the wilderness of Cambridge territory. We dare you to have it out, head-on, with the young whelps here who would call the supposedly unbeatable John Wayne the biggest fraud in history." He, the great right-winger, was being challenged to enter the most traditionally radical and hostile territory on earth. When he received the invitation he laughed and wrote back, "I accept with pleasure your challenge to bring my new motion picture, *McQ*, into the pseudo-intellectual swamps of Harvard Square. I was most happy to find that my age and balding head and gray hair had not made cowards out of the purported gentlemen of the mother college, (sorry to note that there is a weakness in your breeding, but there is a ray of hope in the fact that you are conscious of it.) May the good Lord keep you well until I get there." When he set out from home he told Pat he would ring to let her know if he got out in one piece.

On January 15 1974 he rode into Harvard Square at "High Noon" on top of an armoured personnel carrier. It was icy and snowing, some of the kids threw snowballs. After *McQ* was shown he gave an impromptu press conference for the students. It turned into one of the best performances he ever gave and he enjoyed it as much as anything he had ever done. He ad-libbed the whole session, flying by the seat of his pants all night. One student asked him why he wore a phoney toupee, "It isn't phoney. It's real hair. Of course it's not mine, but it's real." Another, "Has President Nixon ever given you any suggestions for your movies?" was answered, "No, they've all been successful." He responded all night in the same light vein and the students loved it, and warmed to him, recognising the special kind of courage it took to answer questions without knowing what was going to be coming at him and when it was a safe bet that much of it would be hostile. He didn't falter and it was a precious moment that lived on in all their memories. He was thrilled, excited and deeply touched by the reception he was given. Staff at the lampoon later sent him their Brass Balls award, in recognition of his "outstanding machismo and a penchant for punching people in the mouth." It was late when he rang to tell Pat he'd had the time of his life. He felt exhilarated by his contact with the students he called, "Such refreshing young men."

From the success at Harvard he flew straight onto London, which was also in the grip of a bitter, icy winter, to appear on The Parkinson Show. He soon felt less than thrilled and excited. In fact he felt very uncomfortable after developing a terrible hacking cough and high temperature. Michael Parkinson, the talk-show host, felt the full force of his irritability when his opening words of welcome seemed to annoy Duke. He was having some difficulty catching his breath and he coughed throughout the interview. He had walked onto the set in dinner jacket and was immaculate, pristine, and he looked bemused when Parky asked him whether he wanted to sit on a chair or a saddle. His opening question was the old chestnut, "Did you acquire the walk and the talk?"

"Well, I don't know about any walk or talk." His back was up immediately.

"What's kept you at the top so long?"

"Luck."

"You don't resent the charge that in the majority of your films you play yourself?"

"Well, I want to play myself … if myself is what I've been playing. People like me because there's no nuance in what I do, I love lustily, hate heartily, I drive straight ahead. I usually fight something bigger than a petty argument."

"How many of your films do you care to forget?" "Let's see … I've made about two hundred … oh, I guess about 170." It was the first time he relaxed, "You know I try every time, but there's a lot of things that go into making a picture worthwhile." A clip from a film made in 1934 was shown, "That makes it rough doesn't it? I'd like to look like I did then. I was kinda pretty. I got over that in a hurry though."

He was asked the usual follow-up, "What changed things for you?"

"John Ford. We developed a pretty wonderful friendship. He had a great deal to do with my thinking and I met a lot of people through him." All the time he talked Duke played with a ring, he was tense and anticipated the hostility brewing underneath. Before the interview was inevitably steered toward politics he was asked about some of his more spectacular accidents, "Yeah, I've had a few."

"You've got this reputation for being the rough, tough fella, are you really?"

A sad smile played round his mouth, "No ... I'm a very sensitive man."

Parkinson wasn't getting far, "Has anyone ever taken a swing at you in a bar?"

"Yes ... and they've hit me ... They cried when they got back up though."

A few more questions about violence in modern pictures and about *The Quiet Man* and then the sting he had been anticipating all evening. Parkinson plunged into the attack, asking about Watergate and Nixon, and Duke, feeling ill, unable to breathe, gasped as he tried to inhale sufficient oxygen, put a hand to his throat. The last thing he wanted to talk about then was his friend Nixon who was in such deep trouble. He explained briefly that he didn't know what was happening, that Nixon had not at the time been charged with anything and had not been impeached, "I'd rather not discuss it." Nothing Parkinson attempted drew any further response from him. Anger was bubbling inside and he turned away from his host. His eyes wandered round the audience as he wriggled in a chair too small for his vast frame. He fiddled with his hair, his hands and avoided facing Parkinson until he was asked, "Are you bored?"

With a deadly snake-stare and exaggerated drawl he turned at last to meet his attacker face to face, "No."

But he did want to get away and he was struggling almost as badly as the interviewer. They argued about *High Noon* and the days of blacklisting, but Duke'd had enough, "You had to understand what was going on in Hollywood at the time ... It was a long time ago." Carl Forman, writer of *High Noon*, who had escaped to England to avoid the blacklist, had put Parkinson up to the line of questioning, "Ask the old bastard about the blacklist." Duke was too tired to respond and he let it pass without defence. A few words about his Oscar and his image as he aged, "Well, you can't stay young forever. I wish you could. I have tried to make my parts mature with my own physical condition. Growing old doesn't worry me." Sad eyes wandered away, focusing on nothing in particular.

"You've got this amazing constitution, what keeps you in good nick?"

If only Parkinson had known! The question drew a laugh from Duke, "Good whiskey and cigars and cigarettes I guess."

"And what about women? You've been married three times now, what are the problems keeping a Hollywood marriage together?"

Did Parkinson know his long marriage to Pilar was all but over? That he was already developing a deep friendship with another woman? He hung his head, sat still and silent for an awkward moment, the characteristic pause, "Well, it takes a very understanding wife ... and ... er ... (Duke folded his arms folded tightly across his chest as if to protect himself, and sat for a painfully long drawn out spell before continuing slowly) ... it's hard ... very hard ... There are so many things you're required to give your time to, that unless they've been brought up in the business they don't understand ..." Unshed tears welled up in the "very sensitive man's" eyes and he turned away in panic. Perhaps at last Parkinson began to sense something was wrong and he turned the interview in a different direction. However it was not one likely to please the Duke, for once again he was asked about cancer.

"And you still smoke?"

"Yes ... I've been smoking too much. I've been smoking cigars again ... but I'm gonna quit it I guess ... when you get a bad cold"

Parkinson wound the show up, thanking Duke who hung his head again and confessed under his breath, "I just barely made it too ... I'll tell you that!"

From first walking down the steps to meet the enthusiastic audience he knew he shouldn't have attempted the interview, but he simply couldn't back out of his responsibilities. He laughed, got angry, frequently wriggled in his undersized chair, was obviously sad, unable to hide his sense of loss although he didn't mention Pilar specifically. The cough was awesome to hear, and that night marked a watershed in his life. He had gone through the motions of another live interview, had talked about the old days, Ford, films, cancer, violence on the screen, about the Oscars and ageing ... used the same words he had used in countless other interviews, but Parkinson had stirred him by talking about his constitution. He had never considered it before, but here, in London, it was about to fail him for the first time. A London writer commented after seeing the programme which aired on 1st Feb 1974, "He has fought off lung cancer, ill health, old age, various ex-wives, hostile reporters and Harvard undergraduates. No matter how many double scotches or poison pens his person absorbs he just keeps rolling along. Overweight and stiff in the joints he may be, but once hoisted up there, he still sits tall in the saddle ... No matter what, he keeps on coming, bringing a message about ourselves. The public might see him die on screen, but refuses to believe it ... the myth is born."

In the meantime the myth was forced to call a doctor who diagnosed pneumonia. He was put on a course of antibiotics. The cough worsened and he began bringing up blood. To any lung cancer survivor coughing up blood is a terrifying phenomenon and Duke was scared, but despite being advised to rest, he continued the tour to promote his upcoming film and to appear on the Glenn Campbell Special. It was business as usual for Duke and his old saying "I can't quit" was often heard during his pain-filled stay. The producer of the Glenn Campbell Show was worried and said, "Every time Duke coughed I could feel it down to my toes."

His breathing did not improve when he returned home and his cough was both painful and hacking. He was worried and went back to hospital to have his own cancer specialist check him over. Although he was given the all-clear he had suddenly become allergic to perfume, cosmetics and tobacco. He was warned he had to stop smoking and he made a more determined effort. When friends told him he looked rough he laughed but admitted he felt worse than he looked. In fact during his visit to London he had torn a small valve in his heart. It remained undetected for four long years during which time he suffered intense chest pain and on-going breathing difficulties.

He continued to miss Pilar badly but allowed Pat to slip, almost unnoticed, into his life. She had moved to Newport to be closer to him and although he still refused to let her stay over he now let her move her office equipment into his den. Until her own things arrived she sat perched on pillows and books at his oversized desk, she was never allowed to sit in his chair, "Duke was the most generous man that ever lived, but heaven help anyone who sat in his chair!" Pat had become a fixture but he knew that moving her in openly as more than his secretary would be a mistake on many levels. For one thing he still wanted Pilar back and he wouldn't endanger his chances with her needlessly, for another his children continued to wander freely through the house, he wouldn't change that and their welfare remained uppermost in his mind.

He took great pride in his home and even when he was living there alone he enjoyed watching the surprised stares of first-time visitors. They expected it to smell of leather and be full of Western memorabilia, "They probably expect to sit on saddles instead of chairs!" Duke commented dryly after his distasteful brush with Parkinson. In fact everything in it reflected his own good taste. He had lovingly filled it with artefacts from around the world and it had a warm, lived-in feel. His expensive Chinese screens, ornaments, and huge red-lacquered coffee tables always impressed guests. His den, the largest room in the house, was full of memorabilia, awards and honours. It housed a projection room and a full sized pop corn machine, always fully stocked. Friends were regularly invited round on Friday nights to view the latest film releases. It was the room he loved the best. It told the story of his life. Full of fine wood panelling, it housed a huge fireplace, part of his gun collection, it was also where he exhibited his collection of Hopi kachina dolls. In it, resting on a special plinth made by the skipper of *The Goose*, was his Oscar, and the "Fifty years of Hard Work" wall.

It was where he read and replied to his mail, much of which still came from cancer sufferers from all over the world. He gave their letters special attention and he never failed to write back, sharing his own experiences and encouraging them not to give up hope. He tried to respond to all his mail, but he needed somebody to keep his office in some kind of order and Pat came in handy for that and he was glad to move her in. Once there she shielded him from the worst of the hate mail, sometimes she didn't even show the letters to him, but he still responded personally to the ones he did get to see, "You may disagree completely with what I say, but I will defend to the death my right to say it."

Another trip to London marked the next turning point and the end of an era when he deliberately put a full stop to his efforts to win Pilar back. Pat's things had been moved into his den and just before leaving home for England to start filming *Brannigan*, he decided to move her into his life. He had been so ill and lonely in London on his last visit he told her, "I need someone to look after me, so you better make sure your passport is in order, because you're coming with me. And if you behave yourself, I might even let you persuade me to take you to Paris."

Strangely, whilst it had been Pilar who left Duke, she was missing him and at the very instant he decided to let go, she made a last ditch attempt to patch things up. She followed him to London and began to make demands. He found it difficult as she pushed him away one minute and dragged him back the next. She had walked out of his life, and now he confessed in a poignant moment that he believed it was time to let go, "I love you very much but I'm old and tired. I don't feel well. I'm taking a lot of medication and I can't be a real husband to you anymore." He had been lonely and hurt for too long and he had now found a woman who was willing to be all the things he needed. Pilar left him in London and went home, realising she had left it too late, her husband had already moved on.

When they first arrived in London Duke booked Pat into the room next to his but she changed the arrangement, taking another on a different floor of the hotel. She didn't want to alert the press to their blossoming relationship. He was angry, he hated underhand dealings, "Goddam Pat, there's no law against a man having his secretary near him. You're being crazy. There's no need for pretence. We're doing nothing wrong and I'm too goddam old to be playing in a French farce." He decided to move out of the hotel and he rented a house on Cheyne Walk, right on the banks of the Thames overlooking Battersea Park, for the summer.

Soon after they moved in he took Pat to a local restaurant where she was suddenly taken ill. He got her home and sat up with her until 5 am, then reluctantly left her to go off to start his day's work, without ever getting to bed himself. Pat said, "I felt all the same awe-inspired affection for him that so many other people did, but that night I fell in love with him. And I knew beyond any doubt that he cared about me."

And once Pilar went home their way was left clear. Duke's mood softened and he made a determined effort to give Pat the time of her life. He took some days out of his busy schedule to take her to France, "If I don't get you to Paris, I'll never hear the goddamn end of it." He hadn't been able to book a hotel before setting off, "If we can't find anywhere honey we'll sleep on a park bench." Pat murmured, "It was so easy to love Duke."

In London he made many new friends. Reporters fell at his feet and *The Sunday Times* carried an article by Jilly Cooper, then a young writer who had some difficulty getting to meet the actor. Once she found him she stuck close and the memory of the day lived on in her mind, "My abiding image is of a passing bus, full of people waving and cheering at him, of surging crowds and eager fans, people of all nationalities stretching their hands out, trying to touch their hero." Her piece mentioned his amazing propensity for downing bourbons and devouring biscuits as he, "All the while talked in a voice that rolls on like a deep, wide, slow-moving river." He told her about previous visits to England, "I visited Chartwell, because Winston Churchill is one of my heroes. I was pleased to find his study very intimate, not unlike my own." When he was called back on set she followed him. As soon as he finished his scene he strolled off to meet the cheering fans, Cooper wrote, "There is indeed something splendid, heroic, indomitable about the man, like a warrior from Homer … Seeing how he hit the crowd I realised how starved of strong men and heroes we are today." Many years later her memories of the day she met John Wayne still burned brightly, "His sheer size struck me most. A big part of his charm was the obvious gentleness emanating from such a hulk of a man. And he laughed all the time. He found the sycophants who hung on his every whim particularly amusing. He seemed cheerful and completely natural. Charisma poured out of his ears."

The British co-stars of *Brannigan* also found him a delight to work with. Del Henney said, "I can't imagine anyone who had met him not being struck by his presence. He was awesome. When he came onto set he had to duck under the doors and the room grew dark. He took all the light and your breath with it. Perhaps apart from the one famous scene in

The Searchers, I don't think one frame of film has ever captured the impact of what was his real life presence! In my opinion the camera reduced him. Oddly enough, in real life there was no sense of danger about him, in spite of his size. When we first arrived on set we were informed that John Wayne liked to be addressed as Duke, which promoted a few sneers amongst the British actors, myself included, but after I'd met him, if he had wanted to be called God Almighty I wouldn't have argued. He had such vast experience. He knew what each shot would look like before the cameras started rolling. He also knew which shots would be wasted. After the bar room brawl he had to exit into the street after throwing my character out ahead of him. We did the first rehearsal. I go sailing through the door and he follows. He stopped. He looked around and brought his hands up to his face, cupping them like binoculars at the camera and the director, "Hey, Hicox, I didn't travel 3,000 miles to be in a longshot that's gonna be completely useless. Get the camera up here and lets shoot something we're gonna like." He was right of course, and he had said it with enough humour that he didn't sound like a bully, or disrespectful either. He was also very kind to us actors. I had to play a scene with him where I was supposed to be drunk. I felt nervous and self-conscious. He bent down and whispered to me, "Don't act drunk. Imagine I'm two people and talk to the guy on my right. And don't worry about the script. Just say what comes into your head." He himself had great ease in front of the camera and I just loved his delivery. He was great to work with."

Whilst Duke enjoyed working with such enthusiastic actors he tired easily and he looked forward to going home. He was also relieved that he no longer had to hide how he felt about Pat. He began spending more time with her and let her know she was more than just a convenience to him, "I'm lucky I found you." He no longer bothered what other people thought and when he visited friends he often took her along with him. She was easy to get on with and everyone accepted her position in Duke's life. His children were still sharing their time freely between him and their mother, and they often rushed unannounced into Bayshore Drive on their way home from school, calling out as they tore through, "Hi dad, I love you." He got on with whatever he was doing, seemed to take no special notice, but loved knowing they were around. They seemed to take Pat's presence for granted.

For many years he had filled his life making film after film and now, after finishing *Brannigan*, he rushed straight on to *Rooster Cogburn* which co-starred Hollywood legend, Katharine Hepburn. They first met when they were both working in London. She rushed across Piccadilly Circus to introduce herself, "Oh Mr Wayne, I'm so pleased to meet you. I'm Katharine Hepburn and I'm looking forward to working with you in Oregon next month." He was bowled over by her enthusiasm and instantly took a shine to her. Everyone who saw them together marvelled at the immediate and obvious chemistry. *Rooster Cogburn* threw the two great stars of the Golden Era together for the first time and Duke at least felt sad their paths hadn't crossed earlier. Hal Wallis was responsible for teaming them in another production about the one-eyed Marshall, and when he offered Duke another chance to wear the eye patch he said, "Asking me to play Rooster is like giving me a handful of chocolate bars." He couldn't wait to start and after coming face to face with Miss Hepburn in London he was really excited, "Rooster was a character that fit my pistol. We felt the same way about life. He didn't believe in accommodation, neither do I. But he was a delightful guy. When things weren't serious he was usually half drunk, but he knew his job and straightened up and walked right when it was time. And no matter how drunk or rough he was, he always had some philosophy he pushed at you. It's the best part I ever had. I never had anything else where I had such a chance to tear into a character … to really turn loose and know it will come out all right in the end. Rooster was a mean old bastard and that's me. No one had to teach me to play the part."

Poor Stuart Miller was the man chosen to try to tell Duke how to play Rooster Cogburn, to direct the two mighty legends, one who had spent a lifetime taming the West and the other who had conquered the East, one an arch conservative, the other a committed liberal. Everyone expected spontaneous combustion, sparked either by Duke's temper or Hepburn's outspoken politics. In fact the only trouble on set had little to do with either of the two stars who got on fantastically well. The fireworks only flared because Duke wasn't prepared to be told how to play the "Mean old bastard." He said, "Rooster was a little tired but he was a fighting man who had no intention of giving up the reins, a man still willing to use his fists and still willing to put his life on the line for what was right. No one could teach me about Rooster. I had known him all my life. I knew the way he thought, lived, loved and looked from his gut to his patch."

He was thrilled to have the chance to recreate the character and to work with Hepburn. He was fascinated by her honesty and she was equally charmed by him; like so many before her, she was surprised to find her leading man polite, sensitive, talented, and above all considerate toward her, "He is a real gentleman. I love working with him. But he tells everyone what to do on the set, and I normally get to do that." Wallis consoled her, "The next time he starts doing that just mention *The Alamo* and *The Green Berets*." Hepburn felt sorry for Millar who was working with three bullies, Duke, Wallis and herself.

Duke admired her rare dedication and was particularly impressed when she insisted on riding horses and doing the raft scene herself, because he knew she didn't enjoy doing either, "I'd never met anyone like her. She's so feminine — she's a man's woman … how lucky a man would have been to have found her." When the last scene was wrapped he pushed up the eyepatch, gathered her in his arms and planted a huge kiss on her lips, then thundered, "Damn! There's a woman!" The compliment left her speechless, but later tears welled up as she returned, "What an experience!"

He had arrived on location tired, irritable and generally feeling uncomfortable with life. And, too much the perfectionist, he was soon at logger heads with the director. Duke had no respect for him and when he felt Millar was not doing the job he was quick to jump, calling him a "six-foot-six sonofabitch no-talent!" Still, when Wallis offered to find a replacement Duke refused, "No, Kate and I will just do what we want anyway. There's no point replacing him. We both know what we want to do."

Duke had always enjoyed working on an open set and liked reporters and fans around. Hepburn preferred a closed set. When this potential tinder-box of a problem was mentioned to Duke he laughed, "Relax, I'll talk to her." He ambled to her trailer and asked politely, all charm as the occasion demanded, "Do you really mind my having them around the set? I promise not to let them bother you." And Hepburn fell for it but warned sternly, "So long as they don't bother me!" In fact as soon as she saw him talking to someone she inevitably went across to join the conversation, later saying, "He always seemed to be having so much fun with them, and I'd never done that before. He always teased me as soon as he saw me approaching. He reminded me so much of Spencer Tracy, so full of warm affection. I fell for his charm, and I can hardly believe it."

Whilst they were in Oregon Duke threw a party to celebrate Hal Wallis's birthday. He sent an invitation to Miss Hepburn who explained that she never went out socially. Duke told her, "I know that, but I just wanted you to know that you're invited all the same." She asked if the invitation still held if she popped in for a few minutes. "You're welcome however long you choose to stay. Bring anyone you wish with you too."

"Well, I might bring my brother-in-law, who's in town just now, but it will only be for a few minutes Duke. I don't like parties."

She was one of the first to arrive, "Remember, I'll only be here a few minutes." When she walked in, she turned a picture that she didn't like to face the wall, and helped herself to a plateful of food. She had already told her host that she wouldn't have anything to eat. She was almost the last person to leave that night and Duke happily told anyone who would listen, "She was an absolute delight, the highlight of the evening ... also of my stay in Oregon." He had heard on set that Miss Hepburn collected umbrellas and after that, whenever he saw an unusual one he bought it and sent it to her in New York.

He still enjoyed playing jokes on crew members and now even Pat suffered at his hands. All through filming in Oregon she wore trousers but on the last day she put a dress on. Throughout the day she noticed the crew didn't look directly at her, though she caught a few of them sneaking a look at her knees from time to time. Duke had told everyone she had a false leg and warned them not to mention her dress or her legs. He was taken at his word, after all he was the man who never told lies! All day he walked around the set with a curious smile playing around his mouth. He was nearly bursting by the time he confessed. He added proudly, "Now you can see what a really good actor I am!" He was doing his very best to have fun on location and he wanted everyone else to have a good time.

Miss Hepburn laughed helplessly and in return for the fun and the gifts she later wrote, "From head to toe, he's all of a piece. Big head. Wide blue eyes. Sandy hair. Rugged skin-lined by living and fun and character ... A face alive with humour ... and sharp wit. He's quick, he's sensitive. His shoulders are broad — very. His chest massive — very. When I leaned against him, (which I did as often as possible I must confess) thrilling. It was like leaning against a tree ... And the base of this incredible creation. A pair of small sensitive feet. Carrying this huge frame as though it was a feather. Light of tread. Springy. Dancing. Pretty feet. Very observing. Very aware. A terribly funny man, always ready to laugh. To be laughed at. To answer. To stick his neck out. Outrageous. Spoiled. Self-indulgent. Tough. Full of charm. Knows it. Uses it. Disregards it ... As an actor he has an extraordinary gift. A unique naturalness. A very subtle capacity to think and express and caress the camera — the audience. A secret between them. He's an artist and he's all male, and that's a rarity these days. When you buy a cotton shirt, you want to get good simple long-lasting cotton. No synthetics. That's what you get when you get John Wayne. That's what I got. And as you can see, I liked it ..."

She also pointed out to him that he needed to see a doctor as soon as he got back to California, "Duke, I'm very worried about that cough, it's no ordinary cough, please promise me you'll get it sorted out. You've been using more and more oxygen every day we've been here." He laughed her warning off, "No one can breathe up here, I'll be alright once I get home. I'm probably allergic to something up here. Don't worry about me." Pat agreed with Miss Hepburn and they both harboured dark thoughts about what the trouble might be. Duke felt he was being nagged and the one place in the world he didn't want to go was hospital. He would have ignored the cough, would have taken himself out to sea to recover, but he'd badly injured his knee shooting the raft scene. He had knelt on a cartridge shell and the wound had become raw and very painful, "I'd wrecked it so bad I could hardly bear it. It wouldn't heal up. We managed to finish the film without causing any serious delays but once I got home I had to go straight to hospital. They said I needed surgery to repair the damage." Whilst he was in hospital the cough developed into pneumonia and he was given another course of antibiotics. When the doctors wouldn't release him he commented caustically, "Well, I guess the good thing is I'll loose weight in here."

Duke recovered slowly and spent Christmas 1975 aboard *The Goose*, with Pat, his younger children and some friends. After seven straight months of filming followed by his enforced hospitalisation he finally took the well-earned rest that Pilar had wanted him to take for so long. He sat in the sun, played cards and enjoyed being out on the boat which was "as lit up as old Duke." Throughout the summer of 1976 he travelled, tried to relax, and visited old friends. And the Press were hard on his heels too. They had smelled a story at last, noticing that everywhere he went, on business or pleasure, Pat accompanied him. Duke refused to rise to the bait and simply smiled, he was feeling happy and pleased with life. He had no premonition that here was the calm before the storm.

All year he had been planning his upcoming picture, *The Shootist*, a story about an ageing gunfighter who was dying of cancer. He attended several script conferences and pre-production meetings to discuss a concept that both excited and frightened him. He was a little uncomfortable about the story which he said was too graphic. He called for many changes before finally accepting the part of JB Books. Don Siegel, the director he had missed working with on *Dirty Harry*, went along with most of his demands to soften the character. The two men got on surprisingly well during the meetings. Siegel was an articulate and witty gentleman who had worked with second unit at Warners for most of his career, now he was working on a John Wayne picture and acknowledged, "It gave me the chance to establish myself and to paint some tender, sympathetic scenes as well as brutal mayhem. The opening premise of the picture could have ended it right there, unless we did it brilliantly. I thank Duke for the fact that it didn't bomb, for the fact that the humour in it worked so well. And actually I would say that he got on with me better than with 95% of the other directors he's worked with. Duke happens to be extremely knowledgeable about the making of movies, and he had many excellent ideas … of course he never hesitates to tell you about them! But he was perfect for the part … no one else could have played Books. I also know he was badly affected by the picture. He found it harrowing, an emotional strain."

Duke had never really got over the many psychological aspects associated with his own close call but the part he was to play now intrigued him, "I knew I could play John Bernard Books from absolute personal experience. When I found out I had cancer I can tell you it was something of a shock, like someone hitting me as hard as they could in the solar plexus. This picture gave me an opportunity to talk about that. Naturally, the fact about cancer and my own background drew me to it … it has a lot of things in it that I went through. I thought a lot about death and how I wanted to go, obviously. We don't all get the same chance to go out on both feet that Books gets though." By the time he set off for Carson in the winter he was full of enthusiasm for what he expected to be a great movie, even if he still harboured some personal reservations, "My previous pictures all carried certain messages about how men should live with dignity. This was all about going out in style." He never, at any stage, planned The Shootist as his last picture, but in it he effectively buried his own persona, he later reflected sadly, "Sometimes the irony of that gets to me."

As was his custom he arrived in Carson City some days ahead of schedule. He had only just begun to recover his strength after the bout of pneumonia and his knee surgery but he made a point of going into the local coffee shops and talking to residents so they would get used to seeing him around, "Oh sometimes I feel a little tired, but people come up to me in a friendly manner. I have to let them know I appreciate their continued interest." Once again he was back working at altitude and almost immediately began suffering the consequences. On several mornings he was unable to catch his breath and the haggard look he needed for the film soon turned out to be more authentic than he would have liked, "I got the damned flu. I tried to keep working, but by the end of the first week I could barely hold my head up. I had to take ten days off, the doc called me an old bastard and told me that I was killing myself." A physiotherapist was called in to pound his back in an effort to dislodge fluid that was rapidly building up in his lung, "Jeeze, my life was one misery. Those weeks were some of the worst I ever suffered, worse even than during Katie Elder. The smallest exertion caused me to rush back to the trailer where I kept my oxygen … the tank had to be refilled several times during shooting. To make matters worse, my goddam ear infection returned. The pain was constant and affected my sense of balance. It was one of the only times I ever disturbed production. It's so damn irritating to feel bad when you haven't felt bad all your life. I have been abnormally healthy. Even when they told me I had cancer, I hadn't any pain … nothing … But this year it's been one thing after another … that's the worst thing about getting old … having to use your will power to drive yourself instead of natural physical energy. Before it all came so easy, now I have to push it." He soldiered on through earache and flu, but his cough demanded constant retakes and he became angry, "I felt unprofessional, and there wasn't a goddam thing I could do about it. I was obsessive about finishing on schedule. People who caused delays annoyed the hell out of me, I always hated anyone who caused difficulties, weaklings who delayed work and cost other people money. Now it was me causing a fuss, me who was weak. All I cared about was getting a good job done the best way I could."

The signs that all was not well were clearly visible and Dave Grayson, his long time make-up man, said, "It was as though an entire decade had gathered like an ocean and swept over him all at once." When he first decided to tackle the film he had been excited about it, now he was there on location he was less sure. Suddenly it all seemed too close to home and, had he been anything less than a complete professional, he would have backed out by the end of the first week. To make matters worse he was having unexpected problems with Siegel. They had struck up a close working relationship during early script conferences but once filming got under way they seldom saw eye to eye, they even argued about who was hired to take the publicity stills. Duke's mood swung from tired and irritable to slightly better, but tension might have eased sooner had he not seen a Press release from Siegel, "I know John Wayne eats directors, but I'll give him indigestion." He was hurt by the comment because he thought they were friends. Siegel knew he had caused offence but didn't know how to bring Duke out of his sullen mood in the way people who had known him for longer did. When Duke raged at the photographer that he had insisted on hiring, "I bust my ass to get you this job and you take a picture with a roof growing out of my head!" the reply came back swiftly, "Yes, you're right it is a roof, I thought it was your head." Onlookers were horrified at the flippant remark, but Duke, caught off guard, just laughed.

In the film he played the archetypal Wayne tragic hero as JB Books reaffirms the dignity of the individual in a world that has outgrown his personal code. In the dramatic countdown to the blaze-of-glory shootout in which he rids Carson City of evil, he manages to melt the icy heart of his landlady and save her son from a life of crime. From the opening credits to the final steps of the hero's journey, he is a man shown in terms of violence and action, not for that old man a sedentary death; Books could no more give in to the ravages of disease than he could to a man who had wronged him. His death befitted the life of a man who was the direct descendant of The Ringo Kid, it was also the conclusion to Duke's own legend. The fact that he was brutally shot in the back in what turned out to be the last of "The John Wayne Things" lent it a dreadful finality and many found the experience too painful, "It was like watching an old friend die." Even at its first release audiences were deeply disturbed after fifty years of the familiarity, friendship and safety they had known in Duke's hands. They felt the bitter irony just as keenly as he did himself.

Perhaps intentionally, the film made no clear distinction between Books or Duke, and here was the final coming together of the image and the man. That made the role the toughest of Duke's career and when his character talked about religion and death, saying his soul is what he made it himself, Duke was making a personal connection with his audience. In his final days Books lay his soul bare and prepares to meet his maker in the glare of publicity, so too, when his time came, would Duke. He knew that, just like the character he played, he would be granted no peace in which to die and whilst he might never have intended it to be his last film, he used it to say his own very public goodbyes. In it he laid to rest his vision of the Old West and, at the same time, put the final flourish to his career. There would be no more last stands and he could have made no finer eulogy. *The Shootist* became a beautiful and perfectly timed piece of Hollywood.

When filming was complete the whole crew lined up to get his autograph and Dave Grayson said, "He was quite irresistible. In spite of some of the things he'd done to alienate some of the people on that picture, they still all wanted his autograph ... these were professionals, not fans. It was quite astonishing, and unprecedented." It was almost as if they sensed the unwelcome twist in the tail that was to follow. As soon as he had signed every request he slipped quietly away. He had not enjoyed making *The Shootist*, it had a lot to do with the realisation that the good times had gone forever.

As soon as he got home from location he went back to hospital, terrified of what might be found this time. He was relieved when X-rays revealed nothing sinister, but also worried because he felt worse than ever. He had anticipated a speedy recovery once he got back but instead he was continuously sick and could hardly breathe even at sea level. Any exercise at all left him struggling following the removal of his lung, but now nothing made any difference and even at rest he couldn't suck in sufficient oxygen for his needs. The famous soft drawl became gravelly, and in his ears at least, unpleasant. He felt dizzy and his weight ballooned. From the sixties he had been forced to diet before each new film but whatever he did now he remained bloated with a marked puffiness around his eyes and neck. He had never cared much about his appearance but whatever was wrong now stripped him of the rugged quality he so prized. And his problems weren't purely physical, "I was a little cranky about the way the studio were handling the release of *The Shootist*. In some cities there are no ads ... Nothing, not a goddam thing. There's always a tendency to do that with my pictures, no kidding. They give me less publicity because they figure ... "It's a Wayne picture, it'll do business anyway, why throw money at it?" ... some of my pictures ... Christ ... I wish they HAD been released that way! But I felt irritated about this one ... it was too nice a picture for that to happen." He felt the responsibility and decided to publicise it himself, setting off on a gruelling series of tours to promote it. If the studio were prepared to see it swallowed up he wasn't, "Here was a picture about a man facing life's hardest obstacle, death, the last thing anyone wants to face up to. I couldn't let this one bomb."

He pushed himself all over the world until he could carry on no longer and, weak and ill, he finally went home and back for more hospital tests. The problem that had dogged him for four long years was at last diagnosed as congestive heart failure. The mitral valve, connecting the upper and lower chambers was not closing properly causing blood and other fluid to back up from the heart to his lung, causing the puffiness in the rest of his body. The damage to his heart was thought to be the result of his violent coughing. A cocktail of drugs was prescribed and Duke came to see his medicine cabinet as a reflection of his weakness. He hated taking so much medication and told friends it was responsible for his increasingly bad temper. He began to think he would never feel well again. He complained about an overwhelming dizziness that forced him to stand motionless for long spells as he fought to regain his balance. And if all that wasn't enough he suddenly found himself having to get up several times during the night to use the bathroom. At first he gave little thought to what was an acceptable sign of advancing age, but his condition deteriorated rapidly, and he could find no relief for his discomfort. Finally, forced to admit there was something else going wrong, he jumped to the conclusion that he had prostate cancer. He decided to ignore the constant pain and closed his eyes to the possibilities. He could face no further surgery. He was frustrated and angry with life but still refused to give up on it, "I may fail, but I can't quit." The sentiment that haunted his every waking hour. Each day became frantic and extreme for him and he told Pat, "Every day has to count for something."

Professionally in the months after completing *The Shootist* he chased around everywhere, promoting the film, doing benefits, TV specials and spending hours searching for another good script. When he wasn't working he invited guests to the house, kept busy and filled his days to overflowing. He knew he was ill but was not prepared to go back to hospital again, at least not until he was forced there.

As busy as he was, he took on more, returning to politics in an effort to deflect the mind from the body again, offering his support to both Reagan and Ford, "As long as a man has a project — something to look forward to — there'll always be something important to him. He'll never really get old. If I had nothing to look forward to, I might as well be dead. You know hard work never killed anyone. But you can't turn back the clock. I'll be sixty nine this year, sixty nine goddamned years."

When he did eventually take himself for a check-up the doctor found an enlarged prostate gland, but did not think cancer was present. Duke was given more medication but was warned he would probably need surgery to clear the problem. How he hated the sound of the word. He didn't have cancer, surgery could wait. He delayed as long as he could, finding one excuse after another not to go back to hospital. When he finally succumbed, the procedure was uncomplicated, he suffered little discomfort and he breathed a mighty sigh of relief.

Though he kept busy, the surgery did force him to slow down, and he stayed closer to home than was his usual habit. There was a positive side and the operation gave him extra time to prepare for the festival he loved best; he had invited Pat to spend her first Christmas at his home, as part of the family. The very thought of it excited him. Best of all would be the procession of highly decorated ships and local boats sailing by his patio. Most owners fitted special microphones so they could shout the seasons greetings to him. He held a loudspeaker and bellowed his back to them. Standing on the patio watching the colourful procession was a ritual he would not miss, it was as big a part of Christmas for him as trimming the tree and wrapping and giving his gifts. He always kept a supply of extra presents ready wrapped, in case someone turned up unexpectedly. He collected his presents through the year, either from his mad catalogue sprees or shopping trips around the world. He dedicated a lot of time to the gift hunts and no one ever left his home empty handed at Christmas, whether they had been invited or not. All through the week of solid festivity the house burst at the seams as people floated in and out and whoever happened to be there when dinner hit the table was expected to stay and share the meal. His older children arrived and departed in some unspoken agreement, and his grandchildren swarmed through the house. They were free to do as they pleased in his home. It was noisy and wild, vibrant and alive with their energy and life force. Duke reflected on times gone by.

Throughout the year his health had been failing rapidly, with each week bringing some new problem. In January his great friend Andy Devine died of leukaemia. He was one of Duke's favourite people and they had been friends long before they worked together on *Stagecoach*. They hadn't seen each other for some time but Duke was again left vulnerable by the loss of another dear friend. He attended Devine's funeral at Pacific View Memorial Park. He had always said he wanted to be cremated like his brother and Ward Bond, but that day he commented on the beauty of the spot.

Soon after the funeral he went back to Monument Valley to shoot a commercial. He found the experience particularly harrowing. He wandered away from the film crew to be alone, to remember scenes from some of his most famous pictures. Memories of the old days flooded back. He could almost hear Pappy's voice and see Andy driving the stage along the valley floor; their ghosts returned briefly to remind him of the glory years, then disappeared in a swirl of dust, "All gone, never to return. Nothing remains the same."

He had worked tirelessly all through 1977 to see the Panamanian Zone treaty through but when President Carter invited him to attend the formal ceremony of ratification he was too ill to attend. The cough had grown steadily worse, he could barely walk, and he felt awful. In March 1978 he was rushed back to hospital and an angiogram showed the faulty mitral valve had to be replaced immediately or his heart would fail, Pat said, "When I put my head against his chest things had become so bad it was possible to hear his heart making a gushing sound." But he didn't want to go back into hospital, and even the surgeons were worried about the risk involved in cutting into the chest of a frail seventy year old who only had one lung. They were loath to drag him back into theatre and his chances of survival looked bleak.

Although he sank into a mood of the blackest depression and was particularly angry with the never ending round of doctors appointments, he continued to make business commitments and to plan his future. He signed a contract with ABC to do six two-hour spectaculars, appearing in them as himself. He also came across the galley proofs of a novel that interested him greatly, *Beau John* by Buddy Atkinson, "I loved the humour in it, there was even a part in it for Ron Howard. I so enjoyed working with that young man in *The Shootist.*" Mentally, he was creating a project to keep him going through what he anticipated coming his way, but he could do little more than plan, "I felt so weak I couldn't even pick up my make-up case, and so bad that I could barely breathe." Finally the doctors decided surgery was his only chance and they told him Massachusetts General Hospital was the best in the world for heart operations. A heavily sedated Duke was flown to Boston on the Flour Corporation's private jet on March 29th. He was admitted under the name Marion Morrison; he wanted to avoid reporters and film crews, he felt too ill to talk to them and too sick to be photographed. Despite the blanket of security, the news that he was back in hospital leaked out by the next morning and extra security guards had to be hired to keep strangers out of his room. He didn't want to see anyone and he was uncharacteristically quiet.

Duke had arrived in Massachusetts with chronic bronchitis, one lung, and a serious heart condition and when Dr DeSanctis started a series of pre-surgical tests, one of which was to measure lung capacity, he looked a worried man. Duke had already told the doctor to spare him the details, "You can tell my family, and you can tell Pat, but don't bother telling me," but now he sensed the doctor, who had planned to replace his mitral valve with one from a pig, was being evasive. In fact he considered the risks involved in surgery were too great and he didn't think the dying man he saw now had sufficient strength to survive another lengthy operation. On top of that he didn't want to go down in history as the man who killed John Wayne.

Duke knew DeSanctis was stalling and felt frustrated. Up to that point he had been the one dithering but as soon as he sensed opposition he took control of the situation, suddenly announcing to a shocked Pat, "We're all going out to dinner tonight, you, me, the kids, everyone who's hanging around in the hallway. The pig is being led to slaughter. All systems are go for Monday. Meanwhile we're going to live it up a little."

DeSanctis had warned that he probably wasn't strong enough to survive, but if there was one thing Duke understood it was his capacity to survive and he had pleaded, "Just give me a chance." When the doctor persisted, setting out the risk factors involved he responded testily, "Open that window. You're going to operate on me or so help me I'm going to jump out. Measure the risk factor in that." He was John Wayne and he would rather die than lead the life of an invalid.

The night before the operation the whole family went out for dinner. Everyone at the table was subdued except Duke who seemed to be in high spirits. His doctors had given him permission to have one drink and he ordered, "The largest martini the bartender can concoct." When he was handed his drink he stood up and raised his glass, "To the last supper!"

On April 3 as he was wheeled out of his room he murmured, "Ten horsemen left, but only nine came back ..." Surgery lasted three hours and was later described as "uneventful." His recovery was also uneventful this time although his family were shocked by the sight of the white and battered body as he lay unconscious, strapped to the bed so he wouldn't dislodge any of the tubes. He looked worse than he was, the great survivor had pulled it off again. He regained consciousness quickly but was disorientated and, for some reason, thought he was drowning. A nurse rubbed his forehead until he came round fully and remembered where he was and what had happened. Because of the risk of infection no one was allowed to kiss him, and the family had to squeeze his ankle to demonstrate their affection, and Duke didn't mind, just so long as he had some physical contact. He was encouraged to sit up and once the drains were removed he was soon looking and sounding more like himself as he made an unexpected but remarkable recovery. He didn't want to rest and despite the doctors advising him to give himself a chance to heal up properly he was soon back on his feet. He set off walking and refused to stop, and no one could hold him back.

When he left the hospital he was presented with a mounted mitral valve and he cried as he thanked the staff for their care, "I can't begin to tell you how grateful I am to all of you, I think you'll all understand if I don't suggest we do it over again sometime."

This time when he arrived home he was glad to go straight to his own bed. Pat stayed within shouting distance so he knew he wasn't alone and that things were getting back to normal. He began to look ahead with hope, convinced the suffering was at an end, sure nothing else could go wrong. He began giving serious attention to all the projects he had been planning. And if he was glad to be back home so too it seemed, was everyone else in the world, for no one had expected the fighting Duke to emerge the winner this time. The Press had never stopped referring to his earlier survival, how much more incredible he appeared now. In fact he felt and looked better than he had for years by the time he went home at the end of April 1978. The doctors told him he could live another fifteen years, and he believed them. He felt immortal and told George Burns, then 81 himself, "People have begun to speak about me in the past tense. They wanted to do a TV special for me, like it was my epitaph or something. But I told them I was just getting my second wind."

Newport's neighbourhood nautical fraternity gave him a welcome home fit for a hero, with the entire flotilla, consisting of over five hundred boats, sailing past the bottom of his garden waving flags, blowing whistles and carrying huge banners proclaiming, "Welcome Home, Duke." He stood on the patio with his children to watch and he noticed one boat with a sign that read, "Home is the sailor, home from the sea, And the hunter home from the hill." Lines from Robert Louis Stevenson's poem, "Requiem" that he had himself spoken in the film, *They Were Expendable*. Well the hero was home and all was well in his world.

He bought new sports clothes and resumed his ritual daily dawn walks, either doing laps of his boat or grounds, stopping to talk to whoever he bumped into. He talked about flowers or changes made to local houses, about anything, just because he wanted to be out doing something and because he needed to be with people, talking to anyone so he could feel alive in their company. It was not long before he felt the urge to get back to work and when Bob Hope asked if he'd do a spot on his birthday special he jumped at the chance. It was close to his own birthday and after he had finished his spot Hope wished Duke many more birthdays, "I hope I look as good as you do when I'm *your* age."

"You did," Duke quipped, "I hope you live forever, and mine is the last voice you hear." Bob Hope got in the last word as usual, "I know he's in good shape, because when he left the hospital he offered to shoot it out for the bill."

He looked good but Pat knew something was wrong when he didn't finish his glass of wine after the show, and it was not many days before he became irritable and listless again. He developed a fever, pain, nausea and severe fatigue. When he went for a routine check-up, blood tests revealed hepatitis which he had picked up from a blood transfusion. He was ordered back to bed where he was forced to rest for six weeks. The disease knocked him back and delayed the recovery that had begun so well. He felt so ill that even he did not complain too much about the bed rest. He did complain when he became allergic to alcohol. It was the greatest of the tortures he had so far faced, "I would have died for a drink."

As soon as he started fidgeting and pacing again he knew the time had come to get back to the only world in which he could function. His doctors hated the fact that he was so determined to get back to work again and would have preferred to isolate him on his boat for the summer. It was useless talking to him and they reluctantly gave him the go-ahead, telling him not to overdo things!

He had been troubled about how he could reply to the thousands of letters and cards he had received whilst he was in hospital. The task of sending personal replies had proved to be too much for him. Then he came up with the perfect solution. He was taping a segment for the hundredth anniversary of General Electric and had rehearsed his part of the show with Elizabeth Taylor, Henry Fonda and Michael Landon. On the day it was recorded, without telling anyone his plans, he made an impromptu speech, "This is the first time I have been with many of you since my recent hospital tour. So I'd like to thank you from the bottom of my heart for all your good wishes, telegrams, get well cards, and your *prayers*. They came at a time when I really needed them. I wish I could thank each of you personally, but that's not possible. So I did something else. I got down on my knees and asked God to double them, and send them back to you with the gratitude of a man you've been awfully nice to for a long, long time. Thank you."

Once during that difficult summer he attended a function. He didn't want to go, but Crown Prince Hussein of Jordan had asked to meet him and the State Department pleaded with him to go. He felt grouchy after driving himself to the reception and his mood worsened when he was kept standing around waiting for guests less punctual than he was himself. He felt cold, ill, his head ached and on top of that he couldn't even have a drink. When the Crown Prince finally arrived he was seated at a small table with Duke and some friends. There was little conversation and everyone was on edge. Dinner was ordered. Wine was served. Duke was offered a small taste and he unthinkingly took a sip. His face went red and he started to cough. All the guests in the room sat stunned as he tried to catch his breath and coughed helplessly for a long time. When he finally stopped he grinned at the prince and said, "It's all right with me." Prince Hussein laughed until tears rolled down his face. When he managed to control himself he raised his glass to Hollywood's box-office king and said, "I'll drink to the Duke." Duke's reaction had saved the night, he had retained his dignity and at the same time provided a memorable occasion for everyone else.

One by one his many and wide pleasures had been stripped away, "I keep thinking I am well again, and then when I try to do something, I realize I am not," but it was rare for him to admit weakness and he carried on doing as many TV specials as he could all through that summer.

Other film stars had feared the advent of the small screen, he had been more tolerant because it never touched his pulling power, "Damned little intimidates me." He had never needed to work in TV but the producers had never given up the chase and they remained determined to get their man. After finishing *The Shootist* his intention had been to get back into films but his prolonged ill health drained him and he finally had to admit that any work was better than nothing and he signed his two year deal with ABC, "They really weren't sure what to do with me, I think they signed me to keep me off the other networks rather than for any other reason." Still it gave him something to look forward to and helped him accept there would not be too many new film roles thrown his way, "I held out from television when everyone else went in because I felt I owed the fellas who stuck by me in the movies the same loyalty…. Television was hurting the theatre owners and the studios. Whenever I appear on TV I will only play myself, never a role. But what the hell, they re-run so many of my old pictures I guess it really doesn't matter. Things have changed. Movies are no longer the major entertainment medium. When I was in the business it was an American habit. I enjoyed being part of it. Bad taste in movies produced by pseudo-intellectuals changed all that. I'm no prude but dirty films aren't my style. Never were. So now I figure it's time to get my feet wet in the other field. I'm not sure what ABC has in mind … we'll just see what happens …"

In September he began suffering severe abdominal pain. He felt full and uncomfortable and one morning, as he breakfasted with Pat, he complained that he couldn't finish, his stomach hurt too much. He knew there was something seriously wrong; food tasted bad, he had indigestion and was beginning to have difficulty keeping even small amounts down, meat seemed to settle high in his throat. He was in big trouble and knew he should go back to the doctor. Instead he brushed the discomfort aside, "I can't keep running to the doctor every time I have a little pain. I'm OK." Nevertheless he altered his will to ensure that Pat would be looked after when he died.

By October the pain had become acute and he confessed it felt as if he had swallowed broken glass. He pushed food away in disgust and lost weight with alarming speed. Sleep was impossible and he could find no relief. Pat often caught him wincing in pain and reaching for his stomach when he thought no one was watching. On one of his early morning walks he doubled up and moaned that he had a razor sharp pain across his stomach. Of course he suspected the worst but also said that he couldn't stand the thought of further surgery. Images of John Ford's face as he suffered the torment of stomach cancer were etched in his mind and all his old fears rushed back in. Eventually when he did consult a doctor he was told it sounded like gall bladder trouble, that he would probably need further surgery, but that it wasn't serious. He roared his anger and at first refused to even consider it, nevertheless he was relieved to think he might only be suffering from gall stones …

Christmas evening 1978 had been eventful and by the time Duke's guests finally arrived for dinner his mind was full of the old days. He had decided to postpone any operation until after the holiday. His doctors didn't suspect cancer, and although he knew differently, they had given him the opportunity to put on this last show, "Stomach cancer is rare Duke. There were less than eight cases per one hundred thousand people in America last year. In white males it's even less likely, and the chance of it striking both John Ford and yourself is, statistically, almost impossible." Deep down he knew the truth and statistics meant nothing to him. He saw no point in surgery and continued to tell those concerned with his health, "I don't have time now." When Pat, his friends and family nagged him, he answered, "I have too many engagements. I can't cancel. I *promised*. Just don't keep pushing me. What the hell is all the hurry anyway? I've put up with these pains so long — I can put up with them a bit longer."

The first guests to arrive at the house were deeply shocked when he opened the door. The effort of preparation had left him washed out and he already knew he'd made a big mistake. He no longer felt like entertaining and he could hardly be bothered talking to his children or grandchildren when they burst in. Early in the evening Dave Grayson rang to ask how he was feeling and Duke answered baldly, "I think I have cancer again. Well … you can't win em all." It was the first time he had voiced his fears. Whenever any of his friends had mentioned the possibility of cancer before he had yelled a furious denial, repeating over and over, "I *don't* have cancer." But on Christmas Eve he retired from acting altogether, his role was too difficult to maintain. Before dinner was served he excused himself, "I just don't feel good. I'm really sorry." He looked dreadful and everyone present felt the first stab of anxiety.

He had spent the last ten years of his life telling people that if they were worried they should see their doctor, but he had stubbornly refused to get himself checked out this time. He knew that if cancer was diagnosed everyone would expect another dramatic fight back, he would have to live up to the expectations of others, would have to be the hero again, not for himself, but for friends, family and fans who carried their own image of him in their hearts. He didn't think he could do it, "I'm a dying man, afraid of the dark." On Christmas morning he was in a terrible state but still got up early, knowing this would be the last one he ever shared with humanity. It felt strange and the enormity of what his body was telling him took his breath away, he was "living on the raw edge," not wanting to consider what death might mean to the image.

The man was up but he didn't bother getting dressed and he sat, unshaven, in his robe instead. He was trying to stay calm but it wasn't easy, there were so many dark, sombre thoughts milling around. He felt annoyed with himself, jumpy and on edge, and when he shouted without thought at one of the kids he decided everyone would have a better day if he went back to bed. He sprawled out and stared blankly at the ceiling.

He got no rest but made the most important decision of his life instead. He had cancer and he had to go back to hospital. He was going to start the fight to the death. His Dad had told him long ago, "Don't pick a fight, but if you find yourself in one, make sure you win." He wasn't sure he could win this time but he had to put up some kind of resistance, not for him the JB Books way perhaps, he couldn't go out all guns blazing, but neither could he just give up and lie down to die. He was more than image, he was flesh and blood and he'd always done the best he could with everything at his disposal. The only decision that John Wayne could make was taken in bed on Christmas Morning 1978.

He got up, showered, dressed and rejoined his family, suddenly very calm. He thanked them for putting up with him and again tried to be the perfect host, serving champagne and doing his best to create special memories.

He had continued to visit Pilar regularly and, although she knew he was having some kind of relationship with Pat Stacy, she also believed he wanted her back in his life, "Not being together broke both our hearts." She had long since regretted leaving him and had tested the water on a number of occasions, frequently asking Mary if he was in love with Pat. Mary assured her it was nothing serious, but added, "I don't think you realize how much Duke was hurt by your separation."

He had tried to talk things over with her when he first got back from London some years previously. He had been unable to put his feelings into words then, and when he flushed vividly and withdrew Pilar said, "I knew he needed comfort. I wanted to hold him. But he did what he always did in times of trouble, he turned and ran. The best chance we'd ever had for an honest and open communication evaporated when he fled that day." She later wrote to him to explain how much she still loved and cared about him.

A few days later he walked back into the restaurant, "I got your letter. I want you to know it meant a lot to me. I know it wasn't easy for you to write all those things. You're still a young woman. One of these days, you're going to need more than I can give you and then ..." he added quietly, "I can't do that to you, or to me. Please leave it be now, Pilar." He had told her many times, "You can take everything a man has as long as you leave him his dignity." He fought tooth and nail to hang on to his. In the past he had begged her to go on location with him, to go out on the boat with him, not to leave him. And, knowing how much she hurt both him and his dignity, she had still insisted on living her own life. He was simply too tired to beg any more, he wanted her home but refused to ask, "When you keep giving people chances and they don't take them, you begin to lose your dignity. That's the time to draw the line."

He had learned to let go of the thing he cherished the most, reluctantly allowing Pilar to go her own way. They continued to meet as friends, and he frequently popped into the restaurant to chat about the children and her new life. And she never entirely gave up on him either. She began ringing all the time, pleading with him to see his doctor. Her nagging brought a nostalgic smile to his lips, "This is like old times. I promise honey, I'll go soon."

When the Press picked up the scent of a new relationship in his life they asked if he had any plans to remarry; they all knew he was the marrying kind, but he never had any intention of divorcing Pilar. Mary St John said, "By that time he no longer cared much about anything, least of all about divorce or marriage. He was too ill to care about what anyone else might or might not want. He needed female company and Pat gave that to him, he didn't care about anything but the comfort she brought."

By New Year those closest to him noticed how pale he had become and were worried. He'd promised them that as soon as the holiday was over he would go back to hospital, now he was given no opportunity to renege. The doctor took one look at him and advised him to get straight to UCLA for gall bladder surgery. And Duke knew, though no one confirmed his suspicion, that he had been right all along, he did have cancer; gall bladder surgery was routine and could easily have been carried out locally, there was no reason to go back to UCLA unless he had a tumour. Duke knew the doctor had seen it.

He was scared and felt an urgent need to talk things over with his wife. He admitted he still loved her very much but when he walked into her restaurant just before going back into hospital she knew he was too ill to make any effort toward reconciliation. She was shocked by his appearance and was aware that, even though he had told her he wanted her to move back home, he could not take any sort of strain right then. If she had gone back it would have required effort on his part. She told him she could not give him what he needed. Pilar was stunned by the changes she saw in him, "He was thin and there were new lines of pain drawn into his face." She was surprised when he reached his hand out toward her, "His skin felt hot and dry, but his grip was as strong as ever. I'd missed his touch so much."

"We had a lot of good times didn't we?" he asked, eager for reassurance.

"Yes, sweetheart, and we got three wonderful children to show for it."

"I've been thinking about my life. I guess I'd do it all over the same way except for these last few years. I wish we'd found some way to change that." He held on to her. "It was as though he were hanging on for dear life."

"I've got to tell someone … I'm sick again … I can't eat anymore. Hell

I can't even drink. Take care of the kids, they're going to need you." He pulled her closer.

"I felt like I'd gone home, but I never saw him or felt his touch again."

Even at that late stage he postponed surgery to do an interview for Barbara Walters and ABC News. Walters had never met him before but suspected she was going to like him. In 1977 she had been having a rough time after leaving NBC, and had been heavily criticised by the media. For some reason Duke sent her a telegram, "Don't let the bastards get you down." She had been delighted to receive such a boost from the icon, and she had wanted to interview him ever since. Now he had agreed to talk to her and he invited her to his home and boat. He planned to go into hospital immediately after he had finished taping the programme. She had no idea he was ill nor that he was going into UCLA the next day for major surgery; on his better days he still looked remarkably well. They instantly hit it off. He was excited and wanted to prove he could still do the business. The Walters Show was being called a "special" and he fully intended it to be just that, he had no idea how many more such interviews he would be able to do. Not until the cameras stopped rolling did he casually mention he was going into hospital and Walters was shocked. When she realised how ill he was she worried about some of the questions she had asked and recognised that his answers had been hauntingly open and honest, reflections of his gnawing suspicions.

"What's your idea of a very good day?"

"Well, getting up in the morning. Being still here. As far as I'm concerned I've had enough experience to know that if I open my eyes and look outside and it's a nice, foggy day, it's great. If it's a sunny day, it's beautiful."

"If it's any kind of day, it's OK, huh?"

"If I'm there."

Walters asked, "Are you worried?"

"Not in the least bit. I'm kidding ... No, I'm not worried. I've been around for quite a while, enjoying the fruits of capitalism."

"When you read now, people call you the legendary John Wayne ... Do you feel as if they're writing about ... a man who isn't here any more?"

Duke drawled slowly, "Well, yeah, that's kind of scary....They talk like you're part of the past or something. And rightfully so. I am part of the past. But I also want to be a little part of the future too." Today and the future were what mattered to him, he had said as much on many occasions.

"Do you plan to make any more films?"

"I think so, yeah."

"Do you think you're a good actor?"

Duke answered laughing, secure at last, "I know I'm a good actor."

"Are you, you? Is John Wayne, Marion Morrison, the guy that we see on screen, is he now you? Are you rough and tough, and a hard drinker, and soft with women and hard with men, and …" "Yeah, I think so. Yeah I like to drink. And I like women, and I've probably been a lot softer than I should be on occasion with them. And a lot tougher on some men, mainly myself."

"Can we talk a little bit about women … There was a quote in which you said, "Women scare the hell out of me. I've always been afraid of them."

"True."

"Women scare the hell out of you? Still?"

Duke laughed, "Yeah. I'm scared to death."

"Why?"

"I don't know … you know … it's just …"

"Are you romantic?"

"Very much. Very much so. Easily hurt. Easily hurt."

"You've been separated for five years."

He nodded agreement, "Um-hmm."

"Is that difficult for you?"

He looked less happy, "I probably would have stayed with it if I'd thought there was any …"

"Hope of reconciliation?"

"Or any respect back and forth, you know. I just … it just actually … she's a fine woman. She's the mother of my children. We just lost contact. Completely lost contact. It's sad … that's what happens."

Walters changed the subject, "Do you think of yourself as a sex symbol?"

"I wasn't a sex symbol but there was, I'm sure, a feeling of sex in … in the minds of audiences. I wasn't milk toast in any form. So I suppose there was that …"

"Do you watch your old movies on television?"

"Occasionally, when there's a real oldie …"

"How do you feel?"

"Well, it's kind of irritating to see I was a good-looking, forty year old man, and suddenly, I can look over here and see this seventy-one year old."

"You're not a bad looking fellow now."

"… but I, and I'm not squawking, but you know, it's … you know, you kind of think, "God, I was pretty wonderful then." He continued, "I just want to be around for a long time."

When she asked how he felt about life he answered seriously, "I have a deep faith that there is a Supreme Being. There has to be … The fact that He has let me stick around a little longer, or She's let me stick around a little longer, certainly goes great with me, and I want to hang around as long as I'm healthy and not in anybody's way."

"Has it been a good life?"

"Great for me."

"Do you fear death?"

He hung his head, "Well, I don't look forward to it, because, maybe He won't be as nice to me as I think He will."

Walters begged, "Stick around for a while longer will you?"

"I sure want to!"

On January 10th 1979 he was admitted to UCLA Hospital. He had delayed as long as possible and even on that morning he messed around, putting off his departure, shouting at those trying to hurry him, "Don't rush me." Michael had taken charge of his father's admission and he protected his interest from that day on. The doctors would talk only to him and he passed any news on to the rest of the family and the media. The Press were not informed when he went into hospital, but eventually the news that he had gone in for gall bladder surgery leaked out. Michael said he was in fine health and was strong and fit following his earlier heart operation. Duke was willing to leave things in his son's hands and had no further personal words for any reporter.

John Wayne would, of course, be receiving the very best cancer treatments available but before surgery he was put through a series of exhaustive tests. One of his nurses watched in awe as he began the fiercest of struggles, "He came to us determined that whatever lay in wait would be faced with courage and dignity. We never did rob him of that and whenever I was giving him any treatment, whatever I had to do to him, he would make jokes. He was always laughing. It was so strange to be in a room alone with him and hear that most famous of laughs. He noticed everything, even somehow when he was drugged, he even commented if I wore a new necklace ... he noticed everything going on. To hear that voice never failed to move me. Sometimes I wanted to cry. Sometimes we cried together. Mostly though he laughed. I once asked him where he got his courage. He said he just didn't want to die yet. He told me, "When I contracted this damned illness I decided the only thing I had ever really believed in was truth and life ... in living. Mostly I have told the truth. I want to live. I can't give in now just because the enemy might be stronger than I am. I look at my grandchildren when they come up. I have to put up some kind of fight for them. When they start playing around, up to all kinds of stuff in here, I feel alive, they are life ... they're important to me and I can't give up on them. As long as I have a breath left in me I will be fighting for them ...""

On the morning of the operation Pat arrived at the hospital at six. He was already up and fretting about his younger children, "Pat, you've got to make sure they're all OK about what's going on here today. They ought to know how I'm doing." He was already heavily sedated but nothing quietened him until she promised to keep them informed. As he was wheeled away he laughed brightly, "See you in the movies!" On January 12 at 7:45 am Dr William Longmire began the long operation at the start of another traumatic day.

As soon as he opened Duke's stomach he knew he was operating on a dying man. The tumour was large and he suspected the cancer cells had already spread to other organs and lymph nodes. He removed the whole stomach, including the tumour and gall-bladder, to give him a fighting chance. In *The Shootist* Books was told by his doctor that no operation would save him, "I'd have to gut you like a fish." The reality was worse, Duke's oesophagus, blood vessels, arteries and nerves were severed and later, after the cancerous tissue had been removed, reconnected. All the regional lymph nodes were taken for analysis after an operation lasting over nine hours.

When the family were told half way into the operation that a tumour had been found Pat had a sudden blinding vision of him complaining about the pain in his stomach since October. It was now January, and she asked the doctor how fast cancer spread, "From half an inch to an inch a month, but you don't worry about the rain when the water's up to here," the doctor answered pointing to his throat. Even back in October it had been too late, it may even have been too late when he had his heart surgery earlier that year.

Long before he was out of theatre the press had engulfed the hospital for the start of the death watch. Duke had gone down at 7:45 in the morning, by late afternoon when there was still no news they were onto the story, no gall bladder operation lasted that long. They packed the lobby and the whole unit was in chaos. Reporters claimed to be patients' relatives as they tried to get closer to Duke's room, some donned doctors coats, some got right up to the theatre doors, and one even tried to take photographs of him as he was being operated on

After ten hours he was transferred to intensive care. The doctor told the family, "If he'd not had his heart surgery he would not have withstood the ordeal, but I'm relatively pleased with how he's doing now. We're going to allow him to come round soon. You might even get to see him later tonight."

A statement was immediately released that a low grade tumour had been removed, that there was no evidence that the disease had spread. Duke had no hand in or knowledge of, this statement. In fact the tumour wasn't low-grade, it was a rare and extremely dangerous variety. Surgeons had been unable to detect any sign of tumour outside the stomach but believed there were likely to be microscopic cancerous cells present in the area, the prognosis was poor; he was weak from earlier surgery, he had only one lung, he was older and less fit than in 1964, and the cancer present this time was particularly virulent. For the next few days the press continued to receive the news that Duke was doing well. The world held its breath and waited, eager for news, and the real life tension was as taut as anything he had ever created on screen. Death, just like his life, was coming in the glare of the public eye and the knowledge left him little leeway for the dignity that was so important to him. A life lived in a goldfish bowl meant he had no door to close behind him now. His fight was public property, there was no confidentiality and no holds barred, and the news that he was regaining consciousness flew down the wires as soon as he opened drowsy eyes in the recovery room. Reporters had been told he was there for a gall bladder operation and yet the first word out of Duke's mouth was, "Cancer?" No one with him had the heart to confirm his fears. When he repeated the question, hoping to hear a denial, Pat just smiled her encouragement. He closed his eyes and drifted back to sleep.

The following day the doctor confirmed that he did have cancer again. He explained everything in detail, telling him his stomach had been removed and about the possibility of metastasis. He was told he would have to follow a special diet for the rest of his life because his body would no longer be able to produce the acids necessary to break down foods. "Did you get it all?" The doctor could only tell him they would have to wait for the results of the pathology. If his lymph nodes showed it had spread he would need radiotherapy and chemotherapy.

On that first day he managed to sit up in ICU, still attached to drips and monitors, and he began telling jokes to anyone who would listen. Alice Day, his private nurse, was surprised by the speed of his recovery and she began to think he'd pulled it off again. He was doing well when the news everyone had been dreading arrived, microscopic cancer cells had been found in the lymph nodes taken from the gastric area. He had been up and walking by January 17th and when he was told the worst he showed no reaction at all, he wasn't listening, he didn't want to know. He wanted to believe he was on the mend and didn't begin to take in the enormity of what the doctor was telling him, that in fact the real nightmare was only just beginning. His incredible endurance held firm and he simply ignored the news that he was fighting a losing battle, "The final pathological report of the tissue removed at the operation has disclosed evidence of microscopic metastasis in the gastric lymph nodes that were removed with the stomach. Such microscopic involvement was not detected at the time of the operation or upon the initial gross pathological examination ... There is a probability that it has spread." Everyone but Duke understood there was to be no repeat of 1964.

He'd insisted on complete privacy, "Dying's my own business. I don't want any fuss." There wasn't the slightest chance, and as soon as the news was out the phone never stopped ringing. Friends pleaded to see him and a steady stream of visitors arrived at the hospital. When he was too sick to see them they asked that he was told they'd been asking about him and praying for him. Flowers by the ton were delivered from well-wishers and a nurse read all the cards to him. Pat was left to deal with sack loads of letters. The hospital was under siege, snowed under by tourists, fans, reporters and news crews. Staff were soon at breaking point but no one seemed to mind the havoc their most celebrated patient was causing.

He never asked Pat to stay but the nurses all agreed that he was more comfortable and easier to deal with once she arrived in the morning to take control. He was generally content when she sat in the room with him and, although he didn't particularly want to talk, he enjoyed watching TV with her, "I learn more about my condition from the news than I do from the doctors." He became addicted to game shows, actively participating in them, shouting the answers out at the top of his voice and getting angry when contestants couldn't hear. He had never had much time to watch TV before, now he found he enjoyed many of the programmes.

He persuaded reluctant doctors to allow him to go for short walks around the hospital, no words of warning from them could hold him back, and he began dragging his intravenous trolley behind him as he marched doggedly along the corridors escorted by one of his sons, Pat or his devoted nurse and his life's habit of endless, restless pacing was resumed. Once he felt stronger he even refused to allow anyone to accompany him to the bathroom. With drips, drains and tubes sticking out in all directions he locked nurse Day outside. It was a big triumph in his book, a sign that he was on the mend, a reclamation of a little precious dignity. The IV trolley was dragged around the hospital with him and anything that was attached firmly enough was pulled along in his wake. By January 28th nothing could hold him back and on that day he even managed to walk along the corridor without support. His daily improvement excited him and stunned the medical profession. He felt better, slept less, sat up more, pulled the IV on longer and longer walks and eventually he even began to eat again! The doctors had created a small pouch from his intestine to replace the stomach they had removed, and he knew that even though digestion was going to be difficult he had to make an effort. He felt hungry and tried a thickened apricot drink, it was not long before he was tackling solids. He seemed to have no trouble, and felt triumphant when he managed to keep it down. His evident recovery was steady and remarkable.

An infection in the incision forced him to stay in hospital longer than he wanted but on February 10 he was allowed to go home. He was smuggled out of the back entrance into his waiting motor home. Pat travelled with him and tried to ease his discomfort on the drive back to Newport. Later, when she asked him when his radiation therapy was due to start he said he knew nothing about any further treatment. He had only taken in what he had wanted to hear and he exploded with fury, saying the surgeon told him the tumour had all been removed, and that he was going to be fine, "I'm so sick and tired of treatment and hospitals … I almost want to die."

For the first time in many years he was unable to attend the Arizona bull sale. He wrote to his friends saying he would be there next year and promised that he felt fine. Radiation treatment was due to start six weeks after his surgery, the scars had to be fully healed first. He resented having to suffer further treatment, and the knowledge that he was still in trouble worried him. After the first euphoric days of being allowed home he became withdrawn and didn't want to talk to anyone. The phone rang constantly. Reporters camped outside. Friends who had been told of his improvement began swamping him with invitations. Pat and Michael shielded him from most of this and refused admittance to everyone.

Nurse Alice had gone home with him and was staying at Bayshore Drive to look after her favourite patient. She had never done anything like it before, she told him, "I'm not doing this for *you*, I'm doing it for Dr Longmuir." Duke of course was well aware of his position in Alice's heart, and he did not believe her words, trusting instead the eyes which told him how much she cared about him, despite his often difficult behaviour. During the last weeks she had become another dedicated and loyal friend, "No one could spend any time with him and not fall in love with him." Even the threat of death had done nothing to dent the charisma.

His heart and mind focused on moving forward and his interest in new projects increased. He was determined to make another movie! The thought drove him … But first, radiation.

When he returned to the hospital the radiation target was marked out in purple pen. It covered the central part of his abdomen from the naval to the sternum, and then spread out to include his left side up to the armpit. Every Monday to Friday he drove himself to the hospital where he waited his turn to receive 170 rads. Whilst each treatment was painless, the cumulative effect wasn't. He developed a bright red, burnt patch over the whole target area. He became nauseous and what little appetite he had was lost. He refused to eat or drink and his weight plunged rapidly until he was thinner than he had been in his second year at high school. His mood deteriorated at an equivalent rate. He was a terrible patient and it was a good job that Alice did love him, that she, like Pat, had become his devoted slave, for no one was safe from his anger. He had always been volatile to say the least, but his boiling temper had always been balanced by an equivalent willingness to seek forgiveness. All his life he had despised anything or anyone that he considered petty, now that life was slipping away, he became petty himself. And even that angered him. His dying infuriated him. The smallest discomfort could trigger a show of wild aggression and no one was safe. Luckily Pat stayed with him and understood that his rage damaged him more than it did anyone else. He was having difficulty getting through each day and she wasn't surprised that he felt angry. In 1964 Pilar said his brush with cancer left him a changed man, in 1979 it robbed him of everything he had once been. He had lost control of his life and he was no longer warm, gentle, generous or kind ... he was as mad as hell! The Press carried daily stories about his fierce will to live, in truth he could hardly hold his head up, but they were right about one thing, he was fierce.

He wanted to see Pilar but she didn't want to visit him at home, unsure about the relationship that existed between her husband and his secretary. She continued to talk to him on the phone and understood that he could not be left alone now. He needed more than a nurse and was glad he had Pat. Still, when he told her he was off his food and having difficulty eating, complaining that food smelled bad to him, Pilar sent him special treats from her restaurant. He was supposed to eat small amounts six times a day, but he had trouble keeping anything down. He just didn't want to eat and the man with the most massive appetite never felt hungry again, he never again asked for or wanted food and one of the greatest pleasures in life was lost to him.

However, his lack of appetite for food, didn't reflect a diminishing appetite for life. He was hanging on grimly, still insisting on all his mail being opened and answered and he still received requests to appear on TV shows. He rejected all but one. He had been sent an invitation to present the Best Picture Award at the 1979 Oscar ceremony. He accepted and nothing would prevent him being there that night. He had been offered one last glorious chance. There, at the most glittering Hollywood celebration of all, he could be John Wayne for his public and his profession for the last time. The ceremony took on great significance for him.

That hadn't always been the way he felt. In 1971 when Richard Warren Lewis had written that because of his "squareness" John Wayne remained a "profit without honour in Hollywood," Duke said, "The Oscar meant a lot to me but I really didn't need it. When people say "A John

Wayne picture got bad reviews," it's a redundant sentence … Hell I don't care. People like my movies and that's all that counts, I wasn't hurt not to get an Oscar before *True Grit*." He added later, "As a younger man I never saw the value of it. I knew that when the grip or the cameraman figured out something new … that was the only way things ever really changed in the movies. So awards for actors … they weren't important to me. But then I figured that the Oscar ceremony was actually the only direct communication we get with the public and for that reason I finally accepted membership." In 1979 it became important to him in ways he could never have imagined at the beginning. He had been looking for a way to say goodbye to his world. He had to communicate with his public for the last time, and what better place to do it? He may have been considered "square" by some, but he had been secure in the affections of those unaffected by fashion for fifty years. He felt he owed a huge debt.

And thoughts of the night, planning and preparing for it, also became a valuable diversion. For many weeks he had been living in loose, baggy sports clothes, not caring what he looked like. Now he ordered a new tuxedo. He had one hanging up that he hadn't even worn but it already swamped his thinning frame. He needed a haircut, new shoes, he had to call Dave Grayson to arrange for make-up. There was a lot to organise in a hurry. The medical profession advised him to avoid the extra stress and warned him he wouldn't be up to it. He replied with typical stubbornness, "I'm going to be there." It was something to live for. The only thing that mattered now was being there on the night of April 9th 1979. He planned to give his finest performance, the last show of true grit.

On the morning of the ceremony he drove to the hospital for his regular treatment and then carried on to Los Angeles for rehearsals. By the afternoon he was in great pain and had become very pale. He ate nothing all day. Dave Grayson arrived at Duke's hotel at 6 pm but was told he was sleeping and he waited for him in the lobby. Some of Duke's family approached and tried to prepare him for the condition he was now in, but even so, when he finally went up to the room he was staggered by the sight of a bare chested Duke who laughed, "I thought I'd shock you." He was little more than pallid skin and bone, and the radiation burns across his stomach told Grayson what he had been going through. He laughed back as casually as he could and Duke asked, "Don't you think I look good?"

Grayson retorted, "You look like Hell. I'm going to have to work miracles to get you out on stage."

"It's a miracle your still working at all! I'll just have to get by on my natural beauty I guess."

"That won't get you far!" Grayson whispered under his breath.

"Goddamn. You just have to have the last word don't you!"

As Grayson opened his make-up case Duke told him, still laughing, "Damn, I look so good tonight, I don't think I'll bother with make-up. I don't want to look as though I've already been embalmed." In fact after he dressed and had some light powder applied Grayson was surprised and admitted, "He looked remarkably good." As he was ready to leave the room Duke stopped and confessed, "Actually I am worried about getting through the evening." He was presenting the very last award and already felt weak, he wasn't sure he could survive the ordeal. Grayson knew him well enough to know that however long he was kept standing around, he would be out on stage to make his speech and to hand out that last award, nothing would stop him. He did his best to reassure him and they went together to the VIP lounge to meet up with the rest of Duke's family. As soon as they walked into the room a line of celebrities formed, all eager for his autograph, Grayson said, "It was a stunning tribute. He remained good natured and polite to each and from that moment on he never sat down again until the evening ended." To those people he appeared to be his normal self, moving around, chatting, signing autographs, joking with old friends, it was the start of an amazing performance. He felt hot and uncomfortable and murmured that he needed a drink. Cary Grant rushed to get one.

Standing around, waiting nervously, he had vivid memories of the other times he had done exactly the same thing, usually with his hand wrapped around a large glass of tequila. Tonight there was no tequila, no party planned for after the show, and no guests to entertain. He spoke to Johnny Carson who was hosting the show that year. They'd been friends a long time. Carson appreciated Duke's sense of the ridiculous and the liveliness that had frequently caught him unawares when he was a guest on his show. Tonight was different, Duke was more serious and Carson sensed the significance of the evening for him.

The show progressed too slowly for the impatient Duke who was tiring fast. Before he was called out on stage a re-run of part of the 1978 Oscars ceremony was screened for the audience. Duke had been in hospital having his heart surgery that year, it had been one of the few occasions he had missed. Johnny Carson took everyone's minds back, "Last year at the fiftieth anniversary presentation of the Academy Awards an American institution stood on this stage and said some very heartfelt words about another American institution. Tonight we'd like to relive that moment with you." The clip showed an emotional Bob Hope, "Before we get to the big one here's a word to one of Hollywood's biggest. He's in Boston right now and we want you to know Duke, we miss you tonight. We expect to see you amble out here in person next year, because nobody else can walk in John Wayne's boots."

Carson then introduced "Mr John Wayne." Duke half ran down the stairs and out onto the stage. He then ambled across it with a slower, more deliberate Wayne roll, hand outstretched in greeting to Carson. As he sauntered into the brilliant lights, there was an audible gasp from the audience. He looked graceful, slim, upright and strong, better in many ways than he had looked for the last few years and yet at the same time, nothing could hide the fact that he was close to death. Lawrence Olivier stood up, hands clasped tightly together in front of his face, he was scarcely able to breathe. Gregory Peck clapped and cheered and the distinguished gathering of stars refused to be seated.

The newly ordered tuxedo had arrived several weeks before the show. By the night of the awards it hung loosely on his emaciated frame, and in an effort to give his body some definition and to hide the weight loss he wore a wet suit under his shirt. He was pure elegance, tall and broad shouldered, but he fooled no one who saw him. The audience already knew he had cancer, now they knew he was dying.

They rose as one to salute him, and they continued clapping, many in tears, delaying his speech for several emotion-packed minutes. He stood in shocked amazement, and rubbed the side of his nose with a gesture straight from *Red River*. He fidgeted nervously and ran a hand lightly across his stomach before putting both hands up to demand silence. The reception, the standing ovation, and the genuine warmth he felt coming at him from his peers thrilled him and somehow he managed to stand up long enough to receive their heartfelt good wishes, though at one point he rested his hands on the podium for support. When the audience quietened he began with difficulty, "Thank you ladies and gentlemen. That's just about the only medicine a fella'd ever really need. Believe me when I tell you that I'm mighty pleased that I *am* able to amble down here tonight." He paused for a long time before continuing, swallowing hard and painfully, "Well, Oscar and I have something in common. Oscar first came to the Hollywood scene in 1928. So did I ... We're both a little weather-beaten, but we're still here and plan to be around a whole lot longer." The audience understood they were witnessing the final performance of "one of Hollywood's biggest." He was saying goodbye in the grandest style, at the most fitting of occasions.

He had prepared a statement for the press that was never issued, "I would like to make one comment about the tribute of affection for me last night. It was the result of the dedication of many people. Decades of men and women who entered our business in the 20s, the 30s, the 40s, the 50s and the 60s, and brought our art form to flower by revealing intimate flashes of greatness, of nobility, of humour, of fineness of the inner soul against a growing tendency of today for realism and vulgarities without the relief of the aforementioned beauty and respect for human dignity … but I plead for the guidelines of good taste, so that our peers may be proud of the product carrying the Hollywood seal, rather than have it represent an alphabetical gradation of vulgarity in our pictures."

The effort he put into attending the ceremony left him exhausted but the following weekend, despite all Pat's protests, he went out on *The Wild Goose* with old friends, Ralph and Marjorie Wingfield. He had a special reason for sailing to Catalina that weekend and he even persuaded his doctor to allow him to miss his regular radiation treatment. He had said goodbye to his adoring public, now it was time for the private ones to start. He would never see his beloved island again and he had also taken the heartbreaking decision to sell *The Goose*, his proudest possession. This was to be the final voyage. The sailor was going home from the sea. He took time to look at everything as he remembered the old days. Throughout the trip he talked almost non-stop, telling stories about the times he had gone buffalo hunting on the island with Johnny Weissmuller, about John Ford of course, and the wild trips with Ward Bond, Harry Carey and Victor McLaglen, about days when they'd all been so drunk no one could remember what they had done. He insisted on going for a walk although he was extremely weak. He was desperate to see it all again, and neither Pat nor his friends could dissuade him from making the effort. He kept stopping to look at things that obviously held a special memory, things he had seen a million times before. He became distant, lost in the past. When they finally docked back in Newport he walked away from *The Wild Goose* without looking round at her again. He placed his favourite stetson on Ralph Wingfield's head and murmured, "Looks better on you …" the traditional cowboy farewell.

He continued going for his daily walks but on April 18th he failed to ring Pat at 7 o'clock to see if she wanted to go with him. When she woke later she knew something serious must have happened. She called him to ask what was wrong.

"I'm not walking today, I've been coughing up blood all night."

"Duke, are you out of your mind? Why didn't you call the doctor or me?"

"I thought maybe I'd just die instead."

Pat raced to his house and drove him straight to hospital. Blood poured from his mouth all the way there, and he assumed the cancer had spread to his lung. In fact he had pneumonia again and was inconsolable when he had to be admitted into hospital to be pumped full of more antibiotics.

"Pat, I want you to go home and bring my Smith and Wesson thirty eight." She was tidying his room and thought he was sleeping. His words turned her blood to ice. She didn't turn to face him and acted as though she hadn't heard. "I want to blow my brains out." She continued to ignore him. "*Goddammit, are you deaf?* Do what I tell you, go home and bring my gun." Finally, when she refused to look at him, he cried in rage and desperation until he collapsed exhausted back against his pillow. He never mentioned the gun or said that he wanted to die again. Suicide and John Wayne did not make good partners. To him now, true grit, courage, honour, and all the things he believed in with all his heart meant dying a horrible, pain filled death, it meant putting up with hell and misery until it came for him. The values that had generated his life now carried him toward his end. In the room next to his Pat sat reading the thousands of letters that continued to flood into the hospital offering support, encouragement, and many prayers. Every day they arrived by the sack load from all over the world. He was too tired to reply to them now but Pat continued to read them to him. How could he let the people down who took the trouble to send him their prayers? He found some of them so moving that he was reduced to tears as he listened. It was tough, but he knew he had no option but to carry on.

When any of his family or friends were going to be visiting, either at home or in the hospital, he still took the greatest care with his appearance. He valued his looks now, not because he had any vanity, but because they continued to emphasise the image he had created, he was weak and feeble perhaps, but doing his best to look hard.

Not long after he'd been discharged he was rushed back to hospital once again, suffering acute pain. He was soon in theatre undergoing further surgery to prevent his oesophagus closing up. The doctor was encouraged to find that the problem was only a side effect of the radiation, not the tumour he first suspected. Although the urgent need for further treatment shocked Duke he still demanded to go home again, he would do anything rather than stay in that ward and he was discharged once more. The doctors may have been pleased with themselves but Duke knew the end had come a little closer when no mention was made of continuing his radiation therapy. The doctor said it wasn't worth carrying on, it was doing him no good and was only prolonging the pain. He was happy not to have to continue his daily drive to the torture chamber.

Many friends arrived on his doorstep during the final countdown. When Maureen O'Hara came for the day she ended up staying three and was unable to tear herself away from him. She hadn't seen him for a while and gasped with shock when he opened the front door. They talked non-stop, as though nothing had changed. He roared with the laughter they had always shared. She was a great tonic and he was grateful that she stayed.

As her car pulled away another turned in. Out stepped Claire Trevor Bren, his co-star from *Stagecoach*, and many other films. She and her husband, Milton, had been his close friends for many years. Milton was suffering from a brain tumour and he had come to say his own last goodbyes. As they parted Duke whispered, "Take care of yourself."

All that week a steady stream of guests arrived. He didn't want any of them to leave and he clung tightly to each, unwilling to let any of them go. Time was running out, there were so many friends to see, but those days were all he was given. In early May he collapsed in agony in his kitchen.

He was rushed to his old suite at UCLA where X rays showed an intestinal blockage. On May 1st another operation revealed there was no further hope, little healthy tissue remained. There was no cover up and the Press was immediately informed, "The probability that cancer has spread throughout his body is now greatly increased … I suspect he feels like he just fell off a horse." The doctor who made the statement also told reporters, "John Wayne has volunteered to remain at the hospital where he will join the program of experimental treatment." Duke would not be leaving the hospital alive. Although there was no further regular treatment available for him, he refused to give up, "I have to try. Pat and my kids talked me out of killing myself. Now I have to try to live for them, don't I?" He remained alert, bright and full of unrealistic hope.

He had gone to the most extraordinary lengths all his life to surround himself with people, delighting in company. Now, as the days dragged remorselessly by in UCLA, loneliness and the detached feeling of isolation were the things he hated most about his dying. He sent a forlorn and heart wrenching note to one of his well-wishers, "Your thoughtfulness was very much appreciated. The further out you go, the lonelier it gets. Yours affectionately, Duke." He was a film star, used to the press of the crowd, the surge of bodies against his, and to the very fact that he never could be on his own. Now there was nothing he could do about it, he was going to die and he was going to be on his own. So he hung on as best he could, clinging tightly to loved ones, stubbornly refusing to let go. The doctors did what they could for him, staggered by his continuing survival. They had no idea how long he could go on like this, they had not treated anyone who gripped so tenaciously to the last vestiges of life. He kept asking, "How long? When?" They had no answers because he wasn't following any of the laws of nature they understood. All they knew was that they had not successfully removed the tumour, that radiation had not worked and that it was extremely unlikely that chemotherapy would be successful either. He should have been dead.

The new drugs they tested on him were highly toxic and had drastic and severe side effects. They pleaded with him to stop the program, telling him that the treatment would kill him before the cancer did. Perhaps that was the idea! Then at the last moment they asked him if he wanted to try a radical new drug to boost his own immune system. It was not known at the time if interferon would make any difference to stomach tumours, but Duke agreed to try it anyway. On the day he began receiving the drug a Press release stated, "There has been no mention in any way to Mr Wayne of how long he might live … it is strictly experimental medicine that we have come to … The treatment was suggested to him and he said "Yes."

He received uncomfortable injections, twice daily, once between the fingers and once between the toes but, almost docile now, he no longer complained when nurses attended him. On the second day of the trials he went for his customary stroll, and when other patients asked how he was doing he breezed, "I'm doing just fine thanks. How about you?" In fact the cancer was spreading so rapidly that no treatment made any difference, he had no chance and very little fight left. The doctors badly wanted to keep John Wayne alive. They allowed him to continue with the tests, needles, more tests, examinations, and even, further surgery. Pat believed it would have been fairer to let him slip away and he even began to feel sorry for himself. He could find little peace, but when anyone asked him to stop he told them about the children he had seen receiving the same treatment, if they could cope so could he.

Few people now had access to his room but he was heard laughing the day Ollie Carey visited. She had been so special in his life for so long, becoming almost the mother he had longed for. She had shared his ups and downs and had always been there, offering help and advice. It had been the wife of his boyhood hero who made him accept that he couldn't ever play the role of the bad boy, the coward, or indeed anything other than the man he was, "Duke, you are just an ordinary man … but you have a rare gift. You make unimportant people feel very special." He had cherished Ollie's words and loved her colourful truck-driving use of language, it was what made him laugh that day. He had never understood the gift she talked about, it wasn't something he worked at or developed, it was natural and unconscious, but he had accepted it and used it along the way. Going to the movies, that great American habit, was a collective, almost spiritual experience, and yet that wasn't the level he ever worked on. He only connected to his audience in an individual, personal way, holding private conversations with everyone there about the things that interested or worried them. He shared his most intimate secrets and his

459

love with each one of them. And it was a two way communication. He exposed himself to the camera and, at the same time, touched the rawness in their hearts and minds. The massive John Wayne image hit the audience as a whole, but Marion Morrison saw to it that every unimportant individual left the theatre feeling special, warm, and extraordinary. Jean Luc Goddard had wondered how it was that he could hate John Wayne so bitterly and love him so tenderly at the same time. He hated the political dinosaur, but loved the ordinary man he found hiding behind the multi-layered image. Mark Rydell explained, "I never anticipated we'd be friends. We stood at opposite poles both politically and emotionally. But he's an individual, and a very fair man. He only functions on a one-to-one basis, and his politics become irrelevant when he is talking directly to YOU! Somehow you're vulnerable to his nature. His magnetism is so powerful that the individual can't help but be drawn into his orbit. He opens up a lot of warm and connective feelings, and I have to tell you, I really like him as a man. He's generous, sympathetic and easily moved." It was exactly the same thing that Katharine Hepburn had termed his, "Subtle capacity to caress the audience." What the audience saw on the screen actually had little to do with image, and everything to do with one human being talking to another.

Duke confessed, "I never analysed any of that stuff, but I'm glad they find me warm. I think I have a deep and real feeling for people, I guess that's what they recognise. I hope my fans forget most of my pictures, and remember maybe five good ones ... I don't know ... I just hope they remember me as a good person."

After Ollie's visit he was never left on his own again. Someone stayed in the room with him around the clock; it was usually Pat. They watched the news together, and he tried to stay awake for the Carson Show, he rarely made it, but Pat liked to listen to the peaceful and regular snoring that told her he was comfortable at last.

Duke said he believed in God but he'd never felt the need to go to church, at times calling himself a "Presby-goddamn-terian," at others, a "cardiac Catholic." Whatever he considered himself to be he had stubbornly refused to go to any formal place of worship. He did not understand sectarian argument, nor why the church insisted on interfering in a man's private life, condemning all the things he loved most, sex, alcohol, and gambling. He was a deeply religious man, who did not believe in religion. In 1971 he had been asked if he'd have liked his life to have been different, he replied, "If I had it to do over again, I'd probably do everything I did. But that's not necessarily the right thing to do. But I hope my family and friends will be able to say that I was an honest, kind and fairly decent man." Honesty, kindness and decency had been his religion, he had cleaved loyally to it, he had few worries on his conscience and he didn't go looking for forgiveness now he knew himself to be dying. During the night of May 13 he was sick every few minutes and was in tremendous pain. He could get no rest and admitted, "I don't know how much worse this is going to get." The next morning he agreed to see Father McGrath, an old friend who had called in from Panama. That day was the first he did not go for his customary walk, sitting in a chair in his room instead. Michael said his father received the last rites from Father McGrath but that remained a matter open to conjecture as no one else was present at the meeting.

Even though he had finally accepted defeat, and had possibly made peace with his maker, he continued fighting his corner like a tiger and, still unprepared to let go, he commented, "What a beautiful day," every morning he woke up. He never forgot to ask each child or grandchild how their day had gone, how school had been, how their cold was, how they felt. He still laughed and still tried to make those around him laugh too, he still felt the need to protect his children from what was happening to him. And no one could have carried the burden of image as faithfully as he did during those days. As he lay close to death he truly became John Wayne at last, his endurance then, the stuff of legend. The endeavour of Marion had long been merged with Wayne's endurance, creating a man of "Clay, baked hard, like Texas!"

By the end of May his oesophagus had closed up again and though the surgeons tried, there was nothing more to be done. The tumour completely blocked his insides. He sold *The Wild Goose*. It broke his heart, he was hardly able to put his signature on the bill of sale, and he cried in despair. The whole world watched him die and was inspired by his going down. From early 1979 letters flooded into Government offices, demanding that something was done to honour him and it was obvious that whatever was to be done had to be done quickly. Fellow Americans wanted him to know they acknowledged what he had done for their country. Congressman Barry Goldwater placed a proposal and Congress held a special meeting at which Maureen O'Hara spoke, "Please let us show him our appreciation and love. He is a hero and there are so few left." She suggested the title for the congressional medal of honour, "John Wayne: American." President Carter quickly agreed to the legislation for a gold medal to be struck. On Duke's seventy second birthday he received a letter from the White House telling him about it. He woke feeling miserable, it was one of his worst times despite the letter and the efforts of his family to make it a special day. They all brought presents and cards but he hardly noticed. He was given the strongest painkillers and left to sleep. The cake prepared by hospital staff was left in the fridge. His gifts lay around the room, unopened. He slept most of the next day too, but woke late in the afternoon feeling a little happier. He and his children celebrated his birthday then, and although he did manage to laugh, he still couldn't face opening the presents. They were eventually sent back to his home to await his return!

On May 29 he gave up. He was put on a permanent morphine drip. He stopped shouting at the nurses and merely turned onto his side to allow them to treat him. The hallucinations started and he began drifting from this world, going to strange lands peopled by men and women from different times and places. He walked in parades amongst horses and laughing children. Bright lights flashed in his eyes and memories sprang into his mind of so many premieres, ceremonies and functions. He was used to flash bulbs going off in his face. He could see bright lights in the distance … the lights of a film set perhaps … or something else entirely. He didn't know, but he was accustomed to arc lights, he felt at home and the vision of brightness held no fear. The pain eased.

"Hello Duke." It was Alice. He didn't have the strength to mumble a reply. She was holding his hand. "Are you OK?" He sqeezed her fingers and closed his eyes. He wasn't on his own and that was all that mattered. When he looked up again there was Alice or Pat or one of his children, and when he allowed himself to drift toward eternity he saw the welcome company of so many of his friends and ancestors. He wasn't alone after all, he would never be on his own again. His hold on life slackened. He lay still, concentrating. He could hear someone pottering around the room. Decisions had to be made today. He'd borne enough, he was not getting up again … "Whether you like it or not, you're a man, you're stuck with it. You're gonna find yourself standing your ground and fighting when you oughta run, speaking out when you oughta keep your mouth shut, doing things that seem wrong to a lot of people, but you'll do them all the same … you're gonna spend the rest of your life getting up one more time than you're knocked down …" The words rang in his ears. Well he simply couldn't get up again.

Alice held his hand and noticed how warm and dry it felt, a huge paw that retained its strong grip. He smiled, "I once asked my boy, Ethan, to draw a picture of a valley. When he showed it to me he had written underneath, "The Valley Beyond by Ethan J Wayne, for my wonderful father." That's all. That's how I want them to remember me. He once told me I was his hero …" Alice had not been a John Wayne fan, but she loved him dearly, "He was the same man in hospital that he appeared in his films. He was as polite as could be reasonably expected, given the circumstances. He was gentle and laughter was never far from his lips. He remained full of pranks, right up to the end. I knew he had to be scared, no man could die as he was without fear in his heart, but he got on with living each day in the most dignified way he could find. He was a brave man."

"Let's get you scrubbed up and ready for action." She used his own soap and when she had finished he felt better, clean and fresh. He had been watching her carefully, he had reached a decision. "Alice, I had a strange dream during the night. I was talking to someone about the kids. My family has been so important to me. There's no thrill in the world like a little daughter or son loving you … it's too bad they have to grow up and lose that warm, gentle approach to life … but I guess the world's a rough place. There was never enough time for us as a family, I really wish I'd taken a little more care about allowing myself to become involved in public affairs. It was too much. Having so little private life sometimes broke up my own personal relationships. I never wanted it to happen, they were precious to me. You haven't met my wife … I loved her so much, I still do, tremendously … I wish I'd held on more tightly, not let go." His mind was wandering but he suddenly asked to see the doctor.

"Doc, I've had enough. I want you to stop trying. I'm ready." Alice smiled in relief, glad it would soon be over for him and the doctor nodded his approval, "I think we should just leave you alone now." On May 31st his intravenous food supply was stopped. Not many days before he had been struggling along the hallways, talking to everyone he met, now the urge to walk faded rapidly.

Katharine Hepburn had written an ode to his body, "Massive, all of a piece, rugged, a man's body … a face alive with humour …" He now weighed 160 pounds, there was no fat or muscle left and the only thing left of him that Hepburn had so admired were the extraordinary blue eyes. The rugged, leathery skin was white, thin and lined with pain. She had mentioned his massive hands, they appeared bigger than ever now, compared to the rest of his thin, scarred body. The 1964 scar from his lung cancer operation was still raised and thickened, partly because he had been operated on again through the same incision. The 1978 heart surgery scar ran from just below his neck to the centre of his chest. It crossed the one from the lung operation. He had a fresh, dark purple scar running the length of his stomach, and another one close to it from a second operation. He was covered by deep red radiation burns and black bruises from the tests, IVs, and morphine injections. So much for Hepburn's ode to the wonderful body!

Once the treatment stopped he wanted Pat there with him. He kept jumping suddenly, telling her that bright lights kept flashing and he asked, "Did you see that one?" He often seemed to be half asleep, dreaming, but with eyes wide open as he followed some action going on before him. When he woke he knew he had been dreaming and was still able to distinguish between what was real and what wasn't. Pat was afraid, knowing he was preparing to leave.

The day after he told her about the lights she left him in Alice's care so she could go to bathe and change at the motel. When she returned Alice informed her that his blood pressure was falling rapidly. The newspapers immediately ran stories that he was loosing his battle and the nation held its breath, waiting and praying with Pat and the rest of the Wayne family. Pilar came from Newport to stay close by in a local hotel, and although he constantly asked about her, she was not allowed to visit him. All through the first week of June he slipped in and out of consciousness. He was thirsty but even water would no longer go down. The morphine was increased to combat the extreme pain although he continued to demand that it was reduced when his children were due to visit.

And still, into the second week of June, he waited for the end. His family gathered at the hospital and doctors told them that June 9th would be the day. He slept peacefully as his respiration and blood pressure dropped alarmingly, all day his vital signs fell until he was scarcely alive. The longest day slipped past like so many others and suddenly at 9 o'clock in the evening his eyes flickered open. For the next three hours he was alert, laughing and joking. He knew where he was and recognised everyone there, he talked happily with them all, keeping everyone amused, just like in the old days. He sounded and acted like his old self. He watched TV with his children for a while and was completely lucid, pain free and best of all, he was happy. The bright blue eyes shone and he enjoyed those three hours as though they were the most important ones in his life. The kids recognised all his familiar seething, restless energy and Pat later called it his final burst of life force. She believed he consciously made that one last effort in an attempt to give his family something positive to hold onto and remember him by in the days, months and years to come.

He fell asleep and didn't wake or rouse all through that night or the next day. His personal effects were removed from the room. A nurse placed a shroud in a drawer. Everything was prepared and ready. All Duke's business was taken care of.

On the morning of Monday June 11th his blood pressure dropped again and his breathing started coming in quick, shallow gasps. Pat stood next to the bed, afraid to move away and she talked to him without knowing if he could hear. He sank into a heavy coma and when Alice came on duty she knew he would not regain consciousness. She refused to leave him and sat watching him closely as he laboured to breathe. She finally paged his children and when they got there he was gasping. There was an increasing interval between each breath but each time they thought he had given up, he suddenly drew in another great gulp of air …

… Finally, at 5:23 pm on June 11th 1979 the room fell silent.

"No man knows the hour of his ending, nor can he choose the place or the manner of his going. To each it is given to die proudly, to die well, and this is, indeed, the final measure of the man." — Louis L'Amour *Hondo*